D1472687

NERVOUS INHIBITION

NERVOUS INHIBITION

PROCEEDINGS OF THE SECOND FRIDAY HARBOR SYMPOSIUM

Edited by

ERNST FLOREY

Associate Professor of Zoology
University of Washington

SYMPOSIUM PUBLICATIONS DIVISION

PERGAMON PRESS

OXFORD · LONDON · NEW YORK · PARIS

1961

PERGAMON PRESS LTD.
Headington Hill Hall, Oxford
4 & 5 Fitzroy Square, London W.1

PERGAMON PRESS INC.
122 East 55th Street, New York 22, N.Y.
1404 New York Avenue, N.W., Washington 5, D.C.

PERGAMON PRESS S.A.R.L.
24 Rue des Écoles, Paris Vᵉ

PERGAMON PRESS G.m.b.H.
Kaiserstrasse 75, Frankfurt am Main

Library of Congress Card No. 61-9788

Printed in Great Britain by
ADLARD AND SON LTD., DORKING, SURREY

FOREWORD

It is often said that international conferences should ideally be composed of a small group of specialists in a field that has been selected because of the rapidity of its development. A further ideal requirement would be that the venue should provide an atmosphere of informality and ease.

The Symposium on Nervous Inhibition at Friday Harbor on 31 May to 4 June 1960 fulfilled all these requirements in ample measure, and it was agreed by all to have been a most stimulating and enjoyable occasion. The formal sessions gave adequate time for good discussion, which perhaps was further encouraged by the absence of any recording devices. The discussions were remarkable for their forthrightness and for the degree to which severe criticisms could be made and accepted without the embarrassment of emotional reactions. The present volume gives the papers that were presented at the Conference, with no doubt many modifications that resulted from the discussions. They will bring back many pleasant and profitable memories to those who were fortunate enough to be participants or observers. For others these papers will illustrate the many types of investigation that are leading to new concepts in regard to the working of the nervous system.

I cannot resist the attempt to give some suggestion of the atmosphere of the Conference, which was partly derived from the peace and beauty of the surroundings and the excellent weather, but which in large measure was due to the planning and superb organization. The two and a half hour journey on the ferry from Anacortes out to Friday Harbor already enabled the participants to renew old friendships or make new ones. The location of the Faculty Club and Cottages in the woods fronting the water with the Olympic Mountains beyond provided the most attractive background for a conference that it would be possible to imagine. The Faculty Club gave us ease, informality and comfort as well as excellent meals. A special feature was the whistle that woke us up, called us to the conferences, and to the meals; so much so that we found ourselves salivating at the sound of the whistle! There were many occasions of hospitality: a lovely evening with a salmon-barbecue party at a beach on the other side of the island; an evening display of the Marine Laboratories; a gay final dinner at the Roche Harbor Restaurant; a saki party at Dr. Hayashi's cottage; and several parties at the Director's house. Walking in the woods and boating gave occasions for informal discussion and a renewal of vitality for the more formal conference occasions, and between conferences there was always the sun-bathed terrace where we had lunch and morning and afternoon coffee.

For all these amenities that added so much to the enjoyment and success of the Conference we have firstly to thank Dr. and Mrs. Florey, Professor and Mrs. Martin, and Dr. Fernald, together with Mrs. Chapman. The University of Washington has an excellent Marine Biological Station at Friday Harbor and speaking on behalf of all participants we are very grateful to them for making it available for the Conference. Finally, special thanks are due to the National Science Foundation for the financial support that made this Conference possible. It will be agreed that this publication is an appropriate tribute to the Foundation.

JOHN C. ECCLES

PREFACE

THIS book is the result of the International Symposium on Nervous Inhibition that was held at the Friday Harbor Laboratories of the University of Washington from 31 May to 4 June 1960. The published papers are not necessarily identical with the talks as they were given at the Symposium; several of them have been worked over and some of them were expanded. It is hoped that the book represents and reviews present knowledge of the so varied phenomena of nervous inhibition. It was the idea behind the whole Symposium to give recognition to the fact that states of inhibition or of temporary inexcitability produced by nerve cells are as important for the co-ordinated and co-ordinating function of the nervous system as are the excitatory states of central or peripheral neurons and of effector cells. Furthermore, it was the aim of the Symposium to permit an interchange of ideas between neurophysiologists primarily concerned with vertebrates, and those more interested in invertebrates, in order to stimulate and encourage the mutual interest in the universal phenomena of nervous inhibition and in order to create a greater awareness of the range of phenomena of nervous inhibition. The list of participants represents many diverse fields of physiology and the topics were chosen to cover as many diverse kinds of inhibition as possible.

The International Symposium was sponsored by the Division of Regulatory Biology of the National Science Foundation. The encouragement and financial support received from this organization is gratefully acknowledged. It made possible the participation of experts from Australia, France, Great Britain, Japan, Hungary and Canada, in addition to those coming from various institutions of the United States. The publication of the Symposium Volume is also subsidized by the National Science Foundation.

Early in the planning of the symposium, the Director of the Friday Harbor Laboratories, Dr. R. L. Fernald, established an *ad hoc* committee consisting of A. W. Martin, A. H. Whiteley, with myself as chairman. This committee was responsible for the planning of the meeting and the administration of funds. Dr. Fernald deserves credit for making it possible to accommodate all participants and a number of interested colleagues and graduate students from the University of Washington at the Friday Harbor Campus and to make all facilities of the Laboratories available to the guests. Already in the early stages of planning, it was agreed that if the Symposium had to be held within the limits of a small group of participants, we all should make at least that part of our contribution to the meeting which consisted in our formal presentation available to the larger scientific community and to those who could not participate in person. This spirit of responsibility made it possible to assemble all manuscripts of the individual papers within three months after the end of the Symposium.

This Symposium has helped to establish several new concepts, most important, perhaps, that of presynaptic inhibition. During the extensive discussions it was recognized that it is not permissible to generalize observations made on one organ and in one species as occurring in all members of the whole phylum, since the diversity of mechanisms may be as great among closely related species as it is among representatives of different phyla. On the other hand, it became quite clear that all the different observations permit general hypotheses of certain physiological phenomena, which are of value in the understanding and the interpretation of functions occurring in any given species.

It is unfortunate that the extensive and most lively discussions cannot be printed. No provision was made to record the arguments and, quite frankly, the discussions would not have been as free and uninhibited as they were, had everybody been conscious of the fact that his words would be recorded and printed.

Obviously, not all differences of opinion have been resolved to the satisfaction of every participant. In so far the book does not represent a unified system of hypotheses. Here the reader must make his own judgment on the basis of the facts that are amply given in the various papers, and on the basis of the criteria set down in several presentations. On the other hand, a study of the discussions of the many diverse phenomena will reveal a remarkable unity of concepts. It is indeed astonishing that the terminology used to describe and analyze inhibition in such diverse systems as the vertebrate heart and the crustacean stretch receptors is nearly identical, indicating a unity of facts, perhaps not suspected by many.

All participants deserve credit for their formal and informal contributions to the success of the Symposium. Whoever was invited to the meeting was asked to participate in the planning, and the whole conference developed almost organically and without strains and efforts. Special thanks, however, are due to Sir John Eccles and Professor Ragnar Granit. Without their early encouragement and support, the Symposium would not have materialized.

On behalf of all participants, I wish to thank Dr. R. L. Fernald and Dr. and Mrs. A. W. Martin for their hospitality at the social evenings, and Mrs. Grace Y. Chapman, the Symposium Secretary, for her charming and continuous assistance in matters personal and official.

The help of Sra. Marta Orrego de Sánchez in the preparation of the Index is gratefully acknowledged.

We are indebted to the publishers and their American and West Coast representatives, Mr. D J. Raymond and Mr. D. Shearer, for their enthusiastic co-operation.

Seattle, Washington   ERNST FLOREY

LIST OF PARTICIPANTS

DR. A. ARVANITAKI, Faculté de Science, Université de Lyon, Lyon, France.

DR. THEODORE H. BULLOCK, Department of Zoology, University of California at Los Angeles, Los Angeles, California.

DR. N. CHALAZONITIS, Faculté de Science, Université de Lyon, Lyon, France.

DR. MELVIN J. COHEN, Department of Biology, University of Oregon, Eugene, Oregon.

MR. WAYNE CRILL, Department of Physiology and Biophysics, University of Washington, Seattle, Washington.

DR. DAVID R. CURTIS, Department of Physiology, Australian National University, Canberra, Australia.

DR. JOSEF DUDEL, Department of Pharmacology, Harvard Medical School, Boston, Massachusetts.

PROFESSOR SIR JOHN ECCLES, Department of Physiology, Australian National University, Canberra, Australia.

DR. ROBERT P. ERICKSON, Department of Physiology and Biophysics, University of Washington, Seattle, Washington.

DR. CARLOS EYZAGUIRRE, Department of Physiology, University of Utah, Salt Lake City, Utah.

DR. GERTRUDE FALK, Department of Pharmacology, University of Washington, Seattle, Washington.

DR. PAUL FATT, Biophysics Department, University College, London, Great Britain.

DR. ROBERT L. FERNALD, Department of Zoology, University of Washington, Seattle, Washington.

DR. ELISABETH FLOREY, Seattle, Washington.

DR. ERNST FLOREY, *Chairman*, Department of Zoology, University of Washington, Seattle, Washington.

PROFESSOR RAGNAR GRANIT, Nobel Institute for Neurophysiology, Karolinska Institutet, Stockholm, Sweden.

DR. HARRY GRUNDFEST, Department of Neurology, Columbia University, New York, New York.

DR. H. K. HARTLINE, Rockefeller Institute, New York, New York.

DR. TAKASHI HAYASHI, Department of Physiology, School of Medicine, Keio University, Tokyo, Japan.

Dr. G. Adrian Horridge, Gatty Marine Laboratory, The University, St. Andrews, Fife, Scotland.

Dr. Otto F. Hutter, Department of Physiology, University College, London, Great Britain.

Dr. Suhayl Jabbur, Department of Physiology and Biophysics, University of Washington, Seattle, Washington.

Dr. Thelma T. Kennedy, Department of Physiology and Biophysics, University of Washington, Seattle, Washington.

Dr. Robert L. King, Department of Physiology and Biophysics, University of Washington, Seattle, Washington.

Dr. Stephen W. Kuffler, Department of Pharmacology, Harvard Medical School, Boston, Massachusetts.

Dr. W. K. Livingstone, Camp Sherman, Oregon.

Dr. David P. C. Lloyd, Department of Physiology, Rockefeller Institute, New York, New York.

Mrs. David P. C. Lloyd, New York, New York.

Mr. Newell Mack, Department of Physiology and Biophysics, University of Washington, Seattle, Washington.

Dr. Arthur W. Martin, Department of Zoology, University of Washington, Seattle, Washington.

Mrs. Arthur W. Martin, Seattle, Washington.

Dr. Donald M. Maynard, Department of Zoology, University of Michigan, Ann Arbor, Michigan.

Dr. Hugh McLennan, Department of Physiology, University of British Columbia, Vancouver, B.C., Canada.

Miss Harriet J. Merwin, Department of Zoology, University of Washington, Seattle, Washington.

Dr. K. Miyata, Department of Physiology, Nihon University, Tokyo, Japan.

Mr. Russell W. Morse, Department of Physiology and Biophysics, University of Washington, Seattle, Washington.

Dr. K. Nagai, Department of Physiology, Nihon University, Tokyo, Japan.

Dr. Harry Patton, Department of Physiology and Biophysics, University of Washington, Seattle, Washington.

Dr. Dominick P. Purpura, Department of Neurological Surgery, Columbia University, New York, New York.

Dr. James B. Ranck, Department of Physiology and Biophysics, University of Washington, Seattle, Washington.

Dr. Theodore C. Ruch, Department of Physiology and Biophysics, University of Washington, Seattle, Washington.

Dr. ALMA STOIBER, Department of Physiology and Biophysics, University of Washington, Seattle, Washington.

Dr. JOHN SZENTÀGOTHAI, Department of Anatomy, University of Pecs, Dischka u 5, Pecs, Hungary.

MR. JOHN THORNTON, Department of Zoology, University of Washington, Seattle, Washington.

Dr. ARNOLD L. TOWE, Department of Physiology and Biophysics, University of Washington, Seattle, Washington.

Dr. WILLIAM G. VAN DER KLOOT, Department of Pharmacology, New York University, New York, New York.

Dr. ARTHUR H. WHITELEY, Department of Zoology, University of Washington, Seattle, Washington.

Dr. C. A. G. WIERSMA, Division of Biology, California Institute of Technology, Pasadena, California.

MRS. C. A. G. WIERSMA, Pasadena, California.

Dr. J. WALTER WOODBURY, Department of Physiology and Biophysics, University of Washington, Seattle, Washington.

Symposium Secretary—MRS. GRACE Y. CHAPMAN

CONTENTS

Page

Inhibitory Neurons: a Survey of the History of their Discovery and of their Occurrence
  by C. A. G. WIERSMA 1

Varieties of Inhibitory Processes
  by HARRY GRUNDFEST 8

A Study of Some Twentieth Century Thoughts on Inhibition in the Spinal Cord
  by DAVID P. C. LLOYD 13

Anatomical Aspects of Inhibitory Pathways and Synapses
  by J. SZENTÀGOTHAI 32

Inhibitory Pathways to Motoneurons
  by J. C. ECCLES 47

Regulation of Discharge Rate by Inhibition, Especially by Recurrent Inhibition
  by RAGNAR GRANIT 61

The Synaptic Mechanism for Postsynaptic Inhibition
  by J. C. ECCLES 71

The Change in Membrane Permeability during the Inhibitory Process
  by PAUL FATT 87

Neuromuscular Synaptic Activity in Lobster
  by HARRY GRUNDFEST and JOHN P. REUBEN 92

Neuromuscular Synaptic Activity in the Crab (*Cancer magister*)
  by ERNST FLOREY and GRAHAM HOYLE 105

Presynaptic Inhibition at the Neuromuscular Junction in Crayfish
  by JOSEF DUDEL and STEPHAN W. KUFFLER 111

Ion Movements during Vagus Inhibition of the Heart
  by O. F. HUTTER 114

On the Problem of Impulse Conduction in the Atrium
  by J. W. WOODBURY and W. E. CRILL 124

Page

Inhibition in Molluscan Hearts and the Role of Acetylcholine
by ERNST FLOREY and HARRIET J. MERWIN . . . 136

Cardiac Inhibition in Decapod Crustacea
by DONALD M. MAYNARD 144

Chemopotentials in Giant Nerve Cells (*Aplysia fasciata*)
by N. CHALAZONITIS 179

Excitatory and Inhibitory Processes Initiated by Light and Infra-red
Radiations in Single Identifiable Nerve Cells (Giant Ganglion Cells
of *Aplysia*)
by A. ARVANITAKI and N. CHALAZONITIS 194

On the Anatomy of the Giant Neurons of the Visceral Ganglion of
Aplysia
by THEODORE H. BULLOCK 233

Inhibitory Interaction in the Retina and its Significance in Vision
by H. K. HARTLINE, F. RATCLIFF and W. H. MILLER . . . 241

Excitatory and Inhibitory Processes in Crustacean Sensory Nerve Cells
by C. EYZAGUIRRE 285

Excitation, Inhibition and the Concept of the Stimulus
by ERNST FLOREY 318

Excitation by Hyperpolarizing Potentials. A General Theory of
Receptor Activities
by HARRY GRUNDFEST 326

The Identification of Mammalian Inhibitory Transmitters
by DAVID R. CURTIS 342

Inhibitory Transmitters—A Review
H. MCLENNAN 350

Further Observations Concerning the Inhibitory Substance Extracted
from Brain
by K. LISSÁK, E. ENDRÖCZI and E. VINCZE 369

Extraction of an Excitatory Substance from Dog's Brain
by TAKASHI HAYASHI, KAZUO NAGAI and KEISABURO MIYATA . 376

Comments on the Excitine–Inhibitine Hypothesis
by TAKASHI HAYASHI 378

Physiological Mechanism of Producing Excitatory Transmitter in the
Brain of Dogs
   by TAKASHI HAYASHI   385

Complete Cure of Natural Epilepsy of Dogs by β-Hydroxy-γ-amino-
butyric Acid Introduced into their Ventricles
   by TAKASHI HAYASHI and KAZUO NAGAI   389

The Organization of the Primitive Central Nervous System as Suggested
by Examples of Inhibition and the Structure of Neuropile
   by G. ADRIAN HORRIDGE   395

Inhibition and Occlusion in Cortical Neurons
   by A. L. TOWE   410

The Influence of the Cerebral Cortex on the Dorsal Column Nuclei
   by S. J. JABBUR and A. L. TOWE   419

Ontogenetic Analysis of Some Evoked Synaptic Activities in Superficial
Neocortical Neuropil
   by DOMINICK P. PURPURA   424

Inhibition in the Neuro-endocrine Systems of Invertebrates
   by WILLIAM G. VAN DER KLOOT   447

Conclusion
   by ERNST FLOREY   459

Author Index   461

Subject Index   467

INHIBITORY NEURONS:
A SURVEY OF THE HISTORY OF THEIR DISCOVERY
AND OF THEIR OCCURRENCE

C. A. G. WIERSMA

California Institute of Technology, Division of Biology

THE presence of inhibitory phenomena in nervous activity has long been recognized, and many hypotheses have been advanced regarding its nature. Among these, the simplest, namely that central inhibition is the result of the activity of specific inhibitory fibers, has received less attention than many others. It is the purpose of this paper to consider the reasons why this came about and also to ponder the feasibility of its revival.

Although inhibition of one type or another appears as part and parcel of many if not most coordinated actions of the nervous system, even of rather primitive forms (see Horridge's paper, this volume, p. 395), its treatment has hardly been in accord with its importance. If this may seem an overstatement, I may refer to the first two volumes on neurophysiology of the *Handbook of Physiology*, in which mention of inhibition is made on a surprisingly small number of pages in less than half of the chapters of the first volume, and does not appear at all in the second.

A major reason for this is undoubtedly the difficulty of the necessary investigations, which always have to refer to excitation. In addition, there are so many different ways in which inhibitory phenomena do or could come about, that anybody asked to explain a given instance may well hesitate even to start speculation on a solution.

From the beginning the number of "inhibitory theories" has been large, involving all kinds of processes that on the basis of analogy could be opposed to excitation. To mention a few: inhibition by wave interference and inhibition by anabolic processes. It is quite possible by some (smart) interpretation to see in these the prototypes of modern ideas. But little purpose is served by such a procedure as often the meaning given to the terms used has been so changed, that no comparison is warranted. The main conclusion one reaches after studying these hypotheses is that they present very clever reasoning indeed with the few "facts" at hand; and the main lesson, that without sufficient facts no real progress is possible.

The history of inhibition by specific nerve fibers started when the brothers

Weber in 1845 were convinced that stimulation of the vagus stopped or slowed the heart. Several other more peripheral phenomena, such as inhibition of the intestinal musculature by splanchnic stimulation were brought under the same heading. But very little attention was given to the possibility that centrally a similar mechanism could be present. For instance we find in Richet's (1882) *Physiologie des Muscles et des Nerfs* three different inhibitory theories for the central nervous system discussed, none of which takes inhibitory nerves for central actions into account. This notwithstanding the fact that Richet is often credited with being the first to have described peripheral inhibition in the crayfish. This credit belongs, however, to Biedermann (1887, 1888) who became convinced of it on rather weak evidence, whereas Richet's remark was of the order of a hunch.

Without committing himself, Foster (1880) came closest to visualizing a theory on the basis of inhibitory fibers in his *Text Book of Physiology*. He points out that one view on respiratory inhibition ascribes this to the presence of inhibitory fibers in the ascending vagus. About the descending vagus he states "Here again it is usually said that the pneumogastric contains cardio-inhibitory fibres" and notes that in both these cases the examples are of the action on automatically active structures. Elsewhere he states "But we have seen that active nervous centres are subject not only to augmentative, but also to inhibitory influences." "Hence the cardio-inhibitory centre (in the medulla) might itself be inhibited by impulses reaching it from various quarters." "In other words, the beat of the heart might be quickened by lessening of the normal action of its inhibitory centre in the medulla." This to me appears to contain the essential features of the presence of a general system of specific inhibitory fibers.

Sherrington (1906) was undoubtedly influenced by these views. He starts out by quoting the vagus, the Anodonta preparation of Pavlov (1885), and the crayfish peripheral inhibition. The latter were the first instances of inhibitory action on a non-automatic active structure. But then, rather than accepting inhibitory fibers, Sherrington conceives of specific inhibitory endings, as branches of axons which have also excitatory function. His reasons for this view are varied and rest on such observations as the increased reflex excit-ability after strychnine. Another difficulty he could not solve by purely inhibitory axons was the fact that in rhythmic reflexes, such as the scratch reflex, continuous stimulation of certain sensory fibers evoked both excitation and inhibition. In his later views (Sherrington, 1925) in which he arrived on the basis of Loewi's vagus substance at the possible presence of excitatory and inhibitory transmitters, he still believed in the dual action of individual neurons.

A very disturbing set of facts for specific inhibitory fibers had in the mean-time developed out of the observations of Wedensky. This well known inhibitory phenomenon, in which excitatory stimulation itself leads to inhibition, had the great attraction that it offered a simple solution, in which only one type of transmission was necessary. In more or less altered forms it became the basis of a considerable number of inhibitory theories, most of which were of electrical nature, and represented the majority viewpoint for several decades from 1900 on. These will be reviewed in this volume by Lloyd.

It is of considerable interest to note that the known examples of specific inhibitory axons came under close scrutiny at this time. Wedensky (1891, 1892) himself was obviously convinced that the vagus inhibition of the heart was similar in nature to that in peripheral muscle, and expressed the conviction that he would be able to show this. I have not found that he really published such experiments. But for the inhibitor of the crayfish, Frölich (1907), who was one of the first to explain central inhibition in these terms, wrote a long paper, claiming to show that it was all done by excitatory impulses. Inhibition would be due to fatigue, weak stimuli fatiguing the closer muscle and strong ones the opener. This was a rather feeble attempt all around, though in certain aspects it resembles modern viewpoints. Sherrington (1906) on his part, discussed the possibility that the motor axons of the one muscle might inhibit the other by specific inhibitory endings.

The fact that Hoffmann (1914) later showed rather convincingly that the peripheral inhibition in the crayfish did depend on specific nerve fibers had little general influence, since so many were already otherwise committed. It also took more than the later proof (Marmont and Wiersma, 1938) that stimulation of these fibers gives, under all physiological circumstances, nothing but inhibition, to revive to the slightest extent the interest in central inhibitory fibers. This did not come about until the discovery of Renshaw (1941) of what are now the cells named after him and especially of course the investigations of Eccles (1957) and his school, which go a long way to show that these structures are purely inhibitory. These developments bring us to present times, in which additional facts have come to light which support the existence of purely inhibitory neurons, as well as a number of other findings, which show that certain inhibitory phenomena are based on different processes.

Bullock, in an as yet unpublished work, has enumerated four processes by which inhibition of a neuron can occur, based on the results of experiments with intracellular electrodes. These he enumerates as follows: "(a) by some degree of refractoriness following a suprathreshold excitatory process; (b) following a subthreshold excitatory postsynaptic potential; (c) inhibition from weak electrical fields acting to reduce ongoing activity already present or the likelihood of its beginning; (d) from specific influx which causes an active synaptic response in the hyperpolarizing direction, the socalled direct inhibition, regarded by some authors as due to the specificity of the transmitter agent, by others as due to specificity of the responding patch of synaptic membrane."

Of these possibilities which do not necessarily exhaust all, the first one is

Wedensky-like in type. It can involve different mechanisms as pointed out by Thesleff (1959) who has recently shown for the phenomena in striated muscle that the endplate becomes desensitized to acetylcholine under these circumstances. Whereas this type of process may never result in true inhibition, such actions might well stop spontaneously active cells. Included in the second case would be instances where the location of the synaptic connection automatically provides for inhibition. Such endings might still be considered to belong to an inhibitory unit, provided all those of such a unit were equal. The third possibility represents field effects. About these I am strongly biased in disfavor, since in my opinion they would tend to produce besides any useful signals, a lot of noise. Furthermore I have seen no evidence yet that proves their natural mode of action. For instance, the electroretinagram appears to be no hindrance to very selective stimulation of different neurons. It may be claimed that this is due to the suppression of unwanted stimulation by the inhibitory collaterals, but if such be the case, the same may work at all places where fields of physiological origin might upset orderly processes, and be one of its main functions. As to the fourth possibility, I want to discuss certain aspects of it later, but point out here that the presence of polarizing potentials is not necessary. In the crayfish muscle fibers inhibition by depolarizing potentials is just as effective as by polarizing ones. Perhaps it would be better to state that the membrane potential is maintained at a definite level at which firing is less likely. It is also questionable if one can distinguish between synapses reacting to a specific transmitter agent and ones with a specific reacting membrane, because both possibilities may be of equal importance. Since acetylcholine can both excite and inhibit as a transmitter agent, the membrane must play a part, but another inhibitory transmitter may never have excitatory properties, and thus be specific.

So far the inhibitory peripheral fibers of the Crustacea have given the best evidence and most complete picture of inhibitory fibers. From these fibers and not from sensory or motor axons, a substance I can be extracted which causes inhibition (Florey and Biederman, 1960). This means that now they completely conform to what purely inhibitory elements should be. However, in the arthropods as a whole, there are still some problems concerning these fibers. Becht (1959) has obtained rather good evidence of the presence of inhibitory fibers in the cockroach, but this only enhances the likelihood that Hoyle's (1955) grasshopper fiber is of inhibitory origin. However, this latter fiber does not inhibit, but conditions the muscle to greater contraction. From the fact that substance I inhibits the stretch receptors, one may tentatively conclude that the inhibitory fibers of these sense cells produce the same inhibitory substance. In this connection I would like to mention that Mr. R. O. Eckert (1960) believes that the functional significance of this sensory inhibition may be like that in *Limulus* eye. He observed that discharge rate of one stretch receptor diminished when neighboring ones are activated.

More centrally located inhibitors have been shown in a number of animals, but the evidence that they are purely inhibitory is less. The work of Tauc (1958) on inhibition in the ganglia of gastropods shows clearly that there exist inhibitory fibers coming from the higher centers which give polarizing potentials in cells of the pedal ganglion. In the crayfish, Hughes and Wiersma (1960) obtained evidence that a specific inhibitory fiber runs from the brain to the abdominal ganglia where it inhibits swimmeret movements. These rhythmic movements can be elicited among other ways by the stimulation of one of two interneurons originating in the brain, and rhythmic discharges remain then present in the motor roots even when the sensory connections with the periphery are severed in the abdominal region. By accepting the presence of "pacemaker" cells which are brought into action by the two triggering fibers and stopped by the inhibitory one, these phenomena can be explained. Note the resemblance of the problems to those of other rhythmic reflexes, such as the scratch reflex, which might possibly have similar explanation. In the cat brain, Desmedt and Mechelse (1958) have recently found a thin tract from the cortex to the cochlear nucleus which on stimulation inhibits click-evoked responses, and they consider it as specifically inhibitory. This would thus be a case in which the inhibitory interneurons were of a very "high" order.

However, for such intracentral tracts the "pure" inhibitory nature may be hard to prove, though for Renshaw cells it appears almost certain that they do not have excitatory endings and the same may be true for other inhibitory elements of the spinal cord at this level. In a number of other cases considerable doubt has arisen about this aspect. Thus Terzuolo and Bullock (1958) consider that the extrinsic inhibitory fiber of the crustacean heart has dual function on different cardioganglionic cells, inhibiting the pacemaker cells and exciting the follower cells. It seems somewhat debatable that their assumption that the excitatory effect is caused by the same fiber, is justified. For though the nerve contains a single inhibitory fiber, it may be asked if this is the only fiber in it, and not accompanied by an accelerator. It would be of importance to investigate this problem with the aid of the transmitter substance.

Another instance that may eventually belong in this column is that of the eccentric neurons of *Limulus* eye. Here it appears as if the collaterals may directly inhibit other eccentric cells. Interestingly enough though, it is possible that they would be completely inhibitory in function, since according to Wilska and Hartline (1941), their central effect consists in an off discharge in the next elements. Thus *Limulus* would develop "negative" prints, which looks like a poor mechanism for vision, because of the resulting loss of information.

The most direct evidence for two types of actions of the synapses made by one neuron is that of the Mauthner's cells of fishes, as described by Retzlaff and Fontaine (1958). Here the excitatory effect on the motor neurons in the tail can hardly be doubted, nor the inhibitory effect on their partner of the other body half. Furthermore, not only do the Mauthner's cells make this collateral connexion on the axon hillock, but presynaptic excitatory fibers of the eighth nerve make similar connexions at the other side. This may well be the outstanding example of the importance of the location of the synapses on the postsynaptic element. However, the spiral structure shown around the axon hillock is almost certainly not of common occurrence, and thus this may be one of those cases in which a special mechanism was developed, which is not generally present, and serves here the special purpose of preventing that these two cells ever fire at about the same time.

In conclusion I would like to make the following remarks. Specific inhibitory neurons are certainly present in nervous systems of different forms including mammals. It is likely from the evidence at hand that they have developed in primitive animals. It is, at present, still debatable how much of the inhibitory phenomena shown in nervous systems can be explained by their action, but this question is now more and more opening up to experimental approach. My own inclination is to predict that a good deal of this type of connexion will be found to be responsible for those inhibitions which are almost momentarily established as well as for some of the long-lasting effects, influenced by tonic inhibitory discharges. Undoubtedly cessation of activity can, even under physiological conditions, be brought about by other means, such as changes of the firing level by hormone influences. By untangling these possibilities and by attacking the problem on different levels of organization, a good deal of important information about and a better understanding of nervous integration appears within reach.

REFERENCES

BECHT, G. (1959) Studies on insect muscles. *Bijdragen tot de Dierkunde* **29** : 5–40.
BIEDERMANN, W. (1887) Zur Kenntniss der Nerven und Nervenendigungen in der quergestreiften Muskeln der Wirbellosen. *Sitzber. Akad. Wiss. Wien Math.-naturw. Kl.* **96** : 8–39.
BIEDERMANN, W. (1888) Über die Innervation der Krebsschere. *Sitzber. Akad. Wiss. Wien. Math.-naturw. Kl.* **97** : 49–82.
DESMEDT, J. E. and MECHELSE, K. (1958) Suppression of acoustic input by thalamic stimulation. *Proc. Soc. Exptl. Biol. Med.* **99** : 772–775.
ECCLES, J. C. (1957) *The Physiology of Nerve Cells.* Johns Hopkins Press, Baltimore.
ECKERT, R. O. (1960) Feedback in the crayfish stretch receptor system. *Anat. Rec.* **137** : 351–352.
FLOREY, E. and BIEDERMAN, M. A. (1960) Studies on the distribution of Factor I and acetylcholine in crustacean peripheral nerve. *J. Gen. Physiol.* **43** : 509–522.
FOSTER, M. (1880) *A Text Book of Physiology* (3rd Ed) Macmillan, New York.
FRÖLICH, F. W. (1907) Die Analyse der an der Krebsschere auftretenden Hemmungen. *Z. allgem. Physiol.* **7** : 393–443.
HOFFMANN, P. (1914) Über die doppelte Innervation der Krebsmuskeln. Zugleich ein Beitrag zur Kenntnis nervöser Hemmungen. *Z. Biol.* **63** : 411–442.
HUGHES, G. M. and WIERSMA, C. A. G. (1960) The co-ordination of swimmeret movements in the crayfish. *J. Exptl. Biol.* **37** (Vol 4)

HOYLE, G. (1955) Neuromuscular mechanisms of a locust skeletal muscle. *Proc. Roy. Soc.* (*London*) B **143** : 343–367.

MARMONT, G. and WIERSMA, C. A. G. (1938) On the mechanism of inhibition and excitation of crayfish muscle. *J. Physiol.* (*London*) **93** : 173–193.

PAVLOV, J. (1885) Wie die Muschel ihre Schaale öffnet. Versuche und Fragen zur allgemeinen Muskel-und Nerven Physiologie. *Arch. ges. Physiol. Pflüger's* **37** : 6–31.

RENSHAW, B. (1941) Influence of discharge on motoneurons upon excitation of neighboring motoneurons. *J. Neurophysiol.* **4** : 167–183.

RETZLAFF, E. and FONTAINE, J. (1960) Reciprocal inhibition as indicated by differential staining reaction. *Science* **131** : 104–105.

RICHET, C. (1882) *Physiologie des Muscles et des Nerfs.* Ballière, Paris.

SHERRINGTON, C. S. (1906) *The Integrative Action of the Nervous System.* Cambridge University Press (1947).

SHERRINGTON, C. S. (1925) Remarks on some aspects of reflex inhibition. *Proc. Roy. Soc.* (*London*) B **97** : 519–545.

TAUC, L. (1958) Processus post-synaptique d'excitation et d'inhibition dans le soma neuronique de l'Aplysie et de l'Escargot. *Arch. ital. biol.* **96** : 78–110.

TERZUOLO, C. A. and BULLOCK, T. H. (1958) Acceleration and inhibition in crustacean ganglion cells. *Arch. ital. biol.* **96** : 117–134.

THESLEFF, S. (1959) Motor end-plate "desensitization" by repetitive nerve stimuli. *J. Physiol.* (*London*) **148** : 659–664.

WEDENSKY, N. (1891) De l'action excitatrice et inhibitoire du courant électrique sur l'appareil neuro-musculaire. *Arch. Physiol.* **23** : 687–696.

WEDENSKY, N. (1892) Des relations entre les processes rhythmiques et l'activité fonctionelle de l'appareil neuro-musculaire excité. *Arch. Physiol.* **24** : 1–10.

WILSKA, A. and HARTLINE, H. K. (1941) The origin of "off responses" in the optic pathway. *Am. J. Physiol.* **133** : P491.

VARIETIES OF INHIBITORY PROCESSES

HARRY GRUNDFEST

Department of Neurology, College of Physicians and Surgeons, Columbia University

INHIBITION is a negative effect, interference with ongoing or incipient activity. Thus the character of inhibitory phenomena may vary depending upon the activity under examination and upon the different processes which enter into that activity. The neurophysiologist usually tends to concentrate his attention on conductile, electrically excitable activity which involves discharge of spikes. However, inhibition, like facilitation, may be studied also in terms of the non-propagated, electrically inexcitable activity of postsynaptic potentials (p.s.p.'s), and in that case the quantitative and even qualitative manifestations of inhibitory phenomena may be different. Among other things, the underlying differences in mode of excitability create different laws for electrically excitable and electrically inexcitable phenomena. By these differences in properties, the interactions of transmissional and conductile activity are complicated.

In his early work Sherrington formulated, though not explicitly, an important distinction among various inhibitory phenomena. The inhibition which he studied in spinal reflexes seemed to him due to active processes, co-equal with excitatory events. He suggested that inhibition might involve activity of synaptic membrane, rather than some "neutral" (or "neutralizing") event. Even when he later suggested that inhibition might perhaps be due to "stabilization" of the excitable membrane, he apparently thought of active interference with the excitatory processes.

However, in principle, both "active" and neutralizing (or "passive") phenomena can produce inhibition. In both types, either synaptic electrically inexcitable membrane may be involved or the conductile electrically excitable membrane may be affected. Thus, different inhibitory mechanisms, acting upon two different electrogenic systems, can give rise to a number of specifically different modes of inhibitory actions and effects.

THE COMPONENTS OF THE TWO ELECTROGENIC ACTIVITIES

In both systems of electrogenic membrane the depolarizing component may be regarded as a mechanism for valving Na^+-conductance, while a repolarizing or hyperpolarizing component is probably more varied in type. The "excitatory" synaptic membranes, like those of primary or of final common path receptor neurons, must produce depolarizing p.s.p.'s or generator potentials, respectively, in order to excite the conductile component. Thus, these electrically inexcitable membranes have both the depolarizing and repolarizing transducer actions. The earlier view that depolarizing synaptic membrane involves merely increased membrane permeability to all ions (i.e. "Bernstein type" of electrogenic activity) apparently does not hold for frog muscle endplates and *Raia* electroplaques, in which the repolarizing factor is probably only increased K^+-conductance. Conductile, electrically excitable membranes also have the two types of transducer components. At present, theoretical emphasis is on the K^+-conductance valving system, but it is not unlikely that in some types of electrically excitable membrane Cl^--valving may also be involved, or may be the principal factor of the repolarizing activity.

ACTIVE SYNAPTIC INHIBITORY PROCESSES

However, membranes also occur in which the Na^+-conductance valving action is absent. In the synaptic membranes some are known in which the K^+-conductance or Cl^--conductance, or both, may occur independently of the absence of the Na^+ component. Under the electrochemical conditions that seem to prevail in excitable cells, the repolarizing transducer action produces relatively little change in membrane potential. The membrane, however, tends to remain at or near the resting potential during this activity. Thus if electrically excitable membrane is present, any stimulus to depolarize and excite the latter membrane is opposed by the "clamping" action of the repolarizing excitable membrane. The action is equivalent to a decrease in membrane resistance, or an increase in its conductance. The result may be a diminution of depolarizing, excitatory p.s.p.'s, or of applied depolarizing electrical stimuli, both effects therefore being inhibitory.

In the absence of electrically excitable membrane, the depolarizing "excitatory" electrogenic activity and the repolarizing "inhibitory" activity produce neither excitation nor inhibition. Thus, in the electrically inexcitable electroplaques of torpedine electric fishes or of the marine teleost *Astroscopus*, the large depolarizing p.s.p.'s do not "excite" another component of the cells. The electrical activity is itself an effector response. Likewise, a hyperpolarizing electrogenesis is not "inhibitory" in the electrically inexcitable gland cells, but signifies the processes associated with excitation of the secretory activity of the gland. Furthermore, in cells that possess electrically excitable membrane, activation of the "inhibitory" synapses may evoke spikes of the cells. This has been observed in cat motoneurons and in crayfish stretch receptors under electrochemical conditions in which activity of the "inhibitory" membrane produces depolarization from the normal resting potential large enough to excite the spike generating membrane.

ELECTRICALLY EXCITABLE INHIBITORY PROCESSES

Membranes in which electrically excitable repolarizing processes occur without that of Na^+-conductance valving are also known and properly should also be termed electrically excitable. As in its electrically inexcitable counterpart, the electrogenic manifestation of this activity is small and may be of either sign, or absent, depending upon the electrochemical condition that set the resting potential. As with repolarizing inhibitory synaptic membrane, the active aspect of this effect is that produced on membrane conductance. It is present in many spike-generating membranes and is well known as rectification. This conductance change may increase and persist for a long time during depolarizing test stimuli and is thus known as "delayed" rectification.

It also occurs in some cells whose active depolarizing electrogenesis is only of the electrically inexcitable variety, such as the slow muscle fibers of frog and certain fibers in crayfish muscle, as well as *Raia* electroplaques. The phenomenon has been studied recently in some detail in the electroplaques and frog muscle fibers, in which absence of depolarizing spike electrogenesis simplifies analysis. The electrically excitable repolarizing component may be due only to K^+-conductance changes or to Cl^-, or to both ions. The conductance change develops slowly, so that once initiated by a depolarizing pulse it may grow after the stimulus for it is terminated. Thus, the "delayed" feature of the conductance change is emphasized. It persists for a considerable time after a brief initiating depolarizing pulse and in *Raia* electroplaques it lasts for almost 1 sec. In the latter cells the electrogenic concomitant of the conductance change may be a slight depolarization, while in the frog muscle fiber it is a hyperpolarization, these aspects depending upon the electrochemical conditions of the system.

The electrically excitable repolarizing or rectifying component may be blocked by applying hyperpolarizing currents or by treatment with pharmacological agents. The p.s.p.'s of frog slow muscle fibers or of *Raia* electroplaques are then correspondingly prolonged. In *Raia* electroplaques the "inhibitory" action of the repolarizing component is only the decrease in electrogenesis of the depolarizing p.s.p.'s. In the case of frog slow muscle fibers, however, the delayed rectification probably diminishes the contraction caused by the depolarizing p.s.p.'s. The repolarizing factor is of prime importance in causing the graded potential of electrically excitable arthropod muscle fibers and the resulting graded contraction of the fibers. Spike-producing electrically excitable membrane is also "inhibited" by the operation of the repolarizing factor, becoming relatively refractory for some time after a response.

NEUTRALIZING, OR PASSIVE EFFECTS

Procedures which interfere with electrogenic transducer actions are also inhibitory, but by preventing activity. Thus, these inhibitory phenomena are "passive". Pharmacological agents which selectively block depolarizing or hyperpolarizing p.s.p.'s, or both types non-selectively, provide the best known examples of this type of action. However, the "inhibitory" effect of synaptic drugs may be complicated by the functional relations of the whole system. Thus, selective block of inhibitory synapses by strychnine or other drugs results in convulsive activity of the central nervous system. Parallel effects may also be observed in electrically excitable membranes. Cocaine and procaine are known to depress activation of both Na^+- and K^+-conductances of squid axons. This may be the mode of action of procaine as a depressant of spikes in eel electroplaques and cat motoneurons. In other cells, however, such as in crustacean muscle fibers, procaine apparently blocks selectively the repolarizing component of the electrically excitable membrane. The result is conversion of the normally gradedly responsive membrane to one that produces large, overshooting spikes.

In electrically excitable membrane two "inactivation" processes apparently occur to counterbalance the activation of Na^+- and K^+-conductance. Block of K^+-inactivation would be an "inhibitory" process. Blockade of Na^+-inactivation has been found to occur and gives rise to one variety of prolonged spikes. This phenomenon therefore is "excitatory". What probably may be related phenomena in electrically inexcitable membranes are "desensitization" and "sensitization" effects. The effects probably depend upon specific drug–membrane interactions. Thus, application of acetylcholine desensitizes *Astroscopus* electroplaques, the response to neural stimulation becoming smaller. Carbamylcholine, however, causes little or no desensitization. For the elucidation of these phenomena, however, more analytical data are required than are currently available.

ELECTRICAL INTERACTIONS

Electrotonic effects, causing depolarization or hyperpolarization of electrically excitable membrane by appropriate synaptic electrogenesis at distant sites in the same cell may be classified as "active" excitatory and inhibitory processes. At least for relatively long stretches the dendrites of cortico-spinal neurons appear to lack a conductile, electrically excitable component. The axodendritic p.s.p.'s of cortical neurons thus probably affect the soma of the cells only by electrotonic spread. The effects are probably important to the complex functioning of the brain, but in experimental situations the tested effects may be small. For example, profound modification of axodendritic electrocortical activity affects the electrical excitability of the corticospinal neurons little or not at all. In contrast, stimulation of the reticular formation which probably activates axosomatic as well as axodendritic inhibitory synapses, causes marked depression of the electrical excitability of corticospinal neurons, as well as changes in electrocortical potentials.

Electrical or "ephaptic" connections between cells occur more frequently than has hitherto been recognized. The primary electrotonic effects are excitatory, since the spike of an active cell would cause a relatively large electrotonic depolarization in other cells. However, hyperpolarizing interactions are theoretically conceivable. Electrical interactions without distinctive anatomical relations also occur and are designated as "field effects". Excitatory and inhibitory effects of this type have been demonstrated between axons in peripheral nerves and in the spinal cord. The dorsal root reflex is probably due to excitation of intraspinal axon terminals by massive nuclear activities excited synaptically by influx in the same or other dorsal root fibers. An inhibitory effect, probably of similar origin, by ephaptic field interactions, has been described in Mauthner cells of goldfish.

INACTIVATOR TRANSMITTERS

It may be appropriate to note at this point that transmitter agents need not be activators of excitatory or inhibitory synapses, but might have quite the opposite effect. Thus, synapse inactivators might be released by some system and depending on the site of this synaptic action they might cause "inhibition" or "excitation". Furthermore, a number of pharmacological agents are known which in addition to being synaptic drugs also affect electrically excitable activity. Thus, a transmitter agent that depolarizes excitatory synapses might also inactivate the conductile membrane of some presynaptic fibers or of the postsynaptic cell.

CONCLUSION

Nearly all of the foregoing examples have been experimentally established. The others are at least likely possibilities which deserve serious consideration in view of the vast complexities of the membranes of living cells. Unfortunately, phenomenological schematizations of "excitatory" and "inhibitory" actions are far too abundant. Especially within the nervous system, with its large variety of anatomically, physiologically and/or pharmacologically distinct species of cell components, extreme complexity of action may be expected and should be sought for analytically rather than by phenomenological verbalizations.

A STUDY OF SOME TWENTIETH CENTURY THOUGHTS ON INHIBITION IN THE SPINAL CORD

David P. C. Lloyd

The Rockefeller Institute, New York

In presenting the following account of thoughts on the subject of central inhibition my purpose is not to make a foray into medical history, for which others are so much better fitted than am I, but to reflect, in so far as I am able, the status of thought on inhibitory mechanism at the present time, and the background from which it has arisen. This necessitates a survey of ideas and their origins, unfashionable as well as fashionable. I would begin with a discussion of the background, then of the overall situation as it stood 20 years ago when direct inhibition as a central action was demonstrated beyond any doubt. Finally, I would touch upon some specific topics of current interest.

It is well to have before us a definition of our subject, and I know of none better than that of Gasser (1937) which serves admirably in, to use his own words, "the absence of an exact definition". Inhibition, then

> "is a term of convenience used without exact definition in connection with a group of phenomena having certain qualities in common. The essential condition is the stoppage or prevention of action through the temporary operation of a process which does not harm the tissue. It is usually also implied that the process results from nervous activity, or imitates the result of nervous activity."

THE BACKGROUND

At the beginning of this century inhibition as a central action was firmly established. Setschenow (1863) had shown that crystals of salt placed on the frog brain stem delayed the time of onset of Türks reflex, and Sherrington had, in his series of papers on reciprocal innervation, left no room for doubt as to the existence of central inhibition and of its role in the genesis of reciprocal action. Attempts had been made to account for inhibition. One finds in these the beginnings of a dichotomy that has played a large role in thought on the mechanism of inhibition and which cannot even today be resolved completely. The sources of this dichotomy lie, on the one hand, in the experiments of the brothers Weber and Weber (1845) on vagal inhibition of the heart in which effect was clearly an action, and, on the other hand, in

13

those of Wedensky (1903) on inhibition of nerve impulses in which effect was clearly a consequence of action. Thus we enter the period under consideration with two alternative ideas prevalent: that of inhibition as an action and that of inhibition as a consequence of action.

An hypothesis as to mechanism of inhibition was presented by Keith Lucas (1917) who set forth his philosophy in these often quoted paragraphs:

> "Are we to suppose that the central nervous system uses some process different from that which is the basis of conduction in peripheral nerves, or is it more probable that the apparent difference rests only on our ignorance of the elementary fact of the conduction process? If we had a fuller knowledge of conduction as it occurs in peripheral nerves, should we not see inhibition, summation, and after-discharge as the natural and inevitable consequences of that one conduction process working under conditions of varying complexity?"

and

> ". . . we should inquire first with all care whether the elementary phenomena of conduction, as they are to be seen in the simple motor nerve and muscle, can give a satisfactory basis for the understanding of central phenomena; if they cannot, and in that case only, we shall be forced to postulate some new process peculiar to the central nervous system."

Keith Lucas notes that McDougall and von Uexküll had put forward hypotheses which account for the phenomena of inhibition by

> "postulating a process unknown to the student of nervous conduction, namely, the passage along nervous paths of a something which can stay and accumulate in one part or another of the nervous system."

Parenthetically, this notion sounds quite modern to our ears today. In presenting his own hypothesis, Keith Lucas gives reference to Verworn and Fröhlich as predecessors, at least in part.

Such was Keith Lucas's prestige that much thought on inhibition for a long time concentrated on inhibition as a consequence, or secondary effect, this despite the blow seemingly dealt when the theory of decremental conduction, a key point in Keith Lucas's specific hypothesis, was held to be invalid (Kato, 1924, and others). However, throughout the works of Sherrington there can be no doubt but that inhibition as a direct action is the preferred hypothesis, and the numerous facts uncovered by him were justification for the point of view. To quote one point made (Eccles and Sherrington, 1931):

> "If the inferences drawn from the present series of experiments are correct, namely, that the inhibition produced by any particular impulse persists for as long as 50 σ, and that excitation and inhibition mutually inactivate each other, then an explanation in terms of the Wedensky effect appears to be impossible."

Although these telling blows militated against the specific hypothesis of Keith Lucas, they did not for long defeat the more general concept of inhibition as a consequence of action, for in the discovery of the subnormal period by Graham (1935) there arose a process known in peripheral nerve that was capable of accounting in large measure for the qualities of inhibition as discussed by Eccles and Sherrington (1931) in relation to the flexor reflex (Gasser, 1937).

It is curious that Keith Lucas in stating his philosophical approach to the problem did not consider as worthy of mention inhibition as a direct action of peripheral nerve fibers, for the vagal inhibition described by the brothers Weber was unequivocally just that. There is, in fact, not a single reference to the Webers in his book *The Conduction of the Nervous Impulse*.

The hypothesis of Keith Lucas, based on refractoriness and decremental conduction, and that of Gasser, based on subnormality, were specific. It could be held that those who believed in inhibition as a direct action had no specific hypothesis to put forward—at least until Loewi (1921) demonstrated the chemical nature of vagal inhibitory action.

This brings us to consideration of another dichotomy of thought in which so-called chemical hypotheses and electrical hypotheses were pitted each sort against the other. I feel it should be made clear that the electrical and chemical hypotheses refer to the mode of synaptic action by means of which inhibition, or for that matter excitation, are brought about. They are thus aspects of the hypotheses of direct inhibition. Hypotheses of indirect inhibition, except for their aim of avoiding the necessity of postulating specifically inhibitory synapses, are fundamentally clear of obligate statements as to the mode of synaptic action itself, whether it be chemical or electrical.

It is interesting that at the time Adrian (1924) wrote on "Some recent work on inhibition" the important rivalry, if such it was, was between the Verworn, Lucas and Adrian hypothesis of indirect inhibition by operation of the Wedensky phenomenon and the "humoral theory", as Adrian called it, based then on evidences of peripheral actions by chemical substances, notably that provided by Loewi (1921).

Through confusion in thought the various hypotheses of indirect inhibition came to be called electrical hypotheses although, as I pointed out, they are not necessarily anything of the sort.

I think it would be correct to say that most electrical hypotheses of transmission, and this includes inhibition in the synaptic action sense, have never reached the dignity of publication. I think it would also be correct to say that the major reasons for this were in the case of excitation to dispose of the unwanted anodes and in the case of inhibition to dispense with the unwanted cathodes. However, an exception was the electrical hypothesis of Brooks and Eccles (1947) that inserted into the monosynaptic reflex inhibitory pathway a subliminally acting interneuron which by generating a synaptic potential would induce, it was supposed, an anelectronic area in the motoneuron subjacent to the inhibitory knob.

In as much as anelectrotonus now has been mentioned for the first time, it is well to digress to take cognizance of the Gaskell effect (1887) for it is probably to be considered the model for much that is discussed today in relation to inhibition. Gaskell demonstrated during vagal stimulation an increase in the demarcation current between normal and damaged regions of the resting tortoise auricle, which is to say anelectrotonus.

One wonders how it was that Keith Lucas failed to consider, along with the Webers' experiments, the Gaskell effect. It presumably could not have been the influence of Einthoven and Rademaker (1916) whose doubts were expressed some two years after Keith Lucas's lectures at University College. The *bona fide* nature of the Gaskell effect was reinstated by Samojloff in 1923 and recently in a most elegant fashion by Castillo and Katz (1955).

It is useful to ponder that which must have been the *conditio sine qua non* of the Gaskell experiment as it would appear in the light of present-day experiments, for which the prototype is the observation by Fatt and Katz (1953) on the crab claw. In a word, the electropositive variation observed by Gaskell depended for its appearance upon a lowering of membrane potential from normal resting level which in this case would have been due to demarcation. Appreciable changes in membrane potential need not accompany vagal inhibition (Trautwein *et al.*, 1956) although they certainly do if the conditions are right.

The occurrence of a "positive variation" clearly is not an essential manifestation of inhibition (Fatt and Katz, 1953; Frank, 1959; Lloyd and Wilson, 1959). Further, if a positive variation is brought out by experimental means, intentional or incidental, the fact of its presence does not delineate the means of its causation, be it electrical or chemical.

To return to the question of the "electrical–chemical" dichotomy, it is easily seen that the chemical hypothesis in its protean form is the simpler and more appealing. The endings in action liberate a substance of one or another chemical species that on encountering the postsynaptic membrane acts to cause excitation or inhibition.

It is clear from the following quotation that Sherrington considered a chemical, or "humoral", hypothesis. In 1925 he wrote:

> "It may further be objected to the scheme that it reduces the afferent neurone-fibre, and the axones of the downstream neurones on which that acts, to somewhat the character of secretory nerves. This, however, would be but in accord with recent evidence in favour of a so-called humoral view of the nervous production of peripheral excitation and inhibition."

Of interest is the fact that Sherrington writing in 1931 with Eccles seems to attribute the view to Samojloff and Kisseleff (1927) in the following words:

> ". . . Samojloff and Kisseleff (1927) inferred that there is a long lasting inhibitory state in the reflex centre, and they suggested that it is a chemical substance of opposite nature to the 'excitatory substance'."

However, in 1933, in the Nobel Lecture we find the following very up-to-date thought:

> "As to inhibition the suggestion is made that it consists in the temporary stabilization of the surface-membrane which excitation would break down. . . . The inhibitory stabilization of the membrane might be pictured as a heightening of the 'resting' polarization, somewhat on the lines of an electrotonus."

The foregoing statement is non-committal as to the sort of action that might bring about the postulated inhibitory stabilization, but in view of the difficulties he and Eccles encountered in reconciling their findings of 1931 with explanation in terms of the Wedensky effect one may suppose that an humoral hypothesis was tacitly assumed the more likely.

Mention has been made of the fact that hypotheses of indirect inhibition are essentially uncommitted with respect to the precise means by which pre-synaptic elements act at their terminal knobs upon subjacent tissue. There exists also an hypothesis of direct inhibition annunciated by Gerard (1932) and greatly elaborated by Gesell (1940), in which mode of action is unspecified. Furthermore, hypothesis of direct action though it be, it is in a sense allied to hypotheses of indirect action in that specifically inhibitory endings are not postulated. Location on the secondary neuron of endings otherwise similar in action is at the heart of this hypothesis. In brief, this hypothesis holds that the motoneuron, for example, is polarized with an external current flowing from axonic pole to dendritic pole. Excitation in the sense of impulse formation takes place at the axon. Synapses at the dendritic pole aid the current and so lead to excitation. Those at the axonic pole tend to cancel the current and so lead to inhibition.

All the general notions so far mentioned contain as part of their structure the orthodox view, born of the neuron doctrine, that neurons affect other neurons at their points of synaptic contact. The orthodoxy was frequently implicit, or perhaps one should say taken for granted. Nevertheless it was there. One should appreciate the fact that attempts to avoid postulation of specifically inhibitory synapses are not the equivalent of breaking with orthodoxy as to the synaptic sites of action by one neuron upon another. But there are notions concerning inhibition that do just that. And so there has arisen yet a third form of dichotomy in thought. On the one hand there are all the hypotheses that include inhibition as a direct synaptic action, or as a consequence of direct synaptic excitatory action. On the other hand there are notions of inhibition arising as a consequence of extrasynaptic action.

Such hypotheses take two forms. The first of these is associated with the name of Beritoff whom I quote from a recent statement (1959):

> "Twenty-five years ago we advanced the idea that at the basis of the inhibition of the nerve elements of the spinal cord and brain stem lies the electrotonic action of slow potentials arising within the dendritic plexuses of the C.N.S. and first of all in the

brain stem reticular formation and substantia gelatinosa Rolandi in the spinal cord. It was thought that the electrotonic action took place by spreading of evoked currents through intercellular fluid to the nearest nerve elements or nerve circuits."

It should be noted that Beritoff is quite emphatic that he did not have a syncytium or reticulum in mind when he, earlier, employed the term "neuropil".

Another expression of this general idea is to be found in the study of "intermittent conduction" by Barron and Matthews (1935). In their formulation fluctuating activity in the grey matter would give rise to a fluctuating potential gradient in collaterals that dip into the grey matter from passing tract fibers and hence to a fluctuating block at the collateral junctions. A significant quotation from their paper is:

"By means of this intermittence the state of the activity of the grey matter as well as the sensory discharge from the periphery may be signalled to the higher centers. The intermittent discharge depends for its frequency on the intensity of the stimulus to the peripheral sense organ, while its interruption depends upon factors influencing the grey matter. Hence such an intermittent stream of impulse signals upward not only information of the stimulus but also the state of the grey matter in some region. So whatever the mechanism of intermittence may be, it seems clear that this inhibition of conduction in a continuous fiber must be a possible mechanism of nervous integration within the central nervous system which does not involve a synapse."

For a brief time it was thought (Obrador and Odoriz, 1936) that a similar action occurred in sympathetic ganglia, but this proved not to be the case (Lloyd, 1938).

The other extrasynaptic hypothesis considers evidences of impulse block in presynaptic fibers by action of impulses in other immediately adjacent presynaptic fibers. Such presynaptic interaction was considered by Renshaw (1946) and subsequently in more specific form by McColloch *et al.* (1950).

This, then, is the background for discussion, and these the thoughts on inhibition that constitute that background.

THE SITUATION 20 YEARS AGO

It is worthwhile at this juncture to turn our minds back 20 years to see what was the situation in 1940, just before the proof of the existence in the spinal cord of direct inhibitory actions changed public opinion in some degree and overcame the reluctance of many to accept specifically inhibitory action in the central nervous system, whatever might be the mechanism, electrical or chemical, at the synapses involved.

The decade prior to 1940 had witnessed the great debate between protagonists of chemical and electrical transmission at nerve terminals. Discussion centered almost exclusively about excitation. Inhibition was an awkward and, therefore, largely neglected action.

Advocates of chemical transmission had peripheral models in that mediators could have excitatory or inhibitory action at different effector loci dependent upon the target organ, but no one, regardless of position held in the great debate, could point to specifically inhibitory synapses, or collaterals, or fibers, in the central nervous system. Furthermore, there was an air of "sleight of hand" in carrying observations on neuro-effector systems, not unchallenged at that, over to consideration of junctions between neurons. It is here that the observations of Kibjakov (1932), Feldberg and Gaddum (1934) and of Feldberg and Vartianin (1934) on sympathetic ganglia played an important role. These observations concerned excitation, however. The only inhibition observed in sympathetic ganglia at that time was of the post-reactional type (Eccles, 1935; Bronk, 1939; Lloyd, 1939) although Marrazzi had ascribed an inhibitory action to adrenaline (1939).

It was during this period that hypothesis of indirect inhibition and hypothesis of electrical transmission became identified in people's minds, presumably because so many felt at the time that any current idea of necessity had to be thrust into one or the other hopper. But whatever one's private or public opinions on the mode of transmission happened to be at the time, the indirect hypothesis of inhibition by operation of the subnormal period was foremost for consideration. Wherever one looked, be it in ganglia or in spinal reflexes, the subnormal period was seen giving rise to decreased response. And signs of antecedent excitation or facilitation were usually present. Eccles and Sherrington's study of the flexor reflex was the most modern and detailed study of the spinal reflex mechanism at work, and the theory of inhibition by subnormality developed by Gasser (1937) was capable of accounting for the evidences of inhibition presented by Eccles and Sherrington (1931).

The pioneering studies of Lorente de Nó on the control of oculomotor neurons belongs to this era. Emphasis was placed upon the action of chains of interneurons and to the qualities their action conferred upon transmission through the reflex center. Lorente de Nó (1936) found the subnormal process a "satisfactory explanation for the delayed block of the circulating impulses and cessation of the activity of the chain". His position is well stated in the following quotation (1936):

> "Since refractoriness of internuncial axons affords a satisfactory explanation of the inhibition of the motoneurons, it does not seem necessary to make the additional assumptions necessary for the establishment of the first hypothesis namely that inhibition is due to an active process taking place in the motoneurons themselves. Of course the possibility of the existence of such a process cannot be ruled out yet, but on the other hand no evidence of it has ever been found in spite of continuous search along different lines."

One will appreciate the fact that the criteria for establishment of inhibition as a direct action in the central nervous system were becoming more rigid and difficult to satisfy as knowledge of central nervous activity grew. And grow it did, due importantly to the fact that electronic means had made possible direct observation of central activity itself. This had great advantage over the older necessity of inferring central events from observation of peripheral events in the causal sequence. A high point in the development of direct recording means and observation was Lorente de Nó's (1939) use of inserted needle electrodes to reveal directly the activity of the chains of interneurons.

The criteria for postulating central inhibition as a direct action as I saw them in 1940 are set forth in the following quotation (Lloyd, 1941):

"Fibers, or synaptic endings of fibers, having an inhibitory action, have often been invoked to provide a mechanism by which to explain central inhibition. There has been no direct evidence to support the contention that such fibers or endings exist in the mammalian central nervous system. Furthermore, subnormality of central neurons serves as a mechanism to explain central inhibition without employing other than known processes, provided central neurons are activated prior to the appearance of inhibition. Activation of central neurons is almost inevitable if the central latency of inhibition is greater than the minimal synaptic delay of approximately $0 \cdot 5$ to $0 \cdot 6$ msec. Therefore, to postulate an active inhibitory process requires a demonstration of inhibition under circumstances which preclude the possibility of subnormality in accounting for a response deficit. In effect, the paths taken by the inhibitory action and the necessary testing excitatory action must not have elements in common before impinging upon the final common path (the motoneurons); the motoneurons must not have been discharged by the conditioning impulses."

It was then shown that certain dorsal root afferent volleys inhibited the monosynaptic reflex elicited by other dorsal root afferent volleys in circumstances that met the criteria for direct action upon the motoneuron (Lloyd, 1941).

SOME TOPICS OF CURRENT INTEREST

At this point a change in approach in this discussion seems indicated to consider specific topics in the problem of inhibition, having developed what seem to me to have been the main avenues of thought, and having made what seems to me to be a fair statement of the position at the onset of the last two decades.

Inhibition—Monism or Pluralism

What is to be included under the heading of inhibition? Obviously the answer to this question to different people is different. In the *Integrative Action* whilst discussing MacDougall's neurin hypothesis Sherrington wrote (1906):

"It appears to me unlikely that in their essential nature all forms of inhibition can be anything but one and the same process."

a passage that was presented again in the 1925 formulation of reflex inhibition.

Thus Sherrington held, and as far as I know always held, a monistic view of inhibition.

On the other hand Gasser (1937) certainly adopted a pluralistic view in writing:

> "Clearly the term 'inhibition' must apply to very different mechanisms. Inhibition of the heart is attributable to the intervention of a humoral substance, acetyl-choline. The cardiac tissue is altered. Inhibition of the flexor reflex is caused by the high threshhold of the internuncial neurons. The so-called 'inhibited' motor neuron is unaltered; it simply has failed to be excited. It is improper, therefore, to speak in terms implying that there is a general explanation of inhibition. One can only describe mechanisms which would be included in that category."

While not adopting a specific view Bremer raised an important question as to what should be included in the category (1947):

> "A fact which no doubt contributes to this confusion is that the term inhibition is rather loosely applied to categories of central depression which are not, or may not be, homologous. For instance it often designates the post-reactional depression of a reflex . . . . This generalization may prove ultimately to be justified by the demonstration of the fundamental identity of mechanisms of these post-reactional refractoriness with the depression of central activity resulting from afferent volleys not evoking themselves any discharge of the same motoneurons, or even any visible discharge But provisionally, and for the sake of clearness, the term inhibition should in the reviewer's opinion, be reserved to central depressions which cannot be attributed to the post-reactional refractoriness of motoneurons. Even with such limitations, there are still great incertitudes as to the phenomenal homogeneity of central inhibitions . . ."

The discovery in 1940 of an undeniable example of direct inhibition seems to have emphasized the monistic view, somewhat along the lines proposed by Bremer. Certainly most of the recent and current research endeavor is the direct offshoot of that discovery. However, it will be my duty in part to "keep the door open" to mechanisms other than those which are discussed in relation to the direct inhibitory process.

The Time Course of Inhibition

Let us state at the outset that inhibition can be brief in duration or prolonged, even when caused by a single afferent volley. In the light of present-day knowledge the least enduring inhibition is that directly imposed upon the motoneurons by a single afferent volley into the myotatic reflex pathways. This has a detectable duration of something less than 15 msec (Lloyd, 1946). Who is to say how long the most enduring would last? A classical example, however, of enduring inhibition in response to a single volley is that of Ballif et al. (1925) which lasted for a second.

Much has been said in the past concerning the duration of the single inhibiting effect. Beritoff (1914, 1924) argued for extreme brevity, the individual process not exceeding 4 msec. On the other hand Eccles and Sherrington (1931) concluded that the inhibition produced by any particular impulse persists for as long as 50 msec. In any event it is agreed that the single inhibitory effect is brief by comparison with evidences of inhibition in the course of integrated activity. At some point everyone, it seems, has found necessary the postulation of delay paths (Forbes), or internuncial chains, to account for prolongation of effect. The point is well made by Liddell in his discussion of "Integration, then and now" (1949). He writes in part:

> "For the scratch reflex of the spinal animal Sherrington suggested the co-operation of at least three neurones, the afferent, the proprio-spinal, and the final common path to the muscles. In light of modern knowledge concerning the fleeting states of activity in single neurones, contrasted with the slow tempo of processes in the integrated scratch reflex it is clear that many side-chains of interneurones must nowadays be postulated."

We are on safe ground if we say that the single inhibitory act exerted at the motoneurons by proprioceptive afferents is one that increments to maximum in 0·5 msec and dissipates exponentially to $1/e$ in 4 msec.

Having in hand a well defined example of central inhibition as a single effect with a well-defined time course, one should be wary of extension to other systems. The presently known example pertains to a very particular reflex path endowed with a very particular sort of afferent fiber, and a very particular sort of neuron, the motoneuron. Other sorts of endings acting upon other sorts of neurons may, and probably do, exert in the spinal cord a "single" inhibitory effect of different dimension.

Place Theory

In many formulations of inhibition location upon the neuron of synaptic knobs, supposedly excitatory or inhibitory, becomes a consideration. Place theory, as it may be called, arises in connection with the hypothesis of Gerard and Gesell already discussed. It appears also in hypothesis considering decremental conduction and in hypothesis of direct inhibition by specific inhibitory action.

Until recently most thought on place theory has been based on physiological induction from anatomical studies on Mauthner's cell (Bartelmez and Hoerr, 1933; Bodian, 1937, 1940). Of more interest, however, for studies on the mammalian spinal cord are those of Sprague (1958) who followed terminal degeneration of various groupings of afferent fibers in regions where motoneurons are known to be excited or conversely to be inhibited by the action of those afferent fibers. Briefly put, degeneration was found on the cell bodies and some dendrites of motoneurons that would be excited monosynaptically by the severed dorsal roots, but was confined to dendrites of those motoneurons that would be inhibited. These findings at the very least assure that place theory, whatever the exact framework may be, must be taken seriously.

One form of hypothesis in which place theory might play a role is an interference hypothesis reconsidered. The recent redemonstration of decremental conduction in nerve by Lorente de Nó and Condouris (1959) serves to focus attention upon decremental conduction generally and upon the properties of the cell body and dendrites in particular. A large body of evidence (Renshaw, 1942; Lloyd, 1951a, b, 1959) testifies to the normal existence of a conduction decrement, at least in the cellulifugal sense, in the dendrites of spinal motoneurons. Assuming that dendritic conduction in the dendrites of spinal motoneurons is decremental also in the cellulipetal sense we have at hand all the necessary requirement for inhibition to take place according to an interference hypothesis of the Keith Lucas type (cf. Lorente de Nó and Condouris, 1959). Whilst thinking in this wise one should not neglect the potentialities, of which we know little, for decremental conduction in the fine presynaptic structures.

Recently another use has been made of place theory which accords well with the anatomical observations of Sprague. Frank and Fuortes (1957) and Frank (1959) have found examples of direct inhibition in which a recordable inhibitory postsynaptic potential is not generated in the inhibited moto-neurons. This effect they call "remote inhibition". One of the two explana-tions advanced is that the inhibitory endings concerned may be located so far out on the dendrites that an intracellular microelectrode in the cell body may not "see" the hyperpolarization otherwise presumed to occur. This is imperceptibly different from an hypothesis of the Keith Lucas type. Their other suggestion concerning remote inhibition supposes a presynaptic block, the inhibitory fibers blocking excitatory presynaptic impulses but not them-selves reaching the motoneuron. This latter suggestion, one will appreciate, is a direct descendant of the ideas advanced by Renshaw (1946) and by McCulloch et al. (1952) which were discussed earlier. It is not a part of place theory.

It is not easy to judge the role that place theory may have in future formula-tions of inhibition. The anatomical evidence of Sprague (1958) is suggestive, but whether or not location of inhibitory endings on dendrites confers some essential quality to their action remains problematical.

Inhibitory Postsynaptic Potential

Positive potentials associable with depression in the spinal cord have been known for some time (Gasser, 1937; Bernhard and Skoglund, 1947; Bernhard et al., 1947). Since the discovery by intracellular recording (Brock et al., 1952) that a so-called inhibitory postsynaptic potential could, as in other tissues, be recorded from motoneurons of the spinal cord much has been made of this deflection, the time course of which somewhat resembles that of direct inhibition. Several pertinent questions must be raised concerning the role of inhibitory postsynaptic potentials.

Firstly, is the i.p.s.p. a necessary accompaniment of inhibition in the monosynaptic reflex system? The answer is as unequivocally no as it is in relation to inhibition of crustacean muscle fiber (Fatt and Katz, 1953). It appears if the motoneurons are known to be partly depolarized (Lloyd and Wilson, 1959) or if there is good reason to suppose they are, as when impaled by intracellular microelectrodes. One might suppose that a background of excitatory internuncial barrage could provide the appropriate conditions for appearance.

Secondly, can i.p.s.p. be regarded as the cause of inhibition? Again the answer is no. A process that need not be present when an effect is registered cannot be the cause of that effect. It can at best have a parallel relationship to a common cause with the effect in question. But further, the time course of i.p.s.p. does not conform with that required for a causal process of inhibition. It begins some considerable fraction of a millisecond after the onset of inhibition (Lloyd and Wilson, 1959) if measurements of its latency are correct, which presumably they are. It reaches a maximum of intensity in 1·5 msec (Coombs et al., 1955) to 2·0 msec (Eccles, 1955) whereas inhibition is maximal at from 0·5 to 0·6 msec. This sort of temporal relation between inhibition and potential change is exactly that found for crab muscle fiber inhibition in 1953 by Fatt and Katz, and their statement:

> "It need hardly be emphasized that the I–potential, as such, has no significance as an inhibitory *agent*" (italics theirs),

is as true for the spinal motoneuron as it is for the crustacean muscle fiber.

When potentials having the direction of increased polarization, which is to say i.p.s.p.'s, are recorded, it seems best to think of them in terms of repolarization in the sense used and discussed by Kolmodin and Skoglund (1958) rather than in terms of hyperpolarization as is frequently done.

Chemical Transmitter Hypotheses of Inhibition

Once convinced of the hypothesis of chemical transmission Eccles (1953) put forward three thinkable hypotheses to account for monosynaptic reflex inhibition, the simplest and most acceptable of which assumed the same transmitter at all endings with specialized "excitatory" and "inhibitory" "subsynaptic" areas.

Later, dissatisfied with these formulations, Eccles et al. (1956) sought to interpose an interneuron in the direct inhibitory pathway, the sole purpose for which was to act as a commutator from excitatory to inhibitory action. In this formulation all primary afferent fibers would be excitatory and would release an excitatory transmitter. Those whose function is to inhibit would excite these interneurons which in turn would release an inhibitory transmitter thereby inhibiting motoneurons.

Unfortunately, this form of chemical hypothesis is not in harmony with a number of carefully made observations and considerations (Frank and Sprague, 1959; Lloyd and Wilson, 1959).

Thus, although a chemical hypothesis is at the present time the more worthy of consideration we have no fully acceptable hypothesis, nor have we sufficient information upon which to build a theory. The search must go on.

The Role of Inhibition

The role of inhibition in reciprocal innervation came into prominence through the series of papers written by Sherrington at the turn of the century. In his own words (Sherrington, 1933):

> "This 'reciprocal innervation' was quickly found to be of wide occurrence in reflex actions operating the skeletal musculature. Its openness to examination in preparations with 'tonic' background (decerebrate rigidity) made it a welcome and immediate opportunity for the more precise study of inhibition as a central process."

A little later in his Nobel Lecture Sherrington remarks:

> "I will not dwell upon the features of reciprocal innervation; they are well known. I would only remark that owing to the wide occurrence of reciprocal innervation it was not unnatural to suppose at first that the entire scope of reflex inhibition lay within the ambit of the taxis of antagonistic muscles and antagonistic movements. Further study of the central nervous action, however, finds central inhibition too extensive and ubiquitous to make it likely that it is confined solely to the taxis of antagonistic muscles."

Sherrington's well considered view is that which is generally held today with vastly more detailed information to hand. This particularly is true of the disynaptic reflex system (Laporte and Lloyd, 1952) of the spinal cord which has as its receptor origin the Golgi tendon organs and its expression in classical reflex physiology as the lengthening reaction. The monosynaptic reflex system of the myotatic reflex is more clearly confined in its fields of action to the requirements of reciprocal innervation (Lloyd, 1946a, b, 1960). In fact the notion is altogether a worthy one that the monosynaptic system in operation is within itself a major factor in the genesis of reciprocal innervation under the command to movement from higher centers.

In describing the integrative role of inhibition in the spinal cord there are altogether four systems to be considered. These are (1) the monosynaptic system, (2) the disynaptic system, (3) the polysynaptic system, and (4) the recurrent system.

The monosynaptic system. The structure of the monosynaptic system is now well known (Lloyd, 1946b; Laporte and Lloyd, 1952; R. M. Eccles and Lundberg, 1958). There is agreement that the inhibitory action arising from the muscle spindle primary endings of one muscle is distributed to the motor nuclei of other muscles in accordance with the requirements of reciprocal innervation.

The functional importance of monosynaptic connection lies in the fact that by this sort of connection the motoneuron inevitably is influenced by action in the peripheral receptor. There is no stage at which the reaction can be blocked. If mechanical change takes place of a sort to excite muscle spindles in one muscle then the motoneurons of all the members joined to it by monosynaptic interconnection, together constituting a myotatic unit (Lloyd, 1946b, 1960), are influenced positively or negatively according to synergic or reciprocal action. Thus no movement is possible without this system coming into play to confer harmony of action in the movement made.

The disynaptic system. In all the relationships of muscles examined (Laporte and Lloyd, 1952) those between muscles which possess monosynaptic interconnection in a given direction, excitatory or inhibitory, proved to contain an element in the opposite sense, inhibitory or excitatory, by means of pathways that possess in their linkage an intercalated interneuron. That the function of the interneurons of the disynaptic system is to serve as a valve seems quite clear. Their role has been described as follows (Lloyd, 1958):

> "To illustrate this (the valve-like action) one returns to consideration of the stretch reflex of the lengthening reaction, with their respective monosynaptic and disynaptic pathways . . . . Not enough difference exists between the stretch threshold of the muscle spindle, afferent end-organ for the stretch reflex, and that of the tendon organ, afferent for the lengthening reaction, to account for the great difference in reflex threshold of the two reflex arcs in the decerebrate animal. Furthermore, in the spinal animal it is the inhibition of the lengthening reaction rather than the excitation of the stretch reflex that is the presenting feature (Henneman, 1951) . . .
>
> "That stretch excitation of autochthonous motoneurons is present at all degrees of stretch follows from the fact that monosynapticity of action implies inevitability of action. That the inhibition may dominate in the spinal animal and yet be held in check in the decerebrate means that the internuncial link of the disynaptic path is open in the former and closed in the latter."

It is, then, by this means that an inco-ordinate clash of reflex effect is obviated in integrative action.

But the disynaptic system has as its field of action one much wider than the myotatic unit and in this wider field of action inhibition only has been found (Laporte and Lloyd, 1952). This external field of action transcends the boundaries of a given region and influences for the most part, but not exclusively, the extensors. The lengthening reaction must be considered as a general collapse of the extensor tonus of the limb.

Polysynaptic systems. Inhibition in polysynaptic systems is inadequately studied, but this is no measure of its importance. The chains of interneurons fashioned into the patterns described by Lorente de Nó (1933) here find their expression in all but a very few reactions of the spinal cord. Although their structure is not known, it is economy of hypothesis to suppose that there are two pools, constituting half-centers after the concept of Graham Brown, that (speaking only of inhibition) are inhibitory to the flexor and extensor final common paths, respectively. Feeding into these would be all the varied influences supra-spinal, spinal and peripheral meeting in convergence on common ground to make of those interneurons a common path to the motoneuron.

The recurrent inhibitory system. The last of the four systems mentioned is that of the recurrent inhibition. This has received the great burden of attention in recent years. From an operational point of view recurrend inhibition is that which takes place in certain motoneuron pools following antidromic stimulation of axons from other motor pools (Renshaw, 1941; Lloyd, 1951b; Eccles *et al.*, 1954; Granit *et al.*, 1957; Brooks and Wilson, 1958). The inhibition is associated with facilitation (Renshaw, 1941; Lloyd, 1951b; Wilson *et al.*, 1960). Although the course of recurrent conditioning, within a nucleus, inhibitory and facilitatory, exactly matches the flows of after-currents about the active motoneurons (Lloyd, 1951b), and hence might seem to be causally related, the effect is generally considered to be due to action of recurrent motor collaterals acting through interneurons, the latter rather widely known as "Renshaw cells".

Opinions vary concerning the functional role of recurrent inhibition. Renshaw (1941) emphasized the local nature of recurrent inhibition, the main influences in his experiments being confined to motoneurons in the same segmental level.

In Eccles' (1955) view the functional significance of the pathway for recurrent inhibition is that of a negative feed-back control over motoneuron activity, which, having no specific distribution, cannot fulfill a co-ordinative role. It is considered as having an anticonvulsant function.

Granit *et al.* (1957) regard the recurrent system as they designed for stabilization of the sustained output of impulses in the stretch reflex. Brooks' and Wilson's (1958) view is somewhat different as they see in the recurrent system a mechanism that serves to assist in preservation of the localized nature of stretch reflexes.

Wilson (1959) has devoted attention to the usually neglected recurrent facilitation which is outside the present main theme. But it is an important consideration that Wilson *et al.* (1960), by a systematic study of the distribution of recurrent facilitation and inhibition, find a pattern that is not unlike that of the inverse myotatic reflex arising from tendon organ, or 1 B, endings. Facilitation is prominently found among flexor groups. Inhibition, of course, is most prominent between synergists in a myotatic unit.

Having in mind the various pieces of evidence concerning action in the recurrent system it would seem a fair assumption that it plays a trigger role in the reversal that takes place on forcible stretching from stretch reflex to lengthening reaction.

As has been mentioned, both spindle and tendon receptors must be active even at moderate stretch for their peripheral thresholds are not greatly different. In the decerebrate animal, the stretch reflex prevails with the antagonist system held in check at the internuncial level of its disynaptic pathway. As the stretch reflex gains in force by increased stretch the recurrent action necessarily increases *pari passu* with it (as parenthetically does the inverse myotatic reflex input). At some point reversal in the reflex taxis of the limb takes place. It seems entirely likely that the recurrent action of the motoneurons is involved and that the motoneurons in effect control the extent to which they can be driven by monosynaptic reflex afferent impingement.

REFERENCES

ADRIAN, E. D. (1924) Some recent work on inhibition. *Brain* **47** : 399–416.
BALLIF, L., FULTON, J. F. and LIDDELL, E. G. T. (1925) Observations on spinal and decerebrate knee-jerks with special reference to their inhibition by single break-shocks. *Proc. Roy. Soc. (London)* B **98** : 589–607.
BARRON, D. H. and MATTHEWS, B. H. C. (1935) Intermittent conduction in the spinal cord *J. Physiol. (London)* **85** : 73–103.
BARTELMEZ, G. W. and HOERR, N. L. (1933) The vestibular club endings in Améivrus. Further evidence on the morphology of the synapse. *J. Comp. Neurol.* **57** : 401–428.
BERITOFF, J. S. (1914) Die zentrale resiproke Hemmung auf Grund der elektrischen Erscheinungen am Muskel I über die Hemmungsrhythmik bei der reflektorischen Innervation. *Z. Biol.* **64** : 175–187.
BERITOFF, J. S. (1924) Über den Rhythmus der reziproken Innervation der antagonistischen Muskeln bei Warmblütern. *Z. Biol.* **80** : 171–192.
BERITOFF, J. S. (1959) On the origin of central inhibition. *XXI Congreso Internacional de Ciencias Fisiológicas.* Buenos Aires.
BERNHARD, C. G. and SKOGLUND, C. R. (1947) Slow positive and negative ventral root potentials accompanying extension and flexion evoked by medullary stimulation. *Acta Physiol. Scand.* 14 Suppl. **47** : 7, 1–12.
BERNHARD, C. G., SKOGLUND, C. R. and THERMAN, P. O. (1947) Studies on the potential level in ventral root under varying conditions. *Acta Physiol. Scand.* 14 Suppl. **47** : 8, 1–10.
BODIAN, D. (1937) The structure of the vertebrate synapse. *J. Comp. Neurol.* **68** : 117–145.
BODIAN, D. (1940) Further notes on the vertebrate synapse. *J. Comp. Neurol.* **73** : 323–337.
BREMER, F. (1947) Nerve and synaptic conduction. *Ann. Rev. Physiol.* **9** : 457–476.
BROCK, L. G., COOMBS, J. S. and ECCLES, J. C. (1952) The recording of potentials from motoneurones with an intracellular electrode. *J. Physiol. (London)* **117** : 431–460.
BRONK, D. W. (1939) Synaptic mechanisms in sympathetic ganglia. *J. Neurophysiol.* **2** : 380–401.
BROOKS, C. M. and ECCLES, J. C. (1947) An electrical hypothesis of central inhibition. *Nature* **159** : 760–764.
BROOKS, V. B. and WILSON, V. J. (1958) Localization of stretch reflexes by recurrent inhibition. *Science* **127** : 472–473.
CASTILLO, J. DEL and KATZ, B. (1955) Production of membrane potential changes in the frog's heart by inhibitory nerve impulses. *Nature* **175** : 1035.
COOMBS, J. S., ECCLES, J. C. and FATT, P. (1955) The inhibitory suppression of reflex discharges from motoneurones. *J. Physiol. (London)* **130** : 396–413.
ECCLES, J. C. (1935) Facilitation and inhibition in the superior cervical ganglion. *J. Physiol. (London)* **85** : 207–238.
ECCLES, J. C. (1953) *The Neurophysiological Basis of Mind: The Principles of Neurophysiology.* Clarendon Press, Oxford.
ECCLES, J. C. (1955) *The Physiology of Nerve Cells.* Johns Hopkins Press, Baltimore.

ECCLES, J. C., FATT, P. and KOKETSU, K. (1954) Cholinergic and inhibitory synapses in a pathway from motor-axon collaterals to motoneurones. *J. Physiol.* (*London*) **126** : 524–562.

ECCLES, J. C., FATT, P. and LANDGREN, S. (1956) Central pathway for direct inhibitory action of impulses in largest afferent nerve fibres to muscle. *J. Neurophysiol.* **19** : 75–98.

ECCLES, J. C. and SHERRINGTON, C. S. (1931) Studies on the flexor reflex—VI. Inhibition. *Proc. Roy. Soc.* (*London*) B **109** : 91–113.

ECCLES, R. M. and LUNDBERG, A. (1958) Integrative pattern of Ia synaptic actions on motoneurones of hip and knee muscles. *J. Physiol.* (*London*) **144** : 271–298.

EINTHOVEN, W. and RADEMAKER, A. C. A. (1916) Über die angebliche positive Strom-schwankung in der Schildkröten Vorkammer bei Vagusreizung nebst Bemerkungen über den Zusammenhang zwischen Kontraktion und Aktionsstrom. *Arch. ges. Physiol. Pflüger's* **166** : 109–143.

FATT, P. and KATZ, B. (1953) The effect of inhibitory nerve impulses on a crustacean muscle fibre. *J. Physiol.* (*London*) **121** : 374–389.

FELDBERG, W. and GADDUM, J. H. (1934) The chemical transmitter at synapses in a sym-pathetic ganglion. *J. Physiol.* (*London*) **81** : 305–319.

FELDBERG, W. and VARTIANEN, A. (1934) Further observations on the physiology and pharmacology of a sympathetic ganglion. *J. Physiol.* (*London*) **83** : 103–128.

FRANK, K. (1959) Basic mechanisms of synaptic transmission in the central nervous system. *IRE Trans. on Med. Electronics* **Me-6** : 85–88.

FRANK, K. and FUORTES, M. G. F. (1957) Presynaptic and postsynaptic inhibition of monosynaptic reflexes. *Federation Proc.* **16** : 39–40.

FRANK, K. and SPRAGUE, J. M. (1959) Direct contralateral inhibition in the lower sacral spinal cord. *Exptl. Neurol.* **1** : 28–43.

GASKELL, W. H. (1887) On the action of muscarin upon the heart, and on the electrical changes in the non-beating cardiac muscle brought about by stimulation of the inhibitory and augmentor nerves. *J. Physiol.* (*London*) **8** : 404–415.

GASSER, H. S. (1937) The control of excitation in the nervous system. *Harvey Lectures* **32** : 169–193.

GERARD, R. W. (1932) Nerve metabolism. *Physiol Revs.* **12** : 469–592.

GESELL, R. (1940) A neurophysiological interpretation of the respiratory act. *Ergeb. Physiol.* **43** : 477–639.

GRAHAM, H. T. (1935) The subnormal period of nerve response. *Am. J. Physiol.* **111** : 452–465.

GRANIT, R., PASCOE, J. E. and STEG, G. (1957) The behavior of tonic α and γ motoneurones during stimulation of recurrent collaterals. *J. Physiol.* (*London*) **138** : 381–400.

KATO, G. (1924) *The Theory of Decrementless Conduction in Narcotised Region of Nerve.* Nankado, Tokyo.

KIBJAKOV, A. W. (1932) Über humorale Übertragung der Erregung von einem Neuron auf das andere. *Arch. ges. Physiol. Pflüger's* **232** : 432–453.

KOLMODIN, G. M. and SKOGLUND, C. R. (1958) Slow membrane potential changes accom-panying excitation and inhibition in spinal moto- and interneurons in the cat during natural activation. *Acta Physiol. Scand.* **44** : 11–54.

LAPORTE, Y. and LLOYD, D. P. C. (1952) Nature and significance of the reflex connections established by large afferent fibers of muscular origin. *Am. J. Physiol.* **169** : 609–621.

LIDDELL, E. G. T. (1949) Integration, then and now. *J. Neurol. Neurosurg. Psychiat.* **12** : 81–85.

LLOYD, D. P. C. (1938) The transmission of impulses by ganglionic direct fibers. *J. Physiol.* (*London*) **93** : 86–89.

LLOYD, D. P. C. (1939) The excitability states of inferior mesenteric ganglion cells following preganglionic activation. *J. Physiol.* (*London*) **95** : 464–475.

LLOYD, D. P. C. (1941) A direct central inhibitory action of dromically conducted impulses. *J. Neurophysiol.* **4** : 184–190.

LLOYD, D. P. C. (1946a) Facilitation and inhibition of spinal motoneurons. *J. Neuro-physiol.* **9** : 421–438.

30 DAVID P. C. LLOYD

LLOYD, D. P. C. (1946b) Integrative pattern of excitation and inhibition in two-neuron reflex arcs. *J. Neurophysiol.* **9** : 439–444.

LLOYD, D. P. C. (1951a) Electrical signs of impulse conduction in spinal motoneurons. *J. Gen. Physiol.* **35** : 255–288.

LLOYD, D. P. C. (1951b) After-currents, after-potentials, excitability and ventral root electrotonus in spinal motoneurons. *J. Gen. Physiol.* **35** : 289–321.

LLOYD, D. P. C. (1958) *The Discrete and the Diffuse in Nervous Action.* James Arthur Lecture. The American Museum of Natural History, New York.

LLOYD, D. P. C. (1959) Temperature and dendritic response of spinal motoneurons. *Proc. Natl. Acad. Sci. U.S.* **45** : 589–592.

LLOYD, D. P. C. (1960) On the monosynaptic reflex interconnections of hind limb muscles. *International Meeting of Neurobiologists.* Elsevier, Amsterdam. 289–297.

LLOYD, D. P. C. and WILSON, V. J. (1959) Functional organization in the terminal segments of the spinal cord with a consideration of central excitatory and inhibitory latencies. *J. Gen. Physiol.* **42** : 1219–1231.

LOEWI, O. (1921) Über humorale Übertragbarkeit der Herznervenwirkung. *Arch. ges. Physiol. Pflüger's* **189** : 239–242.

LORENTE DE NÓ, R. (1933) Vestibulo-ocular reflex arc. *A.M.A. Arch. Neurol. Psychiat.* **30** : 245–291.

LORENTE DE NÓ, R. (1936) Inhibition of motoneurones. *Problems of Nervous Physiology and of Behavior.* Symposium dedicated to Professor I. BERITASHVILI. Tbilisi.

LORENTE DE NÓ, R. (1939) Transmission of impulses through cranial motor nuclei. *J. Neurophysiol.* **2** : 402–464.

LORENTE DE NÓ, R. and CONDOURIS, G. A. (1959) Decremental conduction in peripheral nerve, integration of stimuli in the neuron. *Proc. Natl. Acad. Sci. U.S.* **45** : 592–617.

LUCAS, K. (1917) *Conduction of the Nervous Impulse.* Longmans, Green, London.

MARAZZI, A. S. (1939) Electrical studies on the pharmacology of autonomic synapses—II. The action of a sympathomimetic drug (epinephrine) on sympathetic ganglia. *J. Pharm. Exptl. Therap.* **65** : 395–404.

McCULLOCH, W. S., LETTVIN, J. Y., PITTS, W. C. and DELL, P. C. (1952) An electrical hypothesis of central inhibition and facilitation. *Research Publs. Assoc. Research Nervous Mental Disease* **30** : 87–97.

McDOUGAL, W. (1903) The nature of inhibitory processes within the nervous system. *Brain* **26** : 153–191.

OBRADOR, S. and ODORIZ, J. B. (1936) Transmission through a lumbar sympathetic ganglion. *J. Physiol. (London)* **86** : 269–276.

RENSHAW, B. (1941) Influence of discharge of motoneurons upon excitation of neighboring motoneurons. *J. Neurophysiol.* **4** : 167–183.

RENSHAW, B. (1942) Effects of presynaptic volleys on spread of impulses over the soma of the motoneurons. *J. Neurophysiol.* **5** : 235–243.

RENSHAW, B. (1946) Observations on interaction of nerve impulses in the gray matter and on the nature of central inhibition. *Am. J. Physiol.* **146** : 443–448.

SAMOJLOFF, A. (1923) Die positive Schwankung des Ruhestromes am Verhofe des Schildkrötenherzens bei Vagusreizung (Gaskells Phänomen). *Arch. ges. Physiol. Pfluger's* **199** : 579–594.

SAMOJLOFF, A. and KISSELEFF, M. (1927) Zur Characteristik der Zentralen Hemmingsprozesse. *Arch. ges. Physiol. Pflüger's* **215** : 699–715.

SETCHENOW, I. M. (1863) Note sur les modérateurs des moovements réflexes dans le cerveau de la grenouille. *Compt. rend.* **50–53** : 185–187.

SHERRINGTON, C. S. (1906) *Integrative Action of the Nervous System.* Yale University Press, New Haven.

SHERRINGTON, C. S. (1925) Remarks on some aspects of reflex inhibition. *Proc. Roy. Soc. (London)* B **97** : 519–545.

SHERRINGTON, C. S. (1933) Inhibition as a co-ordinative factor. *Les Prix Nobel en 1932.* P.A. Norstedt, Stockholm.

SPRAGUE, J. M. (1958) The distribution of dorsal root fibres on motor cells in the lumbo-sacral spinal cord of the cat, and the site of excitatory and inhibitory terminals in monosynaptic pathways. *Proc. Roy. Soc. (London)* B **149** : 534–556.

TRAUTWEIN, W., KUFFLER, S. W. and EDWARDS, C. (1956) Changes in membrane charac-teristics of heart muscle during inhibition. *J. Gen. Physiol.* **40** : 135–145.

WEBER, E. F. D. and WEBER, E. H. (1845) Experimenta, quibus, probatur nervos vagos rotatione machinae galvano-magneticae irritatos, motum cordi retardare et adeo intercipare. *Ann. Univ. Med. Milano* **20** : 227.*

WEDENSKY, N. E. (1903) Die Erregung, Hemmung und Narkose. *Arch. ges. Physiol. Pflüger's* **100** : 1–144.

WILSON, V. J. (1959) Recurrent facilitation of spinal reflexes. *J. Gen. Physiol.* **42** : 703–713.

WILSON, V. J., TALBOT, W. H. and DIECKE, F. P. J. (1960) Distribution of recurrent facili-tation in cat spinal cord. *J. Neurophysiol.* **23** : 144–153.

* Not consulted in the original.

ANATOMICAL ASPECTS OF INHIBITORY
PATHWAYS AND SYNAPSES

JOHN SZENTÁGOTHAI

Anatomy Department, University Medical School of Pécs, Hungary

ANATOMICAL information on inhibitory pathways and synapses in vertebrates is scanty. Certain histological types of neurons (Golgi cells), axon collaterals, and synapses on the axon hillock or around the initial segment of the axon have been assumed to be concerned with inhibition. None of these assumptions, however, is based on direct experimental evidence. The development of intracellular recording techniques has recently brought forth evidence that inhibition is exerted at least on motor and some other types of spinal neurons by specific and generally short inhibitory neurons. This concept offers us a chance to investigate some of the better known inhibitory mechanisms in the spinal cord and the brain stem with the methods of experimental neuro-histology.

This approach to the problem is based primarily on the secondary degeneration of synapses, a method which can be exploited in two directions. Histological signs of synaptic degeneration can be directly observed with the aid of impregnation after destruction of nuclei or transection of pathways. Another possibility is to look for the synapses which remain intact after certain experimental interference and sufficient time for complete disintegration and resorption of the nervous elements involved. This procedure is especially rewarding in the pursuit of short neuronal connexions, as assumed to be involved in inhibitory mechanisms. For this purpose we have to destroy the majority of the longer connexions or to isolate smaller parts of the CNS neuronally, leaving the vascular supply intact. Any intact synapse found in such isolated fragments about one or two months after isolation must arise from neurons situated in the isolated part itself. We shall refer to this method briefly as "method of persisting elements".

Since the hypothesis of inhibitory action of synapses located on the axon hillock (Gesell, 1940; Gesell et al., 1954; Retzlaff, 1954, 1957) could neither be proved nor disproved, we resorted to some methods of experimental embryology suited to produce by artificial recombination of tissues simplified "nervous system models" completely lacking any organoid structure or organized pattern of neuronal connexions. If inhibition were based on such minute spatial and geometric relations between neurons, as required by this

32

hypothesis, it should be lacking in preparations with a haphazard arrangement of nervous elements. If on the contrary inhibition were brought about by chemical transmission from certain neurons with a specific metabolic set-up, inhibitory activity could be expected to persist in such models.

1. DIRECT INHIBITION OF MOTONEURONS BY PRIMARY AFFERENTS

The existence of a direct synaptic contact between primary sensory neurons and motoneurons has been known from the early classical descriptions of spinal cord structure. Their existence could be ascertained by secondary degeneration of synapses. The fact postulated by physiological evidence, that only muscle spindle afferents have direct monosynaptic contact with moto- neurons, could be verified histologically in the trigeminal system, where the perikaria of muscular afferents are situated outside the Gasserian ganglion within the mesencephalic tract of the trigeminus (Szentágothai, 1948). Earlier it has generally been supposed that the annulospiral afferents of muscle may have inhibitory endings on motoneurons (Lloyd, 1946; Laporte and Lloyd, 1952; Brock et al., 1952). More recent investigations with intra- cellular recording, however, have led to the assumption that an inhibitory interneuron—probably situated in the intermediate nucleus of Cajal—must be intercalated in the pathway (Eccles et al., 1954). Degeneration of synapses after transection of lower lumbar dorsal roots has given conflicting results (Schimert, 1939; Sprague, 1956; Szentágothai, 1958) probably because of relatively long descending excitatory collaterals of Ia afferents (Eccles et al., 1957). On the whole, however, histological evidence is against assumption of direct inhibitory collaterals to motoneurons of the lumbosacral enlargement of the cord (Szentágothai, 1958).

More recently Lloyd and Wilson (1959) claim direct inhibitory connexions of primary afferents to contralateral motoneurons in S_3. This has been investigated in our laboratory after transection of the dorsal root S_3. Direct dorsal root collaterals crossing the midline are rather rare in other segments (Schimert, 1939), their number is considerable, however, in the small sacral segments. They cross in both commissures, most of them in the middle bundle (faisceau moyen of Cajal) of the dorsal grey commissure, but a fair number is seen also in the anterior white commissure. Most of these collaterals end with terminal knobs on smaller medial cells of the ventral horn. Very few fragments of extremely fine collaterals can be traced into the region of contra- lateral motoneurons, but no degenerating terminal knobs have been found in immediate neighbourhood of motoneurons (Figs. 3 and 4). The difference between the ipsilateral and contralateral side is spectacular (Figs. 1–3). In the S_2 segment there are a few direct sensory neuron collaterals to be traced to

4

the contralateral motoneurons, but these according to the findings of Curtis, Krnjevic and Miledi (1958) may be considered as excitatory ones.

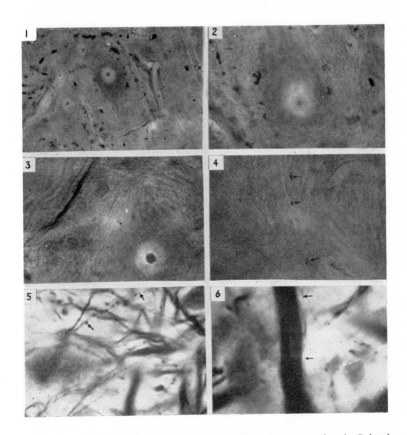

Fig. 1. Degenerated dorsal root collaterals in ipsilateral motor nucleus in S_3 level 4 days after transection of dorsal root S_3. Cat. Nauta method. ×1350.

Fig. 2. Part of Fig. 1 with higher magnification. ×2700.

Fig. 3. Contralateral motor nucleus in S_3 level 4 days after transection of dorsal root S_3. No signs of degeneration around motor neurons. Same slide as Figs. 1 and 2. ×2700.

Fig. 4. Few degenerated fragments (indicated by arrows) found in contralateral motor nucleus S_3 after transection of dorsal root S_3. Compare size and distance of fragments with Fig. 2 of same magnification. Same slide as Figs. 1 and 2.

Fig. 5. Oculomotor nucleus 5 days after focal electrolytic lesion in the region of Darkschewitsch's nucleus. Degenerated very thin fibre indicated by arrows Bielschowsky–Gros method. ×3000.

Fig. 6. Isolated motor horn preparation of the segment L_7 in the dog. Intact fine fibre closely attached to motoneuron dendrite. Bielschowsky–Gros method. ×3000.

2. THE HISTOLOGICAL BASIS OF RENSHAW INHIBITION

Initial motor axon collaterals in the spinal cord have been described by several authors in the last century. Nothing has been known until recently on their synaptic contacts. The findings of Eccles *et al.* (1954) seemed to offer an excellent opportunity for histological control and identification of inhibitory synapses, by the method of persisting elements. The results having been published (Szentágothai, 1958); a diagram suffices to summarize them (Fig. 7). The ventral quadrant of the spinal cord has been isolated at L_7 by splitting the cord longitudinally for about 1 cm, crushing half of the cord at the upper and lower end of the incision, and finally removing the dorsal quadrant of the isolated half. The completely isolated ventral quadrant of the cord receives its blood supply from the vessels of the preserved anterior root. After two months only a small marginal part of the ventral horn remains intact, because of the destruction of the deep anterior fissure arteries, which supply the medial and central parts of the ventral column (Fig. 7, B). In this part of the grey matter only motoneurons and the supposed Renshaw cells are preserved, so that any intact synapse found must either belong to motoneuron initial collaterals or Renshaw cell axons. Not a single terminal knob has been found on several hundred well preserved motoneurons investigated. That terminal knobs of motoneurons may be well preserved in isolated spinal cord segments, emerges from other experiments in which the whole segment has been isolated by crushing the sacral part of the cord at two levels 5 mm apart and transecting the dorsal roots entering the isolated segment. In these preparations intact terminal knobs are seen frequently on motoneurons. Well preserved terminal knobs are found, however, in our isolated ventral horn preparations on smaller cells generally situated on the anterior border of the ventral horn (Fig. 7, C and D), where the motor axons begin to gather into bundles. These observations substantiate the suggestion of Eccles *et al.* (1954a) concerning the pathway of recurrent inhibition. Their evidence for the excitatory nature of these synapses of initial motoneuron collaterals on Renshaw cells, gives weight to the argument that terminal knobs are generally excitatory. We of course looked most thoroughly for intact synapses on motoneurons, since these would have to carry inhibition from Renshaw cells. Unfortunately we could find nothing apart from an extremely fine meshwork of nerve fibers, being apparently in close contact with motoneurons (Fig. 6). It could of course be argued that these are regenerative phenomena evoked by the degeneration of the majority of fibres enveloping the motoneuron. Considering the very fine calibre of the fibres this explanation is not very probable; the abortive regeneration in the CNS always produces rather coarse fibres of varicose character.* Thus our results are not conclusive concerning the inhibitory

---

* In Golgi preparations of isolated slabs of cerebral and cerebellar cortex, where arborization patterns of neurons are so characteristic and well known, no significant regeneration has been observed (Szentágothai, unpublished).

terminals of Renshaw cells on motoneurons. Considering also other analogous findings, it must be assumed that inhibition is exerted on motoneurons and also other types of larger spinal cord neurons by extremely fine synaptic structures probably largely below the resolving power of the light microscope.

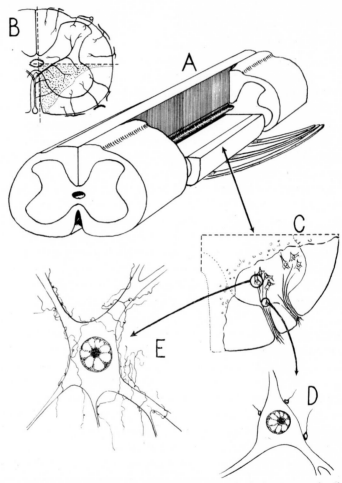

Fig. 7. Diagram illustrating "remaining synapses" in isolated ventral column preparation (A); B shows how arterial supply of the isolated segment is influenced by sagittal and horizontal incisions (broken lines); the dotted region of the isolated ventral quadrant undergoes necrosis. D intact terminal knobs on small (Renshaw) cell located as seen in diagram C. E around motoneurons only a meshwork of extremely fine fibres remains intact.

3. INHIBITORY PATHWAYS OF OCULOMOTOR NEURONS

The oculomotor mechanisms offer wonderful opportunities to investigate the anatomy of inhibitory pathways. Unfortunately the basic physiological facts are only very crudely known. On the other hand the anatomic situation is fairly clear and also conveniently accessible for degeneration experiments. A diagram (Fig. 8) explains the situation. As generally known the cristae ampullares of the labyrinth have strong three-neuron, i.e. bisynaptic, connexions with the extraocular muscles (if the synapse between the receptor epithelium and the primary sensory neuron is neglected). There is a very sharp almost "point to point" projection between the receptors and effectors, each

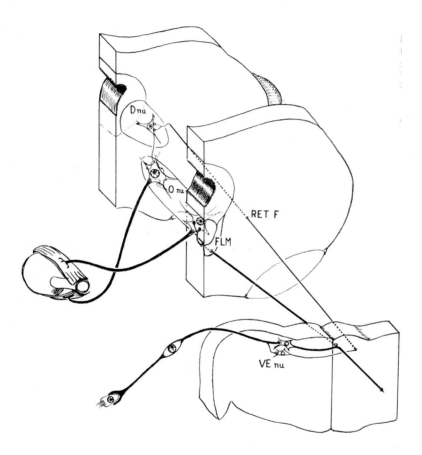

Fig. 8. Diagram illustrating the pathway of reciprocal inhibition in the reflex arc between labyrinth (cristae acusticae) and extraocular muscles. Secondary vestibular neurons ascending in the medial longitudinal fasciculus (FLM) have only excitatory synapses—terminal knobs of rather large size—with oculomotor neurons. Secondary vestibular fibres ascending in the reticular formation (RET F) terminate with end-feet synapses in the region of the Darkschewitsch nucleus on a group of specific inhibitory interneurons (D nu). The mode of connection of these specific neurons with motor ocular neurons (O nu) is not clear. No terminal knob synapses are involved, only extremely fine fibres, the final termination of which cannot be traced under the light microscope.

crista having direct connexions only with two muscles; one of each eye (Szentágothai, 1943, 1950, 1952). These connexions can be brought easily into action by artificial endolymph currents evoked in any one of the semicircular ducts. Reciprocal inhibition in this reflex has a longer latency than excitatory responses, and has apparently quite different pathways. If the medial longitudinal fasciculus is transected between the vestibular and the oculomotor nuclei bisynaptic excitatory responses are abolished, but reciprocal inhibitions are preserved. If on the other hand the whole pons with the exception of the medial longitudinal fascicle is transected the reverse happens, i.e. all bisynaptic excitatory responses are preserved and reciprocal inhibitory responses are abolished (Szentágothai, 1950, 1952).

Tracing these pathways with degeneration methods shows that while secondary vestibular neurons ascending in the medial longitudinal fascicle reach the oculomotor neurons directly and establish synaptic contacts with unusually large terminal knobs, secondary vestibular fibres ascending outside the fasciculus in the reticular formation have no direct access to oculomotor neurons. They terminate, however, with abundant synapses in the region of the Darkschewitsch nucleus and generally in the central grey matter of the midbrain just dorsally and cranially from the oculomotor nucleus. We have been able (Szentágothai and Scháb, 1956) to show that electric stimulation of this region immediately abolishes the effects of even supramaximal labyrinth stimulation by artificial endolymph currents on oculomotor neurons (Fig. 9). However crude this experimental approach, the results suggest as the most simple explanation, that the simplest pathways in the vestibulo–oculomotor reflex are separated anatomically and the inhibitory pathway has an additional short specific inhibitory neuron localized in the anterior midbrain central grey matter. This situation would be analogous to the pathway of reciprocal inhibition suggested by Eccles *et al.* (1954b). The situation is still more favourable, since electrolytic lesions can be placed into the Darkschewitsch nucleus and the anterior central grey matter of the mid-brain without danger to destroy any other pathway or fibre system leading to/through the oculomotor nuclei, an experiment which cannot be performed of course in the spinal cord.

Now again the degeneration findings are rather meagre. Although placing lesions not farther from the border of the oculomotor nucleus than 200 μ not a single degenerated terminal knob could be found and only extremely fine fibres around oculomotor neurons showed signs of degeneration (Fig. 5). They were almost on the border of visibility with the best immersion systems, and their branches can be assumed to be beyond their resolving power. The resemblance between these fine degenerating fibres originating from a region where specific inhibitory neurons must be assumed and the meshwork of the fibres remaining intact in our isolated ventral horn preparations is striking. Both observations suggest that inhibition might be exerted on motoneurons by means of a submicroscopic type of synapse.

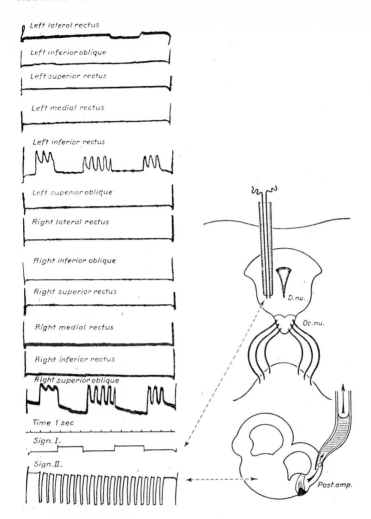

FIG. 9. Inhibition of vestibulo-ocular three-neuron reflexes by electric stimulation of the Darkschewitsch nucleus region. Isolated contractions, among all ocular muscles, in the ipsilateral superior obliquus and contralateral inferior rectus evoked by artificial "from ampulla" endolymph currents in the right posterior semicircular duct (Sign. II, downstroke) are promptly inhibited by electric stimulation of the Darkschewitsch nucleus (Sign. I, upwards). After Szentágothai and Scháb (1956).

4. CLARKE'S COLUMN

Three different types of synapses could be differentiated histologically (Szentágothai and Albert, 1955) in Clarke's column, as explained diagrammatically in Fig. 10, the main histological evidence being demonstrated on microphotograms B, C and D. The main synaptic system of the column derived from muscular afferent neurons entering the cord in lower levels are strange parallel contact synapses of unusual length with occasional very large terminal knobs. They have been called "giant synapses". Their peculiar character is clearly revealed after lower lumbar dorsal root transection

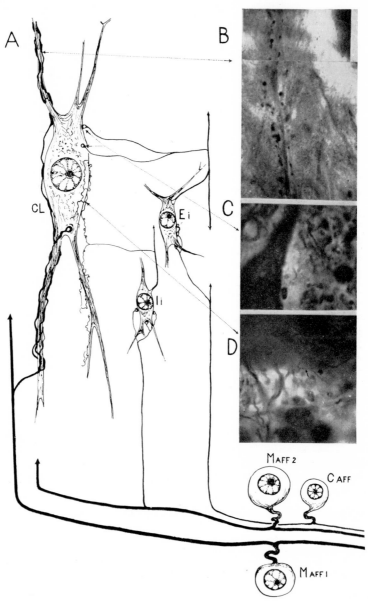

FIG. 10

(Fig. 10, B), when the degenerated fragments of primary sensory neurons can be followed for hundreds of microns surrounding the same Clarke neuron dendrite. The second type are terminal knobs of ordinary size found intact one month after complete de-afferentation of the lower cord (Fig. 10, C), and degenerating after lesions of the lateral funiculus or the grey matter somewhat below their own level. These therefore can be considered as of intraspinal origin. The third type are extremely fine fibres with strange coils and very often closely attached to Clarke neurons, also persisting after complete de-afferentation of the lower cord (Fig. 10, D). Details of contact with Clarke neurons are beyond the power of the light microscope. Since besides the well known direct synaptic action of primary, mostly muscular afferents, two types of interneuronal influence impinge upon Clarke neurons, the synapses of different types can be allocated to the different functions with some probability. The bouton-type apparently belongs to excitatory interneurons as postulated by Holmquist *et al.* (1956) while the fine "coiled" fibre system in analogy to our findings on motoneurons may be considered as the histological basis of inhibitory action as first observed by Laporte *et al.* (1956) and shown by Curtis *et al.* (1958) to be mediated by short interneurons.

5. INHIBITION IN "MODEL NERVOUS SYSTEMS"

Comparison between function and histological structure is especially germane in simplified models produced by artificial recombination of tissues. Completely isolated model nervous systems can easily be obtained by an ingenious method described by Weiss (1950a) but not exploited so far in this

---

Fig. 10. A. Diagram illustrating the three types of synapses identified histologically in Clarke's column. The main synaptic system are the "giant synapses" derived from muscle afferents (M aff 1), which establish extremely long parallel contacts with Clarke (CL) neuron dendrites and have very large boutons terminaux occasionally. Excitatory interneurons (Ei) primarily influenced by cutaneous afferents (C aff) establish synapses with Clarke neurons by means of ordinary end-feet. Inhibitory interneurons (Ii) under synaptic influence from other muscle afferents (M aff 2) may get into synaptic contact with Clarke neurons by means of a meshwork of extremely fine fibres. The microphotographs on right side are giving the histological proofs of this concept. B. Clarke neuron dendrite (in L_3 level) accompanied for hundreds of microns by degenerated fragments of the large parallel contact (giant) synapse, 5 days after transection of dorsal root L_7. Nauta method. C. Intact terminal knob on Clarke neuron (L_3 level) one month after complete de-afferentation of the lower cord (from Th_{10} downwards) by extirpation of all spinal ganglia in the upper and transection of dorsal roots in the lower segments of this part. D. Intact meshwork (arrow) of extremely fine fibres after de-afferentation of the ipsilateral side of the cord (as in case C). Bodian protargol method. $\times 3000$.

problem. Sensory ganglia and/or spinal cord or medulla oblongata fragments of the larval newt are deplanted into the dorsal fin of host larvae of the same species (*Triturus cristatus*, and *Pleurodeles waltli*). An additional limb transplanted nearby serves as indicator of the activity of the isolated model centre. When the preparation begins to function, the host's own spinal cord (i.e. the part underlying the implants) is destroyed in order to exclude interference from the host's own nervous system. In a number of such preparations function and histological structure have thoroughly been compared (Székely and Szentágothai, 1961), and the results can be briefly put as follows.

The muscles of an implanted limb can be innervated successfully only by prospective motoneurons (Weiss, 1950a). If the preparation is built up of medullary neurons only, exclusively irregular spontaneous activity is experienced, which cannot be influenced by physiological stimuli. Reflex activity with responsiveness to natural stimuli (touch) can be achieved if primary sensory neurons (spinal or vagus) are incorporated into the preparation. Both types of activity can be seen in preparations built up of from ten to twenty neurons connected in completely haphazard manner, and without the slightest indication of any organoid character. Terminal knobs are often seen in contact with neurons of medullary origin if primary sensory neurons are present (Figs. 13 and 14). Their preterminal fibres can sometimes directly be traced back to their origin from sensory neurons. Spontaneous activity occurs in preparations lacking terminal knob synapses, and they seem not to be necessary even for true reflexes.

Placing small pieces of filter paper soaked with strychnine on the skin of the dorsal fin covering the deplanted centre greatly enhances spontaneous as well as reflex activity in most of the preparations; in some of them no effect, however, is noticed. No strychnine effect is generally seen during the first few days of developing function, and it disappears again at the onset of metamorphosis, when due to breakdown of circulation in the fin the preparation begins to degenerate. Spontaneous or reflex activity lasts generally for a week or two longer. The strychnine effect is completely independent from the presence or lack of sensory neurons.

Advantage has been taken here of the fact that neurons have early determined specific characters, which enable them to establish effective contacts with certain other types of neurons and perform certain types of functions. These specific properties are retained in spite of considerable disarrangement of nervous structures and complete changes of environmental conditions. They are generally thought to be rooted in the biochemical constitution of the different neuron types (Weiss, 1950b; Sperry, 1955). Since there is reason enough to consider strychnine as specifically blocking the transmission from inhibitory neurons to motoneurons (Coombs *et al.*, 1955; Eccles, 1957), some interesting conclusions can be drawn from observation of such simplified "model nervous systems": (i) arrangement of neurons, cell processes, and interneuronal contacts being completely irregular inhibition cannot be based on any specific localization or geometry of synapses; (ii) being dependent neither from primary sensory nor from motoneurons it must be produced by a third group of neurons acting probably through a humeral agent. These cells may be present or absent in the preparations, and they develop later and degenerate earlier than sensory or motor neurons.

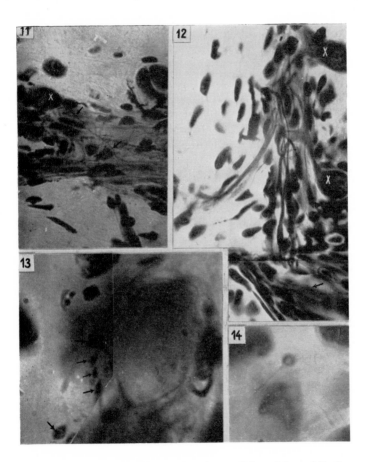

FIG. 11. Deplanted vagus ganglion of larval newt (*Pleurodeles waltli*). Sensory neuron (X) with its process indicated by arrows. Bodian protargol method. × 500.

FIG. 12. Deplanted medulla oblongata, otherwise the same as Fig. 11. Two large motor neurons (X) entering a muscle (arrow) of deplanted limb.

FIG. 13. The same preparation as shown in Fig. 12. Terminal knobs (indicated by arrows) arising from sensory neurons and situated on the surface of motor neurons incorporated in this simplified "nervous system model."

FIG. 14. Same as Fig 13. Terminal knob with its preterminal fibre, which in the preparation can be traced back to deplanted sensory neuron.

6. CONCLUSIONS

On the whole, histological evidence tends to show: (i) that there are no direct inhibitory terminations of sensory neurons reaching motoneurons; (ii) that at least the presence of one additional neuron in the inhibitory pathway has to be assumed in simple reflex arcs;* (iii) that there exists a distinct type of specific inhibitory neurons in the vicinity of the motoneurons, with specific metabolic properties and most probably chemical transmitter activity; and finally (iv) that at least in motoneurons inhibition is not mediated by synapses localized on the axon hillock or the initial segment of the axon.

Unfortunately it has not been possible to identify the inhibitory synapses histologically with certainty. Whenever a pathway yielding monosynaptic excitatory activation is transected, some histologically known type of synapse (in motoneurons the well known boutons terminaux) is found to degenerate after a time interval necessary for secondary degeneration. This is not so in the case of inhibitory pathways. Their destruction does not produce degeneration on the inhibited neuron itself, but generally brings about abundant signs of degeneration of well defined synapses on a group of neurons in the neighbourhood of the cells upon which inhibition is exerted. Thus the histological problem boils down to the detection of synapses between the short specific inhibitory and the motoneurons (or other neurons upon which inhibition is exerted). One should think that this is easy with the aid of Golgi methods. Unfortunately neither in the literature nor in own preparations, especially of the oculomotor system, have such connections been visualized. One must, however, realize that neurites of these smaller types of neurons are not easily stained with Golgi methods and since the problem has arisen only recently, occasionally stained connexions of this type may have passed unnoticed by earlier authors.

However hard we tried to identify these connexions with the aid of experimental histological methods, we found nothing, but extremely fine fibres forming a sparse meshwork between the inhibited neurons. These fibres may be in fairly close contact with the cell surfaces, and their branches must be surely beyond the power of the light microscope. Since almost in any electron microscopical preparation of central nervous organs one can see a wealth of extremely fine elements, which according to size are submicroscopic and from structural properties can be recognized as preterminal and terminal nerve branches, it would be easy to imagine the inhibitory synapses to be submicroscopic. It is a question for physiologists to decide whether, considering the

---

* We have been pointing out repeatedly (Szentágothai, 1952, 1958) the theoretical difficulties which would arise if we were to assume reflex connexions with the same afferent or intermediate neuron giving off excitatory to one and inhibitory synapses to the other (antagonist) muscle group. In this case it would be impossible to let muscles act in different combinations, e.g. muscles *A*, *B* act against *C*, *D* in one and *A*, *D* against *B*, *C* in another combination, etc., as it is very common in labyrinthine eye reflexes.

slow conduction velocities in such extremely fine elements, time relations of inhibition allow such an assumption. The distances to cover are of course short, i.e. of the order of 1–2 mm.

It might be of interest to analyse also other centres from this point of view. Especially the cerebellum, in which the number of different types of synapses on the same final common element, the Purkinje cells and especially the clear and uniform orientation of dendritic and neurite patterns, might present a unique model for the study of such problems. The work of Granit and Phillips (1956) and the three types of inhibition of Purkinje neurons are very promising. Unfortunately stimulation of subcortical structures cannot furnish definitive proof of the histological elements involved, since as already stated by the authors, antidromic excitation of Purkinje axons, orthodromic volleys in their recurrent collaterals, and orthodromic impulses of afferent systems are likely to arrive more or less simultaneously in the cortex under such circumstances. The rapid advance in the understanding of the anatomy of afferent and cortico-cortical connexions in the cerebellum and the oriented character of intracortical systems offers at least from the anatomical point of view favourable chances which might be successfully exploited in the near future. But any statement at present would be necessarily highly speculative.

REFERENCES

BROCK, L. G., COOMBS, S. J. and ECCLES, J. C. (1952) The nature of monosynaptic excitatory and inhibitory processes in the spinal cord. *Proc. Roy. Soc.* (*London*) B **140** : 170–176.

COOMBS, S. J., ECCLES, J. C. and FATT, P. (1955) The inhibitory suppression of reflex discharges from motoneurones. *J. Physiol.* (*London*) **130** : 374–395.

CURTIS, D. R., ECCLES, J. C. and LUNDBERG, A. (1958) Intracellular recording from cells in Clarke's column. *Acta Physiol. Scand.* **43** : 303–314.

CURTIS, D. R., KRNJEVIC, K. and MILEDI, R. (1958) Crossed inhibition of sacral moto-neurones. *J. Neurophysiol.* **21** : 319–326.

ECCLES, J. C. (1957) *The Physiology of Nerve Cells*. Johns Hopkins Press, Baltimore.

ECCLES, J. C., ECCLES, R. M. and LUNDBERG, A. (1957) The convergence of monosynaptic afferents on to many different species of alpha motoneurones. *J. Physiol.* (*London*) **137** : 22–50.

ECCLES, J. C., FATT, P. and KOKETSU, K. (1954a) Cholinergic and inhibitory synapses in a pathway from motor axon collaterals to motoneurones. *J. Physiol.* (*London*) **126** : 524–562.

ECCLES, J. C., FATT, P., LANDGREN, S. and WINSBURY, G. J. (1954b) Spinal cord potentials generated by volley in large muscle afferents. *J. Physiol.* (*London*) **125** : 590–606.

GESELL, R. (1940) Forces driving the respiratory act. *Science* **91** : 229–233.

GESELL, R., BRASSFIELD, C. R. and LILLIE, R. H. (1954) Implementation of electrical energy by paired half centers as revealed by structure and function. *J. Comp. Neurol.* **101** : 331–406.

GRANIT, R. and PHILLIPS, C. G. (1956) Excitatory and inhibitory processes acting upon individual Purkinje cells of the cerebellum in cats. *J. Physiol.* (*London*) **133** : 520–547.

HOLMQUIST, B., LUNDBERG, A. and OSCARSSON, O. (1956) Functional organization of the dorsal spinocerebellar tract in the cat—V. Further experiments on convergence of excitatory and inhibitory action. *Acta Physiol. Scand.* **38** : 76–90.

LAPORTE, Y. and LLOYD, D. P. C. (1952) Nature and significance of reflex connections established by large afferent fibres of muscular origin. *Am. J. Physiol.* **169** : 609–621.

LAPORTE, Y., LUNDBERG, A. and OSCARSSON, O. (1956) Functional organization of the dorsal spinocerebellar tract in the cat—II. Single fibre recording in Flechsigs fasciculus on electric stimulation of various peripheral nerves. *Acta Physiol. Scand.* **36** : 188–203.

LLOYD, D. P. C. (1946) Facilitation and inhibition of motoneurons. *J. Neurophysiol.* **9** : 421–438.

LLOYD, D. P. C. and WILSON, V. J. (1959) Functional organization in the terminal segments of the spinal cord with a consideration of central excitatory and inhibitory latencies in monosynaptic reflex systems. *J. Gen. Physiol* **42** : 1219–1231.

RETZLAFF, E. (1954) Neurophysiological basis for the functioning of paired half-centers. *J. Comp. Neurol.* **101** : 665–687.

RETZLAFF, E. (1957) A mechanism of excitation and inhibition of the Mauthner's cells im teleost. A histological and neurophysiological study. *J. Comp. Neurol.* **107** : 209–225.

SCHIMERT (SZENTÁGOTHAI), J. (1939) Das Verhalten der Hinterwurzelkollateralen im Rückenmark. *Z. Anat. Entwicklungsgeschichte* **109** : 665–687.

SPERRY, R. W. (1955) *Biochemistry of the Developing Nervous System* (ed. by WAELSCH, H.). Academic Press, New York.

SPRAGUE, F. M. (1956) Anatomical localization of excitation and inhibition of spinal motoneurones. *Abstr. XX Int. Physiol. Congr.*, 849–850.

SZÉKELY, G. and SZENTÁGOTHAI, J. (1961) In press.

SZENTÁGOTHAI, J. (1943) Die zentrale Innervation der Augenbewegungen. *Arch. Psychiat. Nervenkrankh.* **116** : 721–760.

SZENTÁGOTHAI, J. (1948) Anatomical considerations of monosynaptic reflex arcs. *J. Neurophysiol.* **11** : 445–459.

SZENTÁGOTHAI, J. (1950) The elementary vestibulo-ocular reflex arc. *J. Neurophysiol.* **13** : 395–407.

SZENTÁGOTHAI, J. (1952) *Die Rolle der einzelnen Labyrinthrezeptoren bei der Orientation von Augen und Kopf in Raume.* Akadémiai kiadó, Budapest.

SZENTÁGOTHAI, J. (1958) The anatomical basis of synaptic transmission of excitation and inhibition in motoneurons. *Acta Morphol. Acad. Sci. Hung.* **8** : 287–309.

SZENTÁGOTHAI, J. and ALBERT, Á. (1955) The synaptology of Clarke's column. *Acta Morphol. Acad. Sci. Hung.* **5** : 43–48.

SZENTÁGOTHAI, J. and SCHÁB, R. (1956) A midbrain inhibitory mechanism of oculomotor activity. *Acta Physiol. Acad. Sci. Hung.* **9** : 89–98.

WEISS, P. (1950a) The deplantation of fragments of nervous system in amphibians—I. Central reorganization and the formation of nerves. *J. Exptl. Zool.* **113** : 397–461.

WEISS, P. (1950b) In Symposia of the Society for Experimental Biology. *Physiological Mechanisms of Animal Behaviour.* Cambridge University Press.

INHIBITORY PATHWAYS TO MOTONEURONS

J. C. ECCLES

Department of Physiology, The Australian National University, Canberra, A.C.T.

IT has now been shown that there are two distinct types of central inhibitory action (cf. Frank and Fuortes, 1957; Eccles, 1961a). One is the conventional type of inhibition that is associated with hyperpolarization of the postsynaptic membrane, and this can appropriately be called postsynaptic inhibition. In contrast, with the other there is no change in the postsynaptic membrane, but instead a depolarization of the excitatory presynaptic terminals that presumably acts by diminishing the output of excitatory transmitter; hence, this type may be called presynaptic inhibition.

POSTSYNAPTIC INHIBITION

I propose firstly to discuss the evidence relating to the simplest inhibitory pathways that are concerned in postsynaptic inhibition, and then briefly to consider more complex situations.

Impulses in the largest afferent fibres (group Ia from the annulospiral endings) of muscle exert a characteristically brief inhibitory action on motoneurons supplying antagonistic motoneurons (Lloyd, 1941, 1946a, b; Renshaw, 1942). There was a detectable inhibition of a monosynaptic reflex discharge even when the inhibitory volley preceded the excitatory by a small fraction of a millisecond. Thus Lloyd (1946a) and Laporte and Lloyd (1952) were led to postulate that Ia inhibitory and excitatory actions on motoneurons have identical central latencies; and hence that inhibition of motoneurons is exerted through a monosynaptic central path, the designation direct inhibition being applied. However, these investigations on the latency of central inhibitory action had the defect that the inhibition was being studied indirectly by relating the interval between the volleys entering the cord to the amount of inhibitory action on the monosynaptic reflex discharge. For our present purpose it is important to note that the central latency of inhibitory action was not measured; it was derived from the least volley interval for effective inhibition by a calculation that has proved to be misleading.

When intracellular recording revealed that inhibitory synaptic action on a motoneuron was associated with a hyperpolarization (the inhibitory postsynaptic potential or i.p.s.p.) which had a comparable time course (Brock *et al.*, 1952), it was concluded that the i.p.s.p. was the cause of the inhibition of reflex discharge and consequently that its latency provided a direct and accurate value for the latency of the inhibitory action. As so measured, the inhibitory latency was almost a millisecond longer than the latency of the monosynaptic e.p.s.p., yet at first an attempt was made to account for this discrepancy merely by the longer conduction time in the longer central inhibitory pathway, which extended for about 15 mm longitudinally in the first investigation. However, systematic testing, as illustrated in Fig. 1,

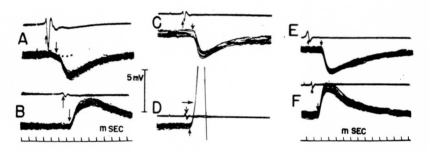

FIG. 1. Intracellular responses from motoneurons (*lower traces*) evoked by various afferent volleys which are recorded from the appropriate dorsal root as it enters the spinal cord (*upper traces*). Upward intracellular deflections signal depolarization and downward hyperpolarization of the motoneuronal membrane. All records are formed by the superposition of about twenty faint traces. The arrows pointing to dorsal root records give times of entry of volleys into the spinal cord, the arrows pointing to intracellular records mark the onsets of the i.p.s.p. or e.p.s.p., i.e. intervals between arrows give the central latencies. With C, D a deep peroneal motoneuron at L_7 level is inhibited by a gastrocnemius volley (C) excited by a deep peroneal volley (D). There was virtually the same length of central pathway yet the latency of the i.p.s.p. was 0·8 msec longer than for the e.p.s.p. With A, the inhibition of the gracilis motoneurons in L_6 by a quadriceps volley had a shorter central pathway than its excitation by a biceps semitendinosus volley, yet the central latency was 0·5 msec longer for the i.p.s.p. With E, F the central inhibitory pathway was about 15 mm longer than the excitatory and the central latency was 0·9 msec longer (Eccles, Fatt and Landgren, 1956).

showed that the longitudinal conduction time could account for only a small fraction of the discrepancy, and that about 0·8 msec could not be so explained (Eccles *et al.*, 1956). Moreover the discrepancy could not be due to a longer delay in the actual synaptic mechanism concerned in producing the i.p.s.p. because there was approximately the same interval (about 0·3 msec) between the arrival of impulses in the respective presynaptic terminals and the onsets of the e.p.s.p. and the i.p.s.p. (Eccles, Fatt and Landgren, 1956). This inference has recently been strongly supported by the finding that stimulation by brief electrical pulses through a microelectrode in the intermediate nucleus evokes e.p.s.p.'s and i.p.s.p.'s of motoneurons with the same brief latencies of about

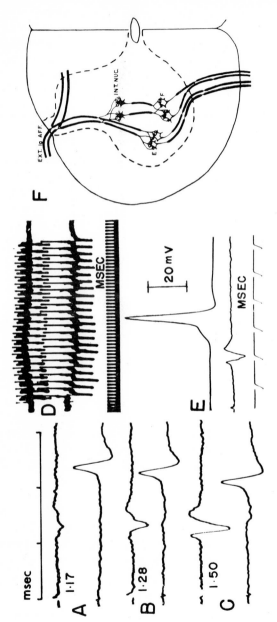

Fig. 2. Lower traces of A–C show extracellular records from an intermediate neuron that was excited by a very small group Ia volley (see upper traces) from biceps-semitendinosus nerve (A). Further increase of the volley merely shortened the latency (B, C). This interneuron was not excited by group Ib impulses from that nerve, or by group I impulses from any other nerve. It followed repetitive volleys even at 450/sec (D). E shows intracellular recording from another type A interneuron, showing the spike arising from an initial e.p.s.p. F shows drawing of monosynaptic excitatory pathway for extensor Ia afferent fibres to extensor motoneurons (E) and the disynaptic inhibitory pathway to flexor motoneurons (F) with a relay in the intermediate nucleus. Note that Ia afferent fibres converge on the intermediate neurons making spatial summation possible.

5

0·5 msec (Eide *et al.*, 1960). It was further found by Eccles, Fatt and Landgren (1956) and by Eccles, Eccles and Lundberg (1960) that the Ia impulses selectively excited interneurons in the intermediate nucleus (Fig. 2), and much evidence indicated that these interneurons had properties that precisely fitted them to be interpolated on the Ia inhibitory pathway, and so to be responsible for the delay of 0·8 msec over and above the monosynaptic excitatory path. For example they were selectively activated by group Ia volleys (Fig. 2A–C, E) responding with brief latencies and high frequencies (Fig. 2D). Finally, R. M. Eccles and Lundberg (1958) showed that spatial summation of Ia afferent impulses was necessary in order for them to produce any i.p.s.p. of moto-neurons, which can be explained only if there are interpolated interneurons that require spatial synaptic activation in order to discharge impulses along the final stage of the inhibitory pathway.

It seemed as if the interneuron had been firmly established as an essential link in the Ia inhibitory pathway, and hence that the simplest inhibitory pathway was disynaptic as shown in Fig. 2F. However, Lloyd and Wilson (1959) and Lloyd (1960) sought to re-establish the monosynaptic inhibitory pathway by an extraordinary manoeuvre. Their attack on the disynaptic hypothesis was based on the very brief central latency of the inhibition which afferent volleys in the second or third sacral roots exert on contralateral motoneurons; but in addition they radically extended their argument to the Ia inhibitory action on motoneurons supplying hind-limb muscles. They sought to undermine all the evidence from intracellular recording by making two bold assertions: that the intracellularly recorded i.p.s.p. is not the primary agent of Ia inhibitory action, but may be a secondary and later manifestation thereof, occurring up to 1 msec later than the onset of inhibition of reflex discharge; that the spike potential recorded intracellularly in the soma cannot be used as a signal of the reflex discharge of an impulse along the axon. Evidently, further experiments were needed in order to resolve this conflict, and they should conform to the requirement of Lloyd and Wilson (1959); namely, that the latency of inhibitory action must be measured on the impulses discharged along the axons in the ventral root. In view of their assertions results derived from intracellular recording are inadmissible.

Figure 3 illustrates measurements of central latency that have been made for the first time on the reflex spike discharge. This method depends on the considerable range in the latency of the individual components of the mono-synaptic reflex discharge (cf. Fig. 3I, J). If the inhibitory action is timed to begin during the dispersed reflex discharges from motoneurons, as illustrated in Fig. 3K, the later components of the complex spike discharge will be delayed or suppressed, so causing a deviation of the inhibited spike from the control, as illustrated in Fig. 3L. The onset of the deviation would be expected to provide an accurate measure of the latency of inhibitory action, and this is illustrated in Fig. 3A–F, where the interval between the entrance into the spinal

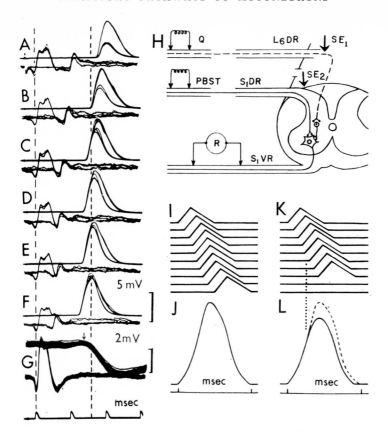

FIG. 3. The experimental arrangements are shown diagrammatically in H. In A–F a monosynaptic reflex spike response (monophasically recorded from S_1VR (*upper traces*)) was generated by an afferent volley from *BST*, which also produced a diphasic spike in the records from the dorsum of the cord (lead SE_1 in H) at the upper level (lower traces). This *BST* volley reached the cord at various times after a maximum group I afferent volley from quadriceps, which is at a fixed position in A–F, its arrival time at the upper L_6 level being given by the left perpendicular broken line. The superimposed traces for each of the testing intervals A–F were formed by firstly photographing eight traces for the *BST* volley alone at 7-sec interval to give the control reflex spike, and then a further eight traces with quadriceps volley in addition. The second vertical broken line at 1·59 msec from the first passes through the onset of the inhibition as signalled by the reflex spikes for all but record A. In G there is an i.p.s.p. produced by the Q volley and intra-cellularly recorded from a *BST* motoneuron at the S_1 segmental level a little later in this same experiment and at the same sweep speed. The manner of production of a record such as C or D is illustrated in the construction, I–L. In I there are schematic reflex spikes in ten fibres dispersed over 0·5 msec, as in a normal monosynaptic reflex, which is derived as in J by summation. Inhibition beginning at the dotted line in K, delays the onset of the sixth to eighth spikes as shown and suppresses the ninth and tenth. As a consequence the summed reflex potential (the continuous line in L) deviates from the control (the broken line in L) at a point just later than the dotted line (Araki *et al.*, 1960).

cord of the inhibitory and excitatory volleys has been diminished progressively from 0·85 to 0·28 msec and correspondingly the deviation point has occurred progressively later on the reflex spike. When, as in Fig. 3A–F, the inhibitory volley is at a fixed position (the first vertical broken line) the deviation points lie close to a second vertical line, which is in this figure 1·58 msec later. This interval gives the central latency for inhibitory action on reflex spike discharge if a small allowance (in this case 0·28 msec) is made for impulse conduction time from its origin in the initial segment of the motoneuron to the recording point on the ventral root (H), i.e. the central inhibitory latency is 1·31 msec. This value is in good agreement with the latency of the i.p.s.p. (1·37 msec) intracellularly recorded from one of the motoneurons that contributed to the reflex spike (G). In a series of six experiments of this type the latency of the i.p.s.p. was sampled in twenty-four motoneurons and was always within 0·1 msec of the central latency for inhibition of the reflex spike discharge.

Similarly, in all of the many series in five experiments with the contralateral inhibition at S_3 level, there was excellent agreement (within 0·1 msec) between the latencies of the intracellular i.p.s.p.'s and of the inhibitory action on reflex spike discharges. Thus the experimental evidence refutes the postulate of Lloyd and Wilson (1959) that there is an earlier inhibitory process having no electrical sign, yet causing the inhibition of impulse discharge and somewhat (up to 1·0 msec) later the i.p.s.p. with its action in inhibiting the spike potentials that are recorded intracellularly in motoneurons. Incidentally this postulate also is at variance with the evidence that the *IS* component of the spike recorded in the motoneuron signals the initiation of the impulse discharged into the ventral root (Coombs *et al.*, 1957). Apparently Lloyd and Wilson have confused the *IS* with the later *SD* spike.

It now remains to summarize in a diagram (Fig. 4) the time course of events when a monosynaptic reflex spike is inhibited by a volley that enters the spinal cord simultaneously, which gives the latest time at which an inhibitory volley can be effective. All the detailed times of the various events are derived from direct measurements. For example, the brief intervals of 0·3 msec (*ESD* or *ISD*) between the arrivals of presynaptic impulses at the synaptic terminals and the initiation of an i.p.s.p. or e.p.s.p. are based on the evidence cited above. Furthermore, the intervals between the onset of the e.p.s.p. and the initiation of spike discharges are also directly observed. The additional delay of about 0·8 msec in the central inhibitory pathway is shown in Fig. 4 to be satisfactorily explained by the synaptic relay in the intermediate nucleus.

As will be argued in another Chapter (Eccles, 1961b), when inhibition is produced by a group Ia afferent volley, the various inhibitory synapses are activated once only and virtually simultaneously. When the size of the group Ia volley is varied, there is merely an alteration in the number of activated synapses, and the time courses both of the reflex inhibition and of the i.p.s.p.

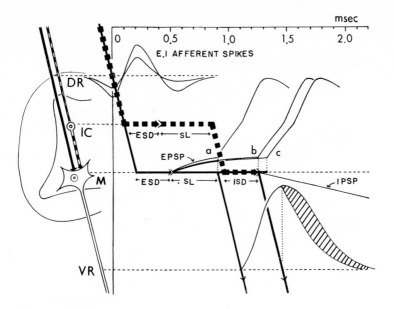

FIG. 4. Diagram showing time course of events during Ia inhibitory action on a monosynaptic reflex spike. The pathways are shown to the left with the mono-synaptic excitatory line in black and the Ia inhibitory line in interrupted black. The remainder of the diagram is constructed both on the same time scale, as shown above, and on the spatial scale of the diagram to the left, except that the potential records are also shown in the conventional manner as rising from base lines at the respective recording sites: dorsal root entry, *DR*; the motoneuron, *M*; and the ventral root, *VR*. The slopes of the lines on the spatial–temporal co-ordinates give the velocities, and delays at regions of junctional transmission are given by lengths of the horizontals there. The spikes discharges by a and b are shown propagating into the ventral root. An I afferent spike arriving synchron-ously with *E*, as shown by records at *DR*, and having an equivalent length of central pathway, is shown delayed for 0·75 msec at the intermediate cell (*IC*) relay; and then after propagating to the motoneuron, having a further delay of 0·3 msec before initiating the i.p.s.p. after a total central latency of 1·35 msec. This i.p.s.p. is just produced in time to delay or suppress (cf. Fig. 3ᴋ) all reflex discharges after *b* (for example *c*), and so is just able to diminish the height of the reflex spike as shown by the hatched area (Araki *et al.*, 1960).

remain virtually unchanged. With inhibitory action from group Ib afferent volleys, the central latency is usually very little longer than with Ia inhibition (cf. Fig. 5ʙ with ᴀ) the pathway being consequently assumed to be disynaptic, though sometimes the duration is long enough to indicate a trisynaptic pathway (Eccles, Eccles and Lundberg, 1957). Moreover, the time course of the i.p.s.p. is often sufficiently long (Fig. 5ᴄ) to indicate that either there are relays through polysynaptic pathways or that there is a brief repetitive discharge of the inhibitory neurons. More prolonged repetitive discharges of inhibitory neurons and consequently a prolonged i.p.s.p. are produced in

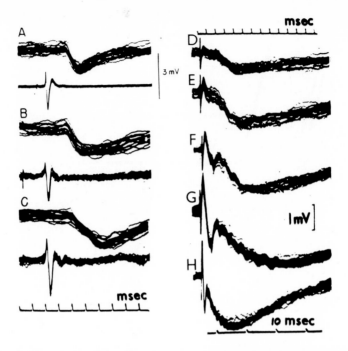

FIG. 5. Time course of the direct i.p.s.p. evoked by Ia impulses (A) and the Ib
i.p.s.p. (B and C). Intracellular recording was made with microelectrodes filled
with 0·6 M K₂SO₄. A was obtained from a biceps posterior-semitendinosus
motoneuron with stimulation of the quadriceps nerve. B and C show the i.p.s.p.'s
evoked in a gastrocnemius motoneuron by group I volleys in the nerves to
plantaris and flexor digitorum longus, respectively (Eccles, Eccles and Lundberg,
1957). Series D–H show intracellular i.p.s.p.'s recorded as in A–C, but evoked by
antidromic volleys in the ventral root, which were progressively larger from D–G.
With G and H the volleys were maximal, but H was recorded at much slower sweep
speed (Eccles, Fatt and Koketsu, 1954).

motoneurons by recurrent impulses in the axon collaterals of motoneurons
(Fig. 5D–H; Eccles, Fatt and Koketsu, 1954). The central latency for this
inhibitory effect indicates that there is no more than one interneuron in the
inhibitory pathway. At least one interneuron also appears to be interpolated
in the inhibitory pathways to motoneurons from groups II and III muscle
afferent impulses, and from cutaneous and joint afferents. When the central
latencies for the excitatory and inhibitory actions of group Ia and Ib muscle
impulses on the cells of origin of the dorsal and ventral spinocerebellar tracts
are compared, there is the same discrepancy of about 0·8 msec that was found
with the Ia action on motoneurons, so likewise an additional interneuron on
the inhibitory pathway may be inferred. Recently also a descending volley in
the pyramidal tract of the monkey was found to have an inhibitory action with

a latency about 1 msec longer than the monosynaptic excitatory action (Preston and Whitlock, 1960).

In summary it can be stated that there is no recorded instance of central inhibitory action directly exerted by primary afferent fibres or by volleys in descending tracts. In every case an interneuron with a short axon is interpolated. It has been suggested that this device is introduced in order to change the chemical transmitter mechanism from an excitatory to an inhibitory type (Eccles, Fatt and Landgren, 1956; Eccles, 1957). It should be noted that, as described in another Chapter (Eccles, 1961b), the specific ionic permeabilities produced by the inhibitory chemical transmitter provide the only hypothesis that can at present account for the membrane hyperpolarization that is characteristic of the i.p.s.p.

PRESYNAPTIC INHIBITION

This type of inhibition is characterized by a diminution of the monosynaptically produced e.p.s.p. with no change in the potential or excitability of the postsynaptic membrane. It was first described by Frank and Fuortes (1957) and by Frank (1959), who termed it remote inhibition because it was exerted remote from the motoneuron soma, though no decision was made between possible presynaptic or postsynaptic sites of action or of the possible modes of action. It has now been shown (Eccles, Kozak and Magni, 1960;

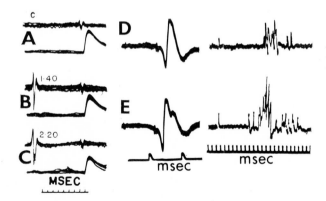

FIG. 6. A–C. Upper traces show dorsal root records and lower intracellularly recorded e.p.s.p.'s set up by a gastrocnemius afferent volley in a gastrocnemius motoneuron. Note that, compared with the control in A, the e.p.s.p. is diminished when preceded by a biceps–semitendinosus volley, the effect of a group Ia volley (B) being much less than a Ia, Ib volley (C). In D and E a biceps–semitendinosus volley of Ia or Ia + Ib composition, respectively, sets up a dorsal root reflex into the nerve to gastrocnemius, which is much larger for Ia + Ib (E) than for Ia only (D). Note difference in time scales for the first and second components of D and E (Eccles, Kozak and Magni, unpublished observations).

Eccles, Eccles and Magni, 1960) that every feature of the e.p.s.p. depression is fully explicable by the demonstrated presynaptic depolarization, which would be effective by its action in depressing the size of the presynaptic impulse and hence decreasing the liberation of excitatory transmitter substance. Such an action appears to be demonstrated in the investigation of Hagiwara and Tasaki (1958) on the squid stellate ganglion.

Presynaptic depolarization of group Ia afferent fibres has been demonstrated both by the increased excitability exhibited to brief testing pulses applied through a microelectrode in the immediate proximity of the presynaptic terminals in the motoneuron nucleus (Fig. 7A–I) and by the generation of impulses in the Ia presynaptic fibres which are observed to be discharged along these fibres as a dorsal root reflex (Fig. 6D, E), particularly when the animal is cool (about 34 °C). Just as with the e.p.s.p. depression the presynaptic depolarization is much more effectively produced by the group I afferents from flexor muscles than by those from extensors. Furthermore, they have approximately the same time course: after a latent period of several milliseconds both reach a maximum at about 15 msec and have a total duration of about 200 msec.

Investigation into the possible mechanisms of production of the presynaptic depolarization has revealed that the conditioning afferent volleys produce a large field potential in the spinal cord (Fig. 7J). This potential is likewise, produced most effectively by the Ib afferent impulses from flexor muscles and it has a time course comparable with the presynaptic depolarization. Since the field is produced by sources at the region of the intermediate nucleus and sinks ventral thereto in the region of the motoneuronal nuclei, a possible explanation is that it is due to the after-hyperpolarization following impulse discharge by the A and B interneurons, particularly the latter (cf. Eccles, Eccles and Lundberg, 1960).

Thus group I afferent volleys from muscle give rise to four events in the spinal cord, which presumably are related because they have such significant features in common: depression of the e.p.s.p. produced by Ia afferent impulses, presynaptic depolarization of Ia afferent fibres, dorsal root reflexes in Ia afferent fibres, and finally the field potential. For example these events are all produced most effectively by Ib afferent impulses from flexors, but also by Ia impulses and by group I impulses from extensors. Again the latency of all is several milliseconds, and with all but the dorsal root reflex the maximum is at about 15 msec and the duration about 200 msec. Presumably the presynaptic depolarization causes the dorsal root reflex in the group Ia afferent fibres, and accommodation accounts for the much briefer duration of the dorsal root reflex.

Since group Ib primary afferent fibres apparently do not penetrate as far as the ventral horn (Eccles, Fatt, Landgren and Winsbury, 1954; Eccles, Eccles and Lundberg, 1957), it may be assumed that the presynaptic depolarization

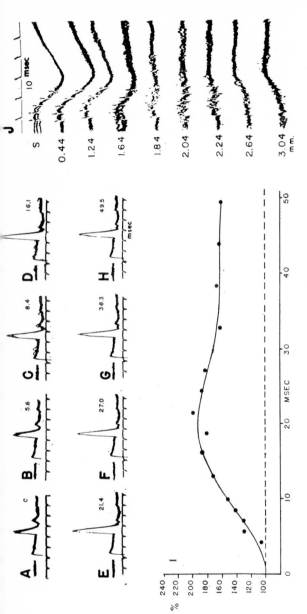

FIG. 7. A–H show spike potentials recorded in the nerve to flexor longus digitorum muscle and evoked by stimulation with brief pulses through a microelectrode in the flexor digitorum motor nucleus. Since the ventral roots were severed, these spikes are produced by group Ia afferent fibres that are excited in the central ramification in the motor nucleus. A gives the control spike size and in B–H the same stimulus was applied at the indicated intervals in milliseconds after conditioning by a group I afferent volley in biceps semitendinosus nerve. The time course of potentiation of the spike is plotted in I, which gives the time course of the depolarization of the Ia afferent terminals. J shows field potentials (upwards deflections signalling negatively) recorded by a microelectrode against an indifferent earth lead at the indicated depths below the cord dorsum; and produced by five group I afferent volleys in the posterior biceps semitendinosus nerve. Each record is formed by the superposition of about ten faint traces.
(Eccles, Eccles and Magni, unpublished observations).

is produced after synaptic relay of the group I afferent volley in the intermediate nucleus. Provisionally, two alternative explanations, electrical or chemical, may be suggested for the mechanism whereby group I muscle impulses produce depolarization of group Ia presynaptic terminals.

According to the chemical hypothesis the intermediate neurons relaying group I impulses make synaptic contact with the presynaptic terminals of primary group Ia afferent fibres, i.e. axo-axonic synaptic contacts are postulated, as shown diagrammatically in Fig. 8A. Impulses discharged from inter-

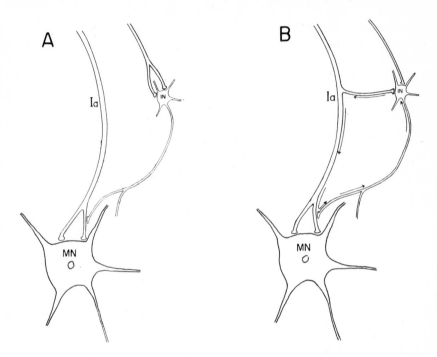

Fig. 8. Diagrams showing possible pathways for presynaptic inhibitory action, which is assumed to have an interpolated interneuron (*IN*). In A the axon of this interneuron is shown making a chemical transmitting synapse on a Ia afferent fibre close to its termination on a motoneuron (*MN*). In B electrical transmitting synapses are shown from the Ia fibre to *IN* and from the axon of *IN* to the Ia fibre near its termination. Arrows indicate path of intracellular current flow (see text).

mediate neurons are assumed to cause the release of transmitter substance at such synapses, which depolarizes the Ia presynaptic terminals. According to this explanation part at least of the potential field is attributable to depolarization of the presynaptic Ia fibres in the ventral horn. However, the slow time course of the depolarization tells against this postulate of axo-axonic chemical transmission. Admittedly the effect is but little longer than the synaptic depolarization of Renshaw cells by recurrent collaterals of motor axons (Eccles, Fatt and Koketsu, 1954; Eccles, Eccles, Iggs and Lundberg, 1961); but both the latency and the rising phase of the presynaptic depolarization are much longer than with Renshaw cells. It would be surprising if a single afferent volley resulted in such a slow onset of synaptic transmitter action.

Alternatively it may be postulated that the presynaptic depolarization results from electrical transmission from the activated intermediate neurons. One version of this postulate would be that, as suggested above, the field potential was generated by the after-hyperpolarization of intermediate neurons following the discharge of an impulse, and that this field directly depolarized the Ia presynaptic fibres. The orientation of the field would effectively give this depolarization. Unfortunately, this version encounters grave difficulties both because the potential field is much less than 1 mV and so would be insufficient to produce a depolarization which would evoke a discharge of impulses in the slightly cooled spinal cord. A further difficulty is that anodal polarization, and therefore depressed excitability, would be expected in the Ia afferent fibres at the depth of the intermediate nucleus and dorsal thereto, whereas hyperexcitability extends right out to the dorsal root, though to a continuously diminishing degree. These two difficulties are both resolved by an alternative version of the electrical hypothesis, it being postulated that the potentials generated by the intermediate neurons are selectively applied to the Ia afferent fibres by two sets of synaptic contacts that have rectification properties so as to allow current flow in the direction of the arrows (Fig. 8B). By one set of connections the Ia afferent fibres have connections to intermediate neurons that allow current to pass from the intermediate neuron into the presynaptic collateral. By the other set of contacts the intermediate terminals form rectifying synapses with the Ia presynaptic terminals in the ventral horn. These synapses selectively allow current to pass from the Ia terminals into the intermediate axonal terminals. This explanation has the merit of explaining why the observed field potential has the same time course as the presynaptic depolarization. Furthermore, rectifying synapses have been shown to exist by Furshpan and Potter (1959).

However, it will be realized that these two alternative explanations are at present speculative, though it is hoped that experimental evidence may soon enable a discrimination to be made between them. At least there appears to be good evidence that the central pathway for presynaptic inhibition involves firstly the Ia and Ib primary afferent fibres, then their synaptic relay in the intermediate nucleus, but thereafter the situation is obscure.

REFERENCES

ARAKI, T., ECCLES, J. C. and ITO, M. (1960). Correlation of the inhibitory post-synaptic potential of motoneurones with the latency and time course of inhibition of monosynaptic reflexes. *J. Physiol (London)*.

BROCK, L. G., COOMBS, J. S. and ECCLES, J. C. (1952) The recording of potentials from motoneurones with an intracellular electrode. *J. Physiol. (London)* 117 : 431–460.

COOMBS, J. S., CURTIS, D. R. and ECCLES, J. C. (1957) The generation of impulses in motoneurones. *J. Physiol. (London)* 139 : 232–249.

ECCLES, J. C. (1957) *The Physiology of Nerve Cells.* Johns Hopkins Press, Baltimore.

ECCLES, J. C. (1961a) The nature of central inhibition. *Proc. Roy. Soc. (London)* B. In press.

ECCLES, J. C. (1961b) The synaptic mechanism for postsynaptic inhibition. This volume, 71–86.

ECCLES, J. C., ECCLES, R. M. and LUNDBERG, A. (1957) Synaptic actions on motoneurones caused by impulses in Golgi tendon organ afferents. *J. Physiol. (London)* 138 : 227–252.

ECCLES, J. C., ECCLES, R. M. and LUNDBERG, A. (1960) Types of neurones in and around the intermediate nucleus of the lumbo-sacral cord. *J. Physiol. (London).* 154 : 89–114,

ECCLES, J. C., ECCLES, R. M., IGGO, A. and LUNDBERG, A. (1961) Electrophysiological investigations on Renshaw cells. *J. Physiol. (London).* In press.

ECCLES, J. C., ECCLES, R. M. and MAGNI, F. (1960) Presynaptic inhibition in the spinal cord. *J. Physiol. (London).* 154 : 28P.

ECCLES, J. C., FATT, P. and KOKETSU, K. (1954) Cholinergic and inhibitory synapses in a pathway from motor-axon collaterals to motoneurones. *J. Physiol. (London)* 126 : 524–562.

ECCLES, J. C., FATT, P., LANDGREN, S. and WINSBURY, G. J. (1954) Spinal cord potentials generated by volleys in the large muscle afferent fibres. *J. Physiol. (London)* 125 : 590–606.

ECCLES, J. C., FATT, P. and LANDGREN, S. (1956) The central pathway for the direct inhibitory action of impulses in the largest afferent nerve fibres to muscle. *J. Neurophysiol.* 19 : 75–98.

ECCLES, J. C., KOZAK, W. and MAGNI, F. (1960) Dorsal root reflexes in muscle afferent fibres. *J. Physiol. (London).* 153 : 48P–49P.

ECCLES, R. M. and LUNDBERG, A. (1958) The synaptic linkage of "direct" inhibition. *Acta Physiol. Scand.* 43 : 204–215.

EIDE, E., LUNDBERG, A. and VOORHOEVE, P. (1960) The synaptic delay at inhibitory synapses. *J. Physiol. (London).* 154 : 30P.

FRANK, K. (1959) Basic mechanisms of synaptic transmission in the central nervous system. *IRE Trans. on Med. Electronics* ME$_4$6 : 85–88.

FRANK, K. and FUORTES, M. G. F. (1957) Presynaptic and postsynaptic inhibition of monosynaptic reflexes. *Federation Proc.* 16 : 39–40.

FURSHPAN, E. J. and POTTER, D. D. (1959) Transmission at the giant synapses of the crayfish. *J. Physiol. (London)* 145 : 289–325.

HAGIWARA, S. and TASAKI, I. (1958) A study of the mechanism of impulse transmission across the giant synapse of the squid. *J. Physiol. (London)* 143 : 114–137.

LAPORTE, Y. and LLOYD, D. P. C. (1952) Nature and significance of the reflex connections established by large afferent fibers of muscular origin. *Am. J. Physiol.* 169 : 609–621.

LLOYD, D. P. C. (1941) A direct central inhibitory action of dromically conducted impulses. *J. Neurophysiol.* 4 : 184–190.

LLOYD, D. P. C. (1946a) Facilitation and inhibition of spinal motoneurones. *J. Neurophysiol.* 9 : 421–438.

LLOYD, D. P. C. (1946b) Integrative pattern of excitation and inhibition in two-neuron reflex arc. *J. Neurophysiol.* 9 : 439–444.

LLOYD, D. P. C. (1960) Spinal mechanisms involved in somatic activities. *Handbook of Physiology* Vol. 2. *Neurophysiology* (ed. by FIELD, J.), pp. 929–949. American Physiological Society.

LLOYD, D. P. C. and WILSON, V. J. (1959) Functional organization in the terminal segments of the spinal cord with a consideration of central excitatory and inhibitory latencies in monosynaptic reflex systems. *J. Gen. Physiol.* 42 : 1219–1231.

PRESTON, J. B. and WHITLOCK, D. G. (1960) Precentral facilitation and inhibition of spinal motoneurones. *J. Neurophysiol.* 23 : 154–170.

RENSHAW, B. (1942) Reflex discharge in branches of the crural nerve. *J. Neurophysiol.* 5 : 487–498.

REGULATION OF DISCHARGE RATE BY INHIBITION, ESPECIALLY BY RECURRENT INHIBITION

RAGNAR GRANIT

From the Nobel Institute for Neurophysiology, Karolinska Institutet,
Stockholm 60, Sweden

PROBLEMS of regulation and control in the mammalian preparation present us with the inherent difficulty of how to analyze equilibria. One tries to disturb them—and a chain of events is mobilized to establish a new state of equilibrium. The combinations and permutations involved in such readjustments are not easily disentangled. In the hope of being able to contribute to the understanding of the role of inhibition in the regulation of activity of the motoneurons it was decided to make a test case out of recurrent inhibition whose circuit is relatively simple and has the advantage of being on the efferent side and hence not subject to as many influences as is the afferent side. It is not possible here to discuss the old work on antidromic inhibition and the early attempts from the beginning of this century to assign a function to the recurrent collaterals of Golgi. A great step forward was taken when Renshaw (1946) discovered the high-frequency discharge to antidromic stimulation of ventral roots in the cells which today we call the Renshaw cells, and when Eccles *et al.* (1954) by different types of experiments found that it paralleled the course of repolarization of the ventral horn cells that was to be expected if antidromic inhibition essentially was recurrent in nature. The work of Brooks and Wilson (1959) and of Wilson (1959) supports the view of the Canberra group; as also does all the work they have done at Canberra since 1954. We make it the basis of our approach that recurrent inhibition repolarizes the motoneurons across an internuncial cell and that it in this respect resembles other polysynaptic inhibitions, a parallel emphasized by Eccles (1957). Most of the work to be considered below is from three papers from the Nobel Institute (Granit *et al.*, 1957, 1960; Granit and Rutledge, 1960). They will be referred to as nos. 1, 2 and 3, respectively.

In paper no. 1 the decerebrate preparation was used and antidromic stimulation of a number of efferent filaments was made to influence the tonic discharge of a functionally isolated cell in a thin ventral root filament. This technique has been used also in papers nos. 2 and 3. To produce a tonic discharge we stimulate by pull on the gastrocnemius–soleus muscle or cut the nerve to this muscle and tetanize its central stump electrically at a

61

rate around 114/sec. In the former case truly tonic cells discharge, in the latter case stimulation will be strong enough to activate tonic responses in cells which normally—to muscular afferents—would respond phasically. With electrical tetanization of muscular afferents the efferent roots have to be cut.

Now there are two ways of stimulating antidromically. In both cases the stimulating electrodes are on the root delivering the filament whose spike we analyze; in one case on the whole remaining root, in the other only on some antidromically active filaments. With extensor reflexes it does not seem to matter much if one selects the most strongly inhibiting adjacent filaments or the whole remaining root.

Let us first consider the tonic stretch reflex as exemplified by the single-fibre preparation responding reflexly to pull on the gastrocnemius–soleus. This situation requires some conceptual clarification. The muscle spindles are responsible for what we call "excitatory drive" which may be regarded as a barrage of impulses that activates a certain number of synaptic knobs per unit time. The result emerges as net depolarizing current P_{dep} across the cell membrane. This process is opposed by repolarizing forces such as orthodromic inhibition from afferents over internuncial cells and natural recurrent inhibition initiated by the firing tonic ventral horn cells themselves. Let the sum total of these opposing forces be P_{pol}. As stated above, antidromic stimulation was proved by Eccles et al. (1954) to repolarize the ventral horn cell. The normal frequency of discharge F_n will be some function of the net depolarizing current which is the algebraic sum of the two opposite forces.

$$F_n = f(P_{dep} + P_{pol}) \qquad (1)$$

Long ago Barron and Matthews (1938) were interested in this function whose right-hand term from now on I shall call *depolarizing pressure*, defining thereby more precisely a term taken from a paper by Phillips (1959). The experimental difficulty is, of course, how to eliminate P_{pol} or to keep it constant. Barron and Matthews tried to stimulate the spinal cord from the outside with a depolarizing current and they published figures for one cell in which F_n was proportional to strength of depolarizing current. The ideal technique for elimination of P_{pol} from equation (1) is to stimulate through an inside microelectrode in the manner of Araki and Otani (1955). Systematic measurements by this technique have been made by Fuortes and Frank who kindly have allowed me to quote unpublished results. The firing frequency of single motoneurons was found to be a linear function of depolarizing current. Slope constants varied from cell to cell and their range of variation was as wide as from 4 to 13·6 imp/sec per mμA. With many cells linear curves running up to 100 imp/sec were obtained. We recall that normal tonic firing of motoneurons is at rates which are but a fraction of this theoretical maximum and later we shall consider the general problem of frequency limitation. For the moment let us return to depolarizing pressure ($P_{\text{dep}} + P_{\text{pol}}$) and use recurrent inhibition as our instrument of analysis.

The simplest approach is to study situations in which depolarizing pressure is constant which means that frequency of discharge F_n is held constant. Assume that we pull out gastrocnemius–soleus to an extension of 10 mm and leave it stretched. In a good, tonic decerebrate animal we shall then find spikes which discharge for minutes at practically constant rates. By definition this means that depolarizing pressure is constant. We then proceed to gauge depolarizing pressure by a brief tetanic burst of antidromic stimulation repeated at regular intervals. This means adding to equation (1) a term P'_{pol} of recurrent inhibition by means of which we measure if the sum $P_{\text{dep}} + P_{\text{pol}}$, as reflected by a constant rate of discharge F_n, really is constant at different moments after onset of pull.

Analysis of an experiment is shown in Fig. 1 from paper no. 3. The reflex rate of discharge of the tonic cell was approximately constant between the two horizontal lines, from 20 to 55 sec after onset of stretch. The tests by constant brief tetani of antidromic stimulation vary in efficacy from moment to moment but the general trend of the result is perfectly definite: as time

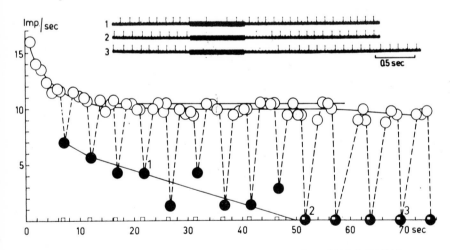

FIG. 1. A 15-mm steady pull on the knee extensors. Tetanic antidromic inhibition at 114/sec inserted for 0·7 sec at regular intervals as marked by oblongs on abscissa (running time). Frequency of discharge constant between the two parallel horizontal lines. Black circles show number of impulses during the periods of recurrent inhibition evaluated in imp/sec. (*Inset*)—Original records at moments marked 1, 2 and 3 in the diagram. Note, that when delayed recovery after recurrent inhibition begins, then discharge frequency fails to reach its original level (at this rate of repetition of antidromic stimulation periods). Discharge stopped for good with last period of stimulation having been five times temporarily silenced (Granit and Rutledge, 1960).

goes on, recurrent inhibition becomes increasingly effective, in fact, inserted at moment 52 sec it succeeded in blocking the cell altogether. The moments 1, 2 and 3, marked in the figure are reproduced in the inset from the original records. We note that the time needed for recovery after a burst of antidromic stimulation increased from 1 to 3 even though between tests the discharge rose to the same level as before.

It is concluded that, since for some reason a constant depolarizing pressure, as gauged by a constant amount of recurrent inhibition, does not deliver a constant inhibitory effect, some concealed factor must be present which is not included in the simple formula (1) relating frequency of discharge to depolarizing pressure. The very first question is whether or not this concealed factor might be a temporal summation of the effects of the individual antidromic bursts so that for this reason the inhibitions actually increase in strength from test to test though—physically speaking—identical as stimuli.

It is not difficult to refute such arguments. To this end we make use of the regularity with which a good tonic motor cell responds to stretches repeated at regular intervals. Then it is possible to make each stretch an individual experiment and throw in the test by recurrent inhibition at any chosen moment in the reflex. Such experiments showed that it really is something behind the discharge of the tonic cell that undergoes a gradual weakening with time leading to a loss of resistance to inhibition. Thus, although the frequency of discharge remains the same and outwardly everything is as before, the stretch reflex in the end has lost the excitatory drive necessary to enable it to withstand a suitably chosen dose of recurrent inhibition.

From this result it is finally concluded that any given frequency of discharge of the motoneuron (F_n), corresponding to a certain depolarizing pressure ($P_{dep} + P_{pol}$), may be run on a greater or lesser amount of surplus excitation. The concept of "surplus excitation" which now is introduced is, as it were, another aspect of what was considered above under the term "frequency limitation". As soon as there is frequency limitation, it is possible to have a surplus of excitatory drive for which there is no equivalent increase of output. Long ago it was shown by Denny-Brown (1929) with the stretch reflex that the output frequency of discharge may be largely independent of the degree of extension of the muscle and I have confirmed this result in a recent study (Granit, 1958). We know very well that the muscle spindles discharge in proportion to extension (Eldred et al., 1953; Granit, 1958) and so, the more the muscle is extended, the greater the excitatory drive. Yet the output frequency is limited to a constant value. If, at different extensions of the muscle, one tests with recurrent inhibition, it is easily shown that the greater the extension and hence the excitatory drive, the better the reflex resists recurrent inhibition. Throughout such experiments F_n can be kept constant. Similarly antidromic stimulation is held constant. In this manner then it is proved that the decisive factor is not the depolarizing pressure, as assayed by constant rate of discharge, but the amount of surplus excitation or excitatory drive by which it is upheld. When the excitatory drive is low the reflex is destroyed by recurrent inhibition. This is what we measure. Early in a stretch reflex there is a good surplus behind the steady frequency of discharge and therefore every loss of depolarizing current resulting from recurrent repolarization is quickly replaced; later on the excitatory drive may be barely sufficient to maintain a given depolarizing pressure (steady output frequency) and so the cell falls an easy prey to repolarization by recurrent inhibition.

One broad generalization following from this work is that in problems of regulation the important intracellular approach which has led to so much conceptual clarification has definite limitations. This is when our concern is with the rules of the game by which frequency of output is determined. It is probably true that in the steady state condition depolarizing pressure determines impulse frequency in accordance with equation (1) and with the results of Fuortes and Frank, mentioned above, with inside stimulation of motoneurons. But up to a point the efficacy of an intercurrent inhibitory force depends on how well any particular depolarizing pressure is defended by excitatory drive. Naturally, efficacy of recurrent inhibition—or any other repolarizing variety of inhibition for that matter—must also depend upon the slope constant by which impulse frequency is related to net depolarizing current. Let us consider the extreme values of Fuortes and Frank, 4 and 13·6 for this slope constant and assume that we are studying two motoneurons adjusted to discharge at the same rate. Assume further that it would be possible to test them by identical amounts of P'_{pol} of recurrent inhibition. Merely because of the different slopes of the two curves (in a diagram relating their impulse frequency to depolarizing current), the effects of recurrent inhibition on the two cells would have to be in the ratio of 4 to 13·6, other things equal. This is clearly because equal amounts of repolarization will reduce frequency of firing in proportion to the constants mentioned.

One might think it unnecessary to introduce this distinction between excitatory drive and depolarizing pressure and instead try to explain our results by an uncertainty in the measurement of firing rate of the motoneurons. In order to reply to this criticism it is possible to design an experiment in which excitatory drive is maintained in spite of a reduction of depolarizing pressure. Thus, with extensor motoneurons, the tonic reflex can be elicited electrically by a maintained afferent tetanus. The depolarizing pressure can at the same time be lowered by pulling on the antagonist flexor muscle tibialis anterior. Exceptionally, in this experiment, the nerve to the flexor must be left intact. By these means it is easy to reduce the firing rate of the extensor motoneuron, used as indicator, in excess of any variation in rate during maintained stretch. When this is done, recurrent inhibition does not

6

silence the firing cell, the reason being that by the electrical tetanization of the extensor afferents excitatory drive is well maintained in spite of the lowered depolarizing pressure. Such experiments show that it is necessary to distinguish between excitatory drive and depolarizing pressure.

In experiments in which the motoneuron has been silenced by recurrent inhibition it is often observed that maintained stretch does not succeed in reactivating the cell although antidromic stimulation is stopped. This is difficult to explain unless one assumes that recurrent inhibition penetrates into the spinal cord beyond the circuit completed with the projections of Renshaw cells upon motoneurons. Frank and Fuortes (1956) showed that neurons located further inside the spinal cord are influenced by antidromic stimulation and this has since been confirmed. It is therefore possible that recurrent inhibition does something to the interneurons which leads to removal of excitatory drive, provided that drive is low.

A general theory of the physiological role of recurrent inhibition follows from the results obtained. The recurrent control will preferentially be directed towards removal of discharges or states of excitation which are badly supported by excitatory drive, lingering after-discharges, subliminal fringes, near-threshold activity in general, and so, as it were, will hold the reflex to its task. The present author has often wondered why interneurons fire at such high rates and why afferent activation often is so much in excess of what is the immediate apparent need (see e.g. in Granit, 1955, p. 247) but it is clear that if excitatory drive is as important functionally as depolarizing pressure, then what superficially looks like excess activity is merely what is required to maintain low-rate operations of neurons provided with recurrent collaterals. As is well known most nervous centres possess recurrent collaterals. The motoneurons are by no means an exception. The views of ourselves (paper no. 1) and Brooks and Wilson (1959) with regard to special functions of recurrent inhibition fit well into this general theory. Also, whatever organizational features be ascribed to the recurrent system, the inhibitory effect will have to be in accordance with the general rule that has emerged from the work now reviewed.

Recurrent inhibition on a tonic discharge can, as we have seen (paper nos. 1 and 3), be made cumulative in the sense that it generally silences the discharge, the intervals between the efferent impulses increasing from spike to spike. This is done by reducing the amount of excitatory drive by which anyone depolarizing pressure is maintained. However, assuming drive to be sufficient, what is then the relation between (control or) normal frequency of discharge F_n and that during recurrent inhibition F_i?

In order to be able to reply to questions of this type it is necessary to be able to vary the firing frequency F_n of any given cell and try recurrent inhibition on it. Many motoneurons are so heavily stabilized in firing rate that they cannot be used in a study of this particular kind. They simply refuse

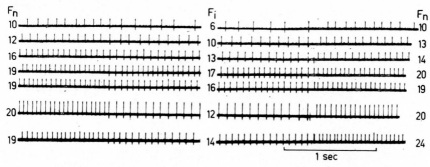

FIG. 2. Records from three experiments showing tonic reflex discharge of single fibre in ventral root to afferent stimulation at repetition rate 114/sec. Normal frequency of discharge F_n 1 sec before and after locking of antidromic shock to firing spike to obtain F_i. Values of F_n and F_i against the records refer to the cut-out portions and not to total period of counting. The first five rows refer to one experiment, the sixth and seventh to two different experiments; the seventh put in to illustrate good rebound (Granit *et al.*, 1960).

to vary their F_n. Others can by electrical afferent stimulation (at 110/sec) at different strengths be made to fire at different rates. By connecting electronically the tonic firing spike to the antidromic shock one can make recurrent inhibition act at the average rate of motoneuron output as in Fig. 2 (paper no. 2). Averaging the rate of discharge over 5 sec before and 5 sec after a 5 sec period of recurrent inhibition one obtains the basic frequency of discharge F_n. The value during recurrent inhibition is the average from the 5-sec period during which it acted. Plotting F_i against F_n gives straight lines of the type shown in Fig. 3 (paper no. 2). F_i is proportional to F_n and this relationship is reminiscent of the results of Hartline and Ratliff (1956) with Hartline's (1949) lateral inhibition in the *Limulus* eye.

This type of experiment also provides us with a method of measuring the potency of recurrent inhibition. In the record of Fig. 4 (paper no. 2) the dashed line is drawn at an angle of 45° in the F_i–F_n diagram to show the theoretical case of absent recurrent inhibition or $F_n = F_i$. B is the result actually obtained. Then concurrent tetanic stimulation of a point, low in the anterior cerebellum, was began and the readings repeated. They are now numbered in the order in which they were taken. The earliest ones fell on a good straight line C with a slope signifying a strong increase in the efficacy of recurrent inhibition. The last values fell better on line D and the effect was not merely visible during concurrent stimulation of the cerebellar point but rose and disappeared so slowly that the numbers underlined, which represent intercurrent controls without simultaneous central stimulation, did not separate out from the others. We also found central inhibitory points in this manner. Koizumi *et al.* (1959) in their work on spinal cord interneurons described one cell which they held to be a Renshaw cell and whose

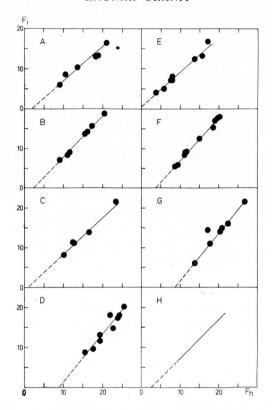

FIG. 3. A–G are curves plotted from experiments in which range of F_n was large. The straight lines have been drawn to reproduce formula $F_n = aF_i + b$. The constants a and b are from A to G: 1·25, 1·0; 0·97, 2·4; 1·08, 1·0; 0·84, 8·9; 1·17, −0·6; 0·92, 3·7; 0·84, 8·8. Curve H is the average from thirty-three experiments, $a = 1·04$; $b = 2·6$ imp/sec (Granit *et al.*, 1960).

rate of discharge could be inhibited by reticular stimulation. I mention this chiefly to show that our method is convenient for studies of this type and to underline that some of the discrepancies in work with Renshaw cells may well have been due to influences of this kind. Considering how little we know about supraspinal mechanisms of control, even for cells which have been studied extensively, much experimentation will be required before we know when and how in complex events Renshaw cells are excited or suppressed. For the time being it would be wrong to look upon them merely as automatic at the spinal level. We know that in truly tonic cells, such as those of soleus, recurrent inhibition is particularly strong (paper no. 1; Kuno, 1959; Eccles *et al.*, 1960) and in those cells it is likely to work in close co-operation with their long-lasting after-hyperpolarization, found by Eccles *et al.* (1958).

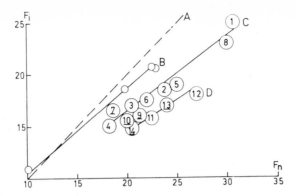

FIG. 4. Plot as in Fig. 3. A, to show graph for $F_n = F_i$. B, initial control of spike drawn to fit $F_n = 1 \cdot 22 \, F_i - 2 \cdot 8$. Stimulation of lower frontal portion of anterior lobe of cerebellum at Horsley–Clarke co-ordinates P6, H2 just contralateral to midline at frequency 300/sec and $9 \cdot 0$ V, coaxial electrode and insulated tip against its shield. Order of observations marked on graph; underlined numerals are observations without stimulation of cerebellum. Curve C drawn to $F_n = 1 \cdot 39 \, F_i - 2 \cdot 8$, D to $F_n = 1 \cdot 58 \, F_i - 2 \cdot 8$ (Granit *et al.*, 1960).

As to other organizational features, we have the results of Brooks and Wilson (1959), Wilson (1959) and of Wilson *et al.* (1959) which show that there is recurrent excitation which is better developed from extensors to flexors than the other way round, because inhibition is the dominant feature between extensors and from flexors to extensors. This is a kind of asymmetrical reciprocal innervation. Eccles *et al.* (1960) emphasize in the first instance nuclear proximity in the spinal cord as the leading organizational feature for recurrent inhibition.

Thus this brief review shows that from many points of view recurrent collaterals deserve to be studied. Recurrent inhibition seems to be dominating in studies of extensors. We have only seen facilitation as rebound.

I might end by saying a few words about limitation of discharge frequency. We have no evidence that recurrent inhibition is decisive, except for the tonic ventral horn cells where it can co-operate with after-hyperpolarization. If we consider equation (1) it is clear that there are two fundamental possibilities: (i) F_n may be cut, as in some of the *Carcinus* fibres of Hodgkin (1948), or it may be cut by accommodation. (ii) Alternatively depolarizing pressure $P_{dep} + P_{pol}$ may be the regulated quantity. It can be shown that the latter generally is the case. Depolarizing pressure is limited by many factors such as limited number of afferent terminals, afferent inhibition, natural recurrent inhibition, after-hyperpolarization. These factors are not easily disentangled; however, it is easily shown that in many cells depolarizing pressure is limited in response to muscular afferents when it still is capable of rising in response to many other types of stimuli. The rule seems to be that depolarizing pressure rather than frequency of discharge is the quantity that the organism in the first instance holds in check.

REFERENCES

ARAKI, T. and OTANI, T. (1955) Response of single motoneurons to direct stimulation in toad's spinal cord. *J. Neurophysiol.* **18** : 472–485.

BARRON, D. H. and MATTHEWS, B. H. C. (1938) The interpretation of potential changes in the spinal cord. *J. Physiol. (London)* **92** : 276–321.

BROOKS, V. B. and WILSON, V. J. (1959) Recurrent inhibition in the cat's spinal cord. *J. Physiol. (London)* **146** : 380–391.

DENNEY-BROWN, D. B. (1929) On the nature of postural reflexes. *Proc. Roy. Soc. (London)* B **104** : 252–301.

ECCLES, J. C. (1957) *The Physiology of Nerve Cells.* Johns Hopkins Press, Baltimore.

ECCLES, J. C., ECCLES, R. M. and LUNDBERG, A. (1958) The action potentials of the alpha motoneurones supplying fast and slow muscles. *J. Physiol. (London)* **142** : 275–291.

ECCLES, J. C., FATT, P. and KOKETSU, K. (1954) Cholinergic and inhibitory synapses in a pathway from motor-axon collaterals to motoneurones. *J. Physiol (London)* **126**: 524–562.

ECCLES, R. M., IGGO, A. and ITO, S. (1960) Personal communication from work in the course of publication.

ELDRED, E., GRANIT, R. and MERTON, P. A. (1953) Supraspinal control of the muscle spindles and it significance. *J. Physiol (London)* **122** : 498–523.

FRANK, K. and FUORTES, M. G. F. (1956) Unitary activity of spinal interneurones of cats. *J. Physiol. (London)* **131** : 424–435.

GRANIT, R. (1955) *Receptors and Sensory Perception.* Yale University Press, New Haven.

GRANIT, R. (1958) Neuromuscular interaction in postural tone of the cat's isometric soleus muscle. *J. Physiol. (London)* **143** : 387–402.

GRANIT, R., HAASE, J. and RUTLEDGE, L. T. (1960) Recurrent inhibition in relation to frequency of firing and limitation of discharge rate of extensor motoneurones. *J. Physiol. (London)*.

GRANIT, R., PASCOE, J. E. and STEG, G. (1957) The behaviour of tonic alpha and gamma motoneurones during stimulation of recurrent collaterals. *J. Physiol. (London)* **138** : 381–400.

GRANIT, R. and RUTLEDGE, L. T. (1960) Surplus excitation in reflex action of motoneurones as measured by recurrent inhibition. *J. Physiol. (London)*.

HARTLINE, H. K. (1949) Inhibition of visual receptors by illuminating nearby retinal areas in the *Limulus* eye. *Federation Proc.* **8** : 69.

HARTLINE, H. K. and RATLIFF, F. (1956) Inhibitory interaction of receptor units in the eye of *Limulus*. *J. Gen. Physiol.* **40** : 357–376.

HODGKIN, A. L. (1948) The local electric changes associated with repetitive action in a non-medullated axon. *J. Physiol (London)* **107** : 165–181.

KOIZUMI, K., USHIYAMA, J. and McC. BROOKS, C. (1959) A study of reticular formation action on spinal interneurons and motoneurons. *Japan J. Physiol.* **9** : 282–303.

KUNO, M. (1959) Excitability following antidromic activation in spinal motoneurones supplying red muscles. *J. Physiol. (London)* **149** : 374–393.

PHILLIPS, C. G. (1959) Actions of antidromic pyramidal volleys on single Betz cells in the cat. *Quart. J. Exptl. Physiol.* **44** : 1–25.

RENSHAW, B. (1946) Central effects of centripetal impulses in axons of spinal ventral roots. *J. Neurophysiol.* **9** : 191–204.

WILSON, V. J. (1959) Recurrent facilitation of spinal reflexes. *J. Gen. Physiol.* **42** : 703–713.

WILSON, V. J., TALBOT, W. H. and DIECKE, F. P. J. (1959) Pattern of recurrent conditioning of spinal reflexes. *Nature* **183** : 824–825.

THE SYNAPTIC MECHANISM FOR POSTSYNAPTIC INHIBITION

J. C. Eccles

Department of Physiology, The Australian National University, Canberra, A.C.T.

It will be convenient if I restrict my account almost entirely to the simplest type of postsynaptic inhibition in the nervous system, namely the inhibitory action of group Ia afferent impulses on motoneurons. There is much evidence that all other types of postsynaptic inhibition have essentially the same synaptic mechanism, both as regards transmitter substance and ionic permeability (Eccles *et al.*, 1954; Coombs *et al.*, 1955a; Eccles, 1957; Curtis, 1959). The differences in time course are attributable either to temporal dispersion or to repetitive discharge of the inhibitory presynaptic impulses.

Intracellular recording reveals that inhibitory synaptic action by a Ia afferent volley causes a brief hyperpolarization of the motoneuronal membrane (Fig. 1A–F). The microelectrode must be filled with a salt having a large anion such as sulphate or citrate, else this inhibitory postsynaptic potential (i.p.s.p.) is likely to be distorted by intracellular changes in ionic composition, as will be seen later. Variations in the size of the group Ia afferent volley cause alterations in the size of the i.p.s.p., but not in its time course, which has characteristically a brief rising phase and a slower, approximately exponential, decay; hence it can be assumed that the i.p.s.p. is produced by a virtually synchronous action of inhibitory impulses, and that each impulse produces an i.p.s.p. having the same time course as those illustrated in Fig. 1A–F for afferent volleys of varying size.

When one comes to consider in detail the synaptic events responsible for the hyperpolarization of the i.p.s.p., it is evident that the increased charge on the motoneuronal membrane must be caused by an electric current outwardly directed across the subsynaptic membrane of the activated inhibitory synapses and inwardly directed across the remainder of the membrane, so hyperpolarizing it, as illustrated in Fig. 2B, D. The time course of this current can be approximately calculated if the electric time constant of the motoneuronal membrane is known (Curtis and Eccles, 1959). This time constant is not directly given by the time course of the membrane potential change produced by application of a rectangular current pulse through an intracellular electrode (Fig. 1, I, K). A considerable allowance has to be made for the distortion produced by electrotonic spread of current along the dendrites.

71

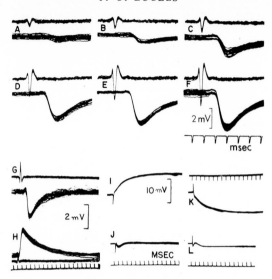

Fig. 1. A–F. Lower records give intracellular responses (i.p.s.p.'s) of a biceps-semitendinosus motoneuron to a quadriceps volley of progressively increasing size, as shown by the upper records, which are recorded from the L_6 dorsal root by a surface electrode, downward deflections signalling negativity. All records are formed by the superposition of about forty faint traces. G shows i.p.s.p.'s similarly generated in another biceps-semitendinosus motoneuron, the monosynaptic e.p.s.p.'s of this motoneuron being seen in H. I–L show changes in potential produced by an applied rectangular pulse of 12×10^{-9} A in the depolarizing and hyperpolarizing directions. I and K being intracellular and J and L extracellular (Curtis and Eccles, 1959). Reproduced by permission from the *Journal of Physiology*.

In Fig. 2A the current flow responsible for the i.p.s.p. has been calculated by assuming that the effective surface of the dendrites is 2·3 times that of the soma, a ratio that was derived from measurements on motoneurons of the lumbosacral cord of the cat (Coombs *et al.*, 1955a). On the basis of measurements of a heterogenous series of motoneuronal pictures published by various authors Rall (1959) argues for a much larger ratio (10–25 or even higher), and consequently for a much longer time constant for the membrane. However, Aitken and Bridger (1961) have measured the somas and dendrites of an extensive series of motoneurons in the lumbosacral region of the cat cord and give measurements both of the relative sizes of the dendrites and soma and of the numbers of dendrites that are in close agreement with the values originally derived for such motoneurons by Coombs *et al.* (1955a) and employed by Coombs *et al.* (1959); hence we may assume that in accordance with Curtis and Eccles (1959) the time course of the inhibitory current is approximately given by the broken line of Fig. 2A. It will be seen that the inhibitory current virtually ceases to flow just after the summit of the i.p.s.p., the decaying phase being due to the passive recovery of the membrane potential.

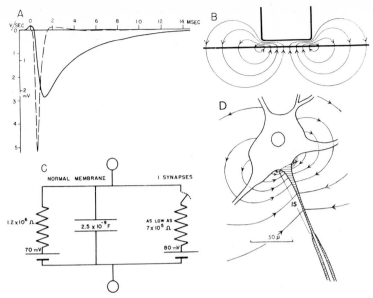

FIG. 2. In A, the mean curve of the i.p.s.p. of Fig. 1G is plotted as a continuous line, and, on the basis of the electric time constant of the membrane determined from Fig. 1I–L, it is analysed to give the time course of the postsynaptic current generating it, as shown by the broken line. In B, the flow of these inhibitory postsynaptic currents is shown. In C there is a formal electrical diagram showing capacity, resistance and battery of the membrane of a standard motoneuron as "seen" by a microelectrode in the soma; on the right side there is in addition a representation of the inhibitory subsynaptic areas of the membrane that are activated in producing the Ia i.p.s.p. Maximum activation of these areas would be indicated by closing the switch (Curtis and Eccles, 1959). Reproduced by permission from the *Journal of Physiology*. D. Diagrammatic representation of current that flows as the i.p.s.p. generated in the soma-dendritic membrane spreads electrotonically to hyperpolarize the initial segment (*IS*) which is the site of initiation of impulses discharged from the motoneuron.

When the motoneuronal membrane is set at a sufficiently high level of hyperpolarization by the application of a steady background current, there is reversal of the inhibitory synaptic current, as is shown by the reversed polarity of the i.p.s.p.'s in the three lower records of Fig. 3A. Plotting of the series partly illustrated in Fig. 3A shows that there is an equilibrium potential of about −80 mV at which the i.p.s.p. is zero, and of course the flow of inhibitory current is then also zero (Fig. 3B). This equilibrium potential for the i.p.s.p. ($E_{i.p.s.p.}$) was in Fig. 3B and C at about 6 mV more hyperpolarized than the normal resting potential. The influence of membrane depolarization in increasing the i.p.s.p. and of hyperpolarization in reversing it leads to the postulate that the inhibitory current is due to the net movement of ions down their electrochemical gradients, and that there is no requirement of a supply

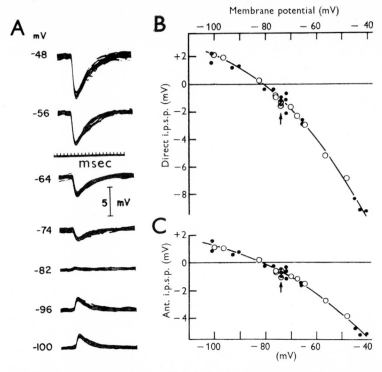

FIG. 3A. I.p.s.p.'s recorded intracellularly from a biceps–semitendinosus moto-neuron by means of a double-barrelled microelectrode. The records, formed by the superposition of about forty faint traces, show the i.p.s.p.'s set up by a quadriceps afferent volley. By means of a steady background current through the other barrel of the microelectrode, the membrane potential has been preset at the voltage indicated on each record, the resting membrane potential being −74 mV (Coombs *et al.*, 1955b). Reproduced by permission from the *Journal of Physiology.*

FIG. 3B. Plotting of measurements from series partly shown in A. Abscissae give the membrane potentials and ordinates the sizes of the respective i.p.s.p.'s. Note that hyperpolarizing i.p.s.p.'s are plotted downwards and depolarizing upwards.

FIG. 3C. Series for same motoneuron, plotted as in B, but i.p.s.p.'s produced by an antidromic volley (Coombs *et al.*, 1955b).

of metabolic energy to ion pumps. The conditions generating the i.p.s.p. are shown in the formal electrical diagram of Fig. 2C, where activation of the I synapses would cause the momentary (for 1 to 2 msec) closure of the switch in the right element of the diagram.

Figure 2C leads one to expect that during motoneuronal depolarization there will be a corresponding increase in the size of the voltage driving currents produced by activated inhibitory synapses; hence the increased i.p.s.p. of the three upper records of Fig. 3A is accounted for. Similarly there

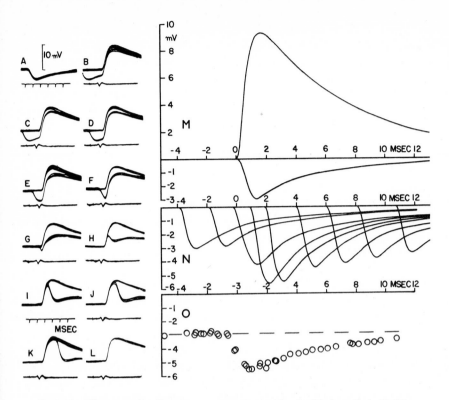

FIG. 4. Biceps–semitendinosus motoneuron with double-barrelled K_2SO_4 electrode, the resting membrane potential being -70 mV. I.p.s.p.'s are set up by quadriceps group Ia afferent volleys, and the e.p.s.p.'s by biceps–semitendinosus afferent volleys. B–K show interaction of i.p.s.p. and e.p.s.p. at various intervals, the control responses being given in A and L respectively. All records were formed by the superposition of about forty faint traces, but the quadriceps afferent volley was only turned on for about half the traces, so that the control e.p.s.p. was superimposed on all records from B to K. Lower traces show the record from the L_7 dorsal root, the quadriceps afferent volley consequently giving a very small spike potential. Same time and potential scales for A–L. M shows tracings of the control e.p.s.p. and i.p.s.p. while N shows an analysis of records like those of A–L. It is assumed that the e.p.s.p. is unaltered by the superimposed i.p.s.p.'s which are themselves greatly potentiated as shown. The peak potentials of the i.p.s.p.'s so determined are plotted in O against the interval between their onset and the onset of the interacting e.p.s.p., part of the series being shown in N. Note that same time scale obtains for M, N and O, zero time being placed at the origin of the e.p.s.p. (Curtis and Eccles, 1959.) Reproduced by permission from the *Journal of Physiology*.

will be potentiation of an i.p.s.p. set up during the depolarization of an e.p.s.p. This is illustrated in Fig. 4, where in the superimposed records of A–L, the i.p.s.p. is increased from its control value of -3 mV to as much as -5.5 mV when the inhibitory currents flow during the maximum of the e.p.s.p. However, when the rising phase of the i.p.s.p. precedes the onset of the e.p.s.p. (Fig. 4B–F), there is no potentiation of the later decaying phase of the i.p.s.p., as is well illustrated in the subtracted records beginning at −4 and −2 msec in Fig. 4N. This absence of effect would be expected if the inhibitory current ceased within 2 msec of its onset as shown in Fig. 2A. On the other hand there is potentiation of the i.p.s.p. when it is generated at any stage of the declining phase of the e.p.s.p., and, as would be expected from Fig. 2C, this potentiation closely follows the time course of the e.p.s.p. (Figs. 4N, O).

Although it has been shown that, by the latency test, the i.p.s.p. is precisely fitted to be the initiator of inhibitory action on reflex discharges (Araki *et al.*, 1960; Eccles, 1961), it is necessary to see whether this good agreement holds for the whole time course of the inhibitory action.

The time course of inhibitory action can be ascertained by observing the depression of a testing monosynaptic reflex discharge at varying times after the conditioning inhibitory volley. In the original descriptions the inhibitory curve so obtained reached a maximum with a volley interval of less than 1 msec, and then declined along an approximately exponential curve with a time constant of about 4 msec (Lloyd, 1946; Laporte and Lloyd, 1952). However, in more recent investigations where special precautions were taken to have the inhibition produced by virtually pure Ia volleys, an initial very rapid phase of decay has declined on to a slowly decaying residuum, as illustrated in Fig. 5A, C (Bradley *et al.*, 1953; Brooks *et al.*, 1957; Araki *et al.*, 1960). Usually inhibitory curves with this double composition were also observed by Jack *et al.* (1959, and personal communication), but occasionally they observed only the brief initial phase. It was suggested that in such circumstances the spinal cord was in particularly good condition and that the membrane potential of the motoneurons was then as high as the equilibrium potential for the i.p.s.p., i.e. that $E_R = E_{\text{i.p.s.p.}}$

Before describing further investigations into the time course of inhibitory synaptic action, it is desirable to show how the double composition of inhibitory curves is related to the mode of operation of inhibitory synapses. It was first suggested by Coombs *et al.* (1955c) that there was a brief intense inhibitory effect superimposed on a more prolonged action that had a time course corresponding to the i.p.s.p., as is illustrated in Fig. 5B, C. It was further suggested that the initial intense inhibition was directly due to the current flow generated by the activated inhibitory synapses, i.e. to the current shown in Fig. 2A. Such currents would directly antagonize the depolarizing currents generated by activated excitatory synapses, their effectiveness being enhanced if superimposed on a depolarization (the e.p.s.p.) already produced by the excitatory synapses. However, the inhibitory current has a duration of no more than 2 msec, and excitatory synapses activated after this time would be antagonized only by the residuum of hyperpolarization. In contrast, at

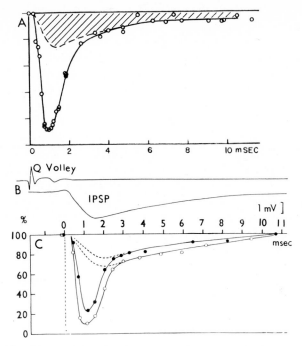

Fig. 5. Reproductions of inhibitory curves in which the inhibitory action of a quadriceps Ia afferent volley is tested by the size of a monosynaptic reflex spike discharged into the ventral root from *BST* motoneurons. The ordinates show the percentage sizes of the reflex spikes, the abscissae the testing volley intervals. The approximate time courses of the components of inhibition attributable directly to the hyperpolarization of the i.p.s.p.'s are shown by the broken lines. In B the quadriceps afferent volley and the i.p.s.p. are shown on the same time scale as in Fig. 5C. A is from Bradley *et al.* (1953) and B, C from Araki *et al.* (1960).

shorter testing intervals the inhibitory action would be due to superposition of the effects due to the inhibitory current and the hyperpolarization; as is illustrated in Fig. 5A, C, where the broken lines approximately separate the two modes of inhibitory action.

Testing for inhibition by the depression of reflex discharge has the disadvantage that the ordinates represent merely the relative population of the discharging motoneurons, and so do not give a direct measure of the intensity of inhibitory action. The most direct measurement is provided by testing excitability by a brief rectangular pulse (about 1 msec in duration) in the depolarizing direction through the intracellular electrode. At each testing interval during the inhibition the intensity of the pulse is adjusted so that it evokes a spike potential in approximately one-half of the trials. When the time course of the inhibitory action is obtained by plotting the reciprocals of current intensities against the testing intervals, it has a time course that displays the same double composition as with testing by reflex inhibition

(Araki *et al.*, 1960). Thus there is again a dual inhibitory action, which is likewise attributable to the inhibitory current and to the hyperpolarization of the i.p.s.p. When the rectangular pulse was much briefer (from 0·1 to 0·2 msec), it had correspondingly to be much more intense, and the initial phase of inhibition was much less prominent (Araki *et al.*, 1960). This is to be expected because the inhibitory current would be much less effective in counteracting the much more intense depolarizing current.

In conclusion it can be stated that the inhibitory synaptic mechanism shown diagrammatically in Fig. 2B, C, D satisfactorily accounts for the time course that is exhibited for inhibition of motoneurons, both of their reflex discharges and of their responses evoked by direct stimulation. Thus these investigations conform with those described above on inhibitory latency in showing that there is no justification for postulating (cf. Lloyd and Wilson, 1959; Lloyd, 1960) that inhibition is due to some process in addition to the potential change (the i.p.s.p.) revealed by intracellular recording and the inhibitory currents that cause that potential change.

As mentioned above, the inhibitory curve has occasionally been found by Jack *et al.* (1959, and personal communication) to exhibit only the brief phase, i.e. to have no phase attributable to the hyperpolarization of the i.p.s.p. Further support for this explanation was derived from the observation that in contrast to e.p.s.p.'s, no i.p.s.p.'s could be recorded as a result of electrotonic transmission to the ventral root as it emerged from the spinal cord (Jack *et al.*, 1959; Lloyd and Wilson, 1959). It was therefore postulated that the intracellularly recorded i.p.s.p. resulted from the lowering of membrane potential due to impalement by the microelectrode. However, a re-investigation (Araki *et al.*, 1960) has shown that i.p.s.p.'s can always be recorded in ventral roots provided that the experimental situation is designed so that it is particularly favourable for the production of i.p.s.p.'s and there is a minimum of complication by superposition of e.p.s.p.'s. For example, in Fig. 6A a quadriceps Ia afferent volley produced the i.p.s.p. electrotonically transmitted from biceps–semitendinosus motoneurons to a S_1 ventral rootlet. The central latencies of the i.p.s.p.'s recorded intracellularly (B) and electrotonically are virtually identical, but, as would be expected, the i.p.s.p. recorded from the ventral root has a slower time course. The relative sizes of the e.p.s.p.'s (C) and i.p.s.p.'s recorded from the ventral root are not at variance with what would be expected from the mean of the intracellular i.p.s.p.'s and e.p.s.p.'s produced similarly in motoneurons (Araki *et al.*, 1960). The mean sizes of the i.p.s.p.'s and e.p.s.p.'s produced by quadriceps and posterior biceps–semitendinosus (*PBST*) volleys on *BST* motoneurons in the lower L_7 or upper S_1 segments were 10 and 90 μV, respectively. Similarly, with stimulation of the S_3 dorsal root, i.p.s.p.'s of appropriate size were regularly recorded from the contralateral S_3 ventral rootlets, the mean size being 28 μV.

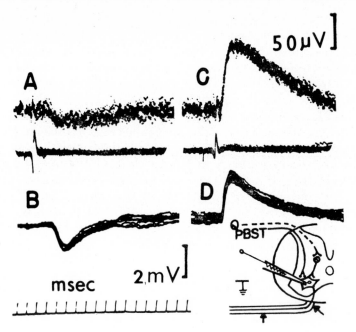

FIG. 6. B and D are intracellular records of i.p.s.p. and e.p.s.p. evoked in a *BST* motoneuron at S_1 segmental level by a Ia quadriceps and a *BST* volley, respectively, as shown in the inset diagram. The upper traces of A, C are the potentials electrotonically conducted from the motoneurons along their motor axons and recorded from an isolated filament of the S_1 ventral root, one electrode being on the filament about 1 mm from its exit from the cord, the other at least 20 mm distally on the isolated filament as shown by the two arrows in the inset diagram. A shows potentials produced by a Ia quadriceps volley, C by a Ia *BST* volley (Araki *et al.*, 1960).

This demonstration of an i.p.s.p. electrotonically propagated to the ventral root establishes that inhibitory synaptic action hyperpolarizes motoneurons that have not had their membrane potential lowered by microelectrode impalement. A similar conclusion may be drawn from the invariable demonstration by Araki *et al.* (1960) that a residuum of reflex inhibitory action continues for many milliseconds after the initial brief phase, as has been illustrated above (Fig. 5c). We may therefore conclude that, even before impalement by microelectrodes, the membrane potential is more depolarized than the equilibrium potential for the i.p.s.p., i.e. that E_R is less than $E_{\text{i.p.s.p.}}$. This conclusion is of importance when considering the ionic mechanism responsible for the inhibitory action.

We have seen that the effects produced in the size and direction of the i.p.s.p. by varying the initial membrane potential correspond precisely to the changes that would be expected if the currents generating the i.p.s.p. were due to ions moving down their electrochemical gradients. These currents would be caused to flow by alterations in the ionic permeability that are produced in the specific inhibitory patches under the influence of the inhibitory transmitter substance. With central synapses the nature of these permeability changes has been investigated by changing the ionic composition of the postsynaptic cell. Thus, electrophoretic injection of chloride ions into motoneurons (Coombs *et al.*, 1955b) or into the cells of Clarke's column (Curtis *et al.*, 1958) causes the i.p.s.p. to change to a depolarizing response (Fig. 7A to 7B). This inversion of the i.p.s.p. would be expected if the inhibitory transmitter acted by making the inhibitory patches highly permeable to chloride ions, which, under such changed conditions, would exhibit a net flow outward down their electrochemical gradient, so depolarizing the membrane. For example, if the normal flux of chloride ions across activated inhibitory patches could be represented as in Fig. 7G, an increased internal concentration of chloride would cause reversal of the net flux, as in Fig. 7H, hyperpolarization giving place to depolarization.

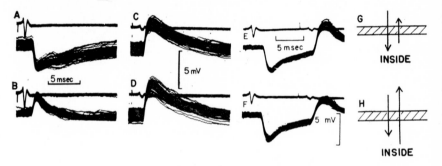

FIG. 7. A and B are i.p.s.p.'s, C and D are e.p.s.p.'s generated in a biceps–semitendinosus motoneuron by afferent volleys as in Fig. 1. A and C were first recorded, then a hyperpolarizing current of 2×10^{-8} A was passed for 60 sec through the microelectrode, which had been filled with 3 M KCl. Note that following this injection of chloride ions the i.p.s.p. was converted from a hyperpolarizing (A) to a depolarizing response (B), while the e.p.s.p. was not appreciably changed (C and D). Passing a much stronger hyperpolarizing current (4×10^{-8} A for 90 sec) through a microelectrode filled with 0·6 M K_2SO_4 caused no significant change (E–F) in either the i.p.s.p. or the later e.p.s.p. G and H represent the assumed fluxes of chloride ions across the membrane before (G) and after (H) the injection of chloride ions, which is shown greatly increasing the efflux of chloride.

In the original investigation (Coombs *et al.*, 1955b) it was also found that electrophoretic injection of several other anions (bromide, nitrate and thiocyanate) changed the i.p.s.p. to a depolarizing response as in Fig. 7B, while such anions as sulphate (cf. Fig. 7E, F), phosphate, acetate and bicarbonate had no such effect. These observations have now been confirmed and extended to many other anions (Araki *et al.*, 1961). The activated inhibitory patches exhibited about the same degree of permeability to eleven species of anion with diameters smaller than 1·32 times K^+ in the hydrated state, and were impermeable to fourteen species of anion with diameters larger than 1·35 times K^+. There was only one slight discrepancy from a size determination: the formate ion exhibited permeability, while the slightly smaller bromate ion (1·32 as against 1·35 times K^+) did not. Hence the simplest assumption is that the inhibitory transmitter has converted the specific inhibitory patches to a sieve-like membrane having pores of a precisely standardized size (cf. Coombs et al., 1955b; Eccles, 1957).

Chloride is the only permeable anion that normally exists in a concentration sufficient to contribute appreciably to the inhibitory ionic current. But, if the i.p.s.p. is produced solely by the net movement of Cl^- ions down their electrochemical gradient, the equilibrium potential for Cl^- ions (E_{cl}) must be at from 5 to 10 mV more polarization than the normal resting membrane potential. This value for E_{cl} could be maintained only if there were a chloride pump (cf. Boistel and Fatt, 1958). With those nerve or muscle fibres where accurate investigation has been possible, it has not been necessary to postulate a Cl^- pump (Hodgkin, 1958; Hodgkin and Horowicz, 1959). Particular attention should therefore be given to the possible role of K^+ ions in contributing to the generation of the i.p.s.p., for there is independent evidence that the equilibrium potential for K^+ ions (E_K) is maintained at 20 mV (or even more) polarization above resting membrane potential of motoneurons, for K^+ appears to be the only ion that contributes appreciably to the afterhyperpolarization following an SD spike potential, which has an equilibrium potential of from -90 to -100 mV (Coombs et al., 1955a; Eccles, Eccles and Ito, unpublished observations).

In the original investigation of the postulate that the net flux of K^+ ions contributes substantially to inhibitory current, Coombs et al. (1955b) compared the effects of passing depolarizing currents out of intracellular microelectrodes that were filled either with Na_2SO_4 or K_2SO_4. It was assumed that the current was carried out of the microelectrode largely by the highly concentrated cations therein, Na^+ or K^+ as the case may be, and that it was passed across the cell membrane partly by an outward flux of cations (largely K^+) and partly by an inward flux of anions (largely Cl^-). Thus an injection out of a K_2SO_4-filled electrode would add K^+ plus Cl^- ions to the cell; and after cessation of the current the normal composition of the cell would be recovered by water moving in to restore osmotic equilibrium and by K^+ and Cl^- ions diffusing out. On the other hand, after Na^+ injection out of the Na_2SO_4 electrode, there would be depletion of the intracellular K^+ and replacement by Na^+, but also much the same increase in Cl^- as with the K^+ injection. It was assumed that in this case also the Cl^- ions would quickly attain equilibrium by diffusion across the cell membrane, a process that is almost complete in 1 min. However, as seen in Fig. 8B, there was a very large change in the $E_{i.p.s.p.}$ (from -80 mV to -35 mV), and it took many minutes

7

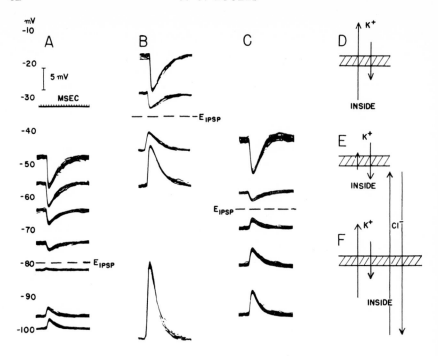

FIG. 8. In A, the i.p.s.p.'s of Fig. 3A are shown arranged with their membrane potentials on the scale indicated by short horizontal lines to the left of A, and the equilibrium potential for the i.p.s.p. is shown by the broken line. B shows the situation from 5 to 40 sec after the passage of a depolarizing current of 5×10^{-8} A for 90 sec through the microelectrode (filled with $0 \cdot 6$ M Na_2SO_4); the i.p.s.p.'s are shown similarly arranged on the same potential scale, the $E_{i.p.s.p.}$ being now -35 mV. C shows, on the same scale, the i.p.s.p.'s obtained during partial recovery at from 3 to 4 min after the electrophoretic injection with the $E_{i.p.s.p.}$ at -66 mV. D and E represent the postulated fluxes of K^+ ions in conditions A and B, respectively, while F gives the postulated fluxes of K^+ and Cl^- ions normally occurring across activated inhibitory postsynaptic membranes.

to recover to the normal value (cf. Fig. 8C). Hence Coombs et al. were led to postulate that the flux of K^+ ions was importantly concerned in the generation of the i.p.s.p., for on this postulate K^+ depletion would cause just such an effect, which would have the slow time course of recovery that depended on the linked Na–K pump.

But it now seems (Ito, 1960, personal communication) that the contribution of Cl^- ions to the more prolonged effect produced by Na^+ injection has been underestimated by Coombs et al. (1955b). After the K^+ injection the Cl^- could easily diffuse out across the membrane with the K^+ ions. After the Na^+ injection and the consequent K^+ depletion, the membrane potential was much diminished, in Fig. 8 from -75 mV to -57 mV in B; as a consequence the diffusion of Cl^- outward would be greatly impeded. Cl^- could only be restored to its initial electrochemical potential within the neuron when the excess Na^+ had been pumped out and replaced by K^+. Thus, even if Cl^- were the only ion that moved freely across the activated inhibitory patches of the postsynaptic membrane, there should be a much slower recovery of the $E_{i.p.s.p.}$ after Na^+ than after K^+ injection. Results such as those of Fig. 8 do not require the further assumption that K^+ ions also move freely across the activated inhibitory patches.

Yet, if K^+ flux does not play a considerable part in the generation of the postsynaptic inhibitory current, it seems impossible to explain how the $E_{i.p.s.p.}$ can be at about 5 to 10 mV more hyperpolarization than the resting potential (Fig. 3) without requiring that E_{Cl} should be maintained at this level by a Cl^- pump (cf. Boistel and Fatt, 1958). No other ion species could substitute for Cl^-, for no other permeable anion would normally be in a concentration to make any appreciable contribution to the inhibitory current. Hence, despite the enigmatic nature of the evidence from cation injection into motoneurons, it seems likely that the postsynaptic inhibitory patches are permeable to K^+ as well as to Cl^-. In the light of our experimental evidence K^+ permeability must be much lower than Cl^-, approximate values being about 20% and 80%, respectively, of the total, as indicated by the relative lengths of the arrows in Fig. 8F (Eccles, Eccles and Ito, unpublished observations).

Investigations on synaptic inhibitory actions at peripheral junctions have indicated that K^+ and Cl^- are likewise the only two ions that are effectively concerned in the postsynaptic inhibitory action (cf. Eccles, 1959). Several examples can be cited: Tauc (1958) has concluded that the i.p.s.p. of the giant cells of *Aplysia* results from an increased permeability to both K^+ and Cl^-; the inhibitory action on crustacean muscle fibres appears to be produced almost entirely by an increase in Cl^- permeability (Boistel and Fatt, 1958); the inhibitory action on crustacean stretch receptor cells is due almost entirely to an increase in K^+ permeability with Cl^- ions playing a subordinate role at most (Kuffler and Edwards, 1958; Edwards and Hagiwara, 1959); finally, vagal inhibition of the heart is similarly due to a large increase in K^+ permeability with little if any increase for Cl^- (Burgen and Terroux, 1953; Trautwein and Dudel, 1958).

Thus these diverse types of inhibitory action are all effected by an increased permeability to either K^+ or Cl^- or to their combination in varying degree. The initial hypothesis has been that the inhibitory postsynaptic membrane functions as a sieve, being permeable to all ions below a critical size in the hydrated state. If, as suggested by Boistel and Fatt (1958), it be further assumed that the pores are charged positively as in Fig. 9B, the membrane would exhibit a selective preference for small anions as against small cations, as occurs with crustacean muscle and mammalian motoneurons. If, on the other hand, the pores are charged negatively (Fig. 9A), the membrane would be selectively permeable to small cations, as occurs with crustacean stretch receptor cells and vertebrate heart muscle.

We have seen that there is a sharp separation between the permeable and impermeable species of anions, and that there is virtually the same permeability of the activated inhibitory patches for the largest permeable ion (formate) as for the smallest (bromide). It may therefore be assumed that, when the inhibitory transmitter acts on the membrane, it brings into existence pores that have a precisely standardized size. In a personal communication Fatt (1960) has suggested that such a happening could be readily envisaged if the pores were permanent structures that were plugged at their external opening and a transmitter molecule acted by momentarily dislodging the plug as illustrated in Fig. 9C, D. For example the transmitter molecule might form a bridge between two receptor sites to which it was momentarily attached, one on the adjacent membrane and the other on the plug as diagrammatically shown in Fig. 9D.

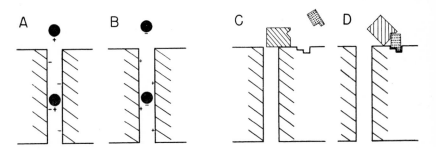

FIG. 9. Schematic representations of pores that are assumed to be the channels for the ionic fluxes through the activated inhibitory patches on motoneurons. In A the pores are negatively charged and so will be selectively permeable to small cations as shown, while in B they are positively charged and so are selectively permeable to small anions, as occurs with the motoneuron. C shows diagrammatically the way in which an inhibitory pore is plugged, an inhibitory transmitter molecule being shown free in the environment. In D this molecule is shown in close steric relationship both to the plug and to an inhibitory receptor site on the postsynaptic membrane. As a consequence the plug has been pulled away from the orifice of the pore, which is opened for the ionic flux that occurs during the brief duration of the transmitter action on the subsynaptic membrane.

In conclusion it can be stated that good explanations can now be offered for the mode of action of postsynaptic inhibition in preventing the reflex discharge of impulses, but there is much uncertainty in other respects. For example, the central inhibitory transmitter substance is as yet unidentified and one can do no more than speculate as above on the manner in which the transmitter acts on the postsynaptic membrane to cause the momentary appearance of pores of precisely standardized size.

REFERENCES

AITKEN, J. T. and BRIDGER, J. E. (1961) Neuron size and neuron population density in the lumbosacral region of the cat's spinal cord. *J. Anat.* In press.

ARAKI, T., ECCLES, J. C. and ITO, M. (1960) Correlation of the inhibitory postsynaptic potential of motoneurones with the latency and time course of inhibition of mono-synaptic reflexes. *J. Physiol. (London).*

ARAKI, T., ITO, M. and OSCARSSON, O. (1961) Anionic permeability of the inhibitory postsynaptic membrane of motoneurones. *Nature* **189** : 65.

BOISTEL, J. and FATT, P. (1958) Membrane permeability change during inhibitory trans-mitter action in crustacean muscle. *J. Physiol. (London)* **144** : 176–191.

BRADLEY, K., EASTON, D. M. and ECCLES, J. C. (1953) An investigation of primary or direct inhibition. *J. Physiol. (London)* **122** : 474–488.

BROOKS, V. B., CURTIS, D. R. and ECCLES, J. C. (1957) The action of tetanus toxin on the inhibition of motoneurones. *J. Physiol. (London)* **135** : 655–672.

BURGEN, A. S. V. and TERROUX, L. G. (1953) The membrane resting and action potentials of the cat auricle. *J. Physiol. (London)* **119** : 139–152.

COOMBS, J. S., CURTIS, D. R. and ECCLES, J. C. (1959) The electrical constants of the motoneurone membrane. *J. Physiol. (London)* **145** : 505–528.

COOMBS, J. S., ECCLES, J. C. and FATT, P. (1955a) The electrical properties of the moto-neurone membrane. *J. Physiol. (London)* **130** : 291–325.

COOMBS, J. S., ECCLES, J. C. and FATT, P. (1955b) The specific ionic conductances and the ionic movements across the motoneuronal membrane that produce the inhibitory post-synaptic potential. *J. Physiol. (London)* **130** : 326–373.

COOMBS, J. S., ECCLES, J. C. and FATT, P. (1955c) The inhibitory suppression of reflex discharges from motoneurones. *J. Physiol. (London)* **130** : 396–413.

CURTIS, D. R. (1959) Pharmacological investigations upon inhibition of spinal neurones. *J. Physiol. (London)* **145** : 175–192.

CURTIS, D. R. and ECCLES, J. C. (1959) The time courses of excitatory and inhibitory synaptic actions. *J. Physiol. (London)* **145** : 529–546.

CURTIS, D. R., ECCLES, J. C. and LUNDBERG, A. (1958) Intracellular recording from cells in Clarke's column. *Acta Physiol. Scand.* **43** : 303–314.

ECCLES, J. C. (1957) *The Physiology of Nerve Cells.* Johns Hopkins Press, Baltimore.

ECCLES, J. C. (1959) Excitatory and inhibitory synaptic action. *Ann. N.Y. Acad. Sci.* **81** : 247–264.

ECCLES, J. C. (1961) Inhibitory pathways to motoneurons. This volume, pp. 47–60.

ECCLES, J. C., FATT, P. and KOKETSU, K. (1954) Cholinergic and inhibitory synapses in a pathway from motor-axon collaterals to motoneurones. *J. Physiol. (London)* **126** : 524–562.

EDWARDS, C. and HAGIWARA, S. (1959) Potassium ions and the inhibitory process in the crayfish stretch receptor. *J. Gen. Physiol.* **43** : 315–321.

HODGKIN, A. L. (1958) Ionic movements and electrical activity in giant nerve fibres. *Proc. Roy. Soc. (London)* B **148** : 1–37.

HODGKIN, A. L. and HOROWICZ, P. (1959) The influence of potassium and chloride ions on the membrane potential of single muscle fibres. *J. Physiol. (London)* **148** : 127–160.

JACK, J., McINTYRE, A. K. and SOMJEN, G. (1959) Excitability of motoneurones during reflex facilitation and inhibition. *Internat. Congr. Physiol. Sci.* **21** : Communications, 136.

KUFFLER, S. W. and EDWARDS, C. (1958) Mechanism of gamma aminobutyric acid (GABA) action and its relation to synaptic inhibition. *J. Neurophysiol.* **21** : 589–610.

LAPORTE, Y. and LLOYD, D. P. C. (1952) Nature and significance of the reflex connections established by large afferent fibers of muscular origin. *Am. J. Physiol.* **169** : 609 -621.

LLOYD, D. P. C. (1946) Facilitation and inhibition of spinal motoneurones. *J. Neurophysiol.* **9** : 421–438.

J. C. ECCLES

LLOYD, D. P. C. (1960) Spinal mechanisms involved in somatic activities. *Handbook of Physiology*, Vol. 2. *Neurophysiology* (ed. by FIELD, J.), pp. 929–949. American Physiological Society.

LLOYD, D. P. C. and WILSON, V. J. (1959) Functional organization in the terminal segments of the spinal cord with a consideration of central excitatory and inhibitory latencies in monosynaptic reflex systems. *J. Gen. Physiol.* **42** : 1219–1231.

RALL, W. (1959) Branching dendritic trees and motoneuron membrane resistivity. *Exptl. Neurol.* **1** : 491–527.

TAUC, L. (1958) Processus post-synaptique d'excitation et d'inhibition dans le soma neuronique de L'Aplysie et de L'Escargot. *Arch. ital. biol.* **96** : 78–110.

TRAUTWEIN, W. and DUDEL, J. (1958) Zum Mechanismus der Membranwirkung des Acetylcholin an der Herzmuskelfaser. *Arch. ges. Physiol. Pflüger's* **266** : 324–334.

THE CHANGE IN MEMBRANE PERMEABILITY
DURING THE INHIBITORY PROCESS

PAUL FATT

From the Biophysics Department, University College, London, England

EVIDENCE for a direct action of the inhibitory nerve impulse on the electrical properties of crustacean muscle was already being sought—and in some measure found—by Biedermann (1887). In 1953 Professor Katz and I described an increase in membrane conductance of the muscle fibre produced by the inhibitory impulse (Fatt and Katz, 1953). It was manifest as a reduction in the displacement from the resting level of potential, the displacement being produced by an applied current. This electrical behaviour was interpreted to indicate an increase in membrane permeability toward ions which, in the resting condition, were in electrochemical equilibrium across the membrane. The ions thus involved were suggested to be either K^+ or Cl^- or both. At the time of this finding an increase in membrane permeability specifically toward K^+ ions was recognized to play a major role in the electrical response of excitable tissue, while Cl^- ions were seen as providing merely a passive electrical leak (Hodgkin, 1951). Nevertheless the possibility of an increase in permeability toward Cl^- as well as toward K^+ was seriously considered from the start as a result of comparing the inhibitory response with the membrane alteration occurring during excitatory junctional activity. At the excitatory junction the nerve impulse produces a transient shift in membrane potential toward a level near zero membrane potential (Fatt and Katz, 1951). This indicates an increase in permeability toward more than a single species of ion. In the frog muscle where the excitatory junctional process has been most fully analysed the ionic currents added by junctional activity are found to reverse at a level of membrane potential making the inside of the fibre between -10 and -20 mV with respect to the outside (Castillo and Katz, 1954). This is about the level to be expected, if in the junctionally active areas the membrane lost all selectivity toward the movement of the various ions known to be present inside and outside the fibre.

In order to examine the possible involvement of the two suggested species of ions in the conductance increase produced during inhibitory activity, experiments were carried out on the opener muscle of the claw of the crayfish, *Astacus fluviatilis* (Boistel and Fatt, 1958). The composition of the bathing solution with respect to K^+ and Cl^- content was varied, and the changes produced in the resting potential and in the level of reversal of the inhibitory response was observed. The observations were made with two microelectrodes inserted close together in a muscle fibre, one being used to apply current while the steady level and transients of membrane potential were recorded by the other. When the K^+ concentration was raised there was an immediate fall in resting potential, roughly in accord with the view that in this range of membrane potentials the conductance was predominantly due to K^+ ions. At this reduced level of membrane potential the inhibitory response appeared as a transient hyperpolarization. Its reversal could be effected by applying an inward current to the muscle fibre, and by this means displace the membrane potential back to about the level existing before the application of the high K^+ solution. The true value of the equilibrium potential, at which junctional activity would produce no additional current flow, would, however, correspond to a somewhat smaller displacement, because of the fact that the shift in membrane potential produced by the current is not uniform throughout the region of the muscle fibre in which junctional activity takes place, but is largest at the position of recording. An additional complication is introduced by the influx of K^+ and Cl^- ions into the muscle fibre in the high K^+ solution, causing the internal Cl^- concentration to rise gradually. Nevertheless the experiment clearly shows that variation in the external K^+ concentration has a greater effect on the resting potential than on the equilibrium potential for inhibition. From this it follows that as a result of junctional activity there is a reduction in the relative contribution to membrane conductance made by K^+ ions. In the complimentary experiment the Cl^- of the bathing solution was replaced by a large organic anion (pyroglutamate and acetylglycine having been used). When Cl^- was completely removed the resting potential fell by from 10 to 20 mV and the inhibitory response appeared as a transient depolarization. The application of an outward current producing a further decrease in membrane potential of several tens of millivolts was necessary to reverse the response, and it was then usually found that on continuing the current the reversal level was driven to a still lower level of membrane potential. Such reversal as was effected is liable to be due to Cl^- ions which had leaked out of the fibre and had accumulated in low concentration immediately outside the membrane. It is concluded from these observations on the effects of the external K^+ and Cl^- concentrations that the inhibitory process involves an increase in the relative contribution of Cl^- to the total membrane conductance. Experiments on varying the K^+ concentration in a Cl^--free solution failed to give evidence of a possible increase in K^+ conductance; the results continued to depend on variations in the movement of Cl^-, now entirely in the outward direction. In this material any increase in membrane permeability toward K^+ produced by inhibitory activity must be of a smaller order of magnitude than the readily demonstrated increase in permeability toward Cl⁻.

In order to inquire into the structural change in the membrane by which the permeability increase just described is brought about, a more speculative course will be followed, the inhibitory response being considered in relation to other types of response of which the membrane is capable. Thus it is reasonable to assume that there would be a basic similarity between the membrane permeability changes occurring in excitatory and inhibitory junctional activity. One of the outstanding features of junctional activity is the great magnitude of the conductance change over the area of the post-junctional cell in which this activity originates. In the frog muscle fibre junctional activity involves the addition of a conductance of about $5 \times 10^{-5} \Omega^{-1}$ to the muscle fibre membrane in an area of 10^{-4} cm² or less (Fatt and Katz, 1951). From this one calculates a minimum conductance for unit area of junctionally active membrane of $0.5 \ \Omega^{-1}$ cm⁻². This exceeds by a factor of 10 the maximum conductance increase occurring for large depolarizations in the squid axon, where the conductance changes, which are involved in the production of the action potential, are due to increases in membrane permeability specifically toward Na⁺ and toward K⁺. Quantities of similar magnitude would probably hold for the excitatory junctional response and for the action potential generating response, respectively, in various types of cells. Moreover a similar high intensity of conductance change would probably hold for inhibitory junctions as for excitatory junctions. The underlying meaning of this is simply that within the small area of junctional contact the total conductance increase must be sufficiently great to allow currents to flow which on spreading into a much larger area of normal membrane will be able to affect the membrane potential significantly and thus control the excitability of the cell with respect to the initiation of an action potential, or in the case of some muscle fibres, to the initiation of contraction. A reasonable inference is that the very drastic increase in permeability required in junctional activity would operate through a different mechanism from that involved in the action potential and would possibly involve a less complex structural organization of the membrane. Thus in the case of excitatory junctional activity the behaviour of the membrane is consistent with the creation of simple holes through which all ions diffusing up to the membrane are able to penetrate. A similar alteration is envisaged to occur in the inhibitory process, though in this case the holes would be of smaller size and thereby capable of discriminating against the passage of larger ions. Furthermore, if the walls of the holes contained fixed positive charges, this would interfere with the passage of cations.

An examination of the electrical behaviour of the crustacean muscle fibre membrane may provide a clue as to how such holes are produced. When an inward current is applied to a fibre in the normal bathing solution the resulting hyperpolarization begins to rise on a time course determined by the charging of the membrane capacity, but after reaching a maximum declines to a lower level in about 50 msec at which it is then maintained (Fatt and Ginsborg, 1958). The delayed increase in membrane conductance on hyperpolarization which this reveals is influenced by procedures which change the internal Cl^- concentration of the fibre. Although the immediate effect of removing Cl^- from the bathing solution is slight, there being usually a decrease in the conductance increase produced for small hyperpolarizations but not for large ones, after soaking the muscle for 1 hr in a Cl^--free solution the increase in conductance on hyperpolarization is nearly abolished. In another experiment the muscle is soaked in a solution of high K^+ concentration for about 30 min, it is then returned to the normal low K^+ solution, and after the resting potential has recovered the increase in conductance on hyperpolarization is found to be increased greatly. In this experiment an increase in the internal Cl^- concentration would have been produced by keeping the muscle in the high K^+ solution. The conclusion is drawn that the conductance increase on hyperpolarization results from an increase in membrane permeability toward Cl^- ions, with the internal Cl^- concentration having the major influence because of the fact that on hyperpolarization the net movement of a negative ion would be outward. (The difference in the effect of internal and external Cl^- would be accentuated by a movement through long pores whereby all the ions contained in a given pore would have to move simultaneously in the same direction.)

This conductance change has no apparent role in the function of the muscle fibre, and is thought of as an accidental property of the membrane. A conductance increase on hyperpolarization has been observed in other types of cells, and has sometimes been described as a breakdown of the membrane brought on by the excessive potential difference across it. For a membrane potential of 100 mV across a membrane thickness of 100 Å (indicated by examination with the electron microscope) the average field strength within the membrane is calculated to be 10^5 V/cm. Dielectric breakdown occurs in most materials at about this field strength, but this cannot be evoked here since it entails the freeing of electrons to conduct the current and this will only occur if there is a total potential difference of at least a few volts available. One therefore has to consider a less elementary process, in which the field causes a charged molecular component of the membrane to be moved, the electrical energy being used to break chemical bonds by which this component is held in its normal position. The structure in question is pictured as acting as a plug, which on being moved from its normal position leaves holes through which ions in the solutions bordering the membrane are able to diffuse. Finally, it is suggested that the inhibitory transmitter operates by breaking the same bonds through a chemical reaction—the reaction involving the receptor body situated on the outer surface of the membrane. This concept, that the nature of the permeability change produced by junctional activity depends on a general structural property of the membrane, is helpful in accounting for some of the variations in the inhibitory process seen in different types of cells.

REFERENCES

BIEDERMANN, W. (1887) Beiträge zur allgemeinen Nerven- und Muskelphysiologie—XX. Über die Innervation der Krebsschere. *Sitzber. Akad. Wiss. Wien* Abt. 3, **95** : 7–40.

BOISTEL, J. and FATT, P. (1958) Membrane permeability change during inhibitory transmitter action in crustacean muscle. *J. Physiol. (London)* **144** : 176–191.

CASTILLO, J. DEL and KATZ, B. (1954) The membrane change produced by the neuromuscular transmitter. *J. Physiol. (London)* **125** : 546–565.

FATT, P. and GINSBORG, B. L. (1958) The ionic requirements for the production of action potentials in crustacean muscle fibres. *J. Physiol. (London)* **142** : 516–543.

FATT, P. and KATZ, B. (1951) An analysis of the endplate potential recorded with an intracellular electrode. *J. Physiol. (London)* **115** : 320–370.

FATT, P. and KATZ, B. (1953) The effect of inhibitory nerve impulses on a crustacean muscle fibre. *J. Physiol. (London)* **121** : 374–389.

HODGKIN, A. L. (1951) The ionic basis of electrical activity in nerve and muscle. *Biol. Revs.* **26** : 339–409.

NEUROMUSCULAR SYNAPTIC ACTIVITY
IN LOBSTER*

HARRY GRUNDFEST AND JOHN P. REUBEN†

Department of Neurology, College of Physicians and Surgeons,
Columbia University, New York

THE neuromuscular systems of the legs of the lobster, *H. americanus*, offer numerous possibilities for electrophysiological and pharmacological studies of the elements that are involved in transmissional processes. At least one inhibitory, and one or several excitatory axons innervate multiterminally the fibers of each muscle. The axons are readily separated in the nerve trunk and the properties of the conductile membrane of each nerve fiber thus may be examined separately. Miniature postsynaptic potentials (p.s.p.'s) occur in both the excitatory and inhibitory synaptic membranes of the muscle fibers and their study permits some degree of analysis of events in the presynaptic terminals, though the latter have as yet proved inaccessible to direct study with microelectrode recordings. As will be described below, there appear to be two distinct action components in the presynaptic terminal region (Reuben and Grundfest, 1960c). Evoked excitatory and inhibitory p.s.p.'s that are produced by stimulating the axons may be studied separately and in combination under various pharmacological and physiological conditions. Their properties may be distinguished from those of the conductile membrane by the distinctive differences between electrically inexcitable transmissional and electrically excitable conductile activities (Grundfest, 1957a, 1959). Furthermore, while the electrically excitable membrane is normally gradedly responsive (Werman and Grundfest, 1961) it may be converted to all-or-none activity by various means (Reuben and Grundfest, 1960a; Reuben *et al.*, 1960a; Werman and Grundfest, 1961). It also exhibits a number of anomalous properties and their analysis (Grundfest, 1960, 1961a; Reuben *et al.*, 1960b) has helped to throw considerable light on the various ionic mechanisms of electrically excitable membrane (Grundfest, 1961a). Thus, interplays of inhibitory and excitatory processes need to be studied in greater detail than as the interaction of only two sets of events in the postsynaptic cell.

* These researches were supported in part by funds from the following sources: Muscular Dystrophy Associations of America, National Institutes of Health, National Science Foundation and United Cerebral Palsy Research and Educational Association.

† Dr. Reuben is a Fellow of the National Science Foundation.

THE CONDUCTILE MEMBRANE OF THE AXONS

While the electrically excitable conductile membrane is relatively less sensitive to most drugs than is synaptic membrane (Grundfest, 1957c, 1958, 1959) it is, nevertheless, also affected by various synaptic agents. Thus D-tubocurarine, eserine and procaine, all of which inactivate the synapses of eel electroplaques, also modify and eventually may block activity in the electrically excitable membrane (Altamirano et al., 1955; Grundfest, 1957b). Phenethylamine (PEA), which has several actions on the lobster neuromuscular junctions (Bergmann et al., 1959; Reuben et al., 1959), blocks conduction in the excitatory and inhibitory axons (Fig. 1). The block is reversible. GABA (γ-aminobutyric acid) and picrotoxin, both of which affect profoundly the activity of other sites in the system (Grundfest et al., 1959; Reuben et al., 1959), do not affect conduction in either axon.

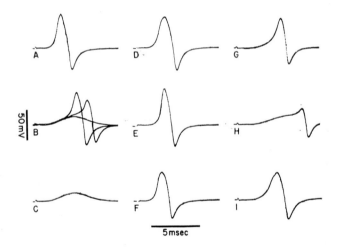

FIG. 1. Effects of drugs on conductile membrane of the axon. An exciter axon was used in this preparation. It was stimulated in the region of the leg proximal to the body with the recording electrodes placed distally. The drugs (PEA, GABA and picrotoxin) were applied at a small region between the stimulating and recording electrodes as a drop of a 10^{-3} (w/v) solution. Similar data were also obtained for the inhibitory axon. A. Control spike. B. After applying PEA, conduction block developed as shown by the appearance of a large electrotonic potential under the delayed spike, then further delay of the latter and its disappearance. c. Block of conduction shown before washing out the PEA. D. Recovery on washing. Application of GABA (E) and of picrotoxin (F) did not affect the responsiveness of the membrane. Addition of the fluid changed the recording conditions somewhat as shown by the large stimulus artifacts and the forms of the spikes. G. After reapplying PEA. H. Block nearly complete. I. Recovery on washing with *Homarus* Ringer's solution.

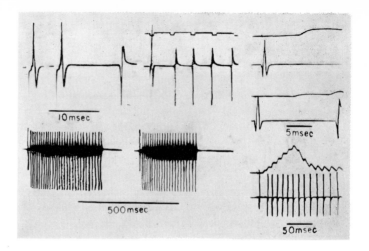

FIG. 2. Repetitive antidromic activity following a single orthodromic impulse in an axon, after applying drugs to the presynaptic terminals. (*Left*)—Serotonin and picrotoxin. (*Upper set*, on faster time base)—Control response before applying drugs. Orthodromic direction indicated by initial negativity (upward) of diphasic spike. After applying drugs the orthodromic spike was followed by an anti-dromic response. This was the first of a burst of repetitive activity seen at half speed on the time base. (*Below*)—Two antidromic trains on a slow time base. (*Right*)—PEA and picrotoxin. Simultaneous recording from muscle fiber (*upper trace*, intracellular recording) and exciter axon (*lower trace*). (*Top*)—E.p.s.p. evoked by an orthodromic nerve impulse. (*Middle*)—The drugs diminished the e.p.s.p., but caused antidromic activity which initiated further e.p.s.p.'s. The first of a train of repetitive spikes and e.p.s.p.'s is seen in this record. (*Bottom*)—The repetitive train and the summated e.p.s.p.'s are seen on a slower time base.

THE CONDUCTILE MEMBRANE OF THE TERMINALS

When PEA, or one of various other agents, is applied to the neuromuscular junctions themselves along with picrotoxin, a single impulse evoked by stimulating either axon leads to a burst of antidromic repetitive impulses (Reuben *et al.*, 1959). These impulses (Fig. 2), which must originate at or near the nerve terminals, are propagated into the axon and are thence distributed to all the muscles innervated by the fiber. These impulses also cause orthodromic effects that may be recorded intracellularly in the muscle exposed to the drugs (Figs. 3 and 4). PEA itself depresses the p.s.p.'s of the muscle fibers. Picrotoxin suppresses the i.p.s.p.'s, while it does not affect the e.p.s.p.'s (Grundfest *et al.*, 1959). The repetitive presynaptic activity caused by the combined actions of the two drugs thus results in only excitatory p.s.p.'s which are now large and prolonged, because of summation and facilitation of the repetitively evoked responses (Fig. 3). Vertebrate presynaptic terminals are also excited to

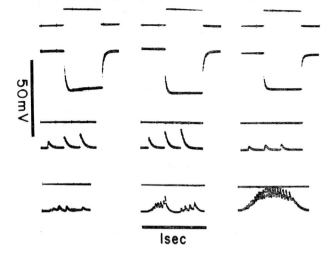

Fig. 3. Differential effects of picrotoxin and PEA on the electrically excitable and synaptic membranes of a muscle fiber. *Lower half* in each set is of intracellular recording. (*Top row*)—Absence of effects on membrane resistance. *Left*, control; *middle*, after picrotoxin; *right*, after PEA. *Upper trace* shows the hyperpolarizing current applied through another intracellular microelectrode. The membrane potential change was about the same in all three records. (*Middle row*)—The e.p.s.p.'s evoked by three stimuli to the axon under the same conditions. After picrotoxin the e.p.s.p.'s increased, indicating that there probably had been considerable spontaneous activity of the inhibitory synaptic membrane which was blocked by the drug. After PEA the e.p.s.p.'s become small. Note that facilitation was present in all conditions indicating that the processes causing this were not affected by the drugs. (*Bottom row*)—Three series of records as PEA and picrotoxin developed their maximal effect on the presynaptic repetitive firing. Note that the pattern of postsynaptic responses to the three orthodromic stimuli was disrupted by the repetitive activity.

repetitive activity (cf. Riker *et al.*, 1959). However, the agents which are effective in these cases did not produce repetitive activity in the lobster axons.

GABA which excites the inhibitory synaptic membrane (Grundfest *et al.*, 1959) also acts antagonistically to picrotoxin on the presynaptic terminals (Fig. 4). However, it does not block the responses of the axons, but eliminates the repetitive activity. The latter is again brought about by adding picrotoxin. Similar effects are also observed on recording from the excitatory and inhibitory axons. They obviously occur at the presynaptic terminals, and therefore the conductile component of the membrane at the terminals is affected differently by the drugs than is the conductile membrane along the axon. It is likely that the repetitive activity of the terminals is a manifestation of prolonged depolarization, either by some type of after-potential, or by prolonged spikes (Reuben and Grundfest, 1960a; Werman and Grundfest, 1961). However, since the details of the electrical activity of the terminals are still unknown, the nature of the actions of the drugs cannot be fully analyzed as

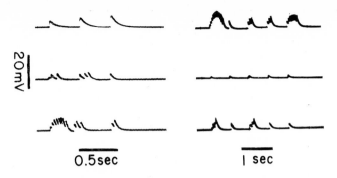

Fig. 4. Effect of GABA on repetitive activity in presynaptic terminals. Intracellular recording from a muscle fiber. (*Left column; upper trace*)—Three control e.p.s.p.'s evoked by stimulating the axon. (*Middle*)—Repetitive activity developing soon after applying PEA and picrotoxin. (*Bottom*)—Further development of repetitive activity in presynaptic terminals indicated by greater summation of e.p.s.p.'s which were produced at higher frequency. Note that repetitive activity disappeared in the second evoked response and that only one repetitive e.p.s.p. occurred in the third sequence. (*Right column*)—Another sequence of repetitive activity following five stimuli to the axon. Recording on a slower time base. Note again the modification in frequency of repetitions and absence after the second orthodromic stimulation. However, the single response was facilitated as were the subsequent responses to the orthodromic stimuli. (*Middle*)—Repetitive activity was abolished on adding GABA. The agent also activated the inhibitory membrane which had been blocked by the picrotoxin. Consequently the e.p.s.p.'s were diminished markedly in amplitude. Note the presence of facilitation despite their effects on both presynaptic terminals and synaptic membrane. (*Bottom*)— Repetitive activity was restored on adding picrotoxin.

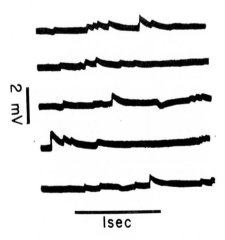

Fig. 5. Spontaneous miniature p.s.p.'s both depolarizing and hyperpolarizing in lobster muscle fiber. Intracellular recording. The hyperpolarizing responses were consistently smaller than the depolarizing responses since the equilibrium potential of the inhibitory synaptic membrane is close to the resting potential.

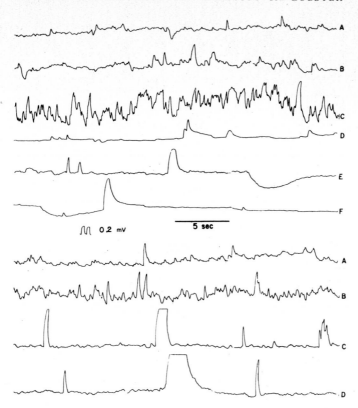

FIG. 6. Modification of spontaneous miniature potentials by NH₄Cl and picrotoxin. Inkwriter recording. (*Upper set*)—A. Control. B. Ten minutes after applying 40 mM NH₄Cl/l. C. Thirty minutes; increase in frequency and amplitude is marked. D. Fifty minutes; frequency becomes low but potentials are of considerable amplitude. E, F. Continuous recording at 90 min. Large depolarizing and hyperpolarizing potentials. (*Lower set*)—In another experiment, picrotoxin was applied and this eliminated the hyperpolarizing potentials. A. Before applying NH₄Cl. B. Thirty minutes after 40 mM NH₄Cl/l. was applied. C, D. Continuous recording at 90 min. Depolarizing potentials were now very large, in the absence of the hyperpolarizing activity.

yet. Nevertheless, the analysis can be extended considerably, by examining the miniature synaptic activities, which presumably arise from "spontaneous" local activity of the presynaptic terminals (Reuben and Grundfest, 1960c).

THE TRANSMISSIONAL MEMBRANES OF THE TERMINALS

The inhibitory as well as excitatory synaptic membrane in lobster muscle fibers produces miniature p.s.p.'s (Fig. 5). They are of considerable amplitude and both types are affected by application of NH₄Cl (Fig. 6), an action

8

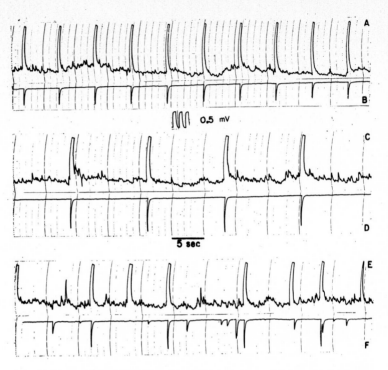

FIG. 7. Localized activity of transmissional presynaptic membrane. Intracellular recordings simultaneously from two muscle fibers, registered with inkwriter. Amplitude calibration applies to upper trace of each set. Lower trace at 1/10 gain. A, B. E.p.s.p.'s recorded on stimulating the excitatory axon were produced simultaneously in both muscle fibers. C, D. Ten minutes after applying serotonin. The e.p.s.p.'s had increased markedly in amplitude. E, F. At 45 min. Spontaneous activity had increased markedly, and large e.p.s.p.'s are seen on lower trace which are independent of activity in muscle fiber recorded on upper trace. The latter also shows large potentials that do not occur on lower trace.

similar to that on frog skeletal muscle (Furukawa *et al.*, 1957). These actions are confined to the local transmissional sites of the presynaptic terminals, since involvement of conductile activity in the axons should have caused synchronous activity in the various muscle fibers. Other agents affect only the terminals of the excitatory axon. Thus, serotonin increases the spontaneous e.p.s.p.'s to the point where they are almost of the same magnitude as evoked e.p.s.p.'s (Fig. 7), but it does not increase the magnitude or frequency of spontaneous or evoked i.p.s.p.'s (Reuben and Grundfest, 1960c). The foregoing data therefore demonstrate that a transmissional component, which is probably secretory in function (Grundfest, 1957a, 1959), has different pharmacological properties from a conductile component, and that the latter differs from the electrically excitable membrane of the rest of the axon. Furthermore, the terminals of the excitatory and inhibitory axons have some pharmacological similarities and also differences.

INTERACTIONS OF THE TRANSMISSIONAL COMPONENTS AT THE SYNAPSE

The large e.p.s.p.'s produced by the action of serotonin show marked facilitation (Fig. 8). Like a number of other agents (Werman and Grundfest,

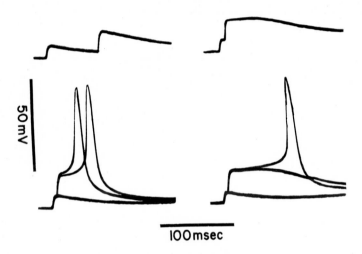

50 mV

100 msec

Fig. 8. Facilitation and summation of e.p.s.p.'s in serotonin-treated muscle fibers. (*Upper set*)—Two e.p.s.p.'s evoked by stimulating axon with paired pulses at different intervals. The closely spaced pairs of e.p.s.p.'s evoked a small graded response of the electrically excitable membrane. (*Below*)—Three sweeps superimposed in each record. A single stimulus evoked a relatively large e.p.s.p. compared with that in untreated muscle fibers, but not large enough to evoke a response of the electrically excitable membrane. The second stimulus produced a facilitated synaptic response which caused a graded response and a spike in the electrically excitable membrane.

1961; Reuben and Grundfest, 1960a), serotonin may convert the gradedly responsive electrically excitable membrane to all-or-none responsiveness, and the summated e.p.s.p.'s after a few nerve volleys evoke spikes. Both e.p.s.p.'s and i.p.s.p.'s are enhanced even more by soaking the preparations in solutions that have the K^+ replaced with Cs^+ (Reuben and Grundfest, 1960d). The p.s.p.'s are now nearly maximal in amplitude (Figs. 9, 10), and show very little facilitation.

The site of action of Cs^+ has not yet been completely identified, but one factor, the electrically excitable membrane may be excluded (Fig. 10). The resting potential of the muscle fibers (-85 mV) is about like that of muscle

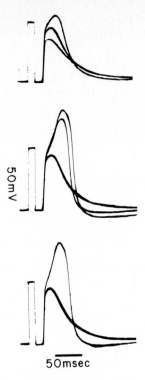

Fig. 9. Large e.p.s.p.'s evoked in muscle fiber that had been soaked in a Ringer's solution in which Cs⁺ had replaced K⁺. The e.p.s.p.'s showed only small facilitation on repetitive stimulation, but the increase was sufficient to evoke graded responses in the electrically excitable membrane. Note the rapid repolarization when the graded responses were produced.

fibers exposed for a short time to zero K^+ (Grundfest *et al.*, 1959; Reuben, 1959). The equilibrium potential of the i.p.s.p.'s is about 7 mV more negative, also as in the case of muscle fibers soaked for a short time in zero K^+, although as shown, the responses in Cs^+ are maximal with single stimuli. When muscles are soaked for some hours in a K^+-free solution the resting potential becomes much more inside-negative (average: $- 110$ mV) and the equilibrium potential for the i.p.s.p.'s is at $- 120$ mV (average). The individual i.p.s.p.'s are nevertheless small and show marked facilitation. The different effects on the resting and equilibrium potentials produced by absence of K^+ or its replacement with Cs^+ appear to be due to the different modes of redistribution of Cl^- in the two experimental situations. The physiological manifestations in the synaptic responses, characterized by the presence or absence of augmentation of the single i.p.s.p., and by the absence or presence of facilitation, are nevertheless evidenced independently of the electrochemical conditions.

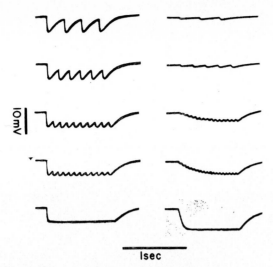

Fig. 10. Differential effects on i.p.s.p.'s in muscle fiber soaked in K+-free Ringer's solution (*right*) and in Cs+-Ringer's solution (*left*). (*Right*)—In the K+-free solution, the individual i.p.s.p.'s were small, but summation and facilitation at higher frequencies of stimulation drove the potential to its equilibrium level about 10 mV negative to the resting potential which was −110 mV. (*Left*)—In the Cs+-Ringer's solution the individual i.p.s.p.'s were large, facilitation was absent and the equilibrium potential was equal to the peak single i.p.s.p. It was about 6 mV negative to the resting potential which was only −85 mV.

Augmentation of the e.p.s.p. to nearly maximal responses by Cs makes possible an estimate with some degree of accuracy of the reversal potential of the e.p.s.p. (Fig. 11). Furthermore, the change in the amplitude of the e.p.s.p. with the membrane potential has a slope of about 0·5. Thus, the conductance change during activity of the excitatory postsynaptic membrane is much less than is the conductance change during maximal activity in the inhibitory postsynaptic membrane. When the latter is excited by GABA the membrane resistance of the normal muscle fiber falls some three- to six-fold, and in Ba+-treated fibers the resistance decreases some twenty-five- to thirty-fold (Grundfest et al., 1959).

CONCLUSION

The foregoing brief survey describes some of the complications that must arise in the functioning of a synaptic system of even moderate degree of organizational complexity. The synaptic membranes themselves and the electrically excitable components of the postsynaptic unit have been neglected at this time to emphasize factors that are ordinarily not considered or insufficiently regarded. Further details of the pharmacological and electro-

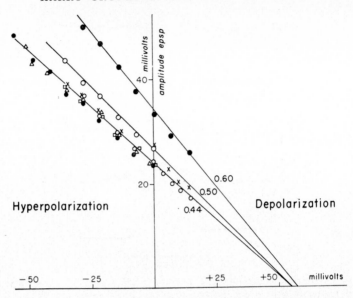

Fɪɢ. 11. Effect of change of membrane potential on the amplitude of the large
e.p.s.p. produced in muscle fibers soaked in Cs$^+$-Ringer's solution. Six muscle
fibers from different preparations, each indicated by a different symbol. The origin
of the abscissa is the resting potential which was about -75 mV in all experiments.
The reversal potential, as estimated by extrapolation, was at about -20 mV.
The slopes of the lines average about 0·5 and indicate that the conductance change
during the e.p.s.p. decreased the membrane resistance to about half.

physiological properties of the transmissional systems and of their interactions
have been given elsewhere (Grundfest, 1957a, b, c, 1958, 1959, 1961b). The
properties of the electrically excitable membrane and their various complexities are also described elsewhere (Grundfest, 1960; 1961a; Reuben and
Grundfest, 1960a; Werman and Grundfest, 1961).

It is of considerable interest to note that the pharmacological properties
differ markedly from those of another decapod crustacean, the crab (Florey
and Hoyle, 1961). Indeed, there also seem to be some differences between
the neuromuscular synapses of crayfish (Boistel and Fatt, 1958) and those
of lobster, but the data on the former are still insufficiently detailed for a
close comparison. The different actions of GABA and picrotoxin on the
presynaptic terminals and on the synaptic membrane in lobster indicate that
general conclusions cannot be drawn about the effects of various drugs.
Thus, while the axodendritic excitatory and inhibitory synapses of the
mammalian cortex are affected in a specific manner by the ω-amino acids
and related compounds (Purpura *et al.*, 1959), they affect various neuraxial
sites of bullfrog differently (Sigg and Grundfest, 1959). The electrophoretic
application of various amino acids on spinal neurons (Curtis, 1961) also

leads to very different results. Substances that are inert on axodendritic synaptic responses act upon the membranes of the spinal neurons. Indeed, the pattern of pharmacological actions of the electrophoretically applied drugs is quite different. Thus, strychnine is ineffective when applied electrophoretically, but exerts its axonal effect, blockade of inhibitory synapses, when injected locally with a fine pipette.

The individual components that have now been identified in synaptic transmission must also interact by pairs, and this interaction in the orthodromic direction is the recognized normal action. Back actions are still insufficiently analyzed, but the initiation of repetitive responses after a single orthodromic nerve impulse emphasizes the need to consider such back effects. They are probably minimal in the back action of electrically excitable activity upon electrically inexcitable membrane, and would be manifested most strongly by actions of the presynaptic terminals on the conductile membrane of the axon.

Such effects would lead to disorganization of the patterns of co-ordinated responses since the repetitive discharges would interfere with the controlled message code of the orthodromic impulses sent out by the central nervous system. Under many conditions they would lead to convulsive activity. An interesting possibility arises in connection with still more complicated neuron organizations than that of lobster neuromuscular junctions. Suppose that an agent which blocks inhibitory synapses in the cortex (like strychnine or the convulsant ω-amino acids) were also to cause repetitive activity in the presynaptic terminals of the ramifying nerve fibers. Various types of avalanching convulsive activity would then develop.

REFERENCES

ALTAMIRANO, M., COATES, C. W., and GRUNDFEST, H. (1955) Mechanisms of direct and neural excitability in electroplaques of electric eel. *J. Gen. Physiol.* **38** : 319–360.

BERGMANN, F., REUBEN, J. P. and GRUNDFEST, H. (1959) Actions of biogenic amines and derivatives on lobster neuromuscular transmission. *Biol. Bull.* **117** : 405.

BOISTEL, J. and FATT, P. (1958) Membrane permeability change during inhibitory transmitter action in crustacean muscle. *J. Physiol. (London)* **144** : 176–191.

CURTIS, D. R. (1961) The assessment of the mode of action of neurone depressants. This volume, p. 342.

FLOREY, E. and HOYLE, G. (1961) Neuromuscular synaptic activity in crabs. This volume, p. 105.

FURUKAWA, T., FURUKAWA, A. and TAKAGI, T. (1957) Fibrillation of muscle fibers produced by ammonium ions and its relation to the spontaneous activity at the neuromuscular junction. *Japan. J. Physiol.* **7** : 252–263.

GRUNDFEST, H. (1957a) Electrical inexcitability of synapses and some of its consequences in the central nervous system. *Physiol. Revs.* **37** : 337–361.

GRUNDFEST, H. (1957b) The mechanisms of discharge of the electric organ in relation to general and comparative electrophysiology. *Progr. in Biophys. and Biophys. Chem.* **7** : 1.

GRUNDFEST, H. (1957c) General problems of drug action on bioelectric phenomena. *Ann. N.Y. Acad. Sci.* **66** : 537–591.

GRUNDFEST, H. (1958) An electrophysiological basis for neuropharmacology. *Federation Proc.* **17** : 1006–1018.

GRUNDFEST, H. (1959) Synaptic and ephaptic transmission. In: *Handbook of Physiology* Vol. I. *Neurophysiology*, p. 147. American Physiological Society, Washington, D.C.

GRUNDFEST, H. (1960) A four-factor ionic hypothesis of spike electrogenesis. *Biol. Bull.* **119** : 284.

GRUNDFEST, H. (1961a) Ionic mechanisms in electrogenesis. *Ann. N.Y. Acad. Sci.* In press.

GRUNDFEST, H. (1961b) Excitation by hyperpolarizing potentials. A general theory of receptor activities. This volume, p. 326.

GRUNDFEST, H., REUBEN, J. P. and RICKLES, W. H., JR. (1959) The electrophysiology and pharmacology of lobster neuromuscular synapses. *J. Gen. Physiol.* **42** : 1301.

PURPURA, D. P., GIRADO, M., SMITH, T. G., CALLAN, D. A. and GRUNDFEST, H. (1959) Structure-activity relations of amino acids and derivatives on central synapses. *J. Neurochem.* **3** : 238.

REUBEN, J. P. (1959) Effect of anion and cation on neuromuscular transmission in *Homarus*. *Federation Proc.* **18** : 127.

REUBEN, J. P., BERGMANN, F. and GRUNDFEST, H. (1959) Chemical excitation of presynaptic terminals at lobster neuromuscular junctions. *Biol. Bull.* **117** : 424.

REUBEN, J. P. and GRUNDFEST, H. (1960a) Further analysis of the conversion of graded to all-or-none responsiveness in the electrically excitable membrane of lobster muscle fibers. *Biol. Bull.* **119** : 334.

REUBEN, J. P. and GRUNDFEST, H. (1960b) Action of cesium ions on the electrically excitable membrane of lobster muscle fibers. *Biol. Bull.* **119** : 334.

REUBEN, J. P. and GRUNDFEST, H. (1960c) Inhibitory and excitatory miniature postsynaptic potentials in lobster muscle fibers. *Biol. Bull.* **119** : 335.

REUBEN, J. P. and GRUNDFEST, H. (1960d) The action of cesium ions on neuromuscular transmission in lobster. *Biol. Bull.* **119** : 336.

REUBEN, J. P., WERMAN, R. and GRUNDFEST, H. (1960a) Properties of indefinitely prolonged spikes of lobster muscle fibers. *Biol. Bull.* **119** : 336.

REUBEN, J. P., WERMAN, R. and GRUNDFEST, H. (1960b) Oscillatory hyperpolarizing responses in lobster muscle fibers. *Fed. Proc.* **19** : 298.

RIKER, W. F., JR., WERNER, G., ROBERTS, J. and KUPERMAN, A. (1959) The presynaptic element in neuromuscular transmission. *N.Y. Acad. Sci.* **81** : 328.

SIGG, E. B. and GRUNDFEST, H. (1959) Pharmacological differences of similarly electro-genic neuraxial sites of bullfrog. *Am. J. Physiol.* **197** : 539–543.

WERMAN, R. and GRUNDFEST, H. (1961) Graded and all-or-none electrogenesis in arthropod muscle. II. The effect of alkali-earth and onium ions on lobster muscle fibers. *J. Gen. Physiol.* In press.

NEUROMUSCULAR SYNAPTIC ACTIVITY IN
THE CRAB (*CANCER MAGISTER*)*

ERNST FLOREY AND GRAHAM HOYLE

Department of Zoology, University of Washington, Seattle 5, Washington, and
Department of Zoology, University of Glasgow, Glasgow

INTRODUCTION

NERVOUS inhibition in crustacean muscles has been divided by Marmont and Wiersma (1938) into two categories, simple and supplemented, according to whether or not the action potentials are attenuated. These are now moie commonly referred to as β- and α-inhibition, following the usage of Katz (1949).

The chemical nature of the transmitters involved in neuromuscular transmission in crustacea is still unknown. There are, however, a few substances which in low concentration affect synaptic activity and membrane behaviour in these animals. Some of these effects resemble those of nerve action, others interfere with synaptic transmission in such a way that they too become useful tools in the experimental approach to processes of excitation and inhibition.

γ-Aminobutyric acid (GABA), which occurs in vertebrate central nervous system, has a powerful inhibitory action in many crustacean synapses. As an active component of Factor I it was considered possible that this compound represents the natural inhibitory transmitter. Edwards and Kuffler (1959) had shown that GABA mimics the action of inhibitory neurons on the stretch receptor cells of crayfish, and Van der Kloot and Robbins (1959) reported that it, like Factor I containing extracts (Florey, 1954), inhibits neuromuscular transmission in the crayfish, possibly by reducing the junctional excitatory potentials.

Picrotoxin blocks the action of inhibitory neurons on the heart-ganglion and on somatic muscle in crayfish (Florey, 1957; Van der Kloot and Robbins, 1959). It also prevents the action of Factor I and GABA on these organs.

Grundfest *et al.* (1959) found that GABA achieved its inhibitory effect on lobster (*Homarus*) muscle by reducing membrane resistance up to tenfold which increased the membrane potential only slightly. Picrotoxin was found to block the action of GABA as well as the inhibitory postsynaptic potentials.

* This investigation was supported by grant B-1451 of the National Institutes of Health, U.S. Public Health Service. It was carried out at the Friday Harbor Laboratories of the University of Washington.

The action of GABA was therefore interpreted as *activation* of inhibitory subsynaptic membrane and that of picrotoxin as *inactivation* of inhibitory synapses.

Lobster muscle is known to show marked α-inhibition. It appeared desirable to have data comparable to those obtained by Grundfest *et al.*, but from one or more of the many crustaceans in which α-inhibition is very slight or unobtainable. This might help to resolve the question as to the importance of the attenuation of excitatory junction potentials in achieving mechanical inhibition.

We have, therefore, examined the membrane changes produced in muscle fibers of two species of crab which do not show much α-inhibition, *Cancer magister* and *Cancer productus*, both by natural excitatory and inhibitory action and also by GABA and picrotoxin.

METHODS

The excitatory and inhibitory nerve fibers supplying the adductor muscle of the dactylus of walking legs were isolated and stimulated through platinum electrodes. The muscle was exposed by cutting away the carapace covering it. The tendon of the adductor muscle was cut. Movements of the dactylus were transduced by allowing it to press against a strain gauge. Routinely two intracellular glass capillary microelectrodes were inserted into the same single muscle fibers, one for recording potential changes and the other for passing current.

A saline medium, composed of 466 mM NaCl, 8 mM KCl, 10 mM $CaCl_2$ and 12 mM $MgCl_2$ was used throughout. The saline and also the drugs, in the same medium, were introduced by perfusion through two hypodermic needles inserted into the carpo-dactylopodite joint. This permitted rapid flushing of all fibers of the test muscle. The preparations were maintained at a temperature of 15–19 °C.

RESULTS

As a preliminary we repeated the experiments of Grundfest *et al.* (1959) on the lobster, *Homarus americanus* (the animals were flown to Friday Harbor from the east coast). Their results were confirmed: large decrease in membrane resistance occurred following the application of GABA, together with attenuation of the junctional potentials.

With crab muscle fibers, GABA (10^{-4} g/ml) produced a marked immediate attenuation of the excitatory junctional potentials and eventually obliterated them (Fig. 1); this action was associated with a progressive fall in tension. The effects were completely reversible by thorough washing with fresh saline medium and they could be repeated several times on the same preparation. In contrast, normal inhibitory transmitter action was not accompanied

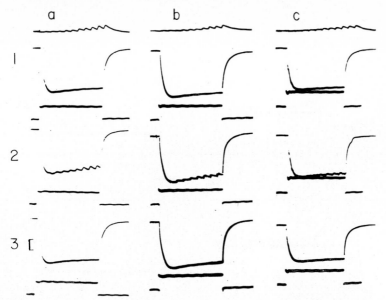

FIG. 1. *Cancer magister*, intracellular records from closer muscle of walking leg. (a), (b) and (c) are sequences obtained from three different fibers. The top records in (1) show the excitatory junctional potentials recorded during stimulation of slow motor axon at normal resting potential, the middle record represents the potential change induced by a hyperpolarizing pulse (monitored in bottom record). In (2) the junction potentials are recorded during application of the hyperpolarizing pulse. Note the minimal enhancement (monitored in the lower records). The records in (3) were obtained as in (2), but the muscle was treated with GABA (10^{-5} g/ml). Note the complete absence of excitatory junction potentials and the slight decrease in membrane resistance.

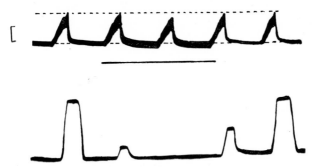

FIG. 2. *Cancer magister*, closer muscle of walking leg. Effect of stimulation of the inhibitory axon with 120 pulses/sec on excitatory junction potentials (fast system) and membrane potential (first line) and on tension development (second line). The electrical record shows slight hyperpolarization during inhibition (horizontal bar) without attenuation of excitatory junction potentials (response to five periods of 0·3 sec stimulation at 100 pulses/sec) while the mechanical record indicates complete inhibition. Voltage calibration: 10 mV.

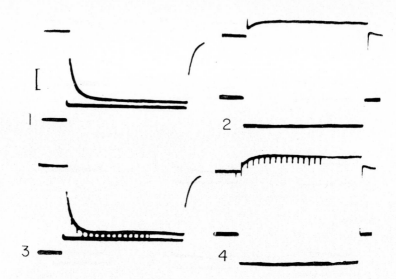

FIG. 3. *Cancer magister*, intracellular record of potential changes induced by hyperpolarizing (1 and 3) and depolarizing square pulses (2 and 4) without (1 and 2) and during (3 and 4) stimulation of the inhibitory axon at 120 pulses/sec. Upper channel records membrane potential, lower channel monitors the applied pulse. Voltage calibration 10 mV. Note the absence of marked permeability change, and the extent of rectification.

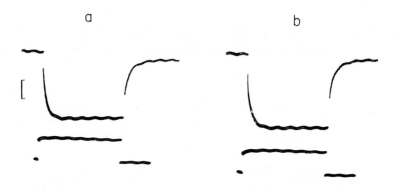

FIG. 4. *Cancer magister*, closer muscle of walking leg. Intracellular record (upper channel) of potential change induced by application of hyperpolarizing square pulse (monitored on lower channel). (a) Normal fiber, (b) fiber treated with picrotoxin 10^{-5} g/ml. Voltage calibration 10 mV. Note slight increase in membrane resistance.

by attenuation of junctional potentials in most fibers, and where attenuation did occur it never exceeded about 15% (Fig. 2).

To determine the membrane resistance change under the influence of GABA, a hyperpolarizing square pulse was applied across the membrane. The magnitude of this pulse was reduced only very slightly, never more than 12%, when GABA (10^{-4} g/ml) was applied (Fig. 1). This is in marked contrast to the results obtained in the lobster muscle. In spite of making penetrations of several hundreds of muscle fibers very few were found in which membrane potential changes could be detected during inhibitory action. Even when the membrane potential was displaced by many millivolts with depolarizing or hyperpolarizing current, the inhibitory potential changes were less than 1 mV (Fig. 3).

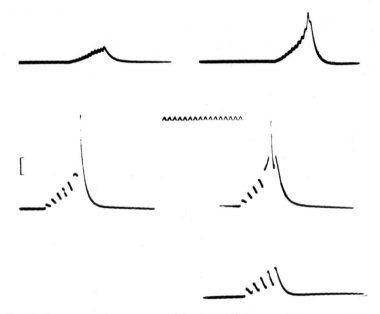

FIG. 5. *Cancer magister*, sequence of five intracellular records from muscle fiber in closer muscle of walking leg, obtained a few minutes after washing off previously applied picrotoxin (10^{-4} g/ml). Note the strong summation of junction potentials which in two instances leads to production of spike. Time base 60 cycle, voltage calibration 10 mV.

Under the influence of picrotoxin (10^{-4} g/ml) a hyperpolarizing square pulse was increased in magnitude at the recording electrode by about 15%, indicating an increase in membrane resistance (Fig. 4). At the same time the junctional potentials were reduced. As the picrotoxin was washed out the reappearing excitatory junctional potentials had a greatly increased decay time, so that they summated to a much greater extent than normally. In several muscle fibers large spikes (60 mV) were elicited by the summated potentials (Fig. 5) although none was present in the untreated preparation even with the highest possible stimulation rate.

In our experience, picrotoxin did not prevent GABA from attenuating excitatory junctional potentials, i.e. the two substances were not antagonistic to each other for these crabs. If applied in more dilute solution, picrotoxin (10^{-5} g/ml) did prevent the inhibition of tension development during stimulation of the inhibitory fiber.

DISCUSSION

The results obtained stand in marked contrast to those obtained from lobsters. The principal difference is that in the crabs neither GABA nor the natural inhibitory transmitter substance cause more than a minute resistance change. It might be that this is due to there being a much smaller subsynaptic membrane area in the crabs, or there might be a genuine smaller permeability change. The marked attenuation of the junctional potentials caused by GABA, as compared with the lack of α-inhibition, means that normal inhibition causes a mechanical inhibition in a different way than GABA. The latter clearly acts by reducing excitatory transmitter action, either as a result of competition for receptor molecules or by reducing the quantity of transmitter released per impulse.

The failure of the natural inhibitory transmitter substance to cause attenuation of the junctional potentials is probably explained by the small resistance change caused by it in the subsynaptic area. This highlights the problem of the true nature of the action of the normal inhibitory transmitter. Since this is not associated with attenuation of junctional potentials it must be due either to the slight repolarization which causes a faster rate of decay of potentials or to a later action in the chain of events coupling excitation to contraction.

REFERENCES

EDWARDS, C. and KUFFLER, S. W. (1959) The blocking effect of γ-aminobutyric acid (GABA) and the action of related compounds on single nerve cells. *J. Neurochem.* **4** : 19–30.

FLOREY, E. (1954) An inhibitory and an excitatory factor of mammalian central nervous system, and their action on a single sensory neuron. *Arch. intern. physiol.* **62** : 33–53.

FLOREY, E. (1957) Further evidence for the Transmitter-Function of Factor I. *Naturwissenschaften* **44** : 424–425.

GRUNDFEST, H., REUBEN, J. P. and RICKLES, W. H. (1959) The electrophysiology and pharmacology of lobster neuro-muscular synapses. *J. Gen. Physiol.* **42** : 1301–1323.

KATZ, B. (1949) Neuromuscular transmission in invertebrates. *Biol. Revs.* **24** : 1–20.

MARMONT, G. and WIERSMA, C. A. G. (1938) On the mechanism of inhibition and excitation of crayfish muscle. *J. Physiol.* (*London*) **93** : 173–193.

VAN DER KLOOT, W. G. and ROBBINS, J. (1959) The effects of gamma-aminobutyric acid and picrotoxin on the junctional potential and the contraction of crayfish muscle. *Experientia* **15** : 35.

PRESYNAPTIC INHIBITION AT THE NEUROMUSCULAR JUNCTION IN CRAYFISH

JOSEF DUDEL AND STEPHEN W. KUFFLER

Neurophysiology Laboratory, Department of Pharmacology, Harvard Medical School,
Boston, Massachusetts

IN crayfish neuromuscular junctions the inhibitory transmitter acts by increasing the permeability of the muscle fiber to certain ions while the membrane potential remains near the resting level (Fatt and Katz, 1953). This postsynaptic inhibitory mechanism seems widespread in different species. In recent experiments on the abductor muscle of the dactyl of the crayfish *Orconectes virilis* a new second mechanism was found. If inhibitory impulses are timed to arrive at the neuromuscular junction from 1 to 6 msec before the excitatory impulses they reduce the excitatory junctional potentials (e.j.p.'s). Under specific conditions it was shown that this e.j.p. reduction could not be brought about solely by a postsynaptic conductance increase and therefore one had to postulate an additional mechanism (Dudel and Kuffler, 1960).

In close analogy with neuromuscular transmission in vertebrates (del Castillo and Katz, 1956) it was shown in the crayfish junction that the e.j.p.'s are made up of quantal units, which are of the same size as the spontaneous excitatory miniature potentials. These units represent a quantal release of transmitter from the excitatory nerve terminals. The quantum content was analyzed by recording through extracellular microelectrodes from single junctional spots which are distributed over the muscle surface.

In Fig. 1A the upper sweep shows e.j.p.'s recorded with an intracellular electrode at a stimulation rate of 1/sec. The lower sweep presents the simultaneous activity at a single junctional area recorded with an extracellular microelectrode. Series of several hundred extracellular e.j.p.'s were analyzed statistically and the size of the quanta and the probability of release of the quanta were determined. For instance, the last extracellular e.j.p. in Fig. 1A was composed of two quanta. At times the single junction fails to release any quanta (arrow). If, as in Fig. 1B, inhibitory impulses preceded the excitatory ones by 2 msec, both the intra- and extracellular e.j.p.'s were reduced. At the same time the number of failures of transmission was increased at the single junctional area (three arrows). In Fig. 2 the same events are illustrated as in Fig. 1, recorded with a fast sweep. In Fig. 2A the extracellular e.j.p. has a

111

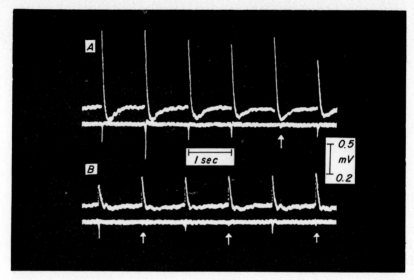

Fɪɢ. 1. Intracellular records (upper sweeps) from a muscle fiber and simultaneous extracellular measurements from single junctional area (lower sweeps) at stimulation rate of 1/sec. ᴀ. Excitatory stimulation alone. ʙ. An inhibitory stimulus is added, preceding the excitatory one by 2 msec. E.j.p.'s are reduced and number of transmission failures in single junctional area (arrows) increased. The diphasic portion in the intracellular records is due to a.c. amplifier.

briefer time course than the intracellular e.j.p. (upper sweep). Out of three excitatory stimuli one failed to release a quantum, while the smaller e.j.p. was composed of two quanta. The arrow marks the arrival of the excitatory nerve impulse near the junctions. In Fig. 2ʙ an inhibitory stimulus was applied 2 msec before the excitatory stimulus (note two extracellularly recorded impulses at arrows). At the single junction under the electrode, transmission failure occurred twice, whereas the third time only one quantum of transmitter was released. It was found by statistical analysis that inhibition did not change the size of the quantum but only decreased the number of quanta contained in the e.j.p.'s. Consequently this type of inhibition acts presynaptically, reducing the probability of release of transmitter quanta from the excitatory nerve endings.

Applied γ-aminobutyric acid (GABA) imitated in all known respects the action of the inhibitory transmitter in crayfish muscle. It was shown that GABA has an inhibitory effect in addition to its postsynaptic inhibitory conductance increase. This and a minimal synaptic delay of 1 msec suggest chemical transmission from the inhibitory to the excitatory nerve terminals in presynaptic inhibition. For details of this work three recent papers should be consulted (Dudel and Kuffler, 1961a, b, c).

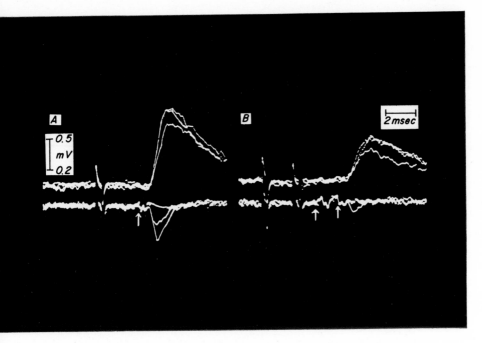

FIG. 2. Simultaneous intra- and extra-cellular records, as in Fig. 1, three con-
secutive junctional potentials superimposed at rate of 1/sec. A. E.j.p.'s alone.
Failure of transmission occurs once in extracellular record. Arrow marks extracellularly recorded motor nerve impulse near the junction. B. Inhibitory stimulus
preceding excitatory one by 2 msec, reducing the intracellular e.j.p.'s and
resulting in two failures of transmission at the single junctional area. Arrows
mark inhibitory and excitatory nerve impulses.

REFERENCES

DEL CASTILLO, J. and KATZ, B. (1956) Biophysical aspects of neuromuscular transmission.
Progr. in Biophys. and Biophys. Chem. **6** : 121–170.
DUDEL, J. and KUFFLER, S. W. (1960) A second mechanism of inhibition at the crayfish
neuromuscular junction. *Nature* **187** : 247–248.
DUDEL, J. and KUFFLER, S. W. (1961a) The quantal nature of transmission and spontaneous
miniature potentials at the crayfish neuromuscular junction. *J. Physiol.* (*London*).
In press.
DUDEL, J. and KUFFLER, S. W. (1961b) Mechanism of facilitation at the crayfish neuro-
muscular junction. *J. Physiol.* (*London*). In press.
DUDEL, J. and KUFFLER, S. W. (1961c) Presynaptic inhibition at the crayfish neuromuscular
junction. *J. Physiol.* (*London*). In press.
FATT, P. and KATZ, B. (1953) The effects of inhibitory nerve impulse on a crustacean
muscle fiber. *J. Physiol.* (*London*) **121** : 374–389.

ION MOVEMENTS DURING VAGUS INHIBITION
OF THE HEART

O. F. HUTTER

Department of Physiology, University College, London

THE arrest of the heart by the vagus nerve has often entered into discussions on nervous inhibition because a favourable experimental situation in this case allowed physiologists to discover long ago something about the site and nature of the inhibitory process. The Webers' original concept of inhibition as a phenomenon distinct from fatigue (Weber, 1846) was challenged for several decades by physiologists who believed that the rhythm of the heart was due to the spontaneous activity of easily exhaustible vagal nerve endings (Schiff, 1858). But the neurogenic theory of impulse formation in the vertebrate heart lost ground as evidence for a direct inhibitory action of the vagus on cardiac muscle accumulated. Thus Gaskell (1883) pointed out that vagus stimulation caused not only arrest of the heart but also weakening of the auricles, and MacWilliam (1883) observed that the sinus venosus of the eel's heart becomes inexcitable during vagus stimulation, that is, it could not be made to contract by direct electrical or mechanical stimuli. In 1887 Gaskell made the discovery that stimulation of the vagus nerve produces an increase in the resting potential of the auricles (Gaskell, 1887). Some workers had difficulty in repeating this observation, or doubted its significance, but Sir William Bayliss (1915) mentions in the *Principles* that he used to demonstrate Gaskell's effect to students of University College and he saw in this phenomenon and in Biedermann's and Pavlov's work on invertebrate muscle convincing evidence that muscular tissue itself undergoes a change under the influence of inhibitory nerves. When the humoral theory of synaptic transmission moved forward as result of Loewi's (1921) work it was therefore possible to fit acetylcholine into the picture as the agent which causes the changes in the heart muscle (Dale, 1937).

A problem since then has been the mode of action of the acetylcholine released by vagal stimulation. That a "mobilization" of potassium ions is involved was indicated by the experiments of Howell and Duke (1908), Lehnartz (1936) and Holland *et al.* (1952a, b). But little progress in the formulation of a coherent hypothesis was made until the general nature of the excitatory synaptic action of acetylcholine was understood. With advance in that field (Fatt and Katz, 1951), the concept of a change in ionic permeability by chemical transmitters was soon applied to the inhibitory situation in the heart, and in 1953 Burgen and Terroux put forward evidence for the hypothesis that acetylcholine and related substances act on cardiac muscle fibres by increasing their permeability to potassium ions (Burgen and Terroux, 1953). Against the background of the ionic theory of electrical activity in nerve and muscle (Hodgkin, 1951) this hypothesis can account satisfactorily for all the features observed during vagal stimulation or application of acetylcholine to auricular and pacemaker fibres (Hoffman and Suckling, 1953; West *et al.*, 1956; del Castillo and Katz, 1957; Hutter and Trautwein, 1956) and it received further support from measurements of membrane resistance (Trautwein *et al.*, 1956; Trautwein and Dudel, 1958).

The aim of the work which is described in this article was to explore how far radioactive isotopes may be usefully employed in the analysis of the mechanism of synaptic inhibition and, if possible, to take advantage of the inherent specificity of this technique to characterize more closely the permeability change produced by acetylcholine in the heart. The experiments were made in collaboration with Dr. E. J. Harris and the principal results have already been reported briefly on previous occasions (Harris and Hutter, 1956; Hutter, 1957; Harris, 1959).

In the selection of a preparation we were influenced by the argument, based on consideration of the situation at the neuromuscular junction, that the permeability channels opened by chemical transmitters may exist in parallel with channels that normally allow the passage of ions. It seemed important therefore to choose a tissue much of whose surface is sensitive to acetylcholine; for a localized increase in ion permeability might well be swamped by the ionic fluxes which go on all the time through ordinary channels. From this point of view the sinus venosus of the frog or tortoise heart seemed promising. Experiments with microelectrodes (Hutter and Trautwein, 1956) had shown that in the sinus venosus the effect of vagus stimulation is often intense enough to render the tissue completely inexcitable and when action potentials could be elicited by direct stimulation their height and duration was found to be so greatly reduced throughout the tissue that a considerable and widespread increase in the permeability to one or more of the ions maintaining the resting potential was indicated.

The sinus venosus also has another advantage for experiments with isotopes: it is so thin that all fibres have virtually free access to the medium. Our estimate of the thickness of the frog's sinus venosus, from measurements of weight and area is about 100 μ, though in the tortoise a muscular band two or three times as thick may exist around the sinoauricular junction. A less desirable property of the sinus venosus is that it contains a good deal of connective tissue in close association with the cardiac muscle fibres. This is reflected in a high proportion of sodium to potassium in the tissue and makes it difficult to determine the ionic concentration in the cardiac muscle fibres.

Once dissected, the preparations were tied to a fine wire and placed in Ringer's solution containing the isotope. They were then either left to "load" for a given length of time and used for an experiment in which the outflow of isotope was studied, or taken out at intervals, washed and counted in order to follow the uptake of the isotope. As the electrical events during vagus inhibition indicated an increase in potassium permeability our first concern was to study the movement of ^{42}K. Fortunately, the normally low concentration of potassium in the extracellular fluid and the thinness of the preparation allow the exchange of ^{42}K to be followed with ease. Thus control experiments showed that the loss of isotope from the extracellular space is virtually complete within 3 min exposure to inactive wash solution and thereafter the efflux of ^{42}K usually proceeded in a practically exponential manner for 1–2 hr. To test the action of acetylcholine in outflow experiments it was added to one or two of the samples of inactive wash solution. Alternatively the sinus venosus was dissected with the vagi attached and arranged in a wax bath allowing easy exchange of wash solution.

Figure 1 shows the effect of vagus stimulation on the efflux of ^{42}K from a frog's sinus venosus. During the first part of the experiment the preparation

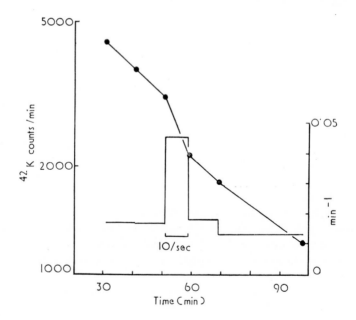

FIG. 1. Efflux of ^{42}K from a frog's sinus venosus into Ringer's solution. Abscissa, time from removal of preparation from solution containing 2·7 mM labelled K. Left ordinate, radioactivity of tissue on a logarithmic scale, obtained by adding together the activity of the wash solutions and the final tissue count. Right ordinate, fraction of labelled K in tissue lost per min. During the third wash period the left vagus was stimulated at 10/sec.

was beating steadily at 24/min and the fractional loss of isotope per min remained substantially constant in two successive control periods. After admission of a fresh lot of wash solution the left vagus was stimulated for 7 min at 10/sec. This caused complete arrest for most of the time and an almost threefold increase in the rate of outflow of ^{42}K. After the end of stimulation the sinus soon resumed its beat and the rate of outflow of ^{42}K returned promptly to almost the initial value. Acetylcholine (2×10^{-7} to 2×10^{-6} g/ml) produces a similar acceleration in the rate of loss of ^{42}K. Differences in the timing of the application of acetylcholine, the duration of the load period and season of the year had little obvious influence on the response, but a matter requiring attention is the exclusion of auricular tissue from the preparation; for although the auricles also show an increase in the rate of ^{42}K efflux under the influence of acetylcholine (see, for instance, Rayner and Weatherall, 1959) the effect is much smaller than in the sinus venosus.

The question may be asked whether the increase in the rate of outflow observed could have arisen secondarily from a change in the electrochemical driving force. In the present inhibitory situation the answer is fortunately clear. During exposure to acetylcholine the preparation is arrested and the inside of the fibres is more negative than the maximum negative potential reached during diastole in the beating preparation (del Castillo and Katz, 1955, 1957; Hutter and Trautwein, 1955, 1956). The force driving potassium out is therefore diminished at all times so an increase in the outflow rate must be taken to signify an increase in permeability. The argument, in fact, leads to the conclusion that the acceleration in the outflow of ^{42}K produced by acetylcholine might be greater could the attending arrest and hyper-polarization be avoided. We have therefore made experiments in which the wash solution contained enough potassium (c. 20 mM) to render the pre-paration quiescent. Under these conditions acetylcholine usually produces a considerably greater effect than is observed when the wash solution contains only 2·7 mM K (Fig. 2).

Further evidence for an increase in potassium permeability by acetyl-choline may be obtained by examining the influx of ^{42}K. One type of experi-ment is illustrated in Fig. 3. Each block represents the amount of isotope taken up by a tortoise sinus venosus in successive 5 min exposures to load solution, the preparation itself being presented to the counter each time after a 3 min wash in an inactive solution. It may be seen that during the fourth and ninth 5 min periods, when the preparation was exposed to acetylcholine, the uptake was considerably greater than during the control periods. Analysis of the preparation at the end of the experiment showed that about 10% of the tissue potassium had exchanged for tracer. This low degree of exchange was probably due to the similar length of wash and load periods, and it accounts for the relative constancy in the amounts of isotopes taken up in successive

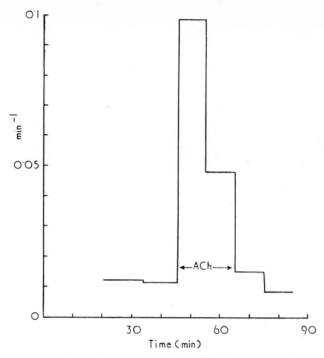

FIG. 2. Effect of acetylcholine on rate of loss of ^{42}K from a quiescent tortoise sinus venosus. Abscissa, time from beginning of efflux. Ordinate, fraction of labelled K in tissue lost per min. The wash solution contained 21·6 mM K throughout the experiment and acetylcholine 2×10^{-6} g/ml between 45–65 min

control periods. When longer load periods were used the exchange of potassium went further towards completion and the increase in the amount of ^{42}K taken up in the presence of acetylcholine was then followed by a series of diminishing increments in radioactivity as is to be expected in the later stages of a load experiment.

As an alternative procedure the sinus venosus of a tortoise was bisected and the two halves used to follow the uptake of ^{42}K from tracer-Ringer with or without acetylcholine. This has the advantage that an inflow curve smoothing out of the error of each assay may be constructed for each preparation, but it involves assumptions about the relative sensitivity and composition of the two halves and uncertainty about how persistent the action of acetylcholine is. In the event an increase in the rate of uptake was usually observed also under these conditions, but the effect was striking only when the extracellular potassium concentration was high (20 mM). How far the influx of ^{42}K from different external potassium concentrations is dependent on metabolic activity has not yet been determined.

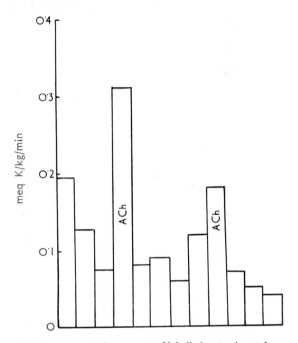

FIG. 3. Each block represents the amount of labelled potassium taken up by a tortoise sinus venosus during successive 5 min exposures to Ringer's solution containing 2·7 mM labelled K. Ordinate scale, milli-equivalents labelled K taken up per min/kg wet weight tissue. During the fourth and ninth period acetycholine 10^{-6} g/ml was added to the ^{42}K Ringer's solution.

The effects of rubidium on excitable tissues resembles that of potassium. In two experiments in which the outflow of ^{82}Rb into Ringer's solution was examined acetylcholine produced an approximately twofold increase in the rate of outflow. As the half life of ^{82}Rb is conveniently long (18·6 days) this isotope could perhaps be used with economy in experiments of this kind.

The striking increase in the rate of movement of potassium under the influence of acetylcholine raises the question of how specific the permeability change is. In particular, it seemed interesting to examine the movement of chloride as there is strong electrophysiological evidence that synaptic inhibition of some tissues is brought about by an increase in permeability to that anion (Coombs et al., 1955; Boistel and Fatt, 1958).

Here a difficulty is met. The specific activity of ^{36}Cl is so low in the relation to the amount of chloride in the cells and the bulk of sensitive tissue available that experiments with this isotope can be made only under limited conditions. We have therefore turned to the more active isotope of bromine. Figure 4 shows the procedure adopted in most outflow experiments with ^{82}Br. The first part of the experiment was conducted at 0°C in order to achieve a better

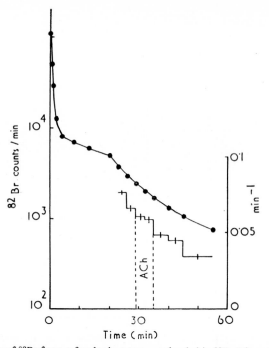

FIG. 4. Efflux of ^{82}Br from a frog's sinus venosus loaded in ^{82}Br-Ringer's solution for 1 hr. Abscissa, time from transfer into inactive Cl-Ringer's solution. Left ordinate, radioactivity in tissue or a logarithmic scale. Right ordinate, rate coefficient for loss of ^{82}Br. Vertical bars give $\pm$ S.E. During the first 20 min the temperature of the inactive wash solution was 0°C, thereafter 20°C. The loss of isotope during the first $\frac{1}{2}$ min of the experiment is not shown. From 29 to 35 min the preparation was arrested by treatment with acetylcholine 5×10^{-7} g/ml. The specific activity of the Br-Ringer's solution was 10^4 counts/min equivalent to $10 \cdot 7 \times 10^{-6}$ mM Br. Tissue weight, lightly blotted, 2·7 mg. Total tissue K, 127×10^{-6} mM.

demarcation between the extracellular and cellular components. After 20 min the preparation was returned to room temperature and it soon started to beat regularly at 44/min. A period of treatment with acetylcholine was then interposed. This causes the usual arrest but evidently had little effect on the movement of bromide. Occasionally a transient or delayed increase in the outflow rate was seen during the action of acetylcholine, but the changes were too irregular and small to justify a positive interpretation of the experiments as a whole. Attempts to test the action of acetylcholine on the uptake of bromide similarly failed to reveal a significant change.

The experiments made with chloride all involved loading preparations in solutions of high $[K_0] \times [Cl_0]$ product, in order to enrich the fibres with chloride; in that sense they were less physiological and more difficult to interpret than the experiments with bromide. They gave opportunity, how-

ever, to examine simultaneously the effect of acetylcholine on the outflow of
^{42}K and ^{36}Cl as the half-life of the two isotopes differs greatly. The rate
constants applying to the outflow of each isotope from a tortoise sinus venosus
loaded in 120 mM ^{42}K ^{36}Cl are shown in Fig. 5. As can be seen acetylcholine
produced its invariable effect on the rate of movement of potassium but the
rate of outflow of chloride showed no obvious response.

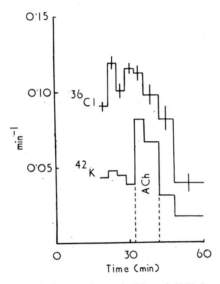

Fig. 5. Effect of acetylcholine on loss of ^{42}K and ^{36}Cl from a tortoise sinus
venosus into Ringer's solution. Abscissa, time from removal of preparation from
a load solution whose principal constituent was 120 mM ^{42}K ^{36}Cl. Ordinate,
rate coefficient for loss of the isotopes. Vertical bars $\pm$ s.e.

How far do these results allow a conclusion as to the specificity of the
permeability increase produced by acetylcholine? It might be supposed, for
instance, that the fibres of the sinus venosus are normally much more permeable to chloride than to potassium; an opening of channels equally
available to both ions might then be expected to produce a relatively greater
effect on the movement of potassium than on the movement of chloride.
This explanation for the absence of a detectable increase in chloride permeability, however, is not in accord with available evidence. Determinations of
the relative contribution of chloride to the membrane conductance of mammalian heart muscle has shown that chloride is less permeant than is potassium at the normal resting potential (Hutter and Noble, 1959). A similar
result has been obtained for frog auricle by Mr. W. E. Crill, University of
Washington, Seattle. Crill (personal communication) has also shown that
the contribution of chloride to the membrane conductance becomes vanish-

ingly small under the influence of acetylcholine, indicating that the anion does not participate in the conductance increase. Furthermore, a rough estimate of the relative fluxes of potassium and bromide in the sinus venosus may be made from the rate constants applying to the outflow of each isotope and the relative concentrations of the two ions in the cell; it also shows that we are not dealing with a highly anion-permeable tissue. There is no reason then to suppose that an additional anion permeability of similar magnitude to the additional potassium permeability would pass unnoticed and we are inclined to conclude that acetylcholine inhibits the sinus venosus by causing a great and specific increase in potassium permeability. In keeping with this conclusion is the observation that the presence of small anions is not essential for the arrest of the sinus venosus by acetylcholine.

It should be added that it is not implied that the movement of potassium through the channels opened by acetylcholine necessarily obeys the same laws as the movement through normally patent channels. Recent experiments (Hutter and Noble, 1960a) have shown that in heart muscle, as in skeletal muscle (Katz, 1949; Hodgkin and Horowicz, 1959; Hutter and Noble, 1960b) the potassium conductance declines when the fibres are depolarized by an outward current. Such rectification need not hold for the potassium conductance added by acetylcholine. The movement of potassium in the chemically opened channels may rather obey the constant field equations (Hodgkin and Katz, 1949) in which case their contribution to the membrane conductance would increase as the preparation is depolarized.

REFERENCES

BAYLISS, W. M. (1915) *Principles of General Physiology* (1st Ed.), p. 407. Longmans, London.

BURGEN, A. S. V. and TERROUX, K. G. (1953) On the negative inotrophic effect in the cat's auricle. *J. Physiol.* (*London*) **120** : 449–464.

BOISTEL, J. and FATT, P. (1958) Membrane permeability change during inhibitory transmitter action in crustacean muscle. *J. Physiol.* (*London*) **144** : 176–191.

DEL CASTILLO, J. and KATZ, B. (1955) The membrane potential changes in the frog's heart produced by inhibitory nerve impulses. *Nature* **175** : 1035.

DEL CASTILLO, J. and KATZ, B. (1957) Modifications de la membrane produites par des influx nerveux dans la région du pace-maker du coeur. In *Microphysiologie comparée des éléments excitables. Colloq. intern. centre nat. recherche sci.* (*Paris*) **67** : 271–279.

COOMBS, J. S., ECCLES, J. C. and FATT, P. (1955) The specific ionic conductances and the ionic movements across the motoneuronal membrane that produce the inhibitory post-synaptic potential. *J. Physiol.* (*London*) **130** : 326–373.

DALE, H. H. (1937) Transmission of nervous effects by acetylcholine. *Harvey Lectures* **23** : 229–245.

FATT, P. and KATZ, B. (1951) An analysis of the end-plate potential recorded with an intra-cellular electrode. *J. Physiol.* (*London*) **115** : 320–370.

GASKELL, W. H. (1883) On the innervation of the heart with especial reference to the heart of the tortoise. *J. Physiol.* (*London*) **4** : 43–127.

GASKELL, W. H. (1887) On the action of muscarin upon the heart, and on the electrical changes in the non-beating cardiac muscle brought about by stimulation of the inhibitory and augmentor nerves. *J. Physiol. (London)* **8** : 404–414.

HARRIS, E. J. (1959) Tracer studies of muscle ions. *The Method of Isotopic Tracers Applied to the Study of Ion Transport* (ed. by COURSAGET, J.). Pergamon Press, London.

HARRIS, E. J. and HUTTER, O. F. (1956) The action of acetylcholine on the movement of potassium ions in the sinus venosus of the heart. *J. Physiol. (London)* **133** : 58–59P.

HODGKIN, A. L. (1951) The ionic basis of electrical activity in nerve and muscle. *Biol. Revs.* **26** : 339–409.

HODGKIN, A. L. and HOROWICZ, P. (1959) The influence of potassium and chloride ions on the membrane potential of single muscle fibres. *J. Physiol. (London)* **148** : 127–160.

HODGKIN, A. L. and KATZ, B. (1949) The effect of sodium ions on the electrical activity of the giant axon of the squid. *J. Physiol. (London)* **108** : 37–77.

HOFFMAN, B. F. and SUCKLING, E. E. (1953) Cardiac cellular potentials: effect of vagal stimulation and acetylcholine. *Am. J. Physiol.* **173** : 312–320.

HOLLAND, W. C., DUNN, C. E. and GREIG, M. E. (1952a) Effect of several substrates and inhibitors of acetylcholinesterase on permeability of isolated auricles to Na and K. *Am. J. Physiol.* **168** : 547–556.

HOLLAND, W. C., DUNN, C. E. and GREIG, M. E. (1952b) Role of acetylcholine metabolism in the genesis of the electrocardiogram. *Am. J. Physiol.* **170** : 339–345.

HOWELL, W. H. and DUKE, W. W. (1908) The effect of vagus inhibition on the output of potassium from the heart. *Am. J. Physiol.* **21** : 51–63.

HUTTER, O. F. (1957) Mode of action of autonomic transmitter on the heart. *Brit. Med. Bull.* **13** : 176–180.

HUTTER, O. F. and NOBLE, D. (1959) Influence of anions on impulse generation and membrane conductance in Purkinje and myocardial fibres. *J. Physiol. (London)* **147** : 16–17P.

HUTTER, O. F. and NOBLE, D. (1960a) Rectifying properties of heart muscle. *Nature* **188** : 495.

HUTTER, O. F. and NOBLE, D. (1960b) The chloride conductance of frog skeletal muscle. *J. Physiol. (London)* **151** : 89–102.

HUTTER, O. F. and TRAUTWEIN, W. (1955) Effect of vagal stimulation on the sinus venosus of the frog's heart. *Nature* **176** : 512.

HUTTER, O. F. and TRAUTWEIN, W. (1956) Vagal and sympathetic effects on the pacemaker fibres in the sinus venosus of the heart. *J. Gen. Physiol.* **39** : 715–733.

KATZ, B. (1949) Les constantes électriques de la membrane du muscle. *Arch. sci. physiol.* **3** : 285–299.

LENHARTZ, E. (1936) Potassium ions and vagus inhibition. *J. Physiol. (London)* **86** : 37–38P.

LOEWI, O. (1921) Über humorale Übertragbarkeit der Herznervenwirkung. *Arch. ges. Physiol. Pflüger's* **189** : 239–242.

MACWILLIAM, J. A. (1883) The physiology of the heart of the eel. *J. Physiol. (London)* **4** : 1–5P.

RAYNER, B. and WEATHERALL, M. (1959) Acetylcholine and potassium movements in rabbit auricles. *J. Physiol. (London)* **146** : 392–409.

SCHIFF, J. M. (1858) *Lehrbuch der Muskel- und Nervenphysiologie*, pp. 187–192. Schauenburg, Lahr.

TRAUTWEIN, W. and DUDEL, J. (1958) Zum Mechanismus der Membranwirkung des Acetylcholin an der Herzmuskelfaser. *Arch. ges. Physiol. Pflüger's* **266** : 324–334.

TRAUTWEIN, W., KUFFLER, S. W. and EDWARDS, C. (1956) Changes in membrane characteristics of heart muscle during inhibition. *J. Gen. Physiol.* **40** : 135–145.

WEST, T. C., FALK, G. and CERVONI, P. (1956) Drug alteration of transmembrane potentials in atrial pacemaker cells. *J. Pharmacol. Exptl. Therap.* **117** : 245–252.

WEBER, E. (1846) Muskelbewegung. In *Wagner's Handwörterbuch der Physiologie* Bd. 3, Abt. 2, pp. 42–48. Vieweg, Braunschweig.

ON THE PROBLEM OF IMPULSE CONDUCTION
IN THE ATRIUM*

J. W. WOODBURY AND W. E. CRILL

Department of Physiology and Biophysics, University of Washington School of Medicine,
Seattle, Washington

CONSIDERABLE evidence supports the view that the action of acetylcholine on pacemaker and atrial tissue is to increase specifically the membrane permeability to potassium ions (Hutter, 1957; Trautwein et al., 1956; Trautwein and Dudel, 1958). Since Dr. Hutter has just given the convincing tracer evidence for this view and Dr. Dudel is in the audience, it seems unnecessary to review here the remaining evidence on the nature of the inhibition of the heart by acetylcholine. Rather, we are going to consider another equally important but less explored facet of cardiac electrophysiology, namely, the mechanism of spread of an all-or-nothing impulse over the atrium. This subject is not altogether unrelated to inhibition in the heart, for some evidence substantiating the present concept of the action of acetylcholine has been gathered in the course of these studies.

An adequate stimulus applied to any point in heart muscle will initiate an impulse which propagates in an all-or-nothing manner throughout the whole muscle. Electrically the tissue behaves like a single excitable cell. On the other hand, electron micrographs (Muir, 1957; Sjöstrand and Andersson-Cedergren, 1960) of cardiac muscle have rather convincingly demonstrated that this tissue is composed of close-packed but discrete cells, each surrounded by a membrane. If the cell membranes have a high electrical resistance, as they do in other tissues, then it is not immediately apparent how an active cell can initiate activity in its neighbors. The simplest possibility is that the mechanism of impulse spread in cardiac tissue is local circuit current flow as it is in nerve and skeletal muscle. Since local circuit spread has been recently brought into question (Sperelakis et al., 1960a, b; Sperelakis and Hoshiko, 1960), the problem, aside from its fundamental interest, has a certain amount of currency.

Fortunately, the local circuit hypothesis can be subjected to a simple and fairly conclusive test. If activity spreads by local circuit flow, then a current flowed through the membrane of one cell by means of an intracellularly placed electrode must have a substantial effect on the potentials of adjacent

* Aided by grants B-1752 and 2B-5269 from the National Institutes of Health.

cells, i.e. the tissue will show electrotonic properties. If electrotonus is not detectable in other cells, impulses cannot spread by local current flow. On the other hand, if potential changes occur in other cells, local circuit spread, although not proven, is rendered highly likely as the simplest mechanism. The data presented here show that there is electrotonic spread of current in tissue and hence support the local circuit mechanism. In 1952, Weidmann showed that electrotonus in Purkinje fibers is accurately described by the cable equations (Weidmann, 1952). He also discussed the problem of impulse conduction in cardiac tissue.

In comparison with investigations of nerve or skeletal muscle fibers, the study of current spread in cardiac muscle is complicated not only by the complex structure of the tissue but also by the spread of the current into two or three dimensions. The structure makes it difficult to decide on an appropriate equivalent electrical circuit for the tissue, while the multidimensional spread makes the theoretical analysis more difficult and the obtaining of adequate experimental data more tedious. Atrial tissue was chosen for this study because it was assumed that current spread in this thin, flat tissue would be limited to two dimensions; i.e. the tissue is thin with respect to a space constant. This assumption appears to be valid, but for somewhat different reasons.

The experimental design is schematized in the upper part of Fig. 1. An electrode is impaled in a cell near the center of a trabecula of an excised rat atrial appendage and a current pulse of 0·1 sec duration is passed through the membrane. The changes in membrane potential produced by the current are measured successively at different distances and angles with another intracellularly placed microelectrode. A series of records obtained at various distances parallel and perpendicular to the edge of the trabecula are shown in the lower part of Fig. 1. Fiber direction is roughly parallel to the trabecula edge. Only the steady-state voltages have been studied. It can be seen in Fig. 1 that the steady-state voltage falls off rapidly with distance at small radii and more rapidly in the perpendicular than in the parallel direction. The decrement of voltage with distance is not exponential, so the space constant cannot be directly estimated. Nevertheless, since potential changes cannot be detected more than a few hundred micra from the current source, the space constant must be of the order of 100 μ. Despite this astonishingly rapid decrement, it is apparent that current applied in one cell appreciably affects the voltage in adjacent cells, for cell dimensions are roughly $15 \times 15 \times 100 \mu$.

Steady-state voltage as a function of distance is plotted in Fig. 2. The abscissa is the radial distance from the stimulating electrode to the recording electrode. The ordinate is the ratio of the change in the steady-state voltage (in millivolts) to the applied current (in microamperes) and therefore has the dimensions of kilo-ohms. The curves for both the parallel and the perpendi-

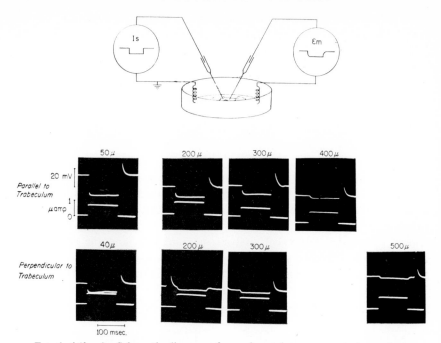

FIG. 1. (*Above*)—Schematic diagram of experimental arrangement. A constant current, I_s, is applied to a cell of a trabecula of a rat atrial appendage through one intracellularly placed microelectrode and the changes in transmembrane potential, ε_m, measured at different distance and angles to the current electrode with another intracellular electrode. (*Below*)—Records of the applied current (*lower trace*) and the resulting voltage changes (*upper trace*). In most of the voltage records there is "anodal break" excitation. The upper row shows the decrement of voltage with distance parallel to the fiber direction and lower row, the fall-off perpendicular to fiber direction. Note that the decrement is much steeper in the latter direction. The S-shape of the potential rise at large distances can barely be distinguished because the time base is too slow.

cular direction show the much greater spatial decrement in the perpendicular direction. The curves are roughly symmetrical about the voltage axis. The dashed lines were drawn by eye.

The phenomena shown in Figs. 1 and 2 have appeared consistently in a number of experiments and are considered not to have been seriously distorted by electrode-inflicted membrane damage. Thus, some trabeculae have been completely mapped without the current electrode becoming dislodged, the resting potential at the current electrode being sufficiently high to maintain excitability at all times. Most of the mapping was done with hyperpolarizing currents since even small depolarizations excited the tissue. This is not surprising because the atria were frequently spontaneously active. Hyperpolarizing break excitation was usually seen (Fig. 1). A further argument for the validity of the results is their reproducibility from point to point

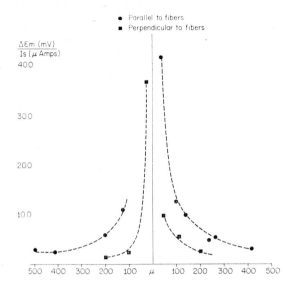

FIG. 2. Spatial decrement of voltage. Abscissa, distance from current applying electrode in micra; circular points, parallel to; square points perpendicular to edge of trabecula (fiber direction). Ordinate, potential change per unit current in mV/μA or kΩ.

in a single experiment and from experiment to experiment. Experiments were done by placing the voltage electrode in surface cells at successively greater distances along a single radius and then returning to the origin to check the zero distance voltage change. If this value had changed appreciably the data were rejected. It is our opinion that the results are a quite valid representation of the electrical properties of the rat atrium.

The significance of these results is quite clear. They make it likely that activity spreads in the atrium by means of local circuit flow because depolarization of one cell produces appreciable changes in the potential of adjacent cells. Strong confirmatory evidence for this view is the finding (Draper and Mya-Tu, 1959; Sano *et al.*, 1959) that conduction velocity is several times faster in the fiber direction than perpendicular to it. This behavior is directly predicted from the observed non-uniform spread of electrotonus. Experiments on the same principle as those Hodgkin (1937) conducted on nerve nearly twenty-five years ago would be required to prove that local circuits are the means of propagation. However, we have clearly established the possible existence of this mechanism, and there seems little point in postulating a more complicated means of intercellular transmission unless compelling evidence is adduced. Sperelakis, Hoshiko and their co-workers (Sperelakis *et al.*, 1960a, b) have recently contended that the transmission of impulses in the heart is not electrical but by a more complicated, relatively unspecified "junctional" transmission. Their evidence is all indirect, and little of it critical in the sense that it does not sharply distinguish between the possibilities. The only evidence presented by these investigators which is apparently not compatible with local circuit propagation is the reversible blocking of conduction in heart by a solution made three times isotonic with sucrose. This effect is probably explained by the electron-micrographic observation that the intercalated disks separate in this solution (S. Scheyer, personal communication). Also, the spread of applied currents is simultaneously greatly reduced or abolished (Crill, unpublished experiments).

The principal question raised by these experiments is not what is the mechanism of spread, but what factors give rise to the short space constant. There is at present insufficient knowledge of the tissue to permit the synthesis of an accurate equivalent electrical circuit. Thus, the first step in evaluating the data is to assume an equivalent circuit and then to see if the measured properties are approximately predicted by the model. The simplest model is that the atrium consists electrically of a single planar cell of practically infinite extent, bounded by two parallel membranes 15 μ apart. The cell is bathed by thick layers of extracellular fluid of negligible resistance. This model is the two-dimensional generalization of the equivalent circuit of a nerve fiber in a large volume of fluid. The equation describing the voltage as a function of distance and time in both models is $\lambda^2 \nabla^2 \varepsilon = \varepsilon + \tau \dot{\varepsilon}$ where λ and τ are the space and time constants, $\nabla^2 \varepsilon$ is the Laplacian of membrane voltage, ε, and $\dot{\varepsilon} = \partial \varepsilon / \partial t$. For the punctate application of current the appropriate form for $\nabla^2 \varepsilon$ is in polar co-ordinates. If ε is a function of r only, i.e. no angular variation in the properties of the tissue, the steady-state solution for which $\varepsilon = 0$ at $r = \infty$ is a zero-order Bessel function of the second kind with imaginary argument. As would be supposed from the geometry of the system, this Bessel function falls off rapidly with distance near the origin, where the membrane area available to current penetration is increasing rapidly.

An attempt was made to fit data of the type shown in Fig. 2 to the appropriate Bessel function. The fit of the data to the theoretical curve is moderately good and considerably better than the fit to an exponential function. A reasonably good approximation to the space constant in the fiber direction is 130 μ. The method of fitting the data was strictly trial-and-error. It appeared that a better fit could have been obtained with additional trials. However, for preliminary analysis the possible improvement in accuracy was not considered worth the extra effort.

An idea of the shortness of this space constant can be obtained by comparing it with the theoretical space constant of the model. Assuming that the specific membrane resistance (R_m) is 1000 Ω cm^2 the spacing, δ, between the parallel membranes is 10 μ and the internal specific resistivity, ρ_i, is 100 Ω cm, then the space constant is $\lambda = \sqrt{[R_m/(r_e + r_i)]} = 1200\ \mu$, where

$r_e = 0$ and $r_i = \rho_i/\delta$. This value can be reduced by 30% if $R_m = 500 \, \Omega \, cm^2$, a value obtained from the time constant of about 5 msec and an assumed membrane capacity of 10 $\mu F/cm^2$. On the other hand, δ could be only $0\cdot34 \, \mu$ if high internal resistance were the reason for the short space constant. This discrepancy (150-fold in dimensions) is so large that the error most probably lies in wrong assumptions on the values of the parameters rather than in the model. There are three terms in the expression for the space constant—the membrane and the internal longitudinal and external longitudinal resistances —for which incorrect values may have been assumed. The short space constant must be the result of a low R_m, of a high r_i or r_e or of a combination of low R_m and high $(r_i + r_e)$. There are at least three possibilities: (i) The spacing between the cells in a trabecula is small, about 200 Å, suggesting that r_e may be sufficiently high. (ii) The internal resistance may be much higher than calculated from a resistivity of 100 Ω cm owing to the presence of intercalated disks in the intracellular current pathways. Since the disks are membrane-like structures, they would be expected to have a rather high resistance. (iii) R_m may be effectively much lower than in other tissues. Before considering these possibilities the structure of trabeculae will be reviewed. It should be added that the present data are sufficient to approximate both R_m and $(r_e + r_i)$ directly but the calculation, which is facilitated by an accurate model, has not yet been made.

Cardiac cells are shaped and stacked somewhat like bricks. A trabecula is roughly a cylinder about 0·5 mm in diameter and several millimeters long. Within the individual trabeculae there are cylindrical bundles about 50 μ in diameter, separated by comparatively large extracellular spaces containing capillaries. The cells within a bundle are closely packed, the space between cell membranes being from 200 to 300 Å. Myofibrils are attached to thickened regions of membrane, the intercalated disks, and appear at regions where Z-bands would be expected (Muir, 1957; Sjöstrand and Andersson-Cedergren, 1960). The membrane is greatly folded in the disk area, the surface area being about ten times greater than that calculated from disk diameter. In contrast to non-disk membrane, the spacing between the opposing faces of the disk is only about 80–100 Å. The cell boundaries in cardiac muscle can be distinguished with certainty only with the electron microscope. This is particularly true of non-disk regions, where the membrane is relatively flat and unthickened. The long dimension of a cell is out of the field in an electron micrograph, so the length cannot be stated with any certainty. It appears to be about 100 μ using a light microscope. If cardiac cells are regarded as circular in cross-section, then a typical diameter would be about 15 μ. The intercalated disks occur in steps, the membrane running parallel to the myofibrils between the steps (Muir, 1957). Eventually, of course, the disk must cross the cell transversely, so the effective diameter of the disk is also 15 μ, if no allowance is made for the folding of the membrane.

10

EXTRACELLULAR FLUID RESISTANCE

At first thought (Crill and Woodbury, 1960) it would appear that the narrow spaces between cells would form a high resistance path for current flow and thus might account for the short space constant. A calculation of the space constant in which it was assumed that the cell was cylindrical with negligible internal resistance and that there was a 200 Å spacing between cells gave the satisfactorily short value of about 60 μ. The matter need be pursued no farther, for these measurements were made on surface fibers and the extracellular resistance could not have been appreciable in comparison with intracellular resistance. Further, the calculation cannot apply even to deep cells since none of these is much more than a half a space constant from a large extracellular space between trabecular bundles. There may be some limitations in this regard during activity when all cells in a transverse plane through a trabecula may be active. The space constant is much shorter and simultaneous activity may limit the current pathways available to internal cells.

INTRACELLULAR AND INTERCELLULAR RESISTANCE

The experimental evidence establishes the fact that a large part of an intracellularly applied current passes through other cells before returning to the indifferent electrode via the extracellular spaces and the bathing medium. The anatomy of a cell suggests that current passes from cell to cell via the intercalated disk. The close spacing and highly folded membrane are both characteristics one would expect to find as means of improving the current transmission. The narrow gap would increase the resistance to current flow parallel to the disk membrane and the increased membrane area would decrease the resistance to current flow through the membrane.

The resistivity of an excitable membrane is 10^7 times that of Ringer's solution, so it is not evident that effective intercellular conduction is assured by the small gap if the disk membrane has the same resistivity as non-disk membrane. The precise calculation of the distribution of current between the extracellular gap and the adjoining disk membrane is a difficult boundary value problem. A satisfactory answer to the question can be obtained, however, by assuming that the whole surface of a cell except the disk is completely depolarized at some instant and calculating the potential in the inter-disk region as a function of radius (Fig. 3). The differential equation describing this situation is $-d\varepsilon/dr = r(\varepsilon_a - 2\varepsilon)/\lambda^2$. The solution for $\varepsilon = 0$ at $r = r_o$ is $\varepsilon = \varepsilon_a\{1 - \exp - (r_o/\lambda)^2 \, [1 - (r/r_o)^2]\}/2$ where $\lambda = \sqrt{(2\delta R_{md}/\rho_e)}$ is the space constant and R_{md} is the specific resistance of disk membrane. The important parameter is evidently $(r_o/\lambda)^2$. The appearance of the space constant squared suggests an "area" constant. Plots of ε against r for different values of (r_o/λ) are shown in Fig. 3. The current density entering the upper cell from the lower, active cell is proportional to ε as shown on the left-hand

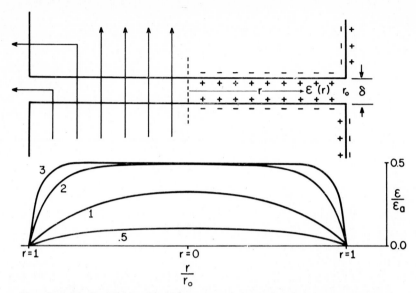

FIG. 3. (*Above*)—Highly simplified schematic diagram of two cells and the intervening gap in the intercalated disk region. The right half defines the various quantities used in calculating the potential profile in the gap and the membrane charge distribution. The left half indicates approximately the current density through the upper membrane due to the current flow between excited and unexcited regions in the lower cell. The current density is simply $\varepsilon/R\sigma_{md}$, where $R\sigma_{md}$ is the specific resistance of the disk membrane ($\Omega\,\mathrm{cm}^2$). (*Below*)—Plot of ε vs. r for the indicated values of the parameter r_0/λ, where $\lambda^2 = 2R_{md}\delta/\rho_i$ and ρ_i is the specific resistivity of myoplasm. It can be seen that most of the current flow from the disk membrane of the lower cell passes through the upper cell if r_0/λ is 3 or more, whereas practically none of it does if r_0/λ is less than 1.

side of Fig. 3. It can be seen that efficient transmission requires that r_0/λ be greater than about 3, whereas there is practically no transmission if the space constant is greater than the cell radius.

The equation for the space constant can be solved for disk resistance, $R_{md} = \rho_e\lambda^2/2\delta$. If $\lambda = r_0/4 = 2 \times 10^{-4}$ cm, $\delta = 80 \times 10^{-8}$ cm and $\rho_e = 50$ Ω cm, then $R_{md} = 1\cdot2\ \Omega\,\mathrm{cm}^2$. This is a maximum value for R_{md}, just sufficient for efficient transmission. Tissue values might well be $0\cdot1$ of this. On the other hand, the surface area of the disk is about ten times the cross-sectional area, so the actual R_{md} might be as large as $12\ \Omega\,\mathrm{cm}^2$. Even $12\ \Omega\,\mathrm{cm}^2$ is a low value, being of the order of the membrane resistance of a squid giant axon at the peak of activity. The resistance of erythrocyte membrane is of the order of $1\ \Omega\,\mathrm{cm}^2$ because it is highly permeable to Cl⁻. Thus the requirements for effective intercellular transmission are stringent but not impossible. Weidmann (personal communication, 1960) has recently obtained evidence from ^{42}K diffusion studies in sheep myocardium that R_{md} is of this same order of magnitude.

If it is assumed that the specific resistance of the disk membranes is of the order of 1 Ω cm^2, the contribution of the disk to intracellular resistance can be calculated. For a cylindrical "cell" 16 μ in diameter the myoplasmic resistance between disks separated by only 40 μ is 0·2 MΩ, the resistance of each disk is 0·5 MΩ and the space constant is 300 μ. On the same basis, the space constant for a two-dimensional model is 850 μ. In this case a space constant of 130 μ requires that the disk resistance be forty times higher or that the disks be forty times closer. Both possibilities seem unreasonable.

MEMBRANE RESISTANCE

A final possibility is that R_m is much lower than in other excitable tissues. R_m would have to be about 25 Ω cm^2, a value more characteristic of excited than resting membrane. However, an alternative possibility is that the effective area of the membrane is much greater than that used in computing the expected space constant from the two-dimensional model. In the formula, R_m refers to the resistance of 1 cm^2 of surface. In a trabecular bundle composed of closely packed cells, the area of excitable membrane in a square centimeter of surface is much greater than 1 cm^2, the exact area depending on the diameter of the individual cells and the effective thickness of the bundle. If the cells were square in cross-section, the actual area would be 4 cm^2 per square centimetre surface and per cell layer. Since no cell is more than a few cell layers from a large extracellular space, the thickness of the tissue in "plane" of the current applying electrode is probably no more than five layers, quite possibly less. From a combination of these two factors, the area of membrane per square centimeter of tissue surface may be as much as 20 cm^2. The true membrane resistance could then be as large as 25 × 20 = 500 Ω cm^2, a reasonable value for R_m.

These calculations are unlikely to be of more than order-of-magnitude accuracy. Nevertheless, the agreement of the calculated value for R_{md} with Weidmann's measurements and the reasonable value of R_m is rather astonishing and constitutes a persuasive if not rigorous argument for the overall validity of the two-dimensional model and the existence of a low disk-membrane resistance. The conclusions drawn are: (i) transmission in cardiac tissue is electrically mediated via low resistance intercalated disks; and (ii) the apparently short space constant for two-dimensional spread is about what would be expected from the cellular structure of cardiac muscle. It is now clear what tissue properties are most important in determining the spread of currents and further study of the temporal as well as the spatial aspects of two-dimensional current spread may lead to a more quantitative analysis of the passive electrical properties of cardiac muscle.

EFFECTS OF ACETYLCHOLINE ON CURRENT SPREAD

Two-dimensional mapping of current spread is a useful tool for studying drug actions on the atrium. Figure 4 shows the effects of 10^{-6} (w/v) acetylcholine on the 3 mV/μA isopotential line of a rat trabecula. It is seen that the acetylcholine reduced the spread of current to about one-half in both the parallel and the perpendicular direction. Such a finding raises the not very

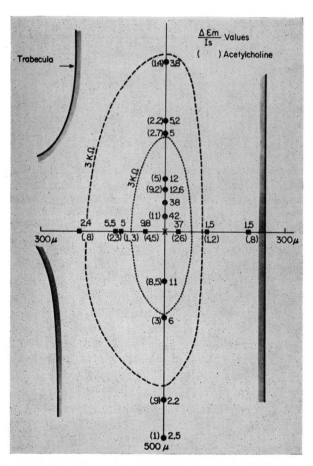

FIG. 4. Isopotential contours on the surface of a trabecula, showing the effect of acetylcholine on current spread. The heavy lines show the boundaries of the trabecula. The map is constructed partly from the data shown in Fig. 2; round points, parallel to fiber direction; square points, perpendicular to it. The numbers by each point give the potential per unit current for that point ; those in parentheses refer to measurements made when acetylcholine was added to the bathing medium (10^{-6} w/v). The outer contour is the 3 k Ω control contour and the inner the 3 k Ω acetylcholine contour. Note the increased spread in the direction of the branch of the trabecula at the left.

probable possibility that acetylcholine acts at the intercalated disks. This possibility is ruled out by the finding that the time constant was reduced by a factor of 4, indicating that the principal change was in R_m.

A few chloride replacement experiments have been done. If chloride is replaced with sulfate, the space constant increases appreciably, about 20%. If acetylcholine is present in the bath, however, replacement of chloride has no effect on the space constant. This is indirect confirmation of Hutter's direct and Trautwein and Dudel's indirect findings that the principal action of acetylcholine is to increase specifically the membrane conductance to potassium.

SUMMARY

The spread of an intracellularly applied current in trabeculae of rat atrial appendage has been mapped in two dimensions. The space constant of voltage decrement is about 130 μ parallel to the fiber direction and about 65 μ perpendicular to fiber direction.

Since the space constant is considerably larger than the cell dimensions, local circuit current flow is the most likely mechanism for the spread of excitation in cardiac muscle.

An approximate mathematical analysis shows that the total specific membrane resistance of an intercalated disk must be 1 Ω cm^2 or less to ensure efficient intercellular transmission by local current flow. This figure is in the range of Weidmann's estimates of disk resistance from diffusion measurements with ^{42}K.

After consideration of a number of possibilities it is tentatively concluded that the principal reason for the short space constant is the large membrane surface area per unit area of muscle surface; the effect is the same as that of a low membrane specific resistance. The calculated disk resistance is too low to have more than about a 25% effect on the space constant.

Acetylcholine (10^{-6} w/v) cuts the space constant in half and the time constant to one-fourth. Thus, the action of acetylcholine is to decrease the membrane resistance. Chloride replacement experiments indicate that acetylcholine specifically increases potassium conductance.

REFERENCES

CRILL, W. E. and WOODBURY, J. W. (1960) Non-uniform two-dimensional electrotonic spread in rat atrium. *Federation Proc.* **19** : 114.

DRAPER, M. H. and MYA-TU, M. (1959) A comparison of the conduction velocity in cardiac tissues of various mammals. *Quart. J. Exptl. Physiol.* **44** : 91–109.

HODGKIN, A. L. (1937) Evidence for electrical transmission in nerve. Part I. *J. Physiol. (London)* **90** : 183–210. Part II. *Ibid.* **90** : 211–232.

HUTTER, O. F. (1957) Mode of action of autonomic transmitters on the heart. *Brit. Med. Bull.* **13** : 176–180.

MUIR, A. R. (1957) An electron microscope study of the embryology of the intercalated disc in the heart of the rabbit. *J. Biophys. Biochem. Cytol.* **3** : 193–202.

SANO, T., TAKAYAMA, N. and SHIMAMOTO, T. (1959) Directional difference of conduction velocity in the cardiac ventricular syncytium studied by microelectrodes. *Circulation Research* **7** : 262–267.

SJÖSTRAND, F. S. and ANDERSSON-CEDERGREN, E. (1960) *The Structure and Function of Muscle* (ed. by BOURNE, G. H.) Vol. 1. Academic Press, New York.

SPERELAKIS, N. and HOSHIKO, T. (1960) Possibility of junctional transmission in cardiac muscle. *Federation Proc.* **19** : 108.

SPERELAKIS, N., HOSHIKO, T. and BERNE, R. M. (1960a) Nonsyncytial nature of cardiac muscle: membrane resistance of single cells. *Am. J. Physiol.* **19** : 531–536.

SPERELAKIS, N., HOSHIKO, T., KELLER, R. F., JR. and BERNE, R. M. (1960b) Intracellular and external recording from frog ventricular fibers during hypertonic perfusion. *Am. J. Physiol.* **198** : 135–140.

TRAUTWEIN, W. and DUDEL, J. (1958) Zum Mechanismus der Membranwirkung des Acetylcholin and der Herzmuskelfaser. *Arch. ges. Physiol. Pflüger's* **266** : 324–334.

TRAUTWEIN, W., KUFFLER, S. W. and EDWARDS, C. (1956) Changes in membrane characteristics of heart muscle during inhibition. *J. Gen. Physiol.* **40** : 135–145.

WEIDMANN, S. (1952) The electrical constants of Purkinje fibres. *J. Physiol.* (*London*) **118** : 348–360.

INHIBITION IN MOLLUSCAN HEARTS AND THE ROLE OF ACETYLCHOLINE

Ernst Florey and Harriet J. Merwin

Department of Zoology, University of Washington, Seattle, Washington

INTRODUCTION

A DISCUSSION of cardiac inhibition would be incomplete if it would not include references to the inhibitory phenomena observed in the hearts of molluscs. Of all the invertebrates only the molluscs have a heart that has morphological and physiological properties that make it comparable with that of the vertebrates. The molluscan heart is chambered; blood enters the atria through large veins and leaves the ventricle through one or two aortae. In most forms the heart receives a double innervation of acceleratory and inhibitory nerve fibers. The great sensitivity of several mollusc hearts to acetylcholine and the fact that acetylcholine causes cardiac inhibition constitutes a further correspondence between the mollusc and the vertebrate hearts.

It is unfortunate that the physiological and biophysical analysis of the molluscan heart is still in a rather infantile stage and lags decades behind the advances made in the study of vertebrate hearts. We will attempt in this paper critically to evaluate the available evidence and to point out some of the interesting problems.

It is worth recalling that the phylum Mollusca includes about ten times the number of species found in the subphylum Vertebrata. Their morphological types range from the snail to the chiton and from the clam to the octopus; a diversity that certainly matches that of the vertebrates. The common features of their anatomy make it possible, however, to group them together and thus we are, in a way, justified in speaking of "the" mollusc heart.

Contrary to textbook doctrine that the heartbeat in molluscs is myogenic there is good evidence that in a number of species there are ganglion cells present in the wall of the atria as well as of the ventricle. In 1934 and 1935 Suzuki described ganglion cells in the auricles and the ventricle of the pearl oyster *Punctada martensi*, of *Ostrea circumpicta*, *Ostrea gigas* (lamellibranchs) and in the auricle and ventricle of six gastropods: *Janthina janthina*, *Hipponyx pilosus*, *Lementina imbricata*, *Cypraea tigris*, *Cellena nigrolineata* and *Cellena eucosmia* (Suzuki, 1934a, b, 1935). Morin and Jullien (1930) found nerve cells

136

in auricle and ventricle of *Murex trunculus*. Suzuki (1935) failed, however, to find nerve cells in the heart of *Lutraria maxima*, Motley (1932) could not detect ganglion cells in the heart of eight species of fresh-water mussels, and Prosser (1940) reported that there are no nerve cells in the heart of *Venus mercenaria*.

The concepts of myogenic and neurogenic origin of the heartbeat are, of course, not mutually exclusive as is demonstrated in the classical case of the *Limulus* heart where a nervous pacemaker dominates a muscular pacemaker, which becomes evident only when the heart ganglion is removed. The presence of ganglion cells in certain hearts poses, however, an interesting problem with regard to the site of action of the extrinsic cardiac nerves. In ganglionated hearts these nerves may well exert their action through the mediation of the ganglion cells of the heart, while in the absence of intracardiac nerve cells the extrinsic nerves may make direct contact with the heart muscle fibers. This question assumes particular importance with regard to the problem of the chemical mediators involved in the regulation of the heartbeat.

In 1940 Prosser demonstrated that an isolated heart of *Venus mercenaria* is inhibited by the perfusion fluid from another *Venus* heart that has been inhibited by stimulation of the visceral ganglion. The isolated heart of *Venus mercenaria* was found to be inhibited by extremely small amounts of acetylcholine (10^{-11} g/ml) (Prosser, 1940; Welsh and Taub, 1948). For this reason the *Venus* heart as well as the heart of many other lamellibranchs are employed as test objects in bioassays for acetylcholine. Welsh and Taub (1948) have studied the action of a large number of modifications of the acetylcholine molecule. Their paper provides excellent evidence for the structure–activity relationship of pharmacological agents. The results imply an interaction of transmitter substance with specific receptor molecules, and a relationship between transmitter and receptor that is comparable to the relationship between substrate and enzyme. Their scheme was extended to include acetylcholine-blocking agents and indicated competitive inhibition of transmitter–receptor interaction. As so often in pharmacological work the elegant picture was somewhat spoiled by the finding that benzoquinonium chloride (Mytolon) was by far the most powerful blocking agent. Its structure has no resemblance to that of acetylcholine.

It is now known that the hearts of a great number of molluscs belonging to the gastropods, lamellibranchs and the cephalopods are inhibited by acetylcholine and that they are accelerated by 5-hydroxytryptamine (5HT) (see the reviews of Krijgsman and Divaris, 1955; Welsh, 1957). For the heart of *Venus mercenaria* it is reasonably well established that acetylcholine is the transmitter substance of the cardio-inhibitory fibers: during nervous inhibition a substance is released which has the same effect on the heart as acetylcholine; eserine prolongs the inhibition resulting from stimulation of the inhibitory nerve supply and Mytolon which prevents the acetylcholine action blocks the action of the inhibitory nerves. Although Welsh (1957) believes that 5HT is the accelerating transmitter in *Venus*, there is little evidence for this other than that this compound occurs in the ganglia of this animal and that the heart is rather sensitive to it. It should be mentioned that Bumpus and Page (1955) found the *Venus* heart to be five to ten times more sensitive to N : N-dimethyl-5-hydroxy-tryptamine than to 5HT.

The transmitter substances of the cardiac nerves of more than 100,000 species of molluscs have not been established. There is evidence, however, that in some species acetylcholine is *not* the inhibitory transmitter to the heart. Of these species the most striking examples are provided by those lamellibranchs in which acetylcholine stimulates the heart and causes systolic contracture (Jullien and Vincent, 1938; Pilgrim, 1954), while stimulation of the visceral ganglion, which gives rise to the cardiac nerves, produces typical inhibition (Diederichs, 1935).

Variation in the ionic composition of the perfusion medium has different effects on the hearts of different molluscs. In his *Comparative Animal Physiology* Prosser (1950) summarizes the data in the literature and states that molluscan hearts are not very sensitive to changes in potassium ion concentration but may be slightly accelerated by increases, and may be stopped in systole by a great excess of potassium. Increase in calcium ion concentration inhibits the pacemaker. In the absence of calcium ions the heart of some molluscs stops in diastole, while that of others stops in systole after considerable acceleration. Magnesium has the same actions as calcium.

We have recently concerned ourselves with a comparison of the actions of acetylcholine and of potassium on the isolated ventricles of lamellibranchs in which acetylcholine causes cardiac inhibition and of lamellibranchs in which acetylcholine causes cardiac acceleration and systolic contracture. Of the former group we selected *Protothaca staminea* and *Mya arenaria*, of the latter *Mytilus californianus* as representative species and experimental animals. The heart of *Mya* and *Protothaca* is inhibited by acetylcholine concentrations as low as 10^{-12} g/ml. Complete diastolic arrest with maximum relaxation can be achieved with concentrations of 10^{-9} g/ml. This is true for unfilled ventricles which are simply suspended in a bath, as well as for ventricles which are filled with perfusing medium and to which acetylcholine is applied to the inside of the heart. It is rather surprising that the outside of filled ventricles is relatively insensitive to acetylcholine. The ratio between inside and outside sensitivity can be as high as 30,000! Since unfilled ventricles are extremely sensitive to acetylcholine applied to the outside we may assume that filling leads to a rotation of acetylcholine-sensitive sites towards the inside of the ventricle. This may well mean that not all of the muscle fiber surface is sensitive to this compound.

If the amount of potassium in the fluid bathing the isolated *Protothaca* ventricle is lowered, the heart rate declines and in the absence of potassium the heart stops in diastole and shows complete relaxation. If the amount of potassium is increased beyond twice the normal concentration, the heart undergoes a contracture. Intermediate concentrations cause acceleration and an increase in amplitude. If a ventricle has been exposed to a medium containing three or four times the normal amount of potassium and if this medium is exchanged for one that contains twice the normal amount of potassium, the ventricle undergoes rapid and complete relaxation and resumes beating with supranormal amplitude a few minutes later. No slowing or relaxation results if the ventricle is returned to normal medium after exposure to a medium containing twice the normal potassium concentration. Acetylcholine and potassium act antagonistically so that a ventricle is more sensitive to the drug if the potassium concentration of the medium is lowered and less sensitive if the potassium concentration is raised (see Fig. 1).

The behavior of the *Mytilus* ventricle is quite different. In this case acetylcholine causes acceleration of the heartbeat and leads to systolic arrest. The same effect is achieved if the ventricle is subjected to a medium which contains no potassium (see Fig. 2). Higher than normal amounts of potassium cause a slowing and relaxation of the heart muscle. As in the case of *Mya* and *Protothaca* the inside of the ventricle is more sensitive to acetylcholine than the outside, the difference in sensitivity is, however, not as great and does not exceed a ratio of 200.

It is interesting in this regard that according to Welsh and Slocombe (1952) anodal current results in decreased heart rate and relaxation in the case of *Venus*, where acetylcholine is inhibitory, and that the same inhibition by anodal current was observed by Jullien and Marduel (1938a) in the heart of *Mytilus* where acetylcholine is excitatory.

The comparison of the effects of acetylcholine and potassium on the two types of lamellibranch hearts offer challenging problems. What is the reason for the opposite actions on the two types of heart? Following the popular concepts that acetylcholine excites neurogenic and inhibits myogenic hearts, one could indeed assume that in the case of *Mytilus* acetylcholine acts on the ganglion cells of the heart rather than on the heart muscle. There are, however, objections to this. First of all, we do not know whether there are nerve cells present in the hearts of *Mya* and *Protothaca*; secondly, we know that the heart of *Ostrea* which contains ganglion cells is inhibited by acetylcholine and the same is true for the cephalopod heart. In addition, we would assume that if acetylcholine acted on the ganglion cells of the heart it would primarily affect the frequency of the heartbeat whereas it actually affects the contraction process much more than the pacemaker rhythm.

The almost instant effect of changes in potassium ion concentration indicates that this ion affects the membrane potential of the cardiac muscle fibers. It is interesting, however, that, at least in *Protothaca* the immediate effect

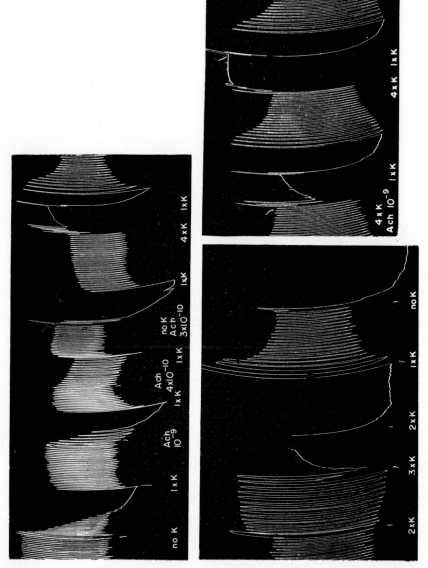

FIG. 1. *Protothaca staminea.* Isolated, unperfused ventricle. Changes in heart beat induced by variation in external potassium (K) concentration and by application of acetylcholine (ACh). The ACh-concentrations are given in g/ml. The K-concentrations are given as multiples of the normal concentration. Composition of the saline medium in mM: NaCl 410, KCl 8, MgCl₂ 47, CaCl₂ 10.

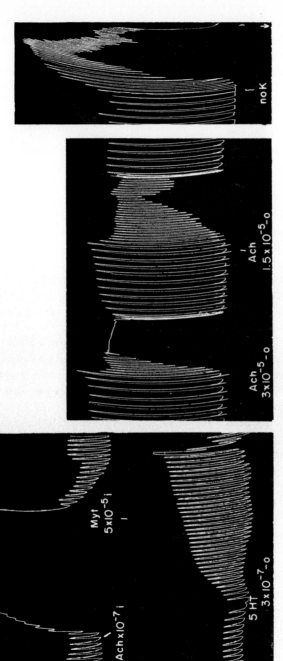

FIG. 2. *Mytilus californianus.* Isolated and cannulated ventricle, internal pressure = 1 cm H₂O. Changes in heart beat induced by application of acetylcholine (ACh), 5-hydroxytryptamine (5HT), Mytolon (Myt) and K-free medium; i denotes application to inside, o application to outside of ventricle. The drug concentrations are given in g/ml. Composition of saline medium in mM: NaCl 410, KCl 8, MgCl₂ 47, CaCl₂ 10.

depends not so much on the absolute level of potassium ion concentration as on the direction of change so that a change from four times to two times the normal potassium concentration has the same effect as a change from normal potassium concentration to a fraction of this amount. It is also striking that in *Protothaca* the effect of a change in potassium ion concentration is minimal if the direction of the change is toward the normal potassium concentration. The fact that the direction of change is more important than the absolute concentration (particularly when the change is toward a concentration other than the normal one) indicates that the internal potassium concentration rapidly follows the outside concentration. If this were true, the effects of altering the concentration of external potassium would be to set up *de novo* a potassium potential which would add to or subtract from a resting potential which is not normally dominated by potassium.

In this regard it appears of interest to refer to the "paradox" observed in other lamellibranch hearts, for instance that of *Clinocardium nutalli*: if the potassium is removed from the medium bathing the heart there is little change in amplitude and frequency of the heartbeat. When the heart is returned to the normal medium after prolonged exposure to the potassium-free medium, it stops in diastole for a period that is proportional to the time of exposure to the potassium-free medium. The phenomenon might be explained by the hypothesis that potassium is lost from the cells and that when they are returned to a medium with normal potassium content, the external potassium concentration is sufficiently high with regard to the internal potassium concentration, so as to set up a potential gradient which reduces the resting potential. The obvious difficulty of this explanation is the fact that the heart becomes inhibited rather than excited.

Thus far it has not been possible successfully to utilize techniques of intracellular recording with microelectrodes since the muscle fibers of lamellibranch hearts have a diameter of not more than 1 or 2 μ. Therefore this analysis rests on deduction rather than direct experimental evidence.

The hearts of molluscs undoubtedly pose intriguing problems which deserve much more serious attention than they have attracted hitherto. If the few observations which we have mentioned provoke interest, argument and more experimentation, our paper has served its purpose.

REFERENCES

BUMPUS, F. M. and PAGE, I. (1955) Serotonin and its methylated derivatives in human urine. *J. Biol. Chem.* **212** : 111–116.

DIEDERICHS, W. (1935) Beiträge zur Physiologie des Muschelherzens. *Zool. Jahrb. Abt. Allgem. Zool. Physiol. Tiere* **55** : 231–280.

JULLIEN, A. and MARDUEL, H. (1938a) Action du courant continu sur le ventricle isolé et pulsant de Moule (*Mytilus galloprovincialis*). *Compt. rend. soc. biol.* **127** : 319–322.

JULLIEN, A. and MARDUEL, H. (1938b) Action du courant continu sur le ventricle isolé et arrêté de la Moule (*Mytilus galloprovincialis*) *Compt. rend. soc. biol.* **127** : 322–325.

JULLIEN, A. and VINCENT, D. (1938) Sur l'action de l'acétylcholine sur le coeur des Mollusques. L'Antagonisme curare-acétylcholine. *Compt. rend. acad. sci.* **206** : 209–211.

KRIJGSMAN, B. J. and DIVARIS, G. A. (1955) Contractile and pacemaker mechanisms of the heart of Molluscs. *Biol. Revs.* **30** : 1–39.

MORIN, G. and JULLIEN, A. (1930) Sur la structure du coeur chez *Murex trunculus. Bull. Hist.* **7** : 79–96.

MOTLEY, H. L. (1932) The histology of the freshwater mussel heart with reference to its physiological reactions. *J. Morphol. and Physiol.* **54** : 415–427.

PILGRIM, R. L. C. (1954) The action of acetylcholine on the hearts of lamellibranch Molluscs. *J. Physiol (London)* **125** : 208–214.

PROSSER, C. L. (1940) Acetylcholine and nervous inhibition in the heart of *Venus mercenaria. Biol. Bull.* **78** : 92–102.

PROSSER, C. L. *et al.* (1950) *Comparative Animal Physiology.* W. B. Saunders, Philadelphia.

SUZUKI, S. (1934a) On the ganglion cells in the heart of the pearl oyster, *Pinctada martensi. Sci. Rep. Tôhoku Imp. Univ.* Ser. IV, **9** : 111–115.

SUZUKI, S. (1934b) On the distribution of ganglion cells in the heart of the oyster. *Sci. Rep. Tôhoku Imp. Univ.* Ser. IV, **8** : 335–344.

SUZUKI, S. (1935) The innervation of the heart of Molluscs. *Sci. Rep. Tôhoku Imp. Univ.* Ser. IV, **10** : 15–27.

WELSH, J. H. (1957) Serotonin as a possible neurohumoral agent: evidence obtained in lower animals. *Ann. N.Y. Acad. Sci.* **66** : 618–630.

WELSH, J. H. and TAUB, R. (1948) The action of choline and related compounds on the heart of *Venus mercenaria. Biol. Bull.* **95** : 346–353.

WELSH, J. H. and SLOCOMBE, A. J. (1952) The mechanism of the action of acetylcholine on the *Venus* heart. *Biol. Bull.* **102** : 48–57.

CARDIAC INHIBITION IN
DECAPOD CRUSTACEA*

DONALD M. MAYNARD

Department of Zoology, University of Michigan, Ann Arbor

DECAPOD Crustacea possess a neurogenic heart. Each heartbeat is normally initiated by nervous activity originating in a cardiac ganglion located on the inner dorsal wall of the heart. The ganglion is considered spontaneously active, for it continues to discharge with little change in pattern when completely isolated from the myocardium. The spontaneous discharge is modulated, however, in crabs and lobster by activity in three regulator fibers originating in the central nervous system and terminating in the heart on the ganglion neurons and possibly on the myocardium. One of the regulator fibers is inhibitory, the other two excitatory. This paper considers the effects of inhibitor fiber activity on the ganglion neurons. Where necessary, details of anatomy, interaction among the ganglion neurons, and action of the accelerator fibers will be presented. Two major aspects of inhibition will be discussed: (1) What are the characteristics of the processes which lead to inhibition of spontaneous or postsynaptic activity in the individual cardiac neurons? (2) What are the effects of depressed excitability in the individual neurons upon the pattern of integrated activity in the total ganglion burst?

ANATOMY

The cardiac ganglion in lobsters, and marine decapods generally, normally contains but nine intrinsic neurons (Alexandrowicz, 1932). In *Homarus americanus* these are arranged along a "Y-shaped" ganglion trunk; in *Panulirus argus* and *Panulirus interruptus*, along a linear trunk (Figs. 1 and 2). The five anterior neurons are larger than the four posterior neurons and are motor units directly responsible for the heartbeat.† The posterior units apparently serve as pacemakers in normal cardiac action, but they are not

* Portions of this investigation were supported by the Grass Trust for Research in Neurophysiology, the William T. Porter Fellowship in Physiology, and grants to T. H. Bullock from the National Institutes of Health. Initial experiments with GABA were performed at the Mental Health Research Institute, University of Michigan.

† In three out of about 150 cardiac ganglia of *Homarus americanus* there were six rather than the usual five anterior large neurons. Personal communication, E. A. Maynard.

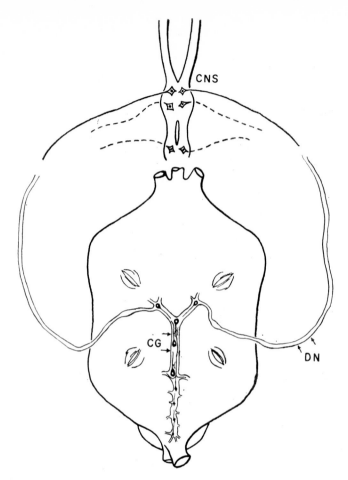

FIG. 1. Diagram of cardiac ganglion *in situ* and regulator fibers (*Homarus americanus*). *CG*, cardiac ganglion; *CNS*, subesophageal ganglia; *DN*, dorsal nerve. *Arrows* indicate usual position of extracellular recording electrodes. *Solid line* represents inhibitor fiber; *dashed lines*, accelerator fibers.

vital for all burst activity (Maynard, 1955). Other functions of the small cells are as yet unknown. Synaptic and electrotonic connections exist between the ganglion neurons, the former presumably in the "neuropile" areas and around the large anterior neuron somata (Fig. 3). In addition to collaterals entering the neuropile and axons extending into the myocardium, cardiac neurons send out processes which branch profusely in a limited area of the myocardium beside the ganglion trunk. These are the dendritic arborizations which presumably function as stretch receptors (Isquierdo, 1931; Alexandrowicz, 1932; Bullock *et al.*, 1954).

11

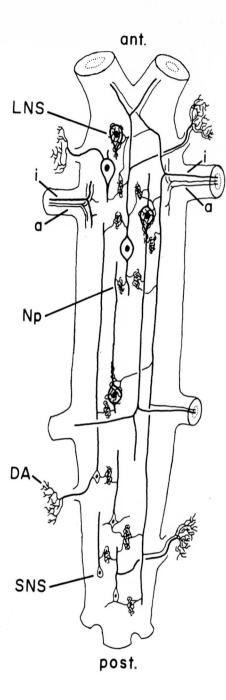

FIG. 2. Diagram of cardiac ganglion (*Panulirus*). The major branches are severed near the trunk; the minor branches are not shown. All of the nerve cells but only a fraction of the ganglionic axons, dendrites, and processes are indicated. *LNS*, large neuron soma: two large cells send axons anteriorly, three send axons posteriorly, all have dendritic arborizations, *DA*, pericellular inhibitor networks, and collaterals to neuropiles, *Np. SNS*, small neuron soma: all small cell axons go anteriorly; pericellular inhibitor networks are absent, but dendritic arborizations and neuropiles are universal. The inhibitor fiber, *i*, and two accelerator fibers, *a*, enter on each side through the dorsal nerve. The inhibitor fiber branches terminate on: *DA*, dendritic arborizations; *LNS*, large neuron soma; and *Np*, neuropiles. Branches also go out into the cardiac muscle and may have terminations in the muscle itself. Entire ganglion 1–2 cm long; width is exaggerated (Maynard, 1954).

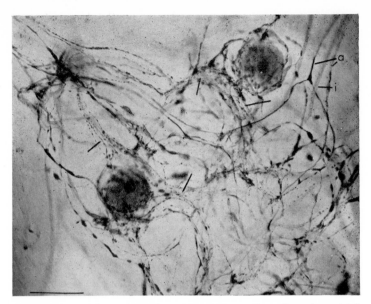

FIG. 3. Cardiac ganglion of *Panulirus interruptus*, portion of trunk containing third and fourth large cells and junction of dorsal nerve (methylene blue stain). Observe thick inhibitor (*i*) and thinner accelerators (*a*) entering from upper right. A number of fine fibers surround cell somata and run along initial segment of axon (arrows). Tangled mass of fine fibers in center of figure is considered "neuropile". Calibration, about 100 μ.

The extrinsic cardioregulatory fibers originate in the thoracic ganglia, probably in the first three segments. In *Panulirus argus* they leave the ventral thoracic ganglion mass in three pairs of nerves. The most anterior (segmental nerve 1) carries the inhibitor fiber, the two more posterior nerves (segmental nerves 2 and 3) carry one accelerator fiber each. All run dorsally through the lateral body musculature and enter the pericardium to unite in the lateral pericardial plexus, a portion of the *pericardial organ* of Alexandrowicz (1953). From each plexus a single *dorsal nerve* runs to the heart. This may contain several fibers near its origin, but only three, one from each of the original nerves, appear to enter the heart and reach the cardiac ganglion (Maynard, 1953).

Alexandrowicz (1932) described two systems of extrinsic fibers; a large-fibered System I (described above) and a small-fibered System II. The present observations suggest that the small-fibered System II may be a portion of the pericardial organ which does not actually enter the cardiac ganglion. All of the following physiological evidence indicates that only the larger System I fibers (one inhibitor, two accelerators) are involved in the present investigations.

In *Panulirus*, the fibers of the dorsal nerve enter the ganglion in the region of the third and fourth large cells; in *Homarus*, slightly anterior to the first two large cells. The inhibitor fiber is generally slightly larger than the two accelerators. Within the ganglion, it branches, sending processes throughout the trunk. Small collaterals enter neuropile tangles or ramify over the large ganglion cell bodies and along the basal portions of their axons (Fig. 3 and Alexandrowicz, 1932). Some larger inhibitor collaterals leave the trunk to end among the "dendritic arborizations" of the large and small cells. Other branches travel into the myocardium in nerves presumably carrying motor fibers from the large cells. There are no fiber networks over the small cell somata, but the inhibitor connects with the small cell dendrites in neuropiles and dendritic arborizations. The inhibitor fiber may end, therefore, on at least three and possibly four regions of a ganglion neuron: (1) on dendritic arborizations; (2) on the cell body (large cells only); (3) on dendrites or collaterals in neuropiles; and possibly, (4) near the endings of motor axons in the myocardium (Fig. 2).

ACTIVITY IN THE CARDIAC GANGLION

Wire electrodes placed on the cardiac ganglion and on the dorsal nerve record two kinds of electrical activity (Fig. 4). First there is the repeating, intermittent burst discharge which originates in ganglion neurons and is limited to the cardiac ganglion. Second there are extrinsic impulses having no direct relation to burst activity or heartbeat which occur both in the dorsal nerve and the cardiac ganglion. They originate in the ventral ganglia and pass through the dorsal nerve to the heart.

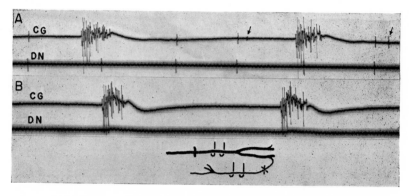

FIG. 4. Extracellular recording from cardiac ganglion and dorsal nerve (*Homarus*). A, before cutting dorsal nerve; B, after cutting dorsal nerve. *CG*, cardiac ganglion; *DN*, dorsal nerve; electrode positions indicated in diagram. Arrows represent accelerator (small) and inhibitor impulses (large) reaching ganglion from opposite side of body. Sixty-cycle ripple on *DN* trace.

Intrinsic Burst

Each of the nine neurons of the ganglion appears to fire several times during the intrinsic burst. The sequence of discharge during a burst may remain essentially unaltered for many minutes, even in the isolated ganglion. The silent period between bursts corresponds with a period of depressed excitability. Many, if not all of the ganglion neurons are capable of spontaneous activity in the absence of synaptic activation. The pattern of discharge of such isolated units, however, generally differs from that of the burst. Consequently, we may assume that the normal, co-ordinated burst depends upon some type of interaction among the ganglion neurons. The small posterior cells usually initiate the burst and have consequently been termed the "pacemakers". The larger, anterior motor neurons have been called the "followers". The burst may continue, however, in the absence of the usual pacemakers, and there is evidence that electrotonic as well as synaptic influences play a role in maintaining the co-ordinated discharge. Aspects of this problem have been considered in the papers of Maynard (1954, 1955, 1960), Hagiwara and Bullock (1957), Bullock and Terzuolo (1957), Bullock (1958), Otani and Bullock (1959), Watanabe (1958), Hagiwara, Saito, and Watanabe (1959).

Although details need not be considered here, Fig. 5, showing intracellular recordings from follower cells in *Panulirus*, demonstrates the complex electrical phenomena which may occur in each cell during each burst. At least four major types of potential changes may occur in ganglion neurons: (1) Electrotonic potentials resulting from slow activity in neighboring units. (2) Generator potentials often leading to spontaneous spike discharges, (3) Propagated action potentials in axons seen as brief spikes from electrodes in the cell body. (4) Synaptic potentials. According to the nature of the presynaptic terminal, synaptic potentials are of at least three kinds; intrinsic excitatory, accelerator, inhibitor (Table 1).

Extrinsic Impulses

Impulses arriving in the cardiac ganglion from the dorsal nerve are of three kinds; one large amplitude spike with an estimated conduction velocity of about 1·5–2 m/sec at 25°C, and two of small amplitude with conduction velocities about half that of the larger spike. All three impulses may be initiated by stimulating the dorsal nerve.

The larger spike is identified as the inhibitor on the following evidence from *Homarus*: (1) When the inhibitor nerve (segmental nerve 1) is cut near the ventral cord, the large spike disappears from the dorsal nerve and ganglion trunk, and the burst frequency of the ganglion may increase. (2) When the distal stump of the cut inhibitor nerve is stimulated, the large spike appears after each stimulus and inhibition returns. Such stimulation

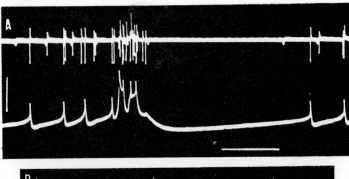

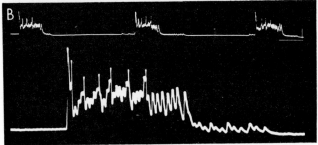

FIG. 5. Intracellular recordings from anterior cardiac neurons (*Panulirus*). A. Follower discharge with spontaneity. Upper trace shows the simultaneously recorded impulse discharge of the entire ganglion trunk. Calibrations for the intracellular potential: 10 mV, time: 100 msec. (Courtesy, Hagiwara and Bullock, *J. Cell. Comp. Physiol.* **50** : 28, 1957). B. Simple follower without spontaneity, the upper and lower traces are from the same cell at different scales. Calibration for upper trace: 10 mV, 500 msec. (Courtesy, Bullock and Terzuolo, *J. Physiol.* (*London*) **138** : 341–364, 1957.)

TABLE 1. POSTSYNAPTIC POTENTIALS IN ANTERIOR CARDIAC GANGLION NEURONS

Presynaptic	Postsynaptic potential	Potentiates spikes
Ganglion neurons, small and large	Depolarizes, defacilitates, summates	yes
Accelerator neurons	Depolarizes, facilitates, summates	yes
Inhibitor neuron	Depolarizes, facilitates, summates	yes
	or	
	Hyperpolarizes, facilitates, summates	no

does not affect the spontaneous activity of the two smaller impulses. (3) If a spontaneously active inhibitor is stimulated without cutting its central connections, the higher stimulus frequency replaces the spontaneous frequency of the inhibitor impulse in the ganglion and increased inhibition occurs. When stimulation stops, a brief post-excitatory depression occurs before spontaneous inhibitor activity resumes, suggesting that the axon carrying spontaneous and "stimulated" inhibitor impulses is the same.

Since there are but three large (1–5 μ) fibers in the dorsal nerve and since only the large impulse described above can be correlated with inhibitory effects, it seems very probable that only one inhibitory fiber passes through inhibitory and dorsal nerves into the ganglion.

A few recordings from the dorsal nerve of *Panulirus interruptus*, in contrast to *Homarus*, show several spikes when the severed inhibitor trunk is stimulated. Simultaneous records from the ganglion, however, show only one impulse, and Terzuolo and Bullock (1958) find but one inhibitory post-synaptic potential upon stimulation of the dorsal nerve. This finding agrees with the observation that certain fibers of the pericardial organ system run in the dorsal nerve to the ligaments and surface of the *Panulirus* heart while they do not appear to do so in *Homarus*. It may be presumed that in the spiny lobster there is also one inhibitor fiber in each dorsal nerve.

Maynard (1953) thought stimulus–response curves in *Panulirus argus* might indicate several inhibitor fibers. This interpretation appears erroneous, however, for the curves may be explained by the present findings that with high stimulus strengths or durations, the inhibitor fiber responds repetitively, and that with high stimulation frequencies (70/sec), it frequently skips stimuli or fails to respond altogether.

When the first accelerator nerve is cut near the thoracic ganglia in *Homarus*, the larger of the two small spikes in the dorsal nerve disappears, but may be elicited again by stimulation of the distal stump. The smaller spike remains after both inhibitor and first accelerator nerve are cut, its frequency unaffected by stimulation of either. A second accelerator like that known to be present in brachyurans (Smith, 1947) and palinurans (Maynard, 1953) may be inferred in *Homarus*. The second accelerator impulse is abolished by cuts in the lateral musculature posterior to the first accelerator nerve. Activity in either or both of these smaller extrinsic fibers is associated with increased activity in the ganglion, confirming their identification as accelerators.

Spontaneous Activity in Regulator Neurons

The inhibitor fiber discharged spontaneously in sixteen out of eighteen bloodless *Homarus* preparations. In six of the sixteen, spontaneous accelerator impulses also occurred, and in two of these six, both accelerators were active. Frequencies varied from 1 to 16 impulses/sec in the inhibitor and up to 36/sec in the accelerators. At lower frequencies, activity was erratic and uneven; at higher frequencies, rhythmic and continuous.

INHIBITION IN THE GANGLION

If the posterior two-thirds of a *Panulirus* ganglion trunk is removed often

only one of the four large anterior cells remains active, firing in a regular
run. Upon stimulation of one inhibitor fiber, an initial inhibition is followed
by recovery or adaptation which eventually levels off at some inhibition
plateau (Figs. 6 and 7). In some preparations, adaptation may continue as
long as 20 sec, but is usually much briefer. When inhibitory stimulation is
stopped, a rebound or post-inhibitory excitation occurs. Both the degree of
inhibition and the extent of the rebound depend upon the frequency of
inhibitor activity.

Figure 8 shows that with brief trains, both the number and frequency of
impulses affect inhibition. At 50/sec, at least three inhibitory impulses may
be necessary before any inhibition of the driven burst is apparent. Frequencies
below 5–10/sec usually have little effect on spontaneous burst discharges,
but complete inhibition may occur at frequencies of 60–70/sec (Maynard,
1953).

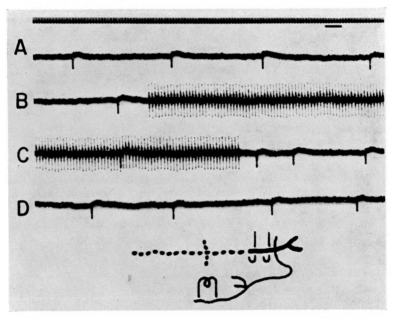

FIG. 6. Inhibition of an isolated, spontaneously active large cell (*Panulirus*).
A through D form a continuous record: A, normal activity; B, inhibitory stimulus
artifact after the first spike, inhibition of spontaneous activity; C, single impulse
during inhibition (adaptation) (there is an increase in frequency, *post-inhibitory
excitation*, at the end of inhibition); D, return to normal activity. The diagram
represents the cardiac ganglion (dotted portion has been removed), dorsal
nerve and inhibitor nerve. Stimulating electrodes are on one inhibitor nerve,
recording electrodes are on the anterior portion of the cardiac ganglion.
Inhibitor stimulation frequency, 50/sec; time signal, 60/sec; time line, 0·1 sec
(Maynard, 1954).

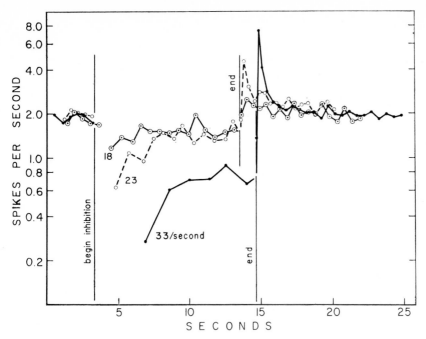

FIG. 7. Isolated large cell, time course of inhibition. (*Panulirus*, same preparation as Fig. 6.) Ordinate, spontaneous activity of ganglion neuron; abscissa, time in seconds. The effect of three different stimulation frequencies is shown: 18/sec, 23/sec, and 33/sec. Cessation of inhibitory stimulation is marked by *end*. Temperature is about 25°C (Maynard, 1954).

Post-inhibitory Events

Latent pause. The latent pause is the interval between the end of inhibitor activity and the first post-inhibitory discharge. Its duration increases with the effectiveness of the preceding inhibition, but decreases with the duration of inhibitor activity and the time since the preceding discharge (Fig. 9). The increase of the latent pause with inhibition suggests a residual depression that ordinarily may be masked by rebound effects. This is illustrated by the preparation shown in Fig. 10 which is driven by an electrical stimulus immediately following a train of inhibitory stimuli adequate for complete inhibition but too brief to induce rebound. As indicated by prolonged latencies, the driven response may show residual inhibition for 0·75 sec after the end of inhibitory stimulation. If such a brief inhibitory train is given to a normal spontaneous preparation, its effectiveness depends upon its position in the interburst period. The later in the period the greater the inhibition but the shorter the latent pause, and vice versa.

Rebound. Post-inhibitory rebound increases with high-frequency inhibitor activity, and for the first 5–10 sec, with prolongation of inhibition. After

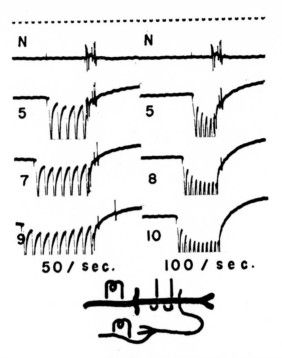

FIG. 8. Inhibitory summation (*Panulirus*). Inhibitor stimulated before driving stimulus with trains of stimuli at 50/sec and 100/sec. Figures give the number of impulses in each train, *N*, normal response to stimulation of ganglion with no inhibition. Stimulating electrodes on inhibitor nerve and posterior ganglion; recording electrodes on anterior ganglion. Time signal, 60/sec (Maynard, 1954).

this, continued inhibition produces little increase in rebound, suggesting a similarity between the time course of development of such post-inhibitory excitation and the time course of adaptation during prolonged inhibition.

Rebound excitation may be quite effective. In many cases it causes greater maximum activity than that produced by high-frequency stimulation of the accelerator nerves. In other preparations, it apparently leads to the phenomenon of paradoxical driving.

Paradoxical driving. As certain preparations age they lose spontaneous activity and fire erratically in small bursts with very long interburst periods. A short train of inhibitory stimuli given in the interburst of such a preparation often may be followed, after a latent pause of about 1 sec, by a burst of ganglionic activity. If the inhibitory train is repeated after a proper interval, a burst again follows so that the previously inactive ganglion can be driven by brief, properly spaced trains of inhibition at a rate somewhat below normal frequencies. Ganglion activity never occurred during inhibitory trains (Fig. 11).

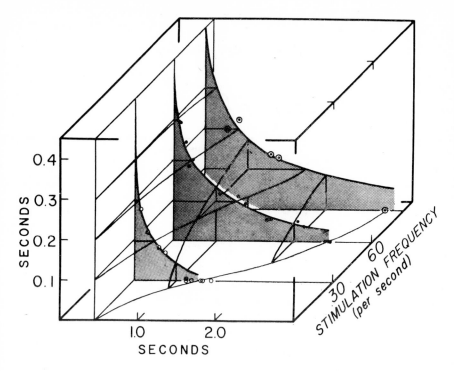

FIG. 9. Relation of latent pause to inhibitory intensity and duration (*Homarus*). Ordinate, latent pause or the interval between the end of inhibition and the first post-inhibitory activity; abscissa (*x*), interval preceding burst, prolonged by inhibition; abscissa (*z*), inhibitor stimulation frequency. The vertical plane at 0·45 sec on the abscissa (*x*) represents the normal burst frequency. Points on the ordinate base line—latent pause, 0—represent first activity during inhibition, and the corresponding value on abscissa (*x*) gives the duration of *initial inhibition* (Maynard, 1954).

The relations between inhibition and the post-inhibitory events are especially clear in these preparations (Fig. 12). An increase in duration of inhibition is followed by an increase in the maximum driving frequency—assumed to measure post-inhibitory excitation—and a decrease in the latent pause. These observations, together with various elaborations, suggest that the probability of discharge of a ganglion neuron within a given period of time after the termination of inhibition is related to at least three distinct phenomena: (1) The depressed excitability directly caused by inhibitor action. (2) The process initiated by such depression which effectively increases excitability and which is presumably responsible for post-inhibitory rebound. (3) The sequence of excitability variations which follow normal intrinsic activity of the ganglion neurons.

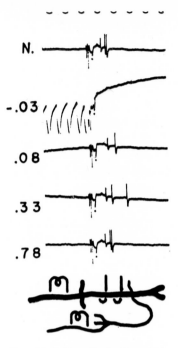

FIG. 10. Inhibitory after effect (*Panulirus*). Twenty-two inhibitory stimuli at 92/sec were given at varying times before the driving stimulus. The numbers to the left represent the interval in seconds between the last inhibitor impulse in the ganglion and the driving stimulus. *N*, normal response. Stimulating inhibitor nerve and posterior ganglion; recording from anterior ganglion. Time signal, 60/sec (Maynard, 1954).

Inhibition of Pacemaker Neurons

The effects of inhibition on the isolated small or pacemaker neuron must be determined indirectly, for it is impossible to isolate a small unit without severing its inhibitory connections. In certain preparations, however, activity in all but one small neuron may be inhibited (see Fig. 20) leaving a functionally isolated unit. Figure 13 diagrams the activity of such a unit firing in repeated trains, not continuous runs. Further inhibition at higher frequencies leads to a progressive decrease in train frequency, maximum spike frequency in the train, number of impulses per train, and mean spike frequency. Adaptation and post-inhibitory rebound occur, so inhibition of the posterior small units is apparently qualitatively similar to inhibition of the anterior followers. There is, however, a quantitative difference; the pacemakers usually require much higher frequencies of inhibitory stimulation for complete inhibition than do the followers.

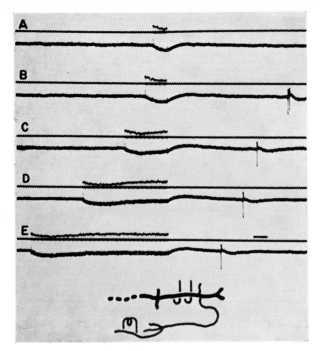

FIG. 11. Paradoxical driving, relation of latent pause to inhibitory duration (*Panulirus*). A through E, increasing duration of inhibitory stimulation: A, no response; B, two-spiked response, long latent pause; C–E, one spike response, decreasing latent pause. Inhibitor stimulation frequency, 100/sec; inhibitor trains repeated every 2·4 sec. Stimulating inhibitor nerve; recording from electrode pair in midcardiac ganglion. Time signal, 60/sec; time line, 0·1 sec (Maynard, 1954).

From the description of inhibitor action on ganglion neuron activity given above, the analysis logically splits in two directions. One proceeds to an examination of the cellular mechanisms which underly the events described, particularly in so far as membrane conductance and potential changes are involved. The other direction takes the events as described and asks how they are altered when the ganglion neuron is placed in a dynamic system and how they in turn affect the total output of the system. It is useful to distinguish between the two aspects, for I think it will become apparent that the terminology and concepts applicable to one, although related, do not necessarily prove the most useful for the other. For example, in so far as the heart beat is concerned, the probability of propagated impulse initiation in motor neurons is the measure of inhibitor activity. In so far as the neuron membrane is concerned, however, one may argue that the appropriate measure of inhibitor activity is the change in relative membrane conductance to specific ions, and that effects on spike probability are secondary.

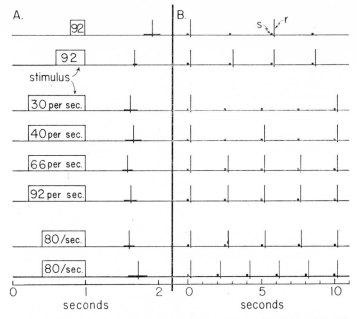

FIG. 12. Paradoxical driving, effects of various parameters of inhibition (*Panulirus*), same preparation as in Fig. 11. Diagram of oscilloscope records. A. Variation of latent pause with duration of inhibitory train, frequently of pulses within train, and frequency of train repetition. Vertical line gives mean of about seven values; horizontal line, range of values. B. Same inhibitor stimulation, slower time scale. Inhibitor trains indicated by small, thick vertical lines; post-inhibitory responses, where they occur, by large vertical lines.

MECHANISMS OF INHIBITION

Membrane potential changes associated with inhibition have been studied by Terzuolo and Bullock (1958) and Otani and Bullock (1959). The following account is derived from their work.

Inhibitory postsynaptic potentials (i.p.s.p.) recorded from follower cells in *Panulirus interruptus* may be hyperpolarizing, depolarizing, or occasionally, both (Fig. 14). Hyperpolarizing potentials generally occur in units with spontaneously occurring generator potentials; depolarizing potentials in pure followers with no spontaneous activity. In contrast to the excitatory p.s.p. initiated by intrinsic neurons, i.p.s.p.'s always facilitate, at times requiring up to 1 sec for complete facilitation, and at higher frequencies summate to a maintained plateau potential. Individual facilitated i.p.s.p.'s usually last several milliseconds and may reach values of several millivolts. Both initial depolarizing and later hyperpolarizing phases of the biphasic i.p.s.p. figured (Fig. 14) facilitated, but only the hyperpolarizing phase summated. With prolonged inhibition, both the individual potential and the summed plateau tend to adapt, returning toward initial membrane potential values (Fig. 16).

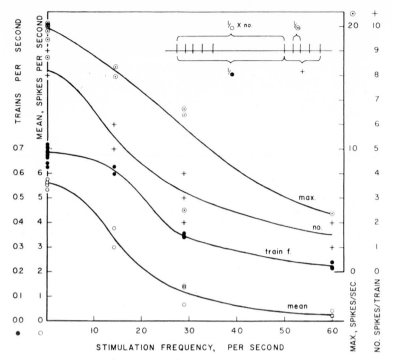

FIG. 13. Single small cell, effect of inhibitor stimulation frequency (*Panulirus*). Ordinate, parameters of spontaneous activity; abscissa, inhibitor stimulation frequency. The pattern of activity in the unit is shown in the diagram, a brief train of high frequency activity followed by a longer recovery period (Maynard, 1954).

The effects of inhibitor activity on the various potentials in the ganglion are not completely known. Generator and oscillating potentials are obviously blocked by the hyperpolarizing potentials, but there is no complete description of their action on the e.p.s.p. or the generation of propagated spikes. In view of the experiments illustrated in Fig. 8, such action may be assumed depressant. Depolarizing i.p.s.p.'s apparently summate with e.p.s.p.'s. This is probably not additive, and in two preparations, the figures (Figs. 14, 15) suggest that summed, depolarizing i.p.s.p.'s result in a depression of individual e.p.s.p.'s. Definite statements on this subject are premature, however. Although I do not feel justified in terming all depolarizing effects of the i.p.s.p. excitatory, there are some instances—usually limited to the non-spontaneous, first two follower neurons in *Panulirus*—in which the depolarizing i.p.s.p. apparently potentiates the generation of spike potentials (Fig. 15). In this sense the i.p.s.p. may be excitatory. Such spike potentiation does not correlate with potentiation of synaptic potentials; the latter in fact diminish in amplitude.

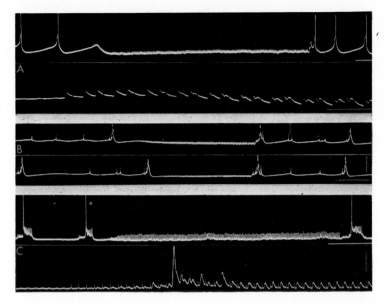

FIG. 14. Inhibitory post-synaptic potentials in follower cells (intracellular recordings, *Panulirus*). A. Spontaneously active cell. Pacemaker potential is interrupted by onset of inhibition (90/sec) which drives the internal potential negative towards a maintained hyperpolarization. Note rebound. Calibration for upper trace, 200 msec. Lower trace at faster film speed, 60/sec inhibitor stimulation. The first stimuli produce only artifacts; clear response is seen beginning with the seventh and is a brief depolarizing, facilitating synaptic potential followed by an hyperpolarizing phase which summates. B. Follower with spontaneity. Synaptic potential hyperpolarizes only, but holds high level of polarization following burst discharge. Calibration; 400 msec, 20 mV. C. Simple follower without spontaneity. Depolarizing synaptic potentials; inhibitor stimulated at 60/sec. In second trace e.p.s.p. from ganglion neurons and i.p.s.p. from inhibitor summate. Note two abortive pacemaker discharges in first line. Calibration, top trace, 1 sec; lower trace, 100 msec, 10 mV. (Courtesy, Terzuolo and Bullock, *Arch. ital. Biol.* **96** : 117–134, 1958.)

Figure 16 provides some bases for understanding the dual action of the inhibitor. As with most i.p.s.p.'s in other systems, the direction of the potential change depends upon the value of the membrane potential, lower membrane potentials leading to hyperpolarizing i.p.s.p.'s, higher membrane potentials, to depolarizing i.p.s.p.'s. A non-spontaneous ganglion neuron such as Unit 1 or 2 in *Panulirus* may consequently be converted into a spontaneous unit with hyperpolarizing i.p.s.p.'s simply by presetting the membrane potential at a lower level. This would mean that the dual nature of the inhibitor fiber does not necessarily require qualitative differences in presynaptic terminations, but rather simply that the postsynaptic elements be on different sides of the reversal potential for the i.p.s.p. The confirmation of such a sup-

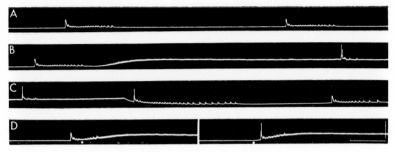

Fig. 15. Potentiation of spike potentials by "inhibition". Follower neuron of *Panulirus*. A. Before stimulation. B. Stimulation of the single inhibitor axon reduces burst frequency and duration, via the pacemakers, but lowers the polarization of the follower and hence two spikes occur which were not present before. Note reduced e.p.s.p. C. Only during post-inhibitory rebound does this cell exhibit a spike in absence of "inhibitory" stimulation. D.The added spikes are not due to the longer interval between bursts because they occur in an escape burst which happens to start soon after the beginning of stimulation (indicated by dots). Calibration, 400 msec, 20 mV. (Courtesy, Terzuolo and Bullock, *Arch. ital. Biol.* **96** : 117–134, 1958).

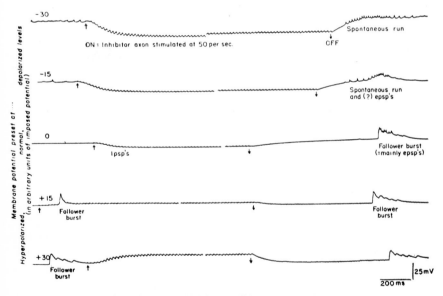

Fig. 16. Effects of membrane potential on inhibitory postsynaptic potentials (*Panulirus*). A large follower cell is penetrated with a single microelectrode used for both polarizing and recording. The single inhibitory axon is stimulated at 50/sec outside the ganglion. The i.p.s.p. facilitates and then slightly adapts with time. A simultaneous effect on the pacemaker cells elsewhere in the ganglion is seen in the follower bursts which show depression during inhibition (see "plus 15") and rebound increase following inhibition. (Courtesy, Otani and Bullock, *Physiol. Zool.* **32** : 104–114, 1958).

position must await conductance measurements across the neuron membranes during inhibition.

One important question regarding inhibitory "excitation" now seems to be whether the membrane potential of certain neurons in the *in situ* ganglion may normally lie above the reversal potential for i.p.s.p.'s. Although some of the units having depolarizing i.p.s.p.'s give reasonably normal discharges during a burst (Fig. 14) others are obviously abnormal (Fig. 15). They produce no propagated spikes and are activated by a single presynaptic unit.

Rebound Effects

Unlike the phenomena of inhibition and adaptation, post-inhibitory rebound is not reflected in underlying membrane potential shifts. Indeed, post-inhibitory spikes may rise from a soma membrane potential several millivolts higher than that found before inhibition (Fig. 16). The rebound appears associated with some process leading to more rapidly developing generator potentials (Fig. 14) and is obvious only when the i.p.s.p.'s hyperpolarize or stabilize the membrane. There is some support, therefore, for the contention that post-inhibitory rebound may be compared with the rebound following release of hyperpolarizing currents or electrotonic depression (Hagiwara and Bullock, 1957).

The results of intracellular recording are generally compatible with the idea that the major effect of activity in the inhibitor fiber is to alter membrane permeability to some specific ion, by analogy with other systems, K^+ or Cl^-. Two observations, however, do not seem to fit directly into the hypothesis. First, biphasic i.p.s.p.'s occur (see also, Tauc, 1958); second, the reversal potential of the summed i.p.s.p.'s may not necessarily be that of the individual i.p.s.p. (Otani and Bullock, 1959). Although it is possible to invoke anatomical distributions of the inhibitor terminals to account for these observations, such an explanation will not be completely acceptable until careful conductance measurements have been made during inhibition.

One criticism has been raised by Dr. C. A. G. Wiersma regarding the interpretation of the above results, i.e. there is no conclusive evidence that unknown accelerator fibers are not being stimulated with the inhibitor and are responsible for such things as the biphasic i.p.s.p.'s This is indeed an important point, particularly when stimulation of the inhibitor is achieved in the dorsal nerve as in at least some preparations of Terzuolo and Bullock (1958) and Otani and Bullock (1959). Although the criticism cannot be completely answered at present, I do feel that the physiological and anatomical evidence presented earlier, and the sharp thresholds for the effects reported by Terzuolo and Bullock (1958) make additional accelerator activity unlikely, at least when the inhibitor fiber is stimulated in segmental nerve 1.

INHIBITION AND PATTERNING

I should now like to consider the effects of inhibition on the pattern of firing of individual units in the total burst. In contrast to the isolated unit, the depression of the excitability of component units in an integrating system may not necessarily lead to a depression of all parameters of activity.

The integrated discharge of the normal, undisturbed ganglion is perhaps best measured by mechanical records of the heartbeat (Fig. 17). Although inhibition often produces a progressive decline in frequency and amplitude and very occasionally may stabilize an irregular beat, in many instances irregular beats of varying amplitude occur during inhibition, or the usual initial inhibition, adaptation, rebound sequence is distorted. The latter instances are perhaps the more interesting, for they imply some deviation from the usual effect of inhibition on the single unit. That they occur in the intact, *in situ* heart indicates that not all such irregular activity can be ascribed to preparation of the semi-isolated ganglion, and consequently it may be expected in normal systems.

The smoothly inhibited heartbeat would presumably be accompanied by ganglion activity such as shown in Fig. 18. Burst duration, burst frequency, and impulses per burst decline together, and the usual sequence of primary inhibition, adaptation, plateau inhibition, and rebound is present as with the single unit. Even in such a preparation, however, all parameters of single unit discharge may not be depressed. Figure 19 diagrams the frequency pattern of a single anterior follower unit in a *Panulirus* ganglion during inhibition.

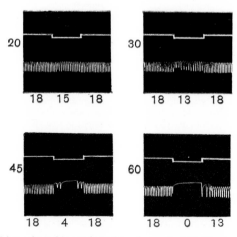

Fig. 17. Inhibition of total heart beat (*Cambarus clarkii*). The numbers below the records show the number of beats per 15 sec; the duration of inhibition is 15 sec, indicated by upper trace. Contraction of heart gives a downward stroke. Frequency of inhibitor stimulation given by numbers to left of records. (Courtesy, Wiersma and Novitski, *J. Exptl. Biol.* **19** : 255–265, 1942).

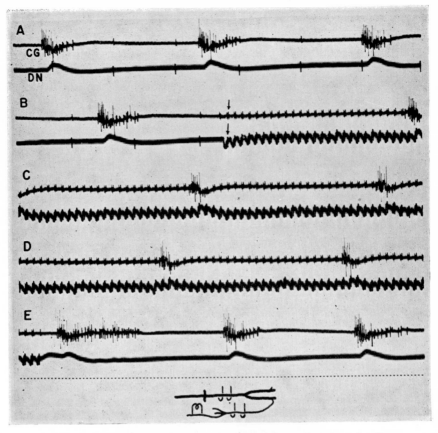

FIG. 18. Inhibition of spontaneous burst activity (*Homarus*). A through E form a continuous record: *CG*, trace from cardiac ganglion; *DN*, trace from dorsal nerve. Spikes in *DN* and between burst in *CG* represent spontaneous activity in the inhibitor fiber. Note that these are absent in E after high-frequency stimulation during inhibition. Arrows in B indicate first response of inhibitor to stimulation. Large deflection in *DN* trace immediately before each inhibitor response to stimulation probably represents activity in muscle surrounding the pericardial cavity. The burst frequency and duration decrease during inhibition. There is also evidence of *adaptation* and *post-inhibitory excitation*. Stimulation frequency, 20/sec (Maynard, 1954).

Burst frequency and impulses per burst are reduced, but the initial maximum impulse frequency seems unaffected or perhaps potentiated by inhibition. Similar patterns have been found in a number of preparations, so relative stability of maximum discharge frequency in followers, while not universal, is by no means unique. It is tempting to ascribe the frequency potentiation to excitatory effects of the inhibitor fiber (compare Fig. 15), but it could equally well result from alterations in the input pattern from other ganglion

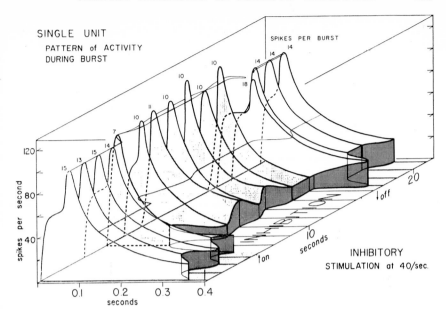

Fig. 19. Inhibition of spontaneous ganglion activity, single unit analysis (*Panulirus*). Ordinate, unit activity; abscissa (*x*), time during burst; abscissa (*z*), time between bursts. The graph portrays a series of vertical planes, each representing the frequency–time curve of one unit during a burst. The distance between these planes represents the time between bursts. Numbers at the top of each plane give the number of impulses of this unit in the respective burst. Inhibited planes are shaded; *on* and *off* indicated beginning and end of inhibition (Maynard, 1954).

neurons. In any event, whether some units are directly excited or not, the total effect of inhibition on such ganglia is a general decrease in the mean number of discharges per unit without drastically altering the co-ordination of the burst.

In contrast to the above, the large follower neurons are often inhibited before pacemaker activity is appreciably disturbed (Fig. 20). The heart contraction may consequently disappear before any gross alteration in burst frequency occurs, or in less extreme instances (Fig. 21) it may occur at irregular intervals which are multiples of pacemaker burst intervals.

Further insight into such activity is provided by an analysis of the frequency patterns of three small units in a *Panulirus* preparation (Fig. 22). The primary unit, the presumed pacemaker, is relatively unaffected by inhibitory stimulation. Burst frequency is only slightly depressed and is not indicated in the figure. During inhibition the second and third units do not fire during every train of the pacemaker. Large units fire only after Unit 3 discharge. During the initial phases of inhibition (bursts 4–11) Unit 2 discharges at every other

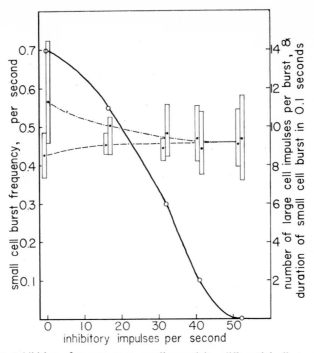

Fig. 20. Inhibition of spontaneous ganglion activity, differential effect on pacemaker and follower units (*Panulirus*). Increasing inhibitor stimulation frequency (abscissa) leads to progressive reduction in number of follower impulses per burst (–○–) before appreciable effect on either mean frequency (— — —) or duration (– – – –) of small unit pacemaker burst. Rectangles give range of values found for duration and frequency of burst at each stimulus frequency.

train of Unit 1. When Unit 2 does become active, its latency is less than usual and more impulses occur at higher frequencies than in the normal burst. This suggests that Unit 2 is hyperexcitable at the time of bursts 5, 7, 9, 11, but hypoexcitable at the time of the intervening bursts. In the later phases of inhibition Unit 2 fires at each burst, but the latency is longer and the frequency of spikes is less than normal. The initial hyperexcitability during odd bursts 5–11 must consequently result from recovery during the increased interburst period rather than a direct excitation by inhibition. As might be expected, as inhibitory adaptation proceeds, and Unit 2 becomes able to follow each Unit 1 train, the large oscillations in excitability are replaced by a more stabilized discharge at subnormal frequencies during each burst. Similar stabilization of alternating beats has been observed upon slight increases in excitability due to accelerator activity (Maynard, 1953).

Unit 3 and the large motor units follow Unit 2 activity only when the latter's discharge frequency during a burst reaches or surpasses normal levels. The heartbeat in this preparation would consequently be irregular

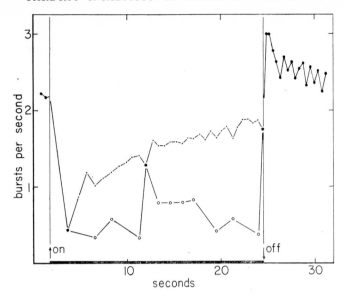

FIG. 21. Inhibition of spontaneous ganglion activity, differential effect on ganglion burst and heart contraction (*Homarus*). Large (●) and small (·) filled circles plot burst frequency; large filled (●) and open (○) circles plot heartbeat frequency. The large filled circles (●) represent points where burst and heartbeat frequencies coincide. During dorsal nerve stimulation not all bursts produced heart contractions and consequently burst frequency (·) and heartbeat frequency (○) diverged. Stimulation at 49/sec began at *on* and stopped at *off*. The inhibitor fiber and one accelerator fiber responded to the stimulus.

(see Fig. 17) and an uncritical evaluation would suggest that inhibition requires several seconds for facilitation and that adaptation is minimal. The actual facts, of course, are directly opposite: adaptation and gradual *increase* in mean excitability of a critical unit lead to complete inhibition of the heartbeat.

A similar condition obtains in another experiment in which the normal pacemaker is replaced by a direct stimulus to the ganglion, and brief trains of inhibition are applied immediately before each burst (Fig. 23). The pattern changes of the large spike complex showing "skipped" bursts and hyper-excitability in bursts F to I recall the responses of Unit 2 above and parallel the behavior of the uninhibited ganglion when driven by electrical stimuli at a frequency just beyond the maximum following frequency. In this instance, however, with interrupted inhibitor trains, several bursts are required to reach the fullest inhibition so skipped bursts and super-normal excitability appear only during the latter portion of the series.

Figure 23 also demonstrates a long-lasting facilitation between inhibitory trains spaced at one second intervals. Terzuolo and Bullock (1958) record similar phenomena in that i.p.s.p. facilitation is more rapid in a second train

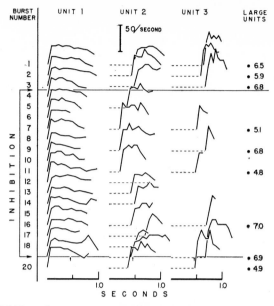

Fig. 22. Inhibition of spontaneous ganglion activity, unit analysis of total burst (*Panulirus*). Units 1, 2 and 3 are small neurons. The pattern of each small unit during a burst is plotted in a separate column. The vertical scale represents impulse frequency, the horizontal, time. Dashed lines represent the interval between the first impulse of unit 1 (0 time) and the first activity in units 2 or 3. The figures in the large unit column give the interval on 0·1 sec between unit 1 activity and the appearance of large cell impulses. Inhibitor stimulation at 36/sec began between bursts 3 and 4 and ended in the middle of burst 19 (Maynard, 1954).

of inhibitor impulses than the first. There is no maintained potential change in the soma between such trains.

One of the most obvious differences between inhibition of the single spontaneous unit and inhibition of the heart beat is the frequent apparent absence of post-inhibitory rebound in the latter. Although in some of the published cases this might be caused by after discharge in the inhibitor fiber, in others (see Fig. 17) a beat just at the end of inhibition with *subsequent* reduction in heart rate makes such explanations involving experimental artifact unlikely. Among the many circumstances which can lead to apparent suppression of rebound, two may be described.

In one preparation, the latent pause of the large units proved so much longer than that of the small, that the large units were often absent from the first post-inhibitory burst. The excitability of the small units was increased only in the first post-inhibitory burst (indicated by more impulses per burst), while the excitability of the large units was increased only in the second post-inhibitory small unit burst (indicated by decreased latency). The total

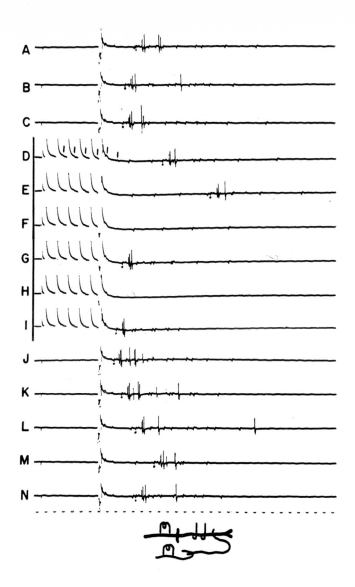

FIG. 23. Inhibition of driven ganglion activity (*Panulirus*). Stimuli applied directly to the ganglion at frequencies of 1/sec evoked a burst response. A–N, responses to successive stimuli. The stimulus artifact is seen as a major break in the baseline. The dot (·) indicates the first potential of the burst complex. Vertical dashes in D point to the inhibitor fiber impulse in the ganglion. A–C, normal response; D–I, six inhibitor stimuli at 50/sec applied to inhibitor nerve before driving stimulus to ganglion; J–N, post-inhibition. Stimulating electrodes on inhibitor nerve and posterior ganglion; recording electrodes on anterior ganglion (see diagram). Time signal, 60/sec, spikes retouched (Maynard, 1954).

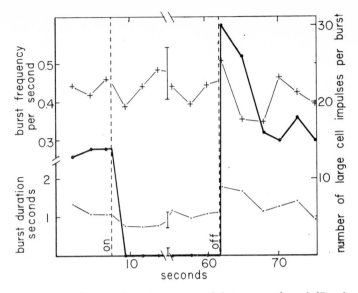

FIG. 24. Post-inhibitory rebound, absence of frequency rebound (*Panulirus*). (+), burst frequency per second; (·), burst duration in seconds; (●), number of large cell discharges per burst. Inhibitor stimulation at 52/sec began at *on*, continued for approximately 50 sec (note break in abscissa), and stopped at *off*. Vertical lines give range of values which occurred during break in abscissa. The large cell discharge, which was almost completely inhibited, and to a lesser extent burst duration, rebound following inhibition while the burst frequency does not.

burst, therefore, superficially failed to show post-inhibitory excitation because of inco-ordination of the component units. A record of the heart beat of such a ganglion would likewise show no post-inhibitory excitation even though it was clearly present in the individual ganglion neurons.

In the second instance (Fig. 24), small units are relatively unaffected by inhibitory activity and show rebound only in increased burst duration. The large units on the other hand, though rebounding in the form of increased number of impulses per burst during post-inhibitory bursts, do not increase the burst frequency. It is likely that the relative effectiveness of a motor axon impulse in producing myocardial tension declines as it occurs later in a train of such impulses. Consequently, though stronger heartbeats may be expected after inhibition, they need not directly reflect the extent of ganglion cell rebound during a burst. As here and in Fig. 17 slightly stronger heartbeats may be associated with appreciably longer inter-burst intervals, and the general impression is one of post-inhibitory depression rather than the post-inhibitory excitation which actually exists.

Primary depression of pacemakers rather than followers occasionally occurs, at least in preparations lacking the normal small cell complement.

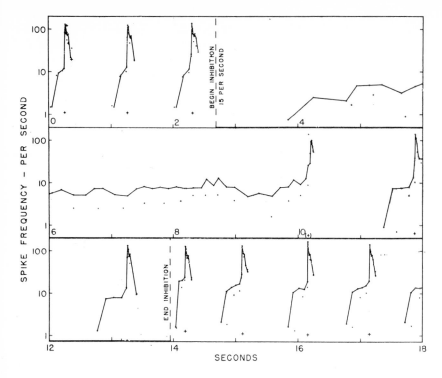

FIG. 25. Inhibition of spontaneous ganglion activity, primary effect on pacemaker (*Panulirus*). Continuous plot of activity against time. (○) and (●) represent large unit spikes; (+), the first of a brief train of pacemaker impulses. Burst activity is indicated by a sudden increase in single unit activity. Note the correlation between absence of pacemaker impulses and absence of bursts (Maynard, 1954).

When this is combined with spontaneous activity in followers, the pattern of Fig. 25 may occur. The released followers discharge in continuous runs at slightly subnormal frequencies, and reorganize into bursts only with the reappearance of the effective pacemaker. Patterns such as this were found only in injured preparations, so they may rarely occur in normal ganglia. The inefficiency of such disorganized activity or fibrillation in pumping fluid through the heart is obvious.

Inhibition and Patterning, Discussion

Both the isolated and interacting unit decrease their mean discharge frequency upon inhibition. In the isolated unit such a decrease is usually accompanied by a corresponding decrease in all pattern parameters (Fig 13). In the interacting unit, the parameters may be relatively independent, and the mean frequency decrease accomplished by several combinations of pattern variation (Fig. 22). It would seem, therefore, that even in such a limited system as the ganglion where the only known synaptic connections between intrinsic neurons are excitatory, the integrating neuron gains striking freedom with respect to its patterned activity. Such a unit may do much more in response to a given stimulus than merely increase or decrease its discharge frequency.

One problem in the analysis of a neural system is the selection of parameters significant in its normal function. In the cardiac ganglion, this difficulty is partially answered. The heart can function as an efficient pump only with co-ordinated contractions which develop intracardiac pressures greater than those in the arteries. These contractions in turn require a co-ordinated burst of nervous activity from the motor neurons. The sequence, amplitude, and duration of contraction of the individual muscle bundles within the heart presumably depend upon the sequence, frequency, and number of discharges arising in particular motor neurons in a given burst. In terms of heart contraction, therefore, the temporal pattern and synchronization of impulse discharge in motor units becomes more significant than such parameters as "average discharge frequency" or non-propagated membrane potential shifts.

Two aspects of the inhibitor junctions seem to favor the retention of some such synchronized and patterned activity during the otherwise disruptive effects of partial inhibition. First, a differential sensitivity to inhibition exists in that spontaneous discharges tend to be blocked more easily in the followers than in the pacemakers. Such a difference insures bursts as long as neurons remain active, and the range of inhibition giving a graded heartbeat becomes determined by the limits of activity of the followers rather than a failure in co-ordination. Second, inhibitor action is reported to facilitate synaptic transmission in some of the followers. If this phenomenon is substantiated, and occurs in the normal ganglion, it must extend the normal limits of follower activity during inhibition and permit effective heartbeats over a wider range of inhibition than otherwise possible.

Under the above conditions, it is not surprising to find burst co-ordination retained at the expense of regularity. Indeed, the reported patterning effects follow directly from the characteristics of the e.p.s.p. and i.p.s.p. described for single units in earlier sections. It is clear, however, that knowledge of single unit characteristics alone could not exclude the very real possibility of indiscriminate reduction in excitability during inhibition and the consequent disruption of the synchronized burst with release of spontaneous, independent motor neuron discharge (see Fig. 25). The latter prediction would require further knowledge of relative sensitivities of the interacting units of a system where, as Fig. 22 shows, a very small excitability change in one unit may lead to much greater and opposite alterations in total system output.

INHIBITORY TRANSMITTERS

Although inhibitor action is probably mediated through some chemical transmitter, little is known of such a substance. Inhibitor agents have been reported in the blood of darkened shrimp, *Paratya* (Hara, 1952), and Alexandrowicz and Carlisle (1953) find extracts of *Maia* pericardial organs which may depress heart rate. Florey (personal communication) reports that extracts of the second superior nerve (the inhibitor) of crayfish stop cardiac ganglion activity. Unfortunately, none of these materials has been applied to the isolated cardiac ganglion.

λ-Aminobutyric acid (GABA) closely mimics the action of inhibitor fibers in the isolated *Homarus* ganglion (Maynard, 1958). It not only depresses burst frequency, but also reduces the number of impulses per burst by cutting off the terminal discharge without drastically altering the initial spike frequency or pattern (Fig. 26). When applied separately to followers or pacemakers, GABA behaves as would be predicted were it the true transmitter (Figs. 27, 28), and permits some direct check on earlier inferences

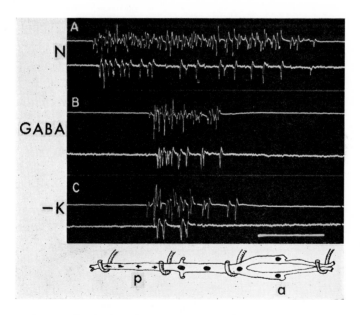

FIG. 26. Effect of GABA on burst pattern, applied to entire isolated ganglion (*Homarus*). A. Normal burst. B. Burst after 10^{-4} M GABA, burst frequency halved. C. Burst in potassium-deficient perfusion fluid to show differences between low K^+ and GABA effects. Upper trace of each record from posterior electrode pair (*p*) emphasizing pacemaker activity; lower trace from anterior electrode pair (*a*) emphasizing follower activity. Time line, $0·1$ sec, spikes retouched.

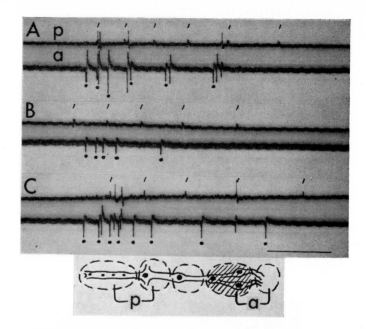

FIG. 27. Effect of GABA on burst pattern, applied to followers only (*Homarus*). A. Normal burst. B. Burst after concentrated GABA solution applied to anterior follower neurons. C. Burst after washing. Upper trace, *p*, from posterior portion of ganglion; lower trace, *a*, from anterior portion of ganglion. (′) indicates impulse originating in posterior cell which is unaffected by GABA; (·) indicates impulse originating in cell between anterior and posterior electrodes, probably large cell 4, which is relatively unaffected by GABA. Note complete inhibition of spikes originating more anteriorly. Diagram shows isolated ganglion laid across five separate pools of perfusion fluid with position of recording electrodes. GABA applied in shaded pool. Time line, 0·1 sec.

regarding the consequences of differential inhibition of the pacemakers and followers.

CARDIO-ACCELERATION

The two cardio-accelerator fibers may be stimulated separately or together. Their effects summate temporally and spatially, and generally increase the frequency and amplitude of the heartbeat (Fig. 29). Rhythmic beats are usually restored to irregular or inactive hearts, but in rare instances, accelerator activity may induce alternating weak and strong contractions in an initially regular beat (Maynard, 1953). In the *Homarus* ganglion, accelerator activity increases spike number and frequency during the burst as well as increasing the burst frequency (Fig. 30). Spike initiation during interburst

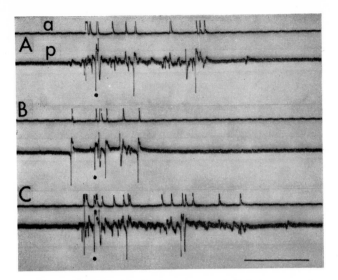

FIG. 28. Effect of GABA on burst pattern, applied to pacemakers only (*Homarus*). A. Normal burst. B. Burst after concentrated GABA solution applied to posterior pacemakers. C. Burst after washing. Upper trace, *a*, from anterior portion of ganglion (follower neurons); lower trace, *p*, from posterior portion of ganglion (pacemaker neurons). (·) marks same spike complex in successive records. Note great reduction in small cell activity and consequent loss of some follower activity. Large downward spikes in trace *p* probably originate in large cells which were not dosed with GABA. Time line, 0·1 sec.

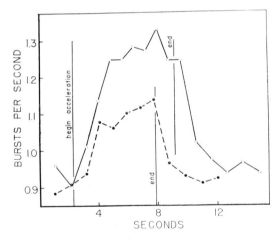

FIG. 29. Acceleration of ganglionic activity, time course and spatial summation (*Homarus*). Ordinate, spontaneous ganglion activity; abscissa, time in seconds. Stimulate accelerator fibers in dorsal nerve at 22/sec. (○), two accelerator fibers respond to each stimulus; (●), one accelerator fiber responds. Note slow growth of acceleration and slow decay to normal activity. Stimulation stopped at *end* (Maynard, 1954).

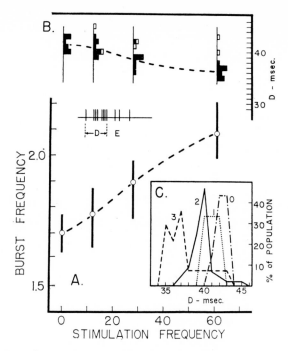

FIG. 30. Effect of accelerator stimulation frequency on parameters of ganglionic activity (*Homarus*). A. Ordinate, spontaneous ganglion activity; abscissa, accelerator stimulation frequency. Vertical lines represent the range, (○) represent means. Diagram of burst in upper left shows an initial portion lasting D msec and a subsequent E portion consisting of 0–3 impulses. Spikes in the preparation could not be assigned to individual neurons; several cells contribute to the impulse pattern shown. B. Ordinate. D. duration of initial portion of burst. A histogram is given at each stimulus frequency showing the distribution of D during acceleration. The curve is drawn through the mean values of D. Open rectangles represent D for the first two bursts of acceleration, presumably before summation is complete. Note that D decreases with acceleration. C. Relation between D and number of impulses in E. The curves are distribution curves for the D values preceding E's with 0, 1, 2, and 3 impulses. There is a positive correlation between shorter D and more impulses in E (Maynard, 1954).

intervals as found by Terzuolo and Bullock (1958) in *Panulirus* was never observed, however, and must be rare in normal *Homarus* ganglia.

Terzuolo and Bullock (1958) find that accelerator activity often produces depolarizing, facilitating, and summating e.p.s.p.'s in *Panulirus* follower cells. They consequently ascribe increases in activity during acceleration to the reduced membrane potentials of individual ganglion neurons. If there is a maximum degree of depolarization, this may account for the observation that marked acceleration in *Homarus* occurs only when the initial burst frequency is below 1·7–2·0 beats/sec and that there appears to be an *absolute* rather than a relative maximum for the response to accelerators

(Wiersma and Novitski, 1942; Maynard, 1953). It seems possible that the excitability increases during acceleration do not involve the same mechanisms as the excitability increases during post-inhibitory rebound, for the latter have not been correlated with depolarizing soma membrane potentials.

Since the time course of facilitation is similar for both inhibitor and accelerator postsynaptic potentials, and since they usually appear to have opposite effects on neuron discharge, one might assume symmetrical and opposite effects on the heart rate. As seen from Fig. 29, however, this is not so. Several seconds are required for maximum acceleratory effects, and adaptation, though presumably present (Wiersma and Novitski, 1942), generally has a longer time course than inhibitory adaptation. Post-acceleratory inhibition is normally absent (Fig. 29 and Maynard, 1953). When both inhibitor and accelerator are stimulated simultaneously in *Homarus*, the time course of inhibition is almost indistinguishable from that observed during stimulation of the inhibitor alone. Wiersma and Novitski (1942) find prolonged post-inhibitory excitation when both accelerator and inhibitor are stimulated together, again indicating the asymmetrical characteristics of inhibition and acceleration.

SUMMARY

Direct cardiac inhibition in the decapod Crustacea is mediated via a single pair of inhibitor neurons which terminate upon the neurons of the cardiac ganglion. As in many other systems, activity in the inhibitor elements results in postsynaptic membrane changes and inhibitory postsynaptic potentials in individual ganglion neurons. Depending upon the membrane potential of the post unit, such i.p.s.p. may be hyper- or de-polarizing. When hyperpolarizing, the facilitated i.p.s.p. leads to a suppression of spontaneous discharges and a reduction in postsynaptic responses. It has been suggested, however, that some ganglion neurons may be normally set at membrane potentials which lead to depolarizing and consequently exciting (?) i.p.s.p. Both facilitation and post-inhibitory rebound are prominent in the ganglion neurons.

The correlation between inhibition of the individual ganglion unit and inhibition of the heartbeat which is the result of the integrated output of the nine ganglion neurons is not always simple. Interactions between the ganglion elements are superimposed on the generalized decrease in excitability caused by inhibitor action, and as a result a single parameter such as heartbeat frequency, duration of beat, or amplitude of beat does not necessarily reflect the degree of inhibition of any individual unit. As an example, such phenomena as adaptation to inhibition or post-inhibitory rebound present in the individual ganglion neuron may be apparently absent in records of the integrated heartbeat.

13

REFERENCES

ALEXANDROWICZ, J. S. (1932) The innervation of the heart of the Crustacea—I. Decapoda. *Quart. J. Microscop. Sci.* **75** : 181–249.

ALEXANDROWICZ, J. S. (1953) Nervous organs in the pericardial cavity of the decapod Crustacea. *J. Marine Biol. Assoc. United Kingdom* **31** : 563–580.

ALEXANDROWICZ, J. S. and CARLISLE, D. B. (1953) Some experiments on the function of the pericardial organs in Crustacea. *J. Marine Biol. Assoc. United Kingdom* **32** : 175–192.

BULLOCK, T. H. (1958) Parameters of integrative action of the nervous system at the neuronal level. *Exptl. Cell Research* Suppl. 5. 323–337.

BULLOCK, T. H., COHEN, M. J. and MAYNARD, D. M. (1954) Integration and central synaptic properties of some receptors. *Federation Proc.* **13** : 20. (Abstract.)

BULLOCK, T. H. and TERZUOLO, C. A. (1957) Diverse forms of activity in the somata of spontaneous and integrating ganglion cells. *J. Physiol. (London)* **138** : 341–364.

HAGIWARA, S. and BULLOCK, T. H. (1957) Intracellular potentials in pacemaker and integrative neurons of the lobster cardiac ganglion. *J. Cellular Comp. Physiol.* **50**: 25–47.

HAGIWARA, S., WATANABE, A.and SAITO, N. (1959) Potential changes in syncytial neurons of lobster cardiac ganglion. *J. Neurophysiol.* **22** : 554–72.

HARA, J. (1952) On the hormones regulating the frequency of the heart beat in the shrimp, *Paratya compressa. Annotationes Zool. Japon.* **25** : 162–171.

ISQUIERDO, J. J. (1931) A study of the crustacean heart muscle. *Proc. Roy. Soc. (London)* B **109** : 229–250.

MAYNARD, D. M. (1953) Activity in a crustacean ganglion—I. Cardio-inhibition and acceleration in *Panulirus argus. Biol. Bull.* **104** : 156–170.

MAYNARD, D. M. (1954) *Direct Inhibition in the Lobster Cardiac Ganglion.* Ph.D. dissertation. University of California, Los Angeles.

MAYNARD, D. M. (1955) Activity in a crustacean ganglion—II. Pattern and interaction in burst formation. *Biol. Bull.* **109** : 420–436.

MAYNARD, D. M. (1958) Action of drugs on lobster cardiac ganglion. *Federation Proc.* **17** : 105. (Abstract.)

MAYNARD, D. M. (1960) Circulation and heart function. *The Physiology of Crustacea* (ed. by WATERMAN, T. H.) Vol. 1, Chap. 5, pp. 161–226. Academic Press, New York and London.

OTANI, T. and BULLOCK, T. H. (1959) Effects of presetting the membrane potential of the soma of spontaneous and integrating ganglion cells. *Physiol. Zool.* **32** : 104–114.

SMITH, R. I. (1947) The action of electrical stimulation and of certain drugs on cardiac nerves of the crab, *Cancer irroratus. Biol. Bull.* **93** : 72–88.

TAUC, L. (1958) Processus post-synaptiques d'excitation et d'inhibition dans le soma neuronique de l'aplysie et de l'escargot. *Arch. ital. biol.* **96** : 78–110.

TERZUOLO, C. A. and BULLOCK, T. H. (1958) Acceleration and inhibition in crustacean ganglion cells. *Arch. ital. biol.* **96** : 117–134.

WATANABE, A. (1958) The interaction of electrical activity among neurons of lobster cardiac ganglion. *Japan. J. Physiol.* **8** : 305–318.

WIERSMA, C. A. G. and NOVITSKI, E. (1942) The mechanism of the nervous regulation of the crayfish heart. *J. Exptl. Biol.* **19** : 255–265.

CHEMOPOTENTIALS IN GIANT NERVE CELLS
(APLYSIA FASCIATA)

N. CHALAZONITIS

Centre National de la Recherche Scientifique, Laboratoire d'Electrobiologie EPHE,
Faculté des Sciences, Université de Lyon, France

INTRODUCTION

IN THIS treatment, we mean by chemopotentials the changes in the electrical activity of nerve cells elicited by a variation in the concentration of CO_2, O_2, H^+ or OH^-. More generally, the term chemopotentials may refer to such electrical changes as are elicited by a variation in the concentration of any metabolite, provided that its action is reversible. Most often, the effects of anoxia or CO_2 on nerve fibres are inhibitory (Gerard, 1932; Lorente de Nó, 1947; Monnier, 1952; Laget and Legouix, 1951; Coraboeuf, 1951; Arvanitaki and Chalazonitis, 1954; Meves, 1955; Straub, 1956). The excitability of the ganglionic chain of some insects seems to be increased by CO_2 (Boistel et al., 1957).

Excitatory actions are well known on some mammalian nerve centres such as the respiratory centre, the carotid body, the aorta paraganglia (Heymans, 1953; von Euler et al., 1939; von Euler and Söderberg, 1952; Gernandt, 1946; Witzleb and Bartels, 1956; Zotterman, 1953), and in some other centres less specialized for CO_2 reception (Bremer and Thomas, 1936; Sugar and Gerard, 1938; Dell and Bonvallet, 1956; Van Harreveld, 1946; Lloyd, 1952–1953; Kolmodin and Skoglund, 1959; Chalazonitis and Sugaya, 1958a, b; Chalazonitis, 1959).

In the present study the effects of anoxia and CO_2 enrichment in Aplysia nerve cells will be discussed. The spontaneous activity of such cells may last many hours and is easily monitored by microelectrodes. The spontaneous activity of invertebrate nerve cells has been studied extensively by a number of authors (Arvanitaki and Chalazonitis, 1955; Bullock, 1958; Bullock and Terzuolo, 1957; Tauc, 1960; among others).

Preliminary studies on the effects of anoxia and CO_2 on spontaneous activity in Aplysia nerve cells have already been published (Chalazonitis and Sugaya, 1958a, b). In this paper the excitatory actions of anoxia and CO_2 will be only briefly mentioned. More space will be devoted to pointing out some of the inhibitory effects, particularly in relation to the three types of electrical activity recognized among the different identifiable cells of Aplysia

179

(Arvanitaki and Chalazonitis, 1957, 1958). (For recent information on inhibition mechanisms relating to nerve cells see Eccles, 1957; Arvanitaki and Chalazonitis, 1957; Bullock, 1958; Fessard, 1959; Grundfest, 1959; Kuffler, 1959.)

1. THE FUNCTIONALLY DIFFERENTIATED NEURONS

Half a dozen of the giant nerve cells of the visceral ganglion of *Aplysia fasciata* are easily identifiable according to their size and their location relative to the nerve trunks (see Fig. 1). Such cells may be divided into three main types, depending upon the patterns of their spontaneous, or synaptically induced electrical activity (Arvanitaki and Chalazonitis, 1958; Chalazonitis, 1959; Tauc, 1960). While the ganglion is bathed in sea water saturated with oxygen the autoactivity observed is long lasting (more than 2 hr) and is observed in 10% of the nerve cells examined.

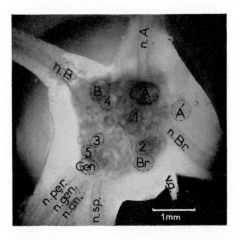

FIG. 1. Dorsal face of *Aplysia fasciata* visceral ganglion.

A, Br, B, Gen, and *A'*, identifiable giant somata. 1, 2, 3, 4, 5, medium-sized somata (100–250 μ diameter) identifiable owing to their vicinities with the former. *n.A.*, pleurobranchial nerve; *n.Br.*, branchial nerve; *n.sp.*, spermathecal nerve; *n.an.*, anal nerve; *n.gen.*, genital nerve; *n.per.*, pericardial nerve; *n.B.*, pleurogenital nerve; *v.g.* ganglionic vessel.

The three types of activity are as follows: The first type is seen in the *A* cell (see Fig. 2). The spikes are of constant, relatively low frequency (0·5–1/sec at 20°C).

The second type is seen in the *Br* cell (see Fig. 2). It is characterized by trains of spikes or slow waves. The duration of the trains is several seconds. The mean spike frequency on each wave is about 4/sec.

The third type is seen in *B* or *Gen* and sometimes in *p.c.r.* cells. It is charac-

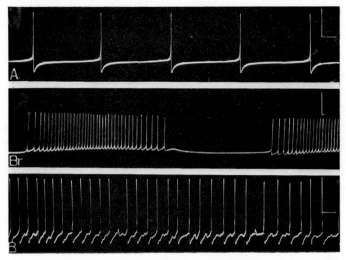

FIG. 2. The autoactivity of the three types of functionally differentiated nerve cells.

A, Autoactivity of the *A* soma. The frequency is relatively low (0·5–1/sec) in the standard experimental conditions (20°C, O_2, sea water). It is fairly constant in the absence of synaptic or antidromic stimulation.

The amplitude of the *A* soma spike is the highest (peak to peak, up to 100 mV) and its duration among the shortest (about 6–7 msec).

Br, Autoactivity of the *Br* soma. Autoactivity by trains of spikes held on slow waves, the period of which is of the order of 25 sec. The duration of each slow wave is here about 10 sec. The mean spike frequency on each wave is about 4/sec.

B or *Gen*, Arhythmic autoactivity. In the absence of any applied stimulus, i.p.s.p.'s are periodically appearing in the spontaneously firing *B* or *Gen* cells, so giving rise to characteristic arhythmias.

Scales for all recordings: 50 mV, 250 msec.

terized by spontaneous arhythmic activity, owing to the intervening hyperpolarizing potentials (see Fig. 2).

Such functionally differentiated cells display a different behaviour under the effect of metabolites. In the present article we are concerned only with the changes resulting from anoxia and injection of exogenous CO_2.

2. EXCITATION-INHIBITION DURING ANOXIA

The first effect is the establishment of an anoxic depolarization. The mean anoxic depolarization for the *Br* and *A* cells is about 1 mV/min at 20°C. The arhythmic cells show lower rates of depolarization. A mean value for the most characteristic among them is not yet established.

If the cells are initially inactive, anoxic depolarization results in firing. In cells that are initially autoactive, the anoxic depolarization leads to cessation of autoactivity. This inhibition appears to be the result of excessive depolarization.*

The latencies required for anoxic inhibition of these cells are given in Table 1.

TABLE 1

	Anoxic inhibition			Reversibility by O_2		
Neuron	Latency: mean values (min)	Number of experiments	Standard deviation	Latency: mean values (min)	Number of experiments	Standard deviation
Br	6	9	2·3	3	6	2
A	13	9	8·5	6·6	5	1·4
Arhythmic cells (*Gen*, *B*, etc.)	45	10				

A careful analysis of the inhibition by anoxia of the *Br* cell shows that:

(a) The presence of oxygen is required for the periodical repolarization of the cell (positive phase of the slow wave, Fig. 2).

(b) Generally a 2-min anoxia (under nitrogen) at 20°C is sufficient to abolish the activity by "trains" because the positive phase of the slow wave is abolished; the resulting activity becomes a steady spike discharge. If we regard the positive phase of the slow wave as a normal periodical inhibition, such primary anoxic effect may be considered as an "inhibition of an inhibition". Under such conditions the *Br* cell behaves as an *A* cell, namely, it fires at a constant, regular frequency.

(c) Finally, after four more minutes of anoxia the activity of the *Br* cell degenerates into damped oscillations and the cell stops firing.

The evolution of the *A* cell activity under anoxia is different. As anoxic depolarization begins, the frequency of the *A* cell first increases, and then, after a total depolarization from 10 to 15 mV, the cell stops firing.

The slow effect of anoxia on the activity of arhythmic cells (*B* or *Gen* or sometimes *p.c.r.*) is not yet clearly understood. These cells are less sensitive to anoxia than are the cells discussed above, and this is probably due to their ceaseless synaptic repolarization by spontaneous inhibitory (hyperpolarizing) neurons.

A possible interpretation of the anoxic inhibitory effects on the soma, observable after the initial excitatory effects, is that the anoxia, at least in some cells, causes an excessive depolarization.

* See also Eyzaguirre and Kuffler (1955) and Granit and Phillips (1956) relating inhibitory effects by excessive depolarization.

The differential sensitivity of the nerve cells under anoxia was also found by Kolmodin and Skoglund in mammalian neurons, the interneurons of the cord being more resistant than the motoneurons. The same authors also found a depolarization of about 5 to 10 mV during 30-sec asphyxia. So, if we assume that about 10 mV/min is an anoxic mean depolarization rate for the mammalian neuron (ten times more than for *Aplysia*'s somata), a parallelism may exist between respiratory rate and depolarization rate: The Q_{0_2} for *Aplysia*'s somata is 170 μl/g per hr, whereas for mammalian nerve cells it is ten times greater (Chalazonitis, 1959; Chalazonitis and Otsuka, 1956).

It would also follow that in systems such as the peripheral nerve system, which has an extremely low respiratory rate, the effects of anoxia upon the resting potential will be comparably slower. This is well known to be the case.

3. BIOCHEMICAL EVENTS DURING ANOXIA

Before discussing this question we shall give some data on the general cyto-chemical organization of these cells.

(a) *Data on the Cytochemical Organization of the Cell*

First, each one of the giant somata has its own capillary net, directly expanded on its surface (Plate I, Figs. 3 and 7; Plate II, Fig. 11). It was found in a series of experiments in which ganglia were injected with Janus green B, that *Br* and *A* are among the cells with the densest vascular nets.

Generally the cytoplasm surrounding the nucleus is more basophilic (Plate I, Figs. 5, 9, 10; Plate II, Fig. 12). Evidence has been presented elsewhere for ascertaining that it is in this region that the maximal dehydrogenase and decarboxylase activities of the cell are to be found (Chalazonitis, 1959).

At the periphery of the highly basophilic cytoplasm one observes a thick, regularly pigmented layer (Plate I, Figs. 5, 9, 10; Plate II, Figs. 13, 14). In the majority of the cells the higher density of this layer is in the axon hillock area of the cell (Plate I, Fig. 9; Plate II, Fig. 13). However, the axon itself is weakly pigmented (Plate II, Fig. 13).

In many cases there is irregular distribution of pigment, some areas having more pigment than others (Plate II, Fig. 14). The pigment is located in small granules, "grains" or lipochondria (Chalazonitis and Arvanitaki, 1956; Young, 1956) (Plate II, Figs. 15, 16).

Lipochondria whose diameter is between 0·8–0·1 μ are highly osmiophilic (Fig. 19) and their cortex is darker than their interior (see Chalazonitis and Lenoir, 1959).

The chemical identification of lipochondria pigments is given elsewhere (Chalazonitis and Arvanitaki, 1956). Here the existence of two pigments, haemoprotein (haemoglobin-like) and carotenoid, is concluded from the data of Table 2.

PLATE I

FIG. 3. View of the surface of an unsectioned visceral ganglion of *Aplysia fasciata*. The naturally orange pigmented nerve cells are distinguishable. Between them, dark coloured vessels and capillaries are also visible owing to the injection of colloidal Janus green through the dorsal artery. The largest cell visible in this field is the *Br* cell at the upper left side. A capillary cluster is directly in contact with the cell. × 60.

FIG. 4. Thick section (100 μ) through the dorsal side of a fixed, frozen visceral ganglion, stained with methylene blue. The connective tissue is stained blue-mauve; the nerve cells, green-blue. Some giant nerve cells are easily identifiable by their situation relative to the nerve trunks. The latter are not visible on this section. The giant upper cell is a *Br* cell. The giant *A* cell is located at the left, centre. × 11.

FIG. 5. Frozen, formalin-fixed section through the visceral ganglion stained with methylene blue. The giant cell in the centre is the *A* cell. The dark blue cytoplasm around the nucleus is the highly basophilic perinuclear cytoplasm. It is surrounded by a peripheral, less basophilic cytoplasm. Quite at the periphery lies a thin dark ring of brownish pigment. The connective tissue is metachromatically stained mauve. The giant *A* cell is always surrounded by numerous smaller "satellite" nerve cells. × 32.

FIG. 6. Section through the *A* soma, formalin fixed, frozen, thionin stained. This preparation was carried out in order to determine the exact position of the micro-electrode tip after having picked up the electrical activity of the cell. One observes the channel made by the tip of the introduced microelectrode. Even in these conditions the cell exhibited autoactivity for more than two hours. Here the nerves are stained brownish, the glial tissue is metachromatically stained red. × 30.

FIG. 7. Vascular net on the *A* cell. Unsectioned preparation injected with a colloidal solution of Janus green. Crossed vessels on the surface of the *A* soma. × 60.

FIG. 8. Section through another *A* soma, prepared as above, but stained with methylene blue. The hole into the nucleus was opened by the tip of the micro-electrode. This soma had been autoactive for more than 5 hr. A blue ribbon-like structure touching the inferior edge of the brownish pigment layer of the *A* soma corresponds to the initial segment of another soma, contracting an axosomatic synapse with the *A* soma. × 40.

FIG. 9. Section of the *Br* soma, prepared as above. Highly basophilic perinuclear cytoplasm surrounded by a peripheral, less basophilic cytoplasm. Between the two lies a very thin dark layer of brownish pigment. The density of this pigment becomes very high at the left side of the cell in the axon hillock area. The connective tissue is metachromatically stained blue-mauve. × 40.

FIG. 10. Another section of the *Br* soma. Formalin–sea water fixed preparation, frozen, sectioned, methylene blue-stained and photographed under higher magnification. Only a quarter of the section is visible. At the upper right side can be seen a portion of the nucleus surrounded by the highly basophilic perinuclear cytoplasm. Towards the periphery lie dark strands of brownish pigment (these are naturally orange (see Fig. 3) but here altered by the fixation procedure) surrounded at the periphery by some less basophilic cytoplasm. × 300.

PLATE I

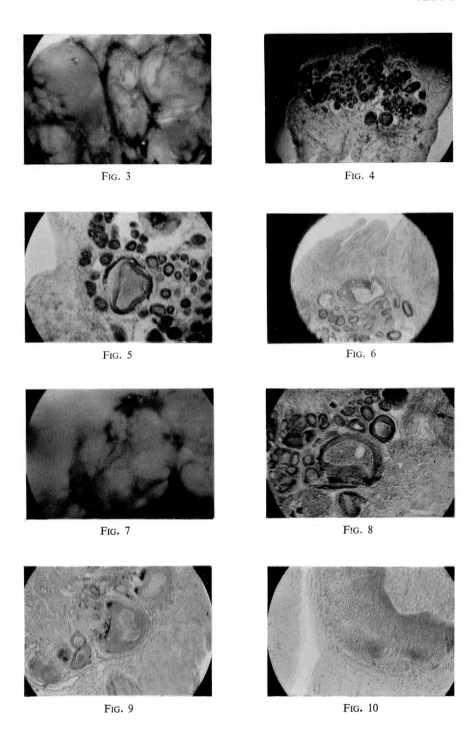

FIG. 3

FIG. 4

FIG. 5

FIG. 6

FIG. 7

FIG. 8

FIG. 9

FIG. 10

PLATE II

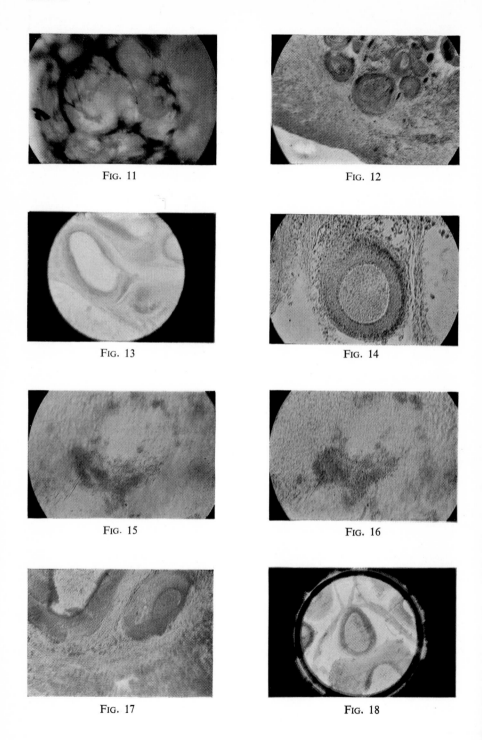

FIG. 11

FIG. 12

FIG. 13

FIG. 14

FIG. 15

FIG. 16

FIG. 17

FIG. 18

PLATE II

FIG. 11. Vascular cluster on the *Gen* (arhythmic) soma. Unsectioned preparation injected with a colloidal solution of Janus green. Thick dark-stained vessel surrounding the soma and thin cluster of capillaries on the apex of the soma. ×60.

FIG. 12. Section through a fixed, frozen, neutral red-stained preparation showing a giant cell, presumably the *B* soma. One sees a dark blue vessel here surrounding the apex of the soma. The maximum of basophilia is shown in the cytoplasm around the nucleus. ×60.

FIG. 13. Section through a fixed, frozen, thionin-stained medium-sized soma. This section shows the axon hillock area with the highest density of orange pigment and the very low basophilia of the emerging axon. ×200.

FIG. 14. Section through another medium-sized cell prepared as above but stained with methylene blue. One observes the pigmented layer of the periphery more developed at the right side. ×280.

FIG. 15. Some pigmented granules or lipochondria distinguishable in the superficial cytoplasm of a fresh nerve cell. These granules are unstained, their natural orange pigment is due to the presence of two chromoproteids; a haemoglobin-like pigment or haemoprotein and a carotenoid. Aggregates of visible granules are in the centre of the micrograph. Beneath, one sees the nucleus of the cell. ×280.

FIG. 16. The same lipochondria after the effect of hypotonic saline (diluted sea water). They swelled and started to coalesce. Such "haemolytic"-like effects are observable also during the action of ether, chloroform or ethanol vapours. ×280.

FIG. 17. Section through two medium-sized nerve cells, fixed, frozen-sectioned and stained with methylene blue. Between the two somata an axonic initial segment of a large diameter is synaptically connected at least to the larger one, for a relatively long distance. At their lower edge both cells are surrounded by a sectioned capillary containing blood cells. ×280.

FIG. 18. Section through a giant soma, after formalin fixation, paraffin inclusion and methylene blue staining. The close contact between a proximal satellite cell (in the centre) and the giant soma, probably belongs to a somatic-synapse. The absence of lipochondrial pigment is due to the alcohol–xylene treatment of the paraffin sections. ×200.

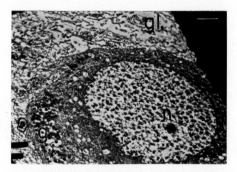

FIG. 19. Electron micrography of *Aplysia*'s soma.

Among the osmiophilic particles such as mitochrondria, endoplasmic reticulum, the grains (*g*)—or "lipochondria", or "lipoid globules"—of from 0·1 to 0·8 μ diameter are the most numerous and by far the most osmiophilic. Preliminary observations on the ultrastructure of these grains have been described elsewhere (Chalazonitis and Lenoir, 1959). The larger ones are aggregated at the periphery of the soma forming groups of variable density, the highest being observable in the axon hillock area. Very often in the other somatic areas the greater density of the lipochondria coincides with the greater thickness of the somatoplasm. The perinuclear cytoplasm is essentially formed of fine osmiophilic granules which correspond to the Nissl substance in this neuron. The same cytoplasm region shows digitations and folds sometimes penetrating deeply into the nucleus and forming bridges there. The thickness of the cytoplasm is not uniform all around the profile of the nuclear membrane, the greater thickness observed just opposite to the most numerous digitations of the perinuclear region. Scale: 5 μ.

TABLE 2. THE PIGMENTS PRESENT IN *Aplysia fasciata* OR *depilans*
NERVE CELLS

Conditions		Absorption bands (mμ)	Pigment
in situ *in vivo*	O₂	579, 542, 490, 463, 418	Haemoglobin-like haemoprotein
	N₂	573–544, 490, 463, 425	
water extract, O₂		579, 542 418	
petroleum ether		480, 450, 425	Carotene-protein
toluene extract		485, 453, 428, 404	
CS₂ extract		510, 478	

It must be emphasized that the lipochondrial haemoprotein stores the oxygen of the soma. A rough estimation gives a figure of 3×10^{-7} M of haemoprotein/g wet neuron, or roughly ten times more per gramme of wet lipochondria.

(b) *Anaerobic Transitions in the Respiratory Catalysts of the Soma*

After this brief description of some results concerning the cytochemical organization of these nerve cells, we return to the question: what are the biochemical events during the latency required for the anoxic inhibition of the electrical activity of the cell?

Let us consider the 6-min latency of the more sensitive cell, the *Br* soma. During the first 2 min of anoxia all the oxygen content in the ganglion is swept out by the nitrogen. This deoxygenation time of the intrasomatic oxyhaemoprotein was determined kinespectrographically by measuring the density of spectrograms as a function of time (Chalazonitis and Arvanitaki, 1956).

During this first phase of anoxia, the *Br* membrane depolarizes by about 2 mV, and, as already seen, the slow wave activity becomes continuous. It is thus reasonable to attribute some regulatory function to the presence of oxygen in the membrane's structure; that is to say, the presence of oxygen is required for repolarization.

After the exhaustion of the oxygen one must consider a second phase, at least equal in duration to the former 2-min phase, during which the DPN in the soma is being reduced anaerobically. The delayed reduction of the DPN is evident from some *in vivo* and *in situ* kinespectrographic experiments showing the delayed reduction of the cytochromes following the complete deoxygenation of the oxyhaemoglobin (Arvanitaki and Chalazonitis, 1952). In view of some data obtained by Chance and co-workers from different cells by simultaneous polarographic and spectrophotometric measurements (Chance, 1954), the delayed reduction time of the DPN *in vivo* could be considered approximately equal to that required for the complete exhaustion of the oxygen. So, during this second phase of anoxia, a further production of CO_2 by the DPN reduction remains possible, although the formation of lactic acid starts simultaneously.

Therefore all oscillographic events described during this second phase (depolarization and changes in the frequency relating to the firing level of each cell) are simultaneous with the total DPN reduction, to the final CO_2 formation and to the incipient lactic acid production.

As the CO_2 is formed and then swept out by the nitrogen, the accumulation of lactic acid on the membrane may be responsible for further depolarization. In fact, extracellular application of lactic acid and of some other weak acids such as succinic and citric acids on *Aplysia*'s somata was found to cause depolarizations which are readily reversible (unpublished).

Finally, the last 2-min anoxic phase in the *Br* cell preceding its inhibition and all further anoxic events in the other cells are *a fortiori* attributable to the further accumulation of products of the anaerobic glycolysis on the membrane.

If we consider now the depolarization events during asphyxia already described by many authors (Kolmodin and Skoglund, 1959; Lloyd, 1952–1953; Van Harreveld, 1946), the CO_2 accumulation on the membrane is highly probable, not only during the second phase,* but even after the reduction of the DPN, because of the proton accumulation in the cytoplasm owing to the anaerobic glycolysis products.

4. EXCITATION-INHIBITION BY INJECTION OF CO_2

The CO_2 action on such differentiated cells seems to be pertinent to this general problem. There is first the common future: CO_2 depolarizes, with a negligible delay, all types of the examined nerve cells. A depolarization of 5 mV is sufficient to elicit the autoactivity of the initially resting cells, or

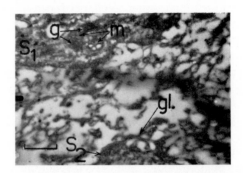

FIG. 20. Electron micrograph of glial junctions with the somatic membrane.
Independently of the well known "long-range" intimate connections between glial cell and somatic membrane, one often observes a filamentous type of glial terminals on the somatic membrane. These glial terminals—about 50 mμ in diameter—are thus connected with the somatic membrane directly or sometimes through small bulges of about 100 mμ of diameter (see (gl) on the membrane of a small somatic portion (S_2)). As the connective tissue of the visceral ganglion normally exhibits contractility, a possible stretch of the non-synaptic portions of the membrane by these glial filaments has to be considered as a probable physiological stimulus for the somata. In the portion S_1 of the upper soma, lipochondria (g) are observable. They are in intimate contact with small mitochondria (m). Nevertheless the majority of lipochondria are not necessarily in contact with mitochondria. Particularly the smaller lipochondria lying deeply in the cytoplasm near the nucleus are held by filamentous processes to the walls of small vacuoles.

---

* As was previously noted, even after the exhaustion of the oxygen DPN is available for some time. This means that during this phase a further production of CO_2 remains possible by the simultaneous dehydrogenation–decarboxylation of the following: 6-phosphogluconate, pyruvate, α-ketoglutarate, D-isocitrate (see Chalazonitis, 1959). During the same phase the deamination of glutamic acid may give α-ketoglutaric acid, its decarboxylation may give GABA, all those products such as CO_2, ammonia, acids, GABA (Curtis et al., 1960; Florey and Florey, 1958; Florey and McLennan, 1955; Hayashi, 1959) being highly important regulators of membrane excitability.

to increase the frequency of the initially autoactive neurons. Further changes in the membrane potential and frequency of firing are characteristic of each cellular type:

(a) A *Cell*

The frequency of firing of the *A* cell increases when this cell is first depolarized by 5–10 mV. When the extent of depolarization exceeds 10–20 mV, the frequency decreases (see Fig. 21).

(b) Br *Cell*

The frequency of the slow waves of the *Br* soma increases when this is first depolarized by about 20 mV. With further depolarization, the slow waves tend to disappear, the spiking becomes continuous and finally the spikes are reduced to damped oscillations (Figs. 21 and 22).

(c) *The Arhythmic Somata*

The arhythmic *B* soma shows an increased frequency when depolarized by no more than about 20 mV.

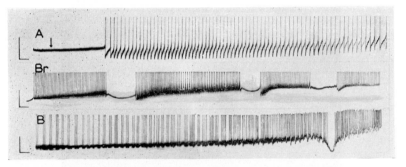

FIG. 21. Effect of carbon dioxide on the activity of the three typical giant somata functionally differentiated. In all cases the carbon dioxide is admitted at the beginning of the recordings (arrow).

A, Giant soma *A*, inactive. The carbon dioxide slightly depolarizes the membrane and initiates the activity. The frequency reaches a maximum 20 sec after the admission of CO_2 and later decreases. Finally the activity ceased a few seconds after the end of the recording (65 sec after the admission of the CO_2).

Br, Giant soma *Br*, initially autoactive in standard conditions (20°C, 100% O_2, sea water), by repetitive trains of spikes, lasting about 10 sec. After the admission of CO_2 the depolarization starts. At this, the frequency of the spike trains increases. Finally, 30 sec after the end of this recording, the activity of the *Br* cell degenerates to damped oscillations and the cell stops firing (see Fig. 22).

B, Soma *B*; its activity is normally arhythmic: the spiking is interrupted by positive potentials. It is strongly depolarized by CO_2 and its frequency is increasing. At the end of the recording one observes a first positive long lasting wave during which all spike emission is inhibited. Two minutes later, after considerable depolarization (almost 60 mV) the activity of the *B* soma completely ceases.

Scales for all recordings: 50 mV, 1 sec.

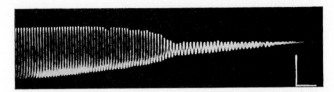

FIG. 22. Damped oscillations ending the *Br* soma activity under the effect of CO_2. After a depolarization higher than 30 mV, the slow repolarizing phases of the *Br* soma are abolished and the activity becomes continuous. In this recording one sees the end of the last spike train. The spike amplitude·decreases and the activity stops in damped oscillations. Scales: 50 mV, 1 sec.

A striking effect is commonly seen in this type of cell. The spiking is periodically interrupted by silent intervals resulting from slow (1–2 sec) hyperpolarizing waves, from 30 to 40 mV in amplitude. These are to be seen as reactive waves elicited by the initial CO_2 depolarization (Fig. 21 and Fig. 23), and facilitated by the summation of i.p.s.p., probably arising from the CO_2-

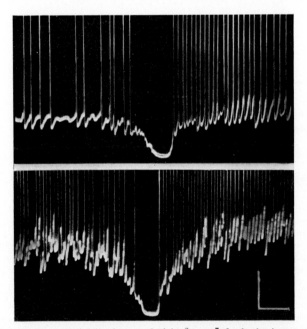

FIG. 23. The long lasting hyperpolarizing waves of arhythmic somata.

When the arhythmic *B* soma is CO_2 depolarized by no more than about 20–30 mV, a hyperpolarizing wave occurs with an amplitude of 30–40 mV and a duration of 1–2 sec. During its falling phase, the activity is completely inhibited and conversely initiated and accelerated during its rising phase. Here also, the frequency is related to the rate of change of the membrane potential rather than to the membrane potential itself. Scales: 25 mV, 1 sec.

stimulated firing of inhibitory interneurons. In this case, of course, if the CO_2 depolarization is permitted to proceed, further spiking will be stopped.

The slopes and the duration of the slow hyperpolarizing waves suggest that they may correspond to high changes in the membrane's conductances, probably of endogenous origin.

5. CHEMICAL CHANGES DURING CO_2 INJECTION

Under the experimental conditions adopted, the mean time required for the appearance of the maximum excitatory effect by CO_2 (maximal frequency) was about 40 sec. Since anoxia does not produce such effects within 40 sec, it seems that the effects of CO_2 may be brought about by direct action upon the membrane. To what extent is the effect of CO_2 attributable to protons produced by the hydrolysis of carbonic acid?

We observed that in the connective tissue surrounding the A cell (in other words, in the tissue close to the A cell membrane), a 0·5 pH unit lowering occurs after 40 sec exposure to CO_2. (Techniques for intracellular pH measurements in nerve cells are given in the literature (Arvanitaki and Chalazonitis, 1954; Caldwell, 1958; Spyropoulos, 1960).) However, it is impossible to attribute the entire action to H^+ ions, because NH_3 vapours, producing OH^- ions in the cell, depolarize and act similarly to CO_2. Thus, the contribution of this amount of H^+ produced by CO_2 to the depolarization is not yet known.* The change in concentration of the CO_2 required for unit depolarization in the *Aplysia*'s cells also remains unknown. But admitting, on the basis of the results of Kolmodin and Skoglund, that 10 mV depolarization in the motoneurons is due to 1 min accumulation of CO_2 after the clamping of the vessel, corresponding to a respiratory rate of 1800 μl/g (wet) per hr (Chalazonitis and Otsuka, 1956) we estimated the extra CO_2 accumulated per gramme (wet) of cells, during 6 sec clamping, to be 10^{-7} M. This amount corresponds to a depolarization of 1 mV.

DISCUSSION AND CONCLUSIONS

Although the relation of O_2 and CO_2 concentration changes to the membrane potential changes and the associated electrical activity could not be analysed in a rigorous quantitative manner, it is already possible to consider the ratio $[O_2]/[CO_2]$ as highly important in determining the excitability and the resting potential of the somatic membrane. By increasing this ratio the resting potential tends to increase, and vice versa.

* Some pH-effect data are already available from Spyropoulos's (1960) work in the case of the squid giant fibre: the resting potential may decrease by about 5 mV for a $-\Delta$pH of 2 units. If we admit that it is possible to get a depolarization of 1 mV with a pH lowering of 0·5 unit, such an effect would be of high importance in the case of spontaneous active cells such as *Aplysia* neurons or the chemoreceptors of higher animals.

In the same way that one often relates the instantaneous value of the resting potential to the excitability of the membrane, one can relate the latter to the instantaneous values of the ratio $[O_2]/[CO_2]$.

Among the three functional types described, namely, the *A* soma of regular frequency, the *Br* soma autoactive on slow waves, and the arhythmic somata, let us first consider the *A* soma because of its relative simplicity.

The behaviour of the *A* cell is easily predictable if we consider the diagram relating its instantaneous frequency vs. its membrane potential (see Fig. 24).

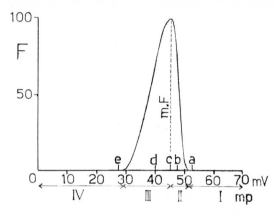

FIG. 24. Curve relating the instantaneous frequency (F) to the membrane potential (*mp*), for an ideal *A* type cell. I, II, III, IV, are line segments of the abscissa into which the frequency of the electrical activity may receive predictable values (see the discussion). *a, b, c, d, e*, possible initial values of the somatic resting potential from which any further shift issued from any change of the ratio $[O_2]/[CO_2]$, may determine a predictable evolution to the instantaneous frequency of the cell (see discussion).

The axis representing the possible values of the membrane potential can be divided into four segments, each segment being related to a distinct electrical activity. Segment I corresponds to zero frequency, being the zone of highest polarization. Segments II and III correspond to the firing zones of the cell. The point dividing these two segments corresponds to the maximum frequency (m.F.). Segment IV corresponds to the maximum depolarization of the cell. After the insertion of a microelectrode into the cell the value of its membrane potential may be represented by the points *a* or *b* if the cell is in good physiological condition.

Thus, if the initial point is situated at *a* the decrease of the ratio $[O_2]/[CO_2]$ will bring it to *b* and perhaps even further from *b* to *c*, *c* being the point corresponding to the maximum firing frequency. Such an effect is an excitatory one. If the ratio $[O_2]/[CO_2]$ is small enough to decrease the membrane potential past *c* to *d* or even to *e*, then this effect is an inhibition through excessive depolarization.

Conversely, the increase of the ratio $[O_2]/[CO_2]$ will cause a hyperpolarization and if initially the cell was at c or b, its spike frequency will tend to decrease (inhibitory effect). But, if the cell's membrane potential is at e or d the spike frequency will increase (excitatory effect on initially depolarized cells).

Prediction of the effects of the $[O_2]/[CO_2]$ ratio changes on the activity of the B cell is more difficult than the prediction of these effects on the A cell: no i.p.s.p.'s are impinging on the latter during CO_2 action. However, the firing of the B cell is periodically inhibited, obviously by the firing of a second cell, inhibitory, which controls its activity. So the behaviour of the B type cell depends not only on the initial level and further displacement of its membrane potential into the firing zone, but also on that of the monitoring inhibitory interneuron being itself under the effect of the $[O_2]/[CO_2]$ changes.

As regards the behaviour of the Br cell, more work is necessary in order to relate it to the $[O_2]/[CO_2]$ ratio changes, because the depolarization required for the transformation of the slow waves into a continuous activity is higher when CO_2 is used than when anoxia is used.

Let us now examine the factors which might control the ratio $[O_2]/[CO_2]$ in the somatic membrane. These factors may be exogenous or endogenous. Exogenous factors are, for instance, the composition of the blood (concentrations of O_2 and CO_2) and the diameter, at a given instant of the capillaries surrounding the soma. Endogenous factors are for instance, the densely accumulated mitochondria near the synaptic portions of the somatic membrane. Arvanitaki and Chalazonitis (1949, p. 549) and more recently Palay (1958), emphasized the possible chemical control of mitochondrial products on the synaptic membrane.* Among such products, CO_2 and other small metabolites, because of their high diffusibility and because of the relative small concentration changes required for a significant shift of the membrane potential, are the first to be considered.

As a general conclusion it is certain that chemosensitivity, recognized in higher animals as a specific property of certain nerve cells (chemoreceptors) is also a general property of any soma. Furthermore, results to be published concerning the higher chemosensitivity of the soma relative to the axon hillock area and to its own axon will give further support to this conclusion.

REFERENCES

ARVANITAKI, A. and CHALAZONITIS, N. (1949) Prototypes d'interactions neuroniques et transmissions synaptiques. Données bioélectriques de préparations cellulaires. *Arch. sci. physiol.* **3** : 547–566.

ARVANITAKI, A. and CHALAZONITIS, N. (1952) Répartition de quelques catalyseurs respiratoires dans l'espace cellulaire des neurones géants (*Aplysia* et *Torpedo*). *Arch sci physiol.* **6** : 213–232.

* DeRobertis (1958) and co-workers have extensively studied the presence of the synaptic vesicles and their changes. Unfortunately the biochemical function of these particles is not yet investigated. Relative to some other possible cytochemical specificities on synaptic terminals, see also Couteaux (1958).

14

ARVANITAKI, A. and CHALAZONITIS, N. (1954) Diffusibilité de l'anhydride carbonique dans l'axone géant, ses effets sur les vitesses de l'activité bioélectrique. *Compt. rend. soc. biol.* **148** : 952–954.

ARVANITAKI, A. and CHALAZONITIS, N. (1955) Potentiels d'activité du soma neuronique géant (*Aplysia*). *Arch. sci. physiol.* **9** : 115–144.

ARVANITAKI, A. and CHALAZONITIS, N. (1957) Réfractivitées introduites par les potentiels positifs du soma neuronique, en activité autoentretenue. *Compt. rend.* **245** : 445–447.

ARVANITAKI, A. and CHALAZONITIS, N. (1958) Configurations modales de l'activité propres à différents neurones d'un même centre. *J. Physiol.* (*Paris*) **50** : 122–125.

BOISTEL, J., CORABOEUF, E. and GUERIN, J. (1957) Le nerf periphérique d'insecte, ses réactions vis à vis du gaz carbonique selon le type des fibres nerveuses. *J. Physiol.* (*Paris*) **49** : 53–56.

BREMER, F. and THOMAS, J. (1936) Action de l'anoxémie, de l'lypercapnie et de l'acapnie sur l'activité électrique du cortex cérébral. *Compt. rend. soc. biol.* **123** : 1256–1258.

BULLOCK, T. H. (1958) Parameters of integrative action of the nervous system at the neuronal level. *Exptl. Cell Research* Suppl. **5** : 323–337.

BULLOCK, T. H. and TERZUOLO, C. A. (1957) Diverse forms of activity in the somata of spontaneous and integrating ganglion cells. *J. Physiol.* (*London*) **138** : 341–364.

CALDWELL, P. C. (1958) Studies on the internal pH of large muscle and nerve fibres. *J. Physiol.* (*London*) **142** : 22–62.

CHALAZONITIS, N. (1959) Chémopotentiels des neurones géants fonctionnellement différenciés. *Arch. sci. physiol.* **13** : 41–78.

CHALAZONITIS, N. and ARVANITAKI, A. (1956) Chromoprotéides et succinoxydase dans divers grains isolables du protoplasme neuronique. *Arch. Sci. physiol.* **10** : 291–319.

CHALAZONITIS, N. and LENOIR, J. (1959) Ultrastructure et organisation du neurone d'*Aplysia*. *Bull. inst. océanog.* No. 1144.

CHALAZONITIS, N. and OTSUKA, M. (1956) Activité succinoxydasique d'éléments sub-cellulaires du cortex cérébral du Boeuf. *Compt. rend.* **243** : 980–982.

CHALAZONITIS, N. and SUGAYA, E. (1958a) Effets anoxiques sur l'autoactivité électrique des neurones géants d'*Aplysia*. *Compt. rend.* **247** : 1495–1497.

CHALAZONITIS, N. and SUGAYA, E. (1958b) Stimulation-Inhibition des neurones géants identifiables d'*Aplysia* par l'anhydride carbonique. *Compt. rend.* **247** : 1657–1659.

CHANCE, B. (1953–4) Enzymes in action in living cells: The steady state of reduced pyridine nucleotides. *The Harvey Lectures* Series 49 : 145–175.

CORABOEUF, E. (1951) L'action particulière du CO_2 sur le nerf myélinisé et son indépendance à l'égard du pH. *Compt. rend. soc. biol.* **145** : 544–547.

COUTEAUX, R. (1958) Morphological and cytochemical observations on the post-synaptic membrane at motor end-plates and ganglionic synapses. *Exptl. Cell Research*, Suppl. **5** : 294–322.

CURTIS, D. R., PHILLIS, J. W. and WATKINS, J. C. (1960) The chemical excitation of spinal neurones by certain acidic aminoacids. *J. Physiol.* (*London*) **150** : 656–682.

DELL, P. and BONVALLET, M. (1956) Mise en jeu des effets de l'activité réticulaire par le milieu extérieur et le milieu intérieur. *XX Internat. Physiol. Congress Rapports* pp. 286–306.

DE ROBERTIS, E. (1958) Submicroscopic morphology and function of the synapse. *Exptl. Cell Research* Suppl. **5** : 347–369.

ECCLES, J. C. (1957) *The Physiology of Nerve Cells*. Johns Hopkins Press, Baltimore.

VON EULER, U. S., LILJENSTRAND, G. and ZOTTERMAN, Y. (1939) The excitation mechanism of the chemoreceptors of the carotid body. *Skand. Arch. Physiol.* **83** : 132–152.

VON EULER, C. and SÖDERBERG, V. (1952) Medullary chemosensitive receptors. *J. Physiol.* (*London*) **118** : 545–554.

EYZAGUIRRE, C. and KUFFLER, S. W. (1955) Processess of excitation in the dendrites and and in the soma of single isolated sensory nerve cells of the lobster and crayfish. *J. Gen. Physiol.* **39** : 87–119.

FESSARD, A. (1959) Les processus de base de l'inhibition centrale. *XXI Congreso Internacional de Ciencias Fisiológicas* pp. 40–46. Buenos Aires.

FLOREY, E. and FLOREY, E. (1958) Studies on the distribution of factor I in mammalian brain. *J. Physiol. (London)* **144** : 220–228.

FLOREY, E. and McLENNAN, H. (1955) Effects of an inhibitory factor (factor I) from brain on central synaptic transmission. *J. Physiol. (London)* **130** : 446–455.

GERARD, R. W. (1932) Nerve metabolism. *Physiol. Revs.* **12** : 469–592.

GERNANDT, B. E. (1946) A study of the respiratory reflexes elicited from the aortic and carotid bodies. *Acta Physiol. Scand.* **11** : Suppl. 35.

GRANIT, R. and PHILLIPS, C. G. (1956) Excitatory and inhibitory processes acting upon individual Purkinje cells of the cerebellum in cats. *J. Physiol. (London)* **133** : 520–547.

GRUNDFEST, H. (1959) Evolution of conduction in the nervous system. *Evolution of Nervous Control* pp. 43–86. American Association for the advancement of Science, Washington, D.C.

HAGIWARA, S. and BULLOCK, T. H. (1957) Intracellular potentials in pacemaker and integrative neurons of the lobster cardiac ganglion. *J. Cellular Comp. Physiol.* **50** : 25–47.

HAYASHI, T. (1959) *Neurophysiology and Neurochemistry of Convulsion.* The Dainihon-Tosho, Tokyo.

HEYMANS, C. (1953) Sino-aortic receptors. *XIX Internat. Physiol. Congress* pp. 44–59. Montreal. (Résumés.)

KOLMODIN, G. M. and SKOGLUND, C. R. (1959) Influence of asphyxia on membrane potential level and action potentials of spinal moto- and interneurons. *Acta Physiol. Scand.* **45** : 1–18.

KUFFLER, S. W. (1959) Synaptic inhibition. *XXI Congreso International de Ciencias Fisiológicas* pp. 27–30. Buenos Aires.

LAGET, P. and LEGOUIX, J. P. (1951) Contribution à l'étude de la chémoception de l'anhydride carbonique. Sensibilité spécifique des nerfs périphériques à ce gaz. *Acta Physiol. Scand.* **22** : 47–53

LI, C. L. and JASPER, H. (1953) Microelectrode studies of the electrical activity of the cerebral cortex in the cat. *J. Physiol. (London)* **127** : 117–140.

LLOYD, D. P. C. (1953) Influence of asphyxia upon the responses of spinal motoneurons, *J. Gen. Physiol.* **36** : 673–702.

LORENTE DE NÓ, R. (1947) A study of nerve physiology. *Studies Rockefeller Inst. Med. Res.* Nos. 131 and 132, New York.

MEVES, H. (1955) Die Wirkung des Wasserstoffionen und der Kohlensäure auf die Nervenleitungsgeschwindigkeit. *Arch. ges. Physiol. Pflüger's* **267** : 249–263.

MONNIER, A. M. (1952) The damping factor as a functional criterion in nerve physiology. *Cold Spring Harb. Symp. Quant. Biol.* **17** : 69–95.

PALAY, S. L. (1958) The morphology of synapses in the central nervous system. *Exptl. Cell Res.* Suppl. **5** : 275–293.

SPYROPOULOS, C. S. (1960) Cytoplasmic pH of nerve fibres. *J. Neurochem.* **5** : 185–194.

STRAUB, R. (1956) The action of CO_2 and pH on the resting potential of myelinated nerve fibres. *XX Internat. Physiol. Congress* pp. 858–860. Bruxelles.

SUGAR, O. and GERARD, R. W. (1938) Anoxia and brain potentials. *J. Neurophysiol.* **1** : 558–572.

TASAKI, I. (1953) *Nervous Transmission.* Charles C. Thomas, Springfield, Illinois.

TAUC, L. (1960) Diversité des modes d'activité des cellules nerveuses du ganglion déconnecté de l'aplysie. *Compt. rend. soc. biol.* **154** : 17–21.

VAN HARREVELD, A. (1946) Asphyxial depolarization in the spinal cord. *Am. J. Physiol.* **147** : 669–682.

WITZLEB, E. and BARTELS, H. (1956) Neue Untersuchungen über den Einfluss verschiedener arterieller Sauerstoff und Kohlensäuredrucke auf die Chemoreceptorischen Aktionpotentiale im Carotissinusnerven. *XX Intern. Physiol. Congress* pp. 974–975. Bruxelles.

YOUNG, J. Z. (1956) The organization within nerve cells. *Endeavour* **15** : no. 57, 5–19.

ZOTTERMAN, Y. (1953) Electrophysiological investigations on afferent fibres from the carotid sinus region. *XIX Internat. Physiol. Congress* pp. 59–66. Montreal.

EXCITATORY AND INHIBITORY PROCESSES INITIATED BY LIGHT AND INFRA-RED RADIATIONS IN SINGLE IDENTIFIABLE NERVE CELLS

(GIANT GANGLION CELLS OF *APLYSIA*)

A. Arvanitaki* and N. Chalazonitis*

RECENT experiments performed in different pigmented cells permitted the recognition of bioelectrical reactivity to light as a widespread cellular property. Moreover, in nerve cells, it has been established that inhibitory processes as well as excitatory ones may be triggered by radiations of different wave lengths (Arvanitaki and Chalazonitis, 1947, 1949a, b and c, 1950, 1958a, 1960; Chalazonitis, 1954).

The approach to such problems at the cellular level holds interest for many reasons. For instance, it is hoped that the knowledge of how light energy specifically trapped by *known molecules* located in *known cellular sites* (see Table 1) leads to electrical work might provide an insight into mechanisms of importance in general neurophysiology. As a matter of fact, photons absorbed by suitable cellular molecules serve to activate or trigger a system to which these molecules are functionally coupled, and which partially converts the absorbed energy into electrical work. But this system is activated just as well by any other stimulus, whether it be electrical, chemical, or mechanical, whose sites and mechanisms of action are, however, less specific than that of the photic stimulus.

It is hoped that this common cellular photosensitivity might be basically compared to that which is at the origin of the performances of a functional photoreceptor cell.

Simultaneous intracellular recordings in many photoactivated nerve cells revealed patterns of activity in which excitation in a given cell is accompanied by inhibition in the immediately neighbouring ones, recalling the "contrasting effects" already known to occur in different receptor organs, in the retina (Hartline, 1941, 1949; Granit, 1947, 1952; Kuffler, 1953; Hartline, Wagner and Ratliff, 1956), in the auditory system (Galambos and Davis, 1944) and, in cerebral patterns of activity (Mountcastle, 1957; etc.). Obviously, the interest

* Centre National de la Recherche Scientifique, Paris.
Laboratoire d'Électrobiologie, Faculté des Sciences, Université de Lyon.
Institut Océanographique, Monaco.

lies in the action of light being here analysed in single cells, by methods permitting *time resolution* as well as *site resolution* of the events.

In this regard pioneer experiments already demonstrating photosensitivity in unstained preparations, but performed on the scale of an organ, muscle or nerve centres (d'Arsonval, 1891; Prosser, 1934), did not afford any analysis at the unitary scale.*

In our approach, we have concentrated on three aspects of the problem:

(a) The cytostructural aspect, involving the identification of the cellular location of the molecules that absorb the light energy, in other words, the site of action of the stimulus.

(b) The biophysical aspect, involving the identification of the intracellular pigments, and allowing some information on the probable biophysical and biochemical transitions initiated by the light.

(c) The electrophysiological aspect, involving the identification of the bioelectrical changes initiated by light and the study of relationships between the incident light energy and the kinetics of the bioelectric processes as recorded by intracellular microelectrodes.

In this venture, we have employed primarily naturally highly pigmented cells (such as cardiac fibres, central nerve cells, plant cells, etc.) (Table 1). Although the pigments found in these cells are mainly involved in such functions as respiration, photosynthesis, etc., they were found to be capable of acting as photoreceptor structures leading to the generation of bioelectric signals.

This review will be limited to the aspects of excitation and inhibition processes induced by light on pigmented nerve cells and to the inhibitory effects determined by radiations of the near infra-red.

It is worthwhile, nevertheless, to quote first fundamental data displayed by experiments on an experimental model of a photoreceptor cell, the isolated giant axon of *Sepia* stained with vital dyes (Chalazonitis, 1954).

---

* On the other hand, the well known photodynamic effects (see Blum, 1941; Lippay, 1929, 1930; Kosmann, 1938; Kosmann and Lillie, 1935; Sandow and Isaacson, 1960) imply sensitization of biological systems to light by dyes (which seldom are *vital*) allowing photochemical reactions in which molecular oxygen takes part. But these reactions have nothing in common with normal oxygen metabolism of living systems. They are irreversible oxidations of cellular structural components, which do not take place thermally in living conditions. The observed and measured effects in photodynamic actions are in general *long latency* injury effects.

In contradistinction, the photoactivation effects considered here are essentially reversible processes of *short latencies*, in which only *functional* reactions are implied. In these, molecular oxygen which takes part is only involved through the respiratory pathway as a result of the increase of the velocity constants of the chain under the action of light (Arvanitaki and Chalazonitis, 1960; Chalazonitis, 1954).

TABLE 1. CYTOSTRUCTURES WHERE THE LIGHT ABSORBING MOLECULES ARE ORGANIZED IN VARIOUS PHOTOACTIVABLE CELLS

Photoactivable cell	Pigments or vital dyes	Absorption bands (mμ)	Subcellular structures where pigments are ordered or dye molecules stacked	References Photo-activation data	References Cytostructural and cytochemical data
Plant cells (*Nitella*)	Chlorophyll Carotenoids	672; 610; 579; 535 491; 471; 436; 417	Chloroplast (lamellae and grana)	Arvanitaki and Chalazonitis, 1949c; 1950	Finean, Sjöstrand and Steinmann, 1953; Steinmann and Sjöstrand, 1955; Wolken and Palade, 1952
Cardiac fibers (*Helix*)	Cytochromes Flavoprotein	605; 564; 550 490; 460	Mitochondria (cristae)	Arvanitaki and Chalazonitis, 1947; Chalazonitis, 1954	Claude and Fullam, 1945; Palade, 1952, 1953; Porter, Claude and Fullam, 1945; Sjöstrand, 1953b
Nerve cells (*Aplysia fasciata*)	Heme-protein Carotene-proteins	579; 542; 418 490; 463	Lipochondria (lamellar and granular structures)	Arvanitaki and Chalazonitis, 1949a, 1958a and 1960	Arvanitaki and Chalazonitis, 1960; Chalazonitis and Arvanitaki, 1951, 1956; Chalazonitis, and Lenoir, 1959
Nerve cells (*Aplysia punctata*)	Tetrapyrrolic pigment Carotenoids	672; 610; 560 482; 447	Lipochondria (lamellar and granular structures)	Arvanitaki and Chalazonitis, 1949b, 1960	Arvanitaki and Chalazonitis, 1960; Chalazonitis and Arvanitaki, 1951, 1956; Chalazonitis and Lenoir, 1959
Retinal photoreceptors	Rhodopsin Porphyropsin Iodopsin Cyanopsin	500 522 562 620	Rods and cones outer segment (lamellae)	Granit, 1947, 1955; Kuffler, 1953; etc.	Robertis and Lasansky, 1958; Moody and Robertson, 1960; Sjöstrand, 1953a, b; Wald, 1950; Wald and Brown, 1956; etc.
Stained giant axon (*Sepia*)(an experimental model of a photoreceptor)	Methylene blue Neutral red	650; 680 510	Cell membrane Neurofilaments Mitochondria	Arvanitaki and Chalazonitis, 1955b; Chalazonitis, 1954	Arvanitaki and Chalazonitis, 1951; Chalazonitis, 1954

EXCITATION OR INHIBITION PROCESSES
INDUCED BY LIGHT

An Artificial Photoreceptor Cell

A *Sepia* giant axon stained with vital dyes such as methylene blue or neutral red behaves as a good photoreceptor cell (Chalazonitis, 1954). Our attention will be limited to several main general features displayed in this model only *in aerobic conditions*.

The excitability and membrane resistance changes induced by the light. Faintly stained with methylene blue, continuously stimulated by 10/sec pulses of equal subliminal intensities, the giant axon of *Sepia* responds in the dark by local damped prepotentials of equal amplitudes.

In the presence of oxygen, the light being turned on, the amplitude of the prepotentials (initiated by the pulses of equal intensities) rapidly increases until a spike is initiated after 2–5 sec of illumination. This may be termed an increase in the excitability induced by light. Simultaneously the response acquires a marked undamped shape. It is noteworthy that in the presence of nitrogen the light induces a reverse effect, a decrease of the excitability.

Using the square pulse technique, it is possible to demonstrate moreover that in the presence of oxygen light induces an immediate increase in the membrane conductance. This is also substantiated by the oscillatory behaviour of the response under illumination, thus indicating that in the analogous circuit representative of the electrical properties of the membrane, the resistance undergoes a decrease (Arvanitaki, 1939; Cole, 1941).

The immediate graded depolarization and early miniature potentials initiated by light. The facts are schematic in the axon stained with neutral red (Fig. 1). At "on", the membrane depolarizes without delay and continues to do so at an increasing rate. At the same time, uncoordinated bumps of miniature potentials are surging. These significantly reveal the recruitment in a quasi-quantal manner of multiple active foci or patches in the illuminated area of the membrane. They recall the miniature responses described by Tasaki and Spyropoulos (1958) and Spyropoulos (1959) in the squid axon membrane under voltage clamp.

The initiation of oscillatory potentials and spiking. As the depolarization of the membrane proceeds, the miniature potentials appear to synchronize into regular oscillations of increasing amplitudes, preluding the spiking (Fig. 1). The kinetics of this generator depolarization is a definite function of the light intensity. It may be shown that the maximum rate and the maximum amplitude of the generator potential, as well as the reverse of the latency of the spikes' initiation, increase roughly as a linear function of the logarithm of the light intensity.

Such bioelectrical reactions, considered as a whole, are by far supra-maximal responses. They may be elicited by flashes of durations shorter

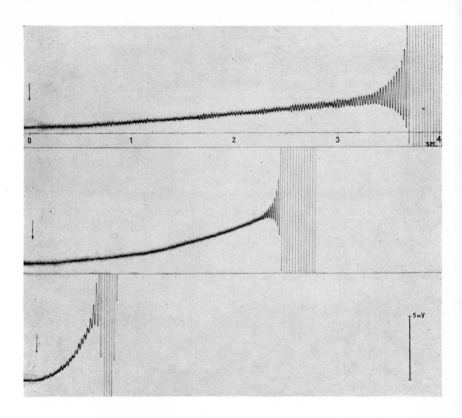

FIG. 1. Photobioelectrical reactions in the stained nerve fibre.

Sepia axon of 300 μ diameter, isolated and stained with neutral red; initially at rest in the dark. Local illumination in the presence of oxygen; 5°C. A narrow beam (0·3 mm width) of light (whole visible, 700–400 mμ) strikes locally the axon at the times signalled by the arrows. Recording microelectrode, 0·5 mm from the illuminated spot. Three successive steady illuminations at increasing intensities, from top to bottom: 1·2, 1·8 and 5·4 × 10⁻⁴ cal g mm⁻² sec⁻¹.

On the exponentially growing generator potential are superimposed irregular miniature potentials, then oscillatory potentials initiating the discharge of spikes. Only the lower portions of the impulses are seen at this high amplification. Following the first impulses of the discharge the membrane potential stabilizes at an upper depolarized state, not seen at this amplification (but see Fig. 3).

than the latency of spikes (although the rate of growth of the generator potential decreases when the light is turned off (Fig. 2) and consequently the initiation of the spikes is delayed).

Obviously, the maximum development of the generator potential and the initiation of the spiking are late secondary reactions, as compared to the primary transitions triggered by the light. In an attempt to determine a threshold value of the photic stimulus, the light energy just sufficient to elicit

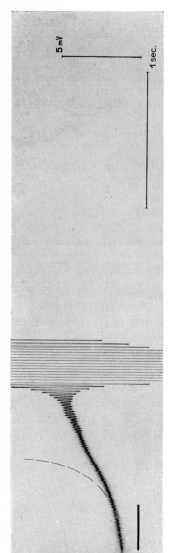

FIG. 2. Axon's response to short illumination.

Record obtained from the same axon as that in Fig. 1. Illumination, during 300 msec as indicated by the horizontal line under the record. Intensity $4 \cdot 5 \times 10^{-4}$ cal g mm^{-2} sec^{-1}. Dotted line traces the course of the depolarization during a steady illumination. Interruption of the light decreases the rate of depolarization and delays the initiation of the discharge.

FIG. 3. Record at low amplification showing the response to illumination ("on" signalled by the arrow), of a neutral red stained *Sepia* axon.

On the falling phase of the spikes a "plateau" becomes progressively conspicuous and finally, following the 12th spike, the membrane potential stabilizes at an upper depolarized state. This lasted for more than 15 sec (white gap). The repolarization process developed spontaneously, bringing back the membrane towards the initial level.

the first detectable bioelectrical response would have to be defined. The latter might be the response to activation of a single patch of the membrane. In such a case, the light threshold energy would approach a few quanta.

Another important feature is the delay of the least detectable photo-bioelectrical reaction. As the rate of development of the generator potential increases exponentially with time, it should be expected that the least measurable delay would tend to a lower and lower value as the sensitivity of the recording device is improved.

Pigmented Nerve Cells—Natural Photoreceptor Cells

The giant nerve cells of *Aplysia* ganglia share with other pigmented photo-activable cells (see Table 1) the common important cytostructural feature of localization of the absorbing molecules in intracellular organelles where they are tightly ordered on fine substructures.

These giant nerve cells have been thoroughly studied for two reasons:

First, they are very densely pigmented. Among the intracellular pigments found in these somata, heme-protein with three main absorption bands at 579, 542 and 418 mμ (in the oxygenated state) and carotene-proteins absorbing mainly at 490 and 463 mμ, have been identified.

The pigments are located in intracellular organelles of approximately 0·7 μ diameter, the lipochondria (or "grains"), (see Chalazonitis, 1961a). The "grains" are organized under the cell membrane into layers and islets at the borders of the highly basophilic deep somatoplasm surrounding the nucleus, as is well seen on sections through the cells. The lipochondria may be isolated by careful microdissection of the cell membrane, or in larger amounts by centrifugation methods (Arvanitaki and Chalazonitis, 1960; Chalazonitis and Arvanitaki, 1951, 1956; Chalazonitis and Lenoir, 1959). The number of lipochondria in a giant cell has been tentatively calculated as being of the order of 10^6 (Arvanitaki and Chalazonitis, 1960).

The second reason was the striking cytological differentiations which allow the recognition of the different cells under the microscope and the experimentation on *given identifiable* somata (see Plate 1). These cells are identifiable not only on account of their constant location, size and shape, but also by the characteristic patterns of their activity (Arvanitaki and Chalazonitis, 1955a, 1958b).

Taking advantage of such a situation, photoactivations have been brought about on given differentiated types of cells: the so-called type A cell, the type Gen cell, and the smaller cells immediately contiguous to these two types.

ASPECTS OF THE RESPONSES TO LIGHT
OF THE A NERVE CELLS

The large type A nerve cells may in the dark be either autoactive by spikes at constant frequencies, or in the resting state. Generally these cells respond to whole light at "on", exhibiting depolarization and spiking. However several A cells respond both at "on" and at "off", less frequently at "off" (Arvanitaki and Chalazonitis, 1958a, 1960), as was known for visual photo-receptors (Hartline, 1938; Granit, 1950; Kuffler, 1953; etc.).

The "off" type response to illumination corresponds properly to an inhibition process at "on". The mixed "on" "off" type response manifests the interference of both the excitation and the inhibition processes. Such a response, even to localized illuminations in cells of a given identity, suggests the interference of two opposite actions exerted by the radiations of the whole visible, one or the other dominating, according to the individual conditions met in the photoactivated cell.

Monochromatic activations. As a matter of fact, cells of the same type may differ by the relative concentrations of the two main intracellular pigments, the heme-protein and the carotene-protein. Accordingly, in a given cell the activation by whole light has been compared to that by monochromatic beams at 579 mμ specifically absorbed by heme-protein molecules and by mono-chromatic beams at 490 mμ absorbed by carotene-protein molecules.

Responses to λ 579 mμ activation reproduce with a much greater efficiency the general data of the excitatory processes elicited by the whole light acti-vations. In an initially resting soma, with a just suitable intensity, a spike generates after a latency of a fraction of a second. At suprathreshold inten-sities, the latency decreases and subsequent spikes are generated at increasing frequencies. If the intensity is kept constant, the frequency increases as a function of the duration of the illumination.

Plotting the spikes' maximum frequency reached during illumination against the logarithm of the light intensity, a reasonably good linear relation has been found. Thus, we may write: $F = k \log I + c$.

With flashes of short durations τ, such that τ be inferior to the latency time, the number of spikes composing the response increases as a function of the product of intensity by duration: $i \times \tau$, which is the energy of the light stimulus. To elicit a given response of N spikes, $i \times \tau$ is constant. To elicit this same response, the energy of a monochromatic λ 579 mμ activating beam is 10–100 times less than that necessary by whole light.

If an A soma was autoactive in the dark, its spiking frequency increases on illumination. The maximum frequency reached is a function of the light intensity (Fig. 8). A short illumination of minute incident energy, 10^{-8} cal g mm^{-2}, is sufficient to bring about a marked transition.

The maximum increase of the frequency reached during illumination has been plotted against the logarithm of the light intensity and data have been compared for whole light and for a monochromatic λ 579 mμ beam in the presence of oxygen, and in the presence of air (Arvanitaki and Chalazonitis, 1960). The relations are linear in all cases, but they are significantly distinct in their slope.

On one hand, the higher the oxygen pressure, the higher the rate of increment of the frequency (or the yielding of the photoactivation process). On the other hand, the efficiency of the activation by the 579 mμ monochromatic beam is higher than that by the whole visible spectrum of equal incident energy.

This fact was consistent with the idea that part of the wave lengths in the whole visible spectrum are inactive, or even inhibitory. In fact, by external microelectrodes in the *Aplysia* nerve cells, earlier data showed that inhibition might occur by λ 490 mμ, which is absorbed by the carotenoid molecules (Arvanitaki and Chalazonitis, 1949b).

Using now the intracellular microelectrode technique (Arvanitaki and Chalazonitis, 1955a, 1958a, b, 1960), it is found that activation of the A type giant soma by a λ 490 mμ beam only occasionally, and with very low efficiency, elicits an "on" response (see Fig. 4). Most frequently it elicits an "off" response, and, if the soma was initially autoactive, it provokes an inhibition of the spiking at "on", its re-establishment at "off" (Fig. 5). In the A type cells, inhibition by 490 mμ is observed mainly in units which on inspection appear rather yellowish, indicating a high concentration of the intracellular carotenoid molecules.

It is also to be noted that the primary immediate effect in this kind of inhibition observed in the A cell is an increase of the membrane potential. Unlike the inhibitory processes to be examined below, no conspicuous inhibitory post synaptic potentials are here superimposed (Fig. 5).

The generator depolarization. Early kinetics of the excitatory process initiated by light. The excitatory effects of the light are fundamentally related to the graded generator depolarization of the cell membrane. This initial bioelectrical response to light is fairly conspicuous in certain nerve cells very densely pigmented, of medium size (diameter 100–200 μ), contiguous to the A cell or to the Gen cell, and extremely sensitive to monochromatic λ 579 mμ light.

Recordings at high amplification showed that initiation of the generator depolarization is fairly synchronous to the incidence of the light stimulus (Fig. 6). This depolarization grows at an increasing rate as the illumination proceeds. The maximum rate is roughly a linear function of the logarithm of the light intensity. By the square pulse technique, it has been established, moreover, that an increase in the membrane conductance is concomitant with the generator depolarization.

When the rate of the generator depolarization reaches a threshold value, spiking is initiated. The reciprocal of the latency of the spiking, as well as the maximum frequency of the spikes in the discharge, are linear functions of the logarithm of the light intensity. Hence, they vary directly with the value of the maximum rate of the generator depolarization. This is well shown in Fig. 6; the maximum frequency of the spiking varies as does the maximum

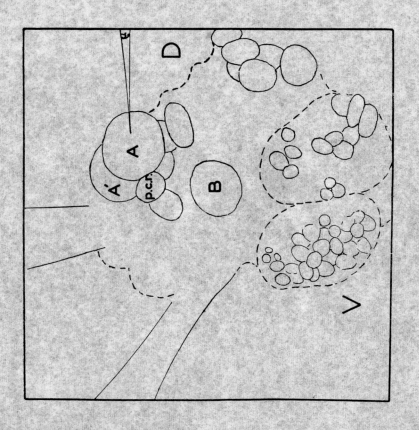

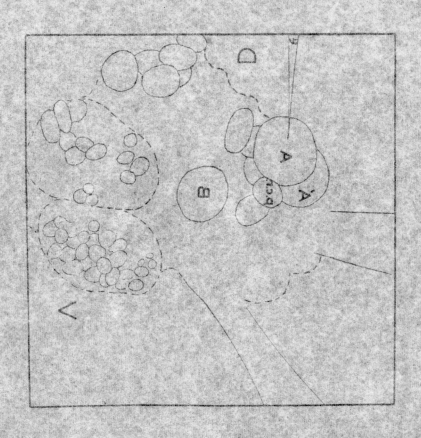

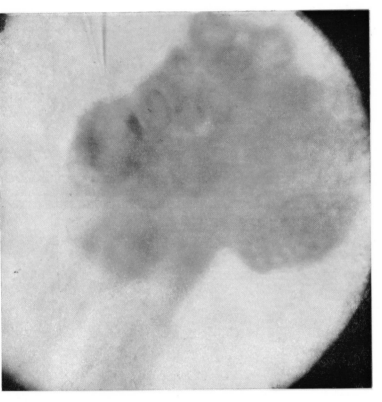

PLATE I. Differential pigmentation among the somata of the visceral ganglia of *Aplysia fasciata*. Photomicrograph *in vivo* of the ganglion in profile. Dorsal face (D) at right; ventral face (V) at left. On the dorsal face, the reddish giant soma A is intensely pigmented. The microelectrode (μ) is seen penetrating into it. Numerous cells on the parieto-genital ganglion, such as the small somata at left of the B cell, are pale yellowish. Magnification $\times 50$.

rate of the depolarization, and is, in the second record, much lower than in the third. The maximum amplitude of the generator potential is, nevertheless, equal in the two.

FIG. 4. The monochromatic activation of the heme-protein (579 mμ) is of higher efficiency than the monochromatic activation of the carotene-protein (490 mμ).

An A cell initially inactive in the dark is here submitted to 3 steady monochromatic illuminations of equal incident intensities (6×10^{-6} cal g mm^{-2} sec^{-1}), alternatively from top to bottom: λ 490 mμ; λ 579 mμ; λ 490 mμ. The discharges initiated at "on" (signalled by arrow) are of higher frequency by the 579 mμ activation.

Calibrations: 80 mV; 0·5 sec.

The generator potential subsides if the light is removed after the maximum depolarization has been attained. If the light is turned off before that time, the rate of the depolarization decreases and a maximum is reached, although later and lower. Thus, with intensities high enough, it is quite possible to elicit bioelectrical responses by flashes of duration as short as some few milliseconds.

According to the intensity of the flashes, graded generator depolarization, with or without spiking, may be initiated (Fig. 7). Again, the maximum rate of the generator depolarization, as well as the maximum frequency of the spikes in the discharge, increase linearly with the logarithm of the intensity of the flash (Fig. 9).

The possibility of eliciting bioelectrical responses by such short flashes is of great theoretical bearing.

In the sequences of reactions initiated by light in the precise cellular site where pigments are located, hence, where light is absorbed, the bioelectrical phenomena start immediately, close to the primary photophysical events. The latter is quantitatively related to the generator depolarization which is the fundamental photobioelectrical reaction at the cellular level.

This notion decreases the value of the bioelectrical reaction threshold towards a much lower order: in a previous work, a 10^3 quanta$_{579}$ threshold energy to elicit an "on" response composed of a single spike was tentatively evaluated (Arvanitaki and Chalazonitis, 1960). But the genesis of a spike marks the attainment of a liminal rate of the generator depolarization, and represents the achievement of a tremendous bioelectric response. Thus, it is now conceivable that a minute detectable depolarization threshold is to be found at lower and lower quantal values.

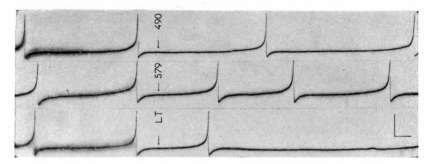

FIG. 5. Inhibition by monochromatic 490 mμ irradiation in certain A somata of high carotene-protein content.

An orange-yellow A soma (concentration of the carotene-protein higher than that of the heme-protein), initially autoactive in the dark, is here submitted to three steady illuminations of different spectral compositions, but of equal incident intensities (6×10^{-6} cal g mm^{-2} sec^{-1}). While the activation of the heme-protein (579 mμ) determines an increase of the spikes frequency (excitation), that of the carotene-protein (490 mμ) determines a decrease (inhibition), without any detectable sign of inhibitory post-synaptic potentials. The response to the activation by the whole visible (L.T.) determines an immediate transitory increase of the frequency, followed by the cessation of the spikes. This is an example of interfering excitatory and inhibitory effects.

Calibrations: 60 mV, and 0·4 sec.

On the nature of the generator depolarization. The generator depolarization might now be recognized as a common process in excitation. It is triggered in different sensory cells by appropriate stimuli. One of the clearest demonstrations of this phenomenon has been in the Crayfish stretch receptor cell (Eyzaguirre and Kuffler, 1955a, 1955b; Kuffler, 1959), whose microanatomy has been studied by Florey and Florey (1955). Generator potentials have been found in the Pacinian corpuscle (Loewenstein and Rathkamp, 1958), in olfactory cells (Ottoson, 1956; Macleod, 1959), and above all in visual photoreceptors, (MacNichol, Wagner and Hartline, 1953; Svaetichin, 1956; Fuortes, 1958 and 1959;MacNichol and Svaetichin, 1958; etc.).

Moreover, generator depolarization has been recorded by external or internal microelectrodes in various central nerve cells: *Aplysia* somata (Arvanitaki and Chalazonitis, 1949d, 1955a, 1958b), crustacean heart ganglia cells (Hagiwara and Bullock, 1957; Watanabe and Bullock, 1959), cortical neurons (Li and Jasper, 1953), and spinal interneurons and motoneurons (Kolmodin and Skoglund, 1958), finally in cardiac pacemaker cells (Dudel and Trautwein, 1958). The association of graded, relatively slow depolarization with discharge of impulses was known as a general phenomenon from previous data on spinal motoneurons (Barron and Matthews, 1938), and on invertebrate nerve fibers and cardiac cells (Arvanitaki, 1938).

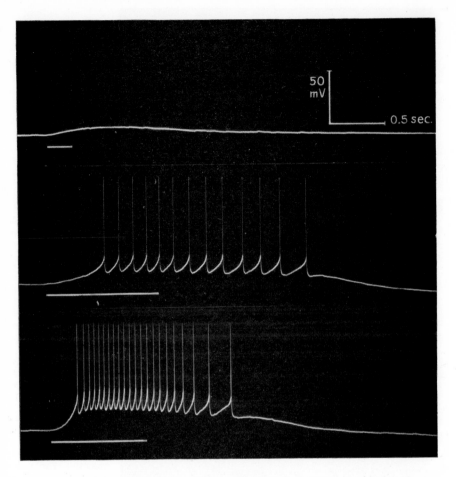

50
mV

0.5 sec.

FIG. 6. Subthreshold and threshold "on" responses to local monochromatic
activations.

Highly photosensitive medium sized nerve cell (150 μ), densely pigmented, initially
inactive in the dark, in the presence of oxygen. It was submitted to three monochromatic (579 mμ) brief irradiations (as indicated by the white horizontal lines
under the recordings), of increasing intensities, successively from top to bottom:
0·05, 0·2 and 2×10^{-6} cal g mm^{-2} sec^{-1}.

At the lower intensity, only a subthreshold photodepolarization (generator
potential) is initiated. At higher intensities, the rate of the generator potential and
the frequency of the spiking increase. Note the slow repolarization wave following
the cessation of the discharge at "off".

The shape of the subliminal generator depolarization, carefully inspected
at high amplification, appeared in many instances to have quite a smooth
contour, without any perceivable superimposed potential change. However,
it frequently occurred that some bumps of regular shape of about 0·1 mV

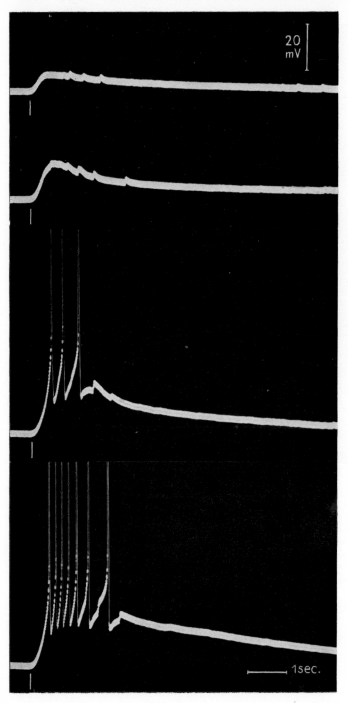

FIG. 7. Graded subthr
old and threshold
sponses of the nerve
to monochromatic flas

Highly photosensitive n
ium sized nerve cell (18
densely pigmented, init
inactive in the dark,
mitted to four monoch
matic (579 mμ) flashe
20 msec (signalled by
vertical bars under the
cordings), of increasing
tensities, from top to
tom: 0·8, 2, 4 and
10^{-6} cal g mm^{-2} sec

The rate of the gener
potential, the freque
and the number of
spikes increase with
intensity. The upper
tions of the spikes are
seen.

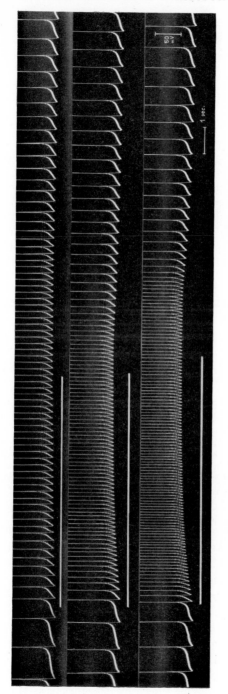

FIG. 8. Responses to light at different intensities in initially autoactive nerve cells. Nerve cell initially autoactive in the dark. Three steady monochromatic (579 mμ) activations, at increasing intensities, successively from top to bottom: 0·15, 0·6 and 1 × 10⁻⁶ cal g mm⁻² sec⁻¹.

Duration of the illumination is slightly different in the three records as indicated by the underlying lines. The depolarization and the frequency of the spikes increase with the intensity of illumination. Note a slow adaptation as indicated by a slight lengthening in the period as the illumination proceeds. At the cessation of the light, the frequency of the spikes decrease towards the initial value in the dark. The upper portions of the spikes are not seen.

15

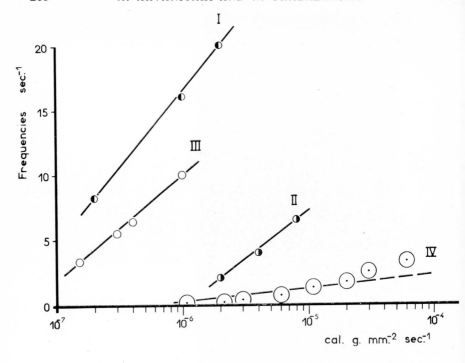

FIG. 9. Maximum increase determined by light in the spikes frequency as function of intensity.

Effects of light intensity on the maximum frequency of firing evoked by the light on initially inactive cells (curves I, II), or the maximum increase of spikes frequency determined by the light on initially autoactive cells (curves III, IV). For curve I, the duration of the illumination was 1 sec; for curve II, 20 msec; for curves III and IV, steady illuminations. Data of curves I, II, III, were obtained from cells of 150–200 μ diameter. Data of curve IV was from a giant A cell (500 μ). Abscissa: $\log_{10}$ incident intensity of light; Ordinate: maximum increase of the spikes frequency.

amplitude and 10 msec duration supervened. The hypothesis that they could be miniature excitatory post synaptic potentials was considered. In effect, some full grown e.p.s.p.'s with an easily identifiable shape are sometimes also superimposed on the subliminal generator depolarization. Yet it is difficult to conclude in favour of a presynaptic bombardment due to the photoactivation of a second soma, because such e.p.s.p.'s may occur even if the illuminating microbeam was carefully restricted to the impaled soma. It is nevertheless possible to imagine that the light would also be adequate to activate directly either the presynaptic terminals or the postsynaptic membrane.

As a matter of fact, the excitability of one or both of these structures is exhausted by illumination, as may be shown by inter-injections of orthodromic stimuli via the afferent nerve. Functional presynaptic potential changes are known to occur (Lloyd, 1949; Wall, 1958; Wall and Johnson, 1958). Furthermore, it is not to be disregarded that presynaptic or synaptic structures might be endowed with some mode of autoactivity.

Thus the question arises whether the generator depolarization is built up by a massive recruitment of e.p.s.p. activities. As generator depolarization has been demonstrated in the axon membrane, however, there is no reason to disregard such a generator potential as having possible intrinsic origins; in addition, an eventual contribution of the activities of the synaptic structures is not excluded.

INHIBITIONS BY LIGHT
IN THE GEN TYPE CELLS

Contrasting to the above, other well identifiable nerve cells of the Gen or of the B type always hyperpolarize when illuminated (Arvanitaki and Chalazonitis, 1958a, 1960). The hyperpolarization is established without appreciable delay and grows to reach from 10 to 20 mV. Simultaneously, series of repeated postsynaptic inhibitory potentials are superimposed at increasing frequencies, and any emission of spikes is consequently inhibited. The amplitude of the hyperpolarization and the frequency of the i.p.s.p.'s increase with the intensity of the activating light. At "off" the membrane repolarizes towards the initial level, the i.p.s.p.'s emission subsides and that of the spikes is re-established.

In an attempt to search for an explanation of these inhibitory actions initiated by light, simultaneous recordings of the electrical activities (Arvanitaki and Chalazonitis, 1959; Chalazonitis and Arvanitaki, 1958) have been systematically performed in many nerve cells contiguous to the cell which was illuminated. Three main features may be distinguished. It happened that the inhibition of the illuminated nerve cell was not accompanied by any obvious transition in the activity of the neighbouring cells. This was a rather rare case which occurred with higher probability at low light intensities.

Secondly, synergic or concurrent inhibition was manifest in neighbouring cells: in many instances the neighbouring cells showed a mere decrease in the frequency of spikes, accompanied by a more or less noticeable repolarization of the membrane, without any detectable superimposed i.p.s.p.'s (Fig. 10). In others, numerous i.p.s.p.'s appeared as well. Time relations between the latter and the i.p.s.p.'s of the illuminated soma were nevertheless not conspicuous (Fig. 11).

Finally, reciprocal excitation–inhibition patterns were repeatedly recorded in illuminated contiguous nerve cells, as illustrated in Fig. 12. At "on", hyperpolarization, i.p.s.p.'s and inhibition of the spiking develop in the Gen cell while depolarization and an increase in the spikes' frequency evolve in a nearby smaller, densely pigmented cell. We have been unsuccessful as yet in attempts to demonstrate consistent time relation between the spikes' emission in the excited cell and the i.p.s.p.'s occurrence in the contiguous inhibited cell. In spite of this failure, a synaptic origin of the inhibition is suggested in these cases. Such patterns already recorded under orthodromic activation in *Aplysia* neighbouring cells (Arvanitaki and Chalazonitis, 1959) reveal subtle interactions between the responding units and draw attention to an underlying elaborate anatomical organization.

> Excitatory and inhibitory interactions have been demonstrated in the vertebrate eye and ascribed to the complex organization of the retina (Granit, 1947, 1955). In the *Limulus* lateral eye conspicuous inhibitions are also present and have been attributed to interactions possibly owing to an elaborate organization supplied by a "plexus" which is an extensive system of cross-connecting strands of nerve fibers, so as to form a three-dimensional network closely associated to the axons of the retinula and eccentric cells (Hartline, 1938, 1941, 1949; Hartline, Wagner and MacNichol, 1952; Hartline, Wagner and Ratliff, 1956). It is to be noted that anatomical investigations in the *Aplysia* ganglia have shown, lying under the cortical giant nerve cells, some analogous network of fine strands of fibres which might perhaps supply similar functions, as above. It also recalls networks as described in other fields by Horridge (1960) and Szentagothai (1960).

As regards the inhibitory processes elicited by radiations in the *Aplysia* cells, one must first consider the hypothesis that in some of the ganglion cells synaptic inhibitions through odd excitation of some interneurons would be implied. The hodological mediation of some underlying organizer plexus might also be inferred. However, besides the above, other inhibitory processes are elicited by light which might suggest other mechanisms, possibly of primary inhibition. For example, there are conspicuous occurrences without latency, when light is "on", of maintained repolarizations free of i.p.s.p.'s. There is also in given cells the permutation from the excitatory type to the inhibitory type of response by merely changing the wave length of the activating radiation without introducing any topological variance. In fact, in the *Sepia* stained axon wherein any means of secondary inhibition is out of the question, excitation may be also turned into inhibition by changing the wave length of the irradiation. To similar inhibitions by light pertains the off response studied by Kennedy (1958) in excised segments of the naturally pigmented pallial nerve of *Mactra*. Such facts suggest that a direct primary inhibition mechanism might in addition be operative through given wave lengths in *Aplysia* nerve cells. This implies that the activated subcellular stru·^ures would be certain intermediary ones, or, indeed, those which func· ɔnally mediate the development of inhibitory processes.

GENERAL INHIBITORY EFFECTS
OF INFRA-RED RADIATIONS

Inhibitory effects of infra-red radiations are noticeable in the *Sepia* axon as well as in the *Aplysia* nerve cells.

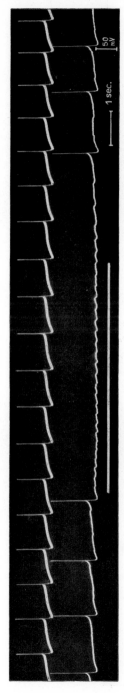

FIG. 10. Inhibitory processes by light on the Gen type nerve cells.

Simultaneous recordings by means of two microelectrodes in the Gen cell (lower record) and in a neighbouring cell (upper record), both initially autoactive. During local illumination of the Gen cell (as indicated by the horizontal white line), hyperpolarization with superimposed i.p.s.p. is evoked in that cell. The effects subside after cessation of the light. Meanwhile, the simultaneous recording in the neighbouring cell (upper), shows only a very slight decrease in its frequency during the illumination, without any sign of superimposed i.p.s.p.'s.

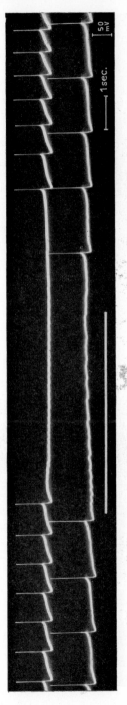

FIG. 11. Concurrent inhibitory effects by light on neighbouring cells.
Simultaneous intracellular recordings in two autoactive nerve cells of the parieto-
genital ganglion. Cessation of the spikes and post synaptic inhibitory potentials
are recorded in both cells, when the light is turned on. Nevertheless, the latencies
of the initiation of the i.p.s.p.'s, and their frequency, the latencies of inhibition
of the spikes, are conspicuously different in the 2 cells. The latencies of reinitia-
tion of the spikings after the cessation of the light are also different.

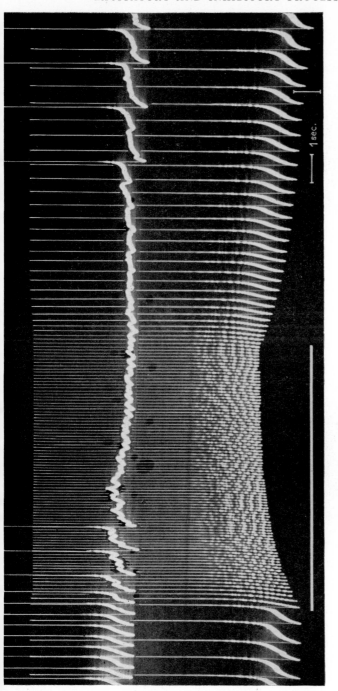

Fig. 12. Reciprocal excitatory and inhibitory effects by light, in two contiguous nerve cells.

Simultaneous intracellular recordings by means of two microelectrodes in two contiguous nerve cells (200 μ diameter) of the parieto-genital ganglion. Both cells were initially autoactive in the dark, with independent frequencies. They were both submitted to light (as indicated by the horizontal line below). The light beam (700–400 mμ) of 0·5 mm width, and 10⁻⁶ cal g mm⁻² sec⁻¹ intensity, covered the two cells. One of the two cells (lower record) depolarized with a quite negligible latency, and its frequency increased to 10/sec. On the cessation of light it repolarized towards a level higher than the initial one. On the contrary, the second cell (upper record) repolarized at "on", repetitive inhibitory post synaptic potentials dominated, the spikes emission stopped. Note that the frequency of the i.p.s.p.'s is without relation to that of the spikes recorded simultaneously in the partner cell. At "off", the cell redepolarized, the frequency of the i.p.s.p.'s decreased and the emission of the spikes was re-established. Voltage calibration: 15 mV for the upper record; 10 mV for the lower record.

The stained axon as a detector of infra-red radiations. At low temperatures the autoactive axon, methylene blue stained, exhibits in the dark an oscillatory behaviour with periodic spike emission. On such a preparation, visible radiations elicit depolarization and increase in the frequency of the spikes (Fig. 13). In contrast, on the same axon, a beam of infra-red radiations induces hyperpolarization, damping of the pre-existing oscillatory activity, and inhibition of spikes emission (Fig. 13a). The effect reverses readily upon the cessation of the infra-red.

In the neutral red stained axon, following the splitting of the repolarization phase of the spike into three components and the uncoupling of the third (see Fig. 4), the membrane potential settles for a long time at a plateau of depolarized level (Arvanitaki and Chalazonitis, 1955b). Tasaki and Hagiwara (1957) have demonstrated in squid giant axon under TEA the existence of such an upper depolarized stable state. If an infra-red beam of threshold intensity is applied during the plateau, the repolarization process is readily initiated (Fig. 14).

The jump in the membrane potential may be 40 mV or more. A similar effect of infra-red injection has been demonstrated by Spyropoulos (1961) in the nodal membrane. The infra-red repolarizing response may be considered in relation to the all-or-none repolarizing response elicited by a "threshold" inward current in the potassium treated squid axon (Segal, 1958) and analysed by Tasaki (1959) on nerve cells in the dorsal root ganglion of the toad.

Inhibitory reactions of the Aplysia *somata to infra-red.* While the response to light of the different identifiable somata may be amphoteric, only inhibitory reactions to infra-red radiations have been as yet recorded. Depending on the identity of the cell, one of the two following inhibitory patterns may be seen:

A mere increase of the membrane potential: This starts without latency at "on" and increases with time to reach a maximum value which is a function of the intensity of the irradiation. The discharge at "off" may be simply considered as a post inhibitory rebound (Fig. 15). As a rule this pattern of inhibition has been recorded in the A type cells.

Initially autoactive cells repolarize at "on", and the emission of spikes is stopped during the irradiation, the length of the pause increasing as a function of the time and the intensity. As expected, autoactive somata, being the more sensitive to the displacement of their membrane potential, react readily to the infra-red radiations. A beam of 10^{-4} cal g mm^{-2} sec^{-1} intensity during 0·2 sec is sufficient to elicit a conspicuous inhibition.

On the immediate increase of the membrane potential, superimposed series of i.p.s.p.'s: This pattern, illustrated in Fig. 17 and Fig. 18, has been mainly recorded in the Gen type cells. Soon after the initiation of the membrane potential increase at "on", a series of i.p.s.p.'s of uniform shape appear

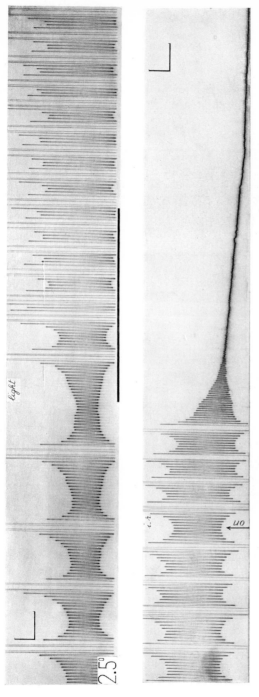

FIG. 13 and 13a. Antagonistic effects of light and infra-red radiations on the giant nerve fibre.

Sepia giant axon (300 μ diameter) stained with methylene blue, autoactive in the dark (local oscillatory activity with periodic emissions of groups of spikes), in the presence of oxygen, 2·5°C. The local illumination (light 700–400 mμ) as indicated by the horizontal line under the record, determines a depolarization and a large increase of the frequency of the spikes' emissions (Fig. 13). In contradistinction, a local beam of the near infra-red (750–4·000 mμ), of equal incident intensity as the light (2×10^{-4} cal g mm^{-2} sec^{-1}) determines on the same axon an immediate increase of the membrane potential and a complete inhibition of the spikes' emission (Fig. 13a). Both the lower and the upper portions of the spikes are not seen at these high amplifications.

Calibrations: 2 mV; 0·25 sec.

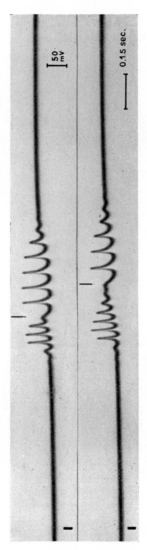

FIG. 14. Abolition by infra-red injection of the "upper depolarized state" on neutral red stained axons.

A "flash" of infra-red radiations (750-4·000 mμ) strikes the axon locally (at the time signalled by the vertical bars at the top of the records), while the upper depolarized state was reached (following the spiking initiated by a flash of light as signalled at the beginning of the records). A repolarization of the order of 40 mV is initiated without any latency by the infra-red injection, bringing transitorily the membrane potential back to the normal level. Here this repolarization is followed by a re-emission of spikes and a restabilization to the upper depolarized state.

with a fairly regular evolution in their frequency as the irradiation proceeds. However, paradoxically, the amplitude of these i.p.s.p.'s does not decrease while the underlying membrane potential increases by 10–15 mV.

As the irradiation is prolonged and the membrane potential increased, a sudden hyperpolarizing jump towards a lower stable state supervenes (Fig. 17), recalling that described above in the axon. At this level the amplitude of the superimposed high frequency i.p.s.p.'s falls to zero. At "off" the membrane redepolarizes towards its initial value, the spiking is re-established with a post inhibitory rebound, and the emission of the i.p.s.p.'s is stopped.

Before the occurrence of the hyperpolarizing jump, the amplitude of the i.p.s.p.'s does not decrease even if the membrane potential surpasses the equilibrium level as marked out by the initial spike's post-hyperpolarization peak. Moreover, this equilibrium level shifts towards a lower value in the post inhibitory discharge spikes.

If the infra-red action is studied with the soma membrane potential previously "fixed" at different levels (Fig. 18), it is seen that only a 5 mV positive displacement is sufficient to determine a relevant decrease in the i.p.s.p.'s amplitude. This is in accordance with previously known data in the spinal motoneuron (Coombs, Eccles and Fatt, 1955), in inhibitory neuromuscular junctions (Fatt and Katz, 1953; Hoyle and Wiersma, 1958a and 1958b; Grundfest, Reuben and Rickles, 1959), in receptor crustacean neurons (Kuffler, 1958; Kuffler and Eyzaguirre, 1955). The displacement of the membrane potential was here brought about merely by varying the temperature of the preparation (Chalazonitis and Arvanitaki, 1957; Chalazonitis, 1961b).

Sensitivity of the above cells to infra-red detection. The change of the tissue's temperature by infra-red may be measured with some accuracy (Chalazonitis, 1954). The surface of the irradiated cell being approximately 10^{-3} mm², the threshold intensity 10^{-4} cal g mm^{-2} sec^{-1} applied for 0·2 sec, the threshold energy is of the order of 10^{-8} cal g and the temperature elevation of the soma has been estimated to be about 0·016 °C (Arvanitaki and Chalazonitis, 1960).

Such evaluations may be useful in comparing the sensitivity to infra-red of these common ganglion nerve cells to that of specialized sense organs. The anatomy and function of the sense organ in the facial pit of Pit Vipers have been thoroughly studied by Bullock and co-workers. The sensory endings were found to be sensitive to a change in temperature of the order of 0·001 °C (Bullock and Diecke, 1956; Bullock and Fox, 1957). This is close to the value found for human thermoreception. Moreover giant synapses of invertebrates are temperature sensitive, as described by Bullock (1956), and isolated invertebrate ganglia, as well as excised nerves, react to rapid warming and cooling (Kerkut and Taylor, 1956; Granit and Skoglund, 1945; Bernhard and Granit, 1946).

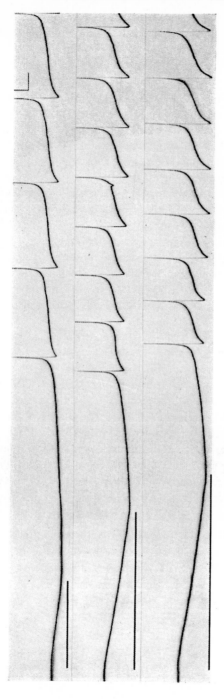

FIG. 15. The hyperpolarizing effects of infra-red radiations in the nerve cell.

A soma on the parieto-branchal ganglion of *Aplysia fasciata*, initially inactive, submitted to the local action of a narrow beam of infra-red radiations (750–4·000 mμ), at 4×10^{-4} cal g mm^{-2} sec^{-1} intensity, with three increasing durations, from top to bottom (as indicated by the underlying lines). Immediately at "on" a large hyperpolarization proceeds as function of the time of irradiation. Immediately at "off" the cell redepolarizes and a discharge of spikes is initiated. The maximum frequency of the latter increases with the energy of the previous infra-red irradiation. The upper portions of the spikes are not seen at this amplification. Calibrations: 20 mV; 0·25 sec.

Fig. 16. Inhibition by infra-red in autoactive nerve cells.
A soma initially autoactive, submitted successively to three local actions of infra-red at the same intensity (10^{-4} cal g mm^{-2} sec^{-1}), with decreasing durations (as indicated by the underlying lines). The length of the pauses that they initiate is function of these durations. Neither the upper nor the lower portions of the spikes are seen. Calibrations: 25 mV; 0·25 sec.

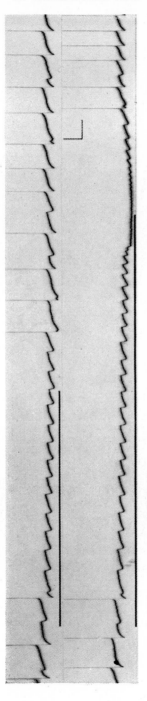

Fig. 17. Hyperpolarizations and high frequency inhibitory post-synaptic potentials by infra-red action.

Gen soma of the parieto-genital ganglion initially autoactive. Two irradiations of equal intensities (2×10^{-4} cal g mm^{-2} sec^{-1}), were successively applied locally to the soma (as indicated by the black lines under each record). They determine an immediate increase of the membrane potential, inhibition of the spikes, increase of the i.p.s.p.'s frequency. During the first 3 sec the two equal irradiations initiate stereotypically an identical sequence of events. The infra-red action being prolonged (lower record), the i.p.s.p.'s reach the highest frequency (24/sec) and the membrane stabilizes at a higher hyperpolarized state. Suppression of the irradiation permits the redepolarization of the membrane, the progressive decrease to zero of the i.p.s.p.'s frequency, and finally the re-emission of the spikes, at higher frequency than initially. The upper portions of the spikes are not seen. Calibrations: 25 mV; 0·25 sec.

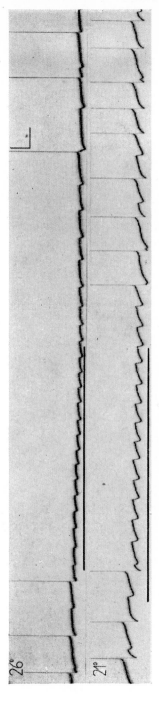

FIG. 18. Comparison of the infra-red effects at two different temperatures. Same soma as in Fig. 17, submitted to infra-red radiations of equal intensity $(2 \times 10^{-6} \text{ cal g mm}^{-2}\text{sec}^{-1})$ at two different temperatures: consecutively at 26 and at 21°C. At 26°C the membrane potential was 5 mV higher than that at 21°C. Accordingly the amplitude of the hyperpolarization by infra-red and that of the superimposed i.p.s.p.'s are lower at 26°C. The upper portions of the spikes are not seen. Calibrations: 25 mV; 0·25 sec.

Mechanisms of the infra-red inhibitions. Infra-red radiations injected in a cell may be operative in various ways: important cellular macromolecules strongly absorb infra-red radiations (Klotz, Griswold and Gruen, 1949; Ambrose and Elliott, 1951a, 1951b; Elliott, 1951). Thus, significant changes in the configuration of the macromolecules and in their interactions may be elicited. Transitions may hence be expected: (1) in functions involving enzyme actions and depending upon specific interactions of these macro-molecules; (2) in functions involving a specific sequence of chemical groups. Such transitions might thus act by introducing changes in the velocity constants of significant chain reactions, in specific loci, and relative to the inhibitory processes observed by infra-red action. The reactions involved might be relevant to those which are actually triggered by the arrival of the inhibitory impulses at the presynaptic terminals. Extensive studies are now available on various blocking molecules extracted from nervous tissue (see Hayashi, 1959), especially γ-aminobutyric acid which accounts for nearly all the activities of Florey's Factor I (Florey, 1954; Florey and MacLennan, 1955a, 1955b; Elliott and Florey, 1956; Wiersma, Furshpan and Florey, 1953)

The spectacular effects of GABA on neuronal activity acquire all the more interest in so far as GABA is involved in energy metabolism in nervous tissue. GABA is formed in the brain from glutamic acid by the action of an enzyme found only in the CNS, an L-glutamic acid decarboxylase. Important relations must exist between the enzymes involved in the metabolism of GABA and those of the tricarboxylic acid cycle. The attraction of such a perspective lies in providing a pattern wherein mechanisms of release of a chemical transmitter would be identified with activation of a definite enzy-matic reaction involved in the normal energy metabolism of the cell. It is obvious that besides the biochemical and electrophysiological information on the GABA properties, knowledge of the cellular loci wherein its enzymatic cycle is implied, and of specific tools to activate the latter, would be highly promising.

DISCUSSION

The value of the foregoing photoactivation data lies mainly in providing means for the analysis of a series of outstanding cellular reactions: among others, the excitatory and inhibitory processes, the generator depolarization, and the integrative processes taking place in sensory and central organs.

The interesting point is here twofold. On one hand, to use injections of light as cellular stimuli is actually to handle an instrumental tool: photons act specifically in definite cellular sites where they are absorbed and there-from act through specific pathways. On the other hand, the fact that the reactions are fairly similar in the nerve cell and in the axon, which is free of synaptic structures, affords several sound conclusions in otherwise contro-versial mechanisms.

Considering the particular case of the generator depolarizations induced by light, the present study reveals them as endowed with strikingly analogous characteristics, whether elicited in highly specialized cells as visual photo-receptors (see Fuortes, 1959), or in cells such as *Aplysia* ganglion somata completely deprived of any photoreceptor function. It has been suggested that the mechanism mediating the generator potential proceeds in the photo-receptor through the release of some chemical transmitter (Fuortes, 1959; Grundfest, 1958). If the same hypothesis could also be adopted for the mechanism of the generator depolarization induced by light in the *Aplysia* soma, we would expect to find in both cells some common, possibly synaptic, fundamental function. But generator depolarization is also elicited by light in the simple stained *Sepia* axon itself, wherein no synaptic structure is implied.

Thus, irrespective of the proper functions of the various cells considered (see above, p. 209), generator potentials may be triggered by stimuli of various nature, by synaptic bombardment, or even by intramural determinants acting in the pacemaker sites of the cell. Hence, in the building up of the generator depolarization, some link common to the different cells and activable by the various kinds of energy, must be implied.

The particular case of the light stimulus is but an aspect in one of the most fascinating and most intensively investigated fields in biology, that which concerns transitions from light to life.

As electrophysiologists, our problem is to situate in time and space the bioelectrical transitions of which the cell membrane is the site, in the long sequence of events initiated on injection of light into the cell. Whatever be the case, the first act is the absorption of a photon by a given molecule in a given cellular site, i.e. the raising of an electron to a higher energy level. In the reactions to light considered here, the input of the electromagnetic energy is on definite cytostructures where the pigment molecules are ordered (granules and lamellae in lipochondria (*Aplysia* nerve cells), cristae in mito-chondria (cardiac cells), lamellae and grana in chloroplasts (plant cells), lamellae in the retinal photoreceptors' outer segment), or where the dye molecules are stacked, as in the stained axon.

An impressive amount of sound information concerning the above sequence is available from works on photosynthesis. Fortunately, on illumination, generator depolarization and spike discharge have been also demonstrated at the cell membrane output, in a suitable plant cell, the Nitella (Arvanitaki and Chalazonitis, 1949c, 1950). Thus, several mechanisms tracked in the processes of plant cells' photoactivation might be suggested as fitting to our problem.

The concentration of absorbing molecules (cytochromes in the mito-chondria, intraneuronal heme-protein and carotene protein in the *Aplysia* lipochondria, stacked dye molecules in the stained axon membrane, visual

16

pigments in the photoreceptors' outer segment) is high enough to justify an approach to excitation and to photo-physical processes from the standpoint of phenomena in the solid state physics, as first suggested by Szent-Györgyi (1941), and worked out in the case of dye molecules aggregates and of chlorophyll molecules in the chloroplast (Bradley and Calvin, 1955; Calvin, 1955, 1959; MacRae and Kasha, 1958; Rabinowitch, 1958; and others; among earlier studies, Kautsky and Hirsch, 1931).

The absorption of a light quantum by a chlorophyll molecule raises it to its excited state; the excited state "wanders around as an exciton" until it finds a point of ionization leading to the creation of a "conduction" electron leaving a "hole" behind. The pair, excited electron and "hole", might move and be found in a site possibly far removed from the original locus of the excitation. This migration theory or energy transfer as proposed by Calvin requires the presence of a relevant cytostructural, highly organized apparatus such as that of the lamellae and grana in the chloroplast where chlorophyll and caro-tenoids are highly concentrated and incorporated in orderly arrays. Such migration of energy might permit, as has been seen in solutions of certain dyes, transfers at distances of nearly one micron from the site of excitation.

The binding energy of the electron-"hole" pair being small, under the mere influence of thermal motion, or the pull of an applied electric field, electron and "hole" might be thrown into separate traps, where they could survive for relatively long periods of time. The whole picture is consistent with the semi-conducting properties found in various dried, organic sub-stances including haemoglobin (Inokuchi, 1951; Eley, Parfitt, Perry and Taysum, 1953; Cardew and Eley, 1959), with the photoconductivity of dried chloroplasts and moreover with the demonstration of the separation of electric charges on illumination of the junction between chlorophyll and carotene. The potential difference (chlorophyll negative with respect to caro-tene) may then be as high as 600–1·300 mV (Arnold and Maclay, 1959). The trapped "holes" can be carried away by some electron donor molecule to form chemical radicals; the trapped electrons are picked up by suitable carriers and transferred to acceptors such as pyridine nucleotides or others. Such space separation of micro-oxidant from micro-reducing loci would be the point at which photoenzymatic processes enter the picture.

Applying the above to the illuminated pigmented nerve cells, cardiac cells, stained axon and even to the retinal photo-receptor, we might envisage the primary photophysical process as the creation of myriads of micro-photobatteries in the cellular sites where photons are absorbed. Proceeding from the creation of micro-oxidant and micro-reducing loci, transitions might be induced into the nearby respiratory chain. In fact data are available indicat-ing a high acceleration of electron transfer in the respiratory chain, in illu-minated cells (Chalazonitis, 1954):

The rate of oxygen consumption of the illuminated axons increases by 205% of the rate measured in dark axons at 12°C.

In anaerobic conditions, the rate of reduction of intracellular hydrogen acceptors (such as methylene blue micro-injected in the cell) is increased by 400% as compared to the rate observed in the dark.

The rate of reduction of cytochrome c in yeast cells is increased by 100% under illumination as compared to the rate in the dark.

The rate of deoxygenation of the intraneuronal heme-protein is accelerated by 100% under light.

But, how might mechanisms of the first detectable photobioelectrical response, i.e. of the generator depolarization, be related, in time and space, to the events in the above sequence? In nerve cells (*Aplysia*), the cell membrane, site of the generator depolarization, is one micron or more distant from the nearest lipochondria wherein the initial photophysical act is performed. In the present state of our knowledge, radiationless electronic energy transfer from lipochondria to the membrane cannot be proved. The transitions in the respiratory chain, initiated on the creation of micro-oxidant and micro-reducing loci, start some 10^{-3} sec later, being thus fairly concomitant to the development of the generator depolarization. Hence, if in the mechanisms of the generator depolarization a chemical mediator has to be invoked, the latter might be relevant to the respiratory metabolism.

> As regards the inhibitory effects elicited by activation of the carotene molecules, the mechanisms are not well understood. Platt (1959) pictures the carotene as an electron donor–acceptor molecule which would act as a very suitable mediator of the electron transfer. If activated, this molecule might be associated with the oxidizing reducing centers and thus interfere with the respiratory chain.

In the methylene-blue or neutral-red-stained axon the dye molecules bind themselves to the axon membrane and aggregate therein, by stacking into polymers. This is a suitable structural device which would allow the application of the exciton theory and might suggest efficient energy transfers. Moreover, both the primary photophysical sequence (excitation of the dye molecule, photoconductivity, migration of energy, oxidant-reducing microspots) and the bioelectrical transitions coincide here on the same cytostructural site, i.e. the cell membrane.

The stained axon might prove to be a very useful experimental model in our analysis. The so-called lamellae of the retinal photoreceptor's outer segment where the pigments are ordered should (according to recent data from Moody and Robertson (1960)) be visualized as the regular, orderly repeating infoldings of a wide differentiated portion of the cell membrane itself. The stained axon might thus be viewed as a rough, primitive replica of the retinal photoreceptor's outer segment, but as one which provides, nevertheless, reliable data. These strongly suggest that at least generator potentials might actually be initiated by light in the retinal photoreceptor cell itself by mechanisms which are not necessarily different from those implied in the stained axon membrane.

The above suggestions stand somewhat outside the traditional paths. They are only tentatively put forward in order to devise useful frames for further investigation. Much work will be necessary in order to ascertain whether they do or do not offer the best way towards an explanation. Fluorescence studies will prove relevant in order to acquire further precise data concerning time and space resolution of the bioelectrical transitions in the sequence of events initiated by the light. The nature of the mechanisms involved in the membrane conductance changes which underly the generator depolarization and the inhibitory hyperpolarization processes induced by the light are of outstanding importance. Here again, the stained axon will prove a useful model for experimentation.

Whatever the mechanisms of the light action may prove to be, the introduction of the light as stimulus into methods of comparative investigations might be a consistently a useful tool in analysis and in the extension of new concepts to the electrophysiological field.

ACKNOWLEDGEMENTS

Permission to reproduce Plate 1 and Figs. 4 and 5 from the *Bulletin de l'Institut Océanographique de Monaco* is gratefully acknowledged.

REFERENCES

AMBROSE, E. J. and ELLIOTT, A. (1951a) Infra-red spectra and structure of fibrous proteins. *Proc. Roy. Soc.* A **206** : 206–219.

AMBROSE, E. J. and ELLIOTT, A. (1951b) Infra-red spectroscopic studies of globular protein structure. *Proc. Roy. Soc.* A **208** : 75–90.

ARNOLD, W. and MACLAY, H. K. (1959) Chloroplasts and chloroplast pigments as semi-conductors. *The Photochemical Apparatus. Brookhaven* **11**, : 1–9.

ARSONVAL, A. D'. (1891) La fibre musculaire est directement excitable par la lumière. *C.R. Soc. Biol.* **43** : 318–320.

ARVANITAKI, A. (1938) *Les variations graduées de la polarisation des systèmes excitables.* Hermann, Paris.

ARVANITAKI, A. (1939) Recherches sur la réponse oscillatoire locale de l'axone géant isolé de *Sepia. Arch. Internat. Physiol.* **49** : 209–256.

ARVANITAKI, A. and CHALAZONITIS, N. (1947) Réactions bioélectriques à la photoactivation des cytochromes. *Arch. Sci. Physiol.* **1** : 385–405.

ARVANITAKI, A. and CHALAZONITIS, N. (1949a) Réactions bioélectriques neuroniques à la photoactivation spécifique d'une hème-protéine et d'une carotène-protéine. *Arch. Sci. Physiol.* **3** : 27–44.

ARVANITAKI A. and CHALAZONITIS, N. (1949b) Inhibition ou excitation des potentiels neuroniques à la photoactivation distincte de deux chromoprotéides (Caroténoïde et chlorophyllien). *Arch. Sci. Physiol.* **3** : 45–60.

ARVANITAKI, A. and CHALAZONITIS, N. (1949c) Catalyse respiratoire et potentiels bio-électriques. *Arch. Sci. Physiol.* **3** : 303–338.

ARVANITAKI, A. and CHALAZONITIS, N. (1949d) Prototypes d'interactions neuroniques et transmissions synaptiques. Données bioélectriques de préparations cellulaires. *Arch. Sci. Physiol.* **3** : 547–566.

ARVANITAKI, A. and CHALAZONITIS, N. (1950) Effets narcotiques sur les biopotentiels neuroniques et sur la catalyse respiratoire. In *Mécanisme de la Narcose, Coll. Internat. C.N.R.S.*, Paris. 195–215.

ARVANITAKI, A. and CHALAZONITIS, N. (1951) Recherches sur la répartition de quelques catalyseurs respiratoires dans l'espace cellulaire. (Axone géant et some neuronique de *Sepia*). *Arch. Sci. Physiol.* **5** : 207–226.

ARVANITAKI, A. and CHALAZONITIS, N. (1955a) Potentiels d'activité du soma neuronique géant (*Aplysia*). *Arch. Sci. Physiol.* **9** : 115–144.

ARVANITAKI, A. and CHALAZONITIS, N. (1955b) Phase descendante à "Palier" de la pointe axonique (*Sepia*). In *Microphysiologie comparée des éléments excitables, Coll. Internat. C.N.R.S.* **67** : 153–158.

ARVANITAKI, A. and CHALAZONITIS, N. (1957a) Réfractivités introduites par les potentiels positifs du soma neuronique, en activité autoentretenue. *C.R. Acad. Sci.* **245** : 445–447.

ARVANITAKI, A. and CHALAZONITIS, N. (1957b) Actions inhibitrices sur la genèse des potentiels positifs du soma neuronique. *C.R. Acad. Sci.* **245** : 1029–1032.

ARVANITAKI, A. and CHALAZONITIS, N. (1958a) Activation par la lumière des neurones pigmentés. *Arch. Sci. Physiol.* **12** : 73–106.

ARVANITAKI, A. and CHALAZONITIS, N. (1958b) Configurations modales de l'activité, propres à différents neurones d'un même centre. *J. Physiol. Paris.* **50** : 122–125.

ARVANITAKI, A. and CHALAZONITIS, N. (1959) Interactions électriques entre le soma géant A et les somata immédiatement contigus. (Ganglion pleuro-branchial d'*Aplysia*). *Bull. Inst. océanogr.* **1143** : 1–30.

ARVANITAKI, A, and CHALAZONITIS, N. (1960) Photopotentiels d'excitation et d'inhibition de différents somata identifiables (*Aplysia*). Activations monochromatiques. *Bull. Inst. océanogr.* **1164** : 1–83.

BARRON, D. H. and MATTHEWS, B. H. C. (1938) The interpretation of potential changes in the spinal cord. *J. Physiol.* **92** : 276–321.

BERNHARD, C. G. and GRANIT, R. (1946) Nerve as a model temperature end organ. *J. Gen. Physiol.* **29** : 257–265.

BLUM, H. F. (1941) *Photodynamic Action and Diseases Caused by Light.* Reinhold Publ. Co., New York.

BRADLEY, D. F. and CALVIN, M. (1955) The effect of thioctic acid on the quantum efficiency of the Hill reaction in intermittent light. *Proc. Nat. Acad. Sci.* **41** : 563–571.

BULLOCK, T. H. (1956) Temperature sensitivity of some unit synapses. *Publ. Staz. Zool. Napoli.* **28** : 305–314.

BULLOCK, T. H., and DIECKE, F. P. J. (1956) Properties of an infra-red receptor. *J. Physiol.* **134** : 47–87.

BULLOCK, T. H. and FOX, W. (1957) The anatomy of the infra-red sense organ in the facial pit of pit vipers. *Quart. J. Micr. Sci.* **98** : 219–234.

CALVIN, M. (1955) The photosynthetic carbon cycle. In *Conférences et Rapports 3e Congrès Internat. Bioch.*, Bruxelles.

CALVIN, M. (1959) From Microstructure to Macrostructure and Function in the Photo-chemical Apparatus. *The Photochemical Apparatus. Brookhaven.* **11** : 160–180.

CARDEW, M. H. and ELEY, D. D. (1959) The semiconductivity of organic substances. Part 3. Haemoglobin and some amino acids. *Disc. Faraday Soc.* **27** : 115–128.

CHALAZONITIS, N. (1954) *Effets de la lumière sur l'évolution des potentiels cellulaires et sur quelques vitesses d'oxydoréduction dans les neurones.* Thèse Sciences, Paris.

CHALAZONITIS, N. (1961a) Chemopotentials in giant nerve cells. (*Aplysia fasciata*). This Volume, p. 179.

228   A. ARVANITAKI AND N. CHALAZONITIS

CHALAZONITIS, N. (1961b) Evolutions differenciées en fonction de la température des caractéristiques de l'activité électrique de quelques neurones identifiables (neurones d'*Aplysia*). *J. Physiol., Paris*. In press.

CHALAZONITIS, N. and ARVANITAKI, A. (1951) Identification et localisation de quelques catalyseurs respiratoires dans le neurone d'*Aplysia*. *Bull. Inst. océanogr.* **996** : 1–20.

CHALAZONITIS, N. and ARVANITAKI, A. (1956) Chromoprotéides et succinoxydase dans divers grains isolables du cytoplasme neuronique. *Arch. Sci. Physiol.* **10** : 291–319.

CHALAZONITIS, N. and ARVANITAKI, A. (1957) Pointes et potentiels positifs du soma neuronique en fonction de la température. *C.R. Acad. Sci.* **245** : 1079–1081.

CHALAZONITIS, N. and ARVANITAKI, A. (1958) Dérivation endocytaire simultanée de l'activité de différents neurones *in situ*. *C.R. Acad. Sci.* **246** : 161–163.

CHALAZONITIS, N. and LENOIR, J. (1959) Ultrastructure et organisation du neurone d'*Aplysia*. Etude au microscope électronique. *Bull. Inst. océanogr.* **1144** : 1–11.

CLAUDE, A. and FULLAM, E. F. (1945) An electron microscope study of isolated mitochondria. *J. Exp. Med.* **81** : 51–62.

COLE, K. S. (1941) Rectification and inductance in the squid giant axon. *J. Gen. Physiol.* **25** : 29–51.

COOMBS, J. S., ECCLES, J. C. and FATT, P. (1955) The inhibitory suppression of reflex discharges from motoneurones. *J. Physiol.* **130** : 396–413.

DUDEL, J. and TRAUTWEIN, W. (1958) Der Mechanismus der automatischen rhythmischen Impulsbildung der Herzmuskelfaser. *Pflüg. Arch. ges. Physiol.* **267** : 553–565.

ELEY, D. D., PARFITT, G. D., PERRY, M. J. and TAYSUM, D. H. (1953) Semiconductivity of organic substances. *Trans. Faraday Soc.* **49** : 79–86.

ELLIOTT, A. (1951) Infra-red dichroism and chain orientation in crystalline ribonuclease. *Proc. Roy. Soc.* A **211** : 490–499.

ELLIOTT, K. A. C. and FLOREY, E. (1956) Factor I—inhibitory factor from brain. *J. Neurochem.* **1** : 181–192.

EYZAGUIRRE, C. and KUFFLER, S. W. (1955a) Processes of excitation in the dendrites and in the soma of single isolated sensory nerve cells of the lobster and crayfish. *J. Gen. Physiol.* **39** : 87–119.

EYZAGUIRRE, C. and KUFFLER, S. W. (1955b) Further study of soma, dendrites and axon excitation in single neurons. *J. Gen. Physiol.* **39** : 121–153.

FATT, P. and KATZ, B. (1953) The effect of inhibitory nerve impulses on a crustacean muscle fibre. *J. Physiol.* **121** : 374–389.

FINEAN, J. B., SJÖSTRAND, F. S. and STEINMANN, E. (1953) Submicroscopic organization of some layered lipoprotein structures (nerve myelin, retinal rods and chloroplasts). *Exp. Cell. Res.* **5** : 557–559.

FLOREY, E. (1954) An inhibitory and an excitatory factor of mammalian central nervous system, and their action on a single sensory neuron. *Arch. int. Physiol.* **62** : 33–53.

FLOREY, E. and FLOREY, E. (1955) Microanatomy of the abdominal stretch receptors of the crayfish (*Astacus Fluviatilis L.*). *J. Gen. Physiol.* **39** : 69–85.

FLOREY, E. and MACLENNAN, H. (1955a) The release of an inhibitory substance from mammalian brain, and its effect on peripheral synaptic transmission. *J. Physiol.* **129** : 384–392.

FLOREY, E. and MACLENNAN, H. (1955b) Effects of an inhibitory factor (Factor I) from brain on central synaptic transmission. *J. Physiol.* **130** : 446–455.

FUORTES, M. G. F. (1958) Generation, conduction and transmission of nerve impulses. *Arch. ital. biol.* **96** : 285–293.

FUORTES, M. G. F. (1959) Initiation of impulses in visual cells of *Limulus*. *J. Physiol.* **148** : 14–28.

GALAMBOS, R. and DAVIS, H. (1944) Inhibition of activity in single auditory nerve fibers by acoustic stimulation. *J. Neurophysiol.* **7** : 287.

GRANIT, R. (1947) *Sensory Mechanisms of the Retina*. University Press, Oxford.

GRANIT, R. (1950) The organization of the vertebrate retinal elements. *Ergebn. der Physiol.* **46** : 31–70.

GRANIT, R. (1952) Aspects of excitation and inhibition in the retina. *Proc. Roy. Soc.* B **140** : 191–199.

GRANIT, R. (1955) *Receptors and Sensory Perception.* Yale University Press, New Haven.
GRANIT, R. and SKOGLUND, C. R. (1945) Effect of temperature on artificial synapse formed by cut end of mammalian nerve. *J. Neurophysiol.* **8** : 211–217.
GRUNDFEST, H. (1957) Excitation triggers in post-junctional cells. In *Physiological Triggers.* 119–151.
GRUNDFEST, H. (1958) An electrophysiological basis for cone vision in fish. *Arch. Ital. Biol.* **96** : 135–144.
GRUNDFEST, H., REUBEN, J. P. and RICKLES, W. H. JR. (1959) The electrophysiology and pharmacology of lobster neuromuscular synapses. *J. Gen. Physiol.* **42** : 1301–1323.
HAGIWARA, S. and BULLOCK, T. H. (1957) Intracellular potentials in pacemaker and integrative neurons of the lobster cardiac ganglion. *J. Cell. Comp. Physiol.* **50** : 25–47.
HARTLINE, H. K. (1938) The discharge of impulses in the optic nerve of Pecten in response to illumination of the eye. *J. Cell. Comp. Physiol.* **11** : 465–478.
HARTLINE, H. K. (1941–1942) The neural mechanisms of vision. *Harvey Lectures* **37** : 39.
HARTLINE, H. K. (1949) Inhibition of activity of visual receptors by illuminating nearby retinal areas in the *Limulus* eye (abstract). *Fed. Proc.* **8** : 69.
HARTLINE, H. K., WAGNER, H. G. and MACNICHOL, E. F. JR. (1952) The peripheral origin of nervous activity in the visual system. In *Cold Spring Harbor Symposia Quant. Biol.* **17** : 125–141.
HARTLINE, H. K., WAGNER, H. G. and RATLIFF, F. (1956) Inhibition in the eye of *Limulus.* *J. Gen. Physiol.* **39** : 651–673.
HAYASHI, T. (1959) *Neurophysiology and Neurochemistry of Convulsion.* Dainihon-Tosho Co. Ltd., Tokyo.
HORRIDGE, G. A. (1961) The organization of the primitive central nervous system as suggested by examples of inhibition, and the structure of neuropile. This volume, p. 395.
HOYLE, G., and WIERSMA, C. A. G. (1958a) Excitation at neuromuscular junctions in crustacea. *J. Physiol.* **143** : 403–425.
HOYLE, G. and WIERSMA, C. A. G. (1958b) Inhibition at neuromuscular junctions in crustacea. *J. Physiol.* **143** : 426–440.
HUTTER, O. F. and TRAUTWEIN, W. (1955) Vagal effects on the sinus venosus of the frog's heart. *J. Physiol.* **129** : 48 P.
INOKUCHI, H. (1951) Electrical conductivity of the condensed polynuclear aromatic compounds. *Bull. Chem. Soc. Japan.* **24** : 222–226.
KAUTSKY, H. and HIRSCH, A. (1931) Neue Versuche zur Kohlensäureassimilation. *Naturwissenschaften.* **19** : 964.
KENNEDY, D. (1958) Neural photosensitivity. *Mactra. Biol. Bull.* **115** : 338.
KERKUT, G. A. and TAYLOR, B. J. R. (1956) Effect of temperature on the spontaneous activity from the isolated ganglia of the slug, cockroach and crayfish. *Nature, Lond.* **178** : 426.
KLOTZ, IR., GRISWOLD, P. and GRUEN, D. M. (1949) Infra-red spectra of some proteins and related substances. *J. Amer. Chem. Soc.* **71** : 1615–1620.
KOLMODIN, G. M. and SKOGLUND, C. R. (1958) Slow membrane potential changes accompanying excitation and inhibition in spinal moto- and interneurons in the Cat during natural activation. *Acta Physiol. Scand.* **44** : 11–54.
KOSMAN, A. J. (1938) The influence of photodynamic sensitization on the electrical and chemical stimulation of muscle and cutaneous nerve endings in the frog. *J. Cell. Comp. Physiol.* **11** : 279–289.
KOSMAN, A. J. and LILLIE, R. S. (1935) Photodynamically induced oxygen consumption in muscle and nerve. *J. Cell. Comp. Physiol.* **6** : 505–515.
KUFFLER, S. W. (1953) Discharge patterns and functional organization of mammalian retina. *J. Neurophysiol.* **16** : 37–68.
KUFFLER, S. W. (1958) Synaptic inhibitory mechanisms. Properties of dendrites and problems of excitation in isolated sensory nerve cells. *Exp. Cell Res. Suppl.* **5** : 493–519.
KUFFLER, S. W. (1959) Excitation and inhibition in single nerve cells. *Harvey Lectures* 1958–1959 : 176–218.

KUFFLER, S. W. and EYZAGUIRRE, C. (1955) Synaptic inhibition in an isolated nerve cell. *J. Gen. Physiol.* **39** : 155–184.

LI, C.-L. and JASPER, H. (1953) Microelectrode studies of the electrical activity of the cerebral cortex in the cat. *J. Physiol.* **121** : 117–140.

LIPPAY, F. (1929) Über Wirkungen des Lichtes auf den quergestreiften Muskel. I. Versuche mit sichtbarem Licht an sensibilisierten Kaltblütermuskeln. *Pflüg. Arch. Ges. Physiol.* **222** : 616–639.

LIPPAY, F. (1930) Über Wirkungen des Lichtes auf den quergestreiften Muskel. II. Versuche mit sichtbarem Licht an sensibilisierten Kaltblütermuskeln. Fortsetzung. *Pflüg. Arch. Ges. Physiol.* **224** : 587–599.

LLOYD, D. P. C. (1949) Post-tetanic potentiation of response in monosynaptic reflex pathways of the spinal cord. *J. Gen. Physiol.* **33** : 147–170.

LOEWENSTEIN, W. R. and RATHKAMP, R. (1958) The sites for mechano-electric conversion in a Pacinian corpuscle. *J. Gen. Physiol.* **41** : 1245–1265.

MACLEOD, P. (1959) Premiéres données sur l'électro-olfactogramme du Lapin. *J. Physiol. Paris.* **51**: 85–92.

MACNICHOL, E. F. JR. and SVAETICHIN, G. (1958) Electric responses from the isolated retinas of fishes. *Amer. J. Ophthalmol.* **46** : 26–46.

MACNICHOL, E. F., JR., WAGNER, H. H. and HARTLINE, H. K. (1953) Electrical activity recorded within single ommatidia of the eye of *Limulus*. *XIX Congr. Internat. Physiol.*, Montréal. 582.

MACRAE, E. G. and KASHA, M. (1958) Enhancement of phosphorescene ability upon aggregation of dye molecules. *J. Chem. Phys.* **28** : 721.

MOODY, M. F. and ROBERTSON, J. D. (1960) The fine structure of some retinal photoreceptors. *J. Biophys. Biochem. Cytol.* **7**: 87–93.

MOUNTCASTLE, V. B. (1957) Modality and topographic properties of single neurons of cat's somatic sensory cortex. *J. Neurophysiol.* **20** : 408–434.

OTANI, T. and BULLOCK, T. H. (1959) Effects of presetting the membrane potential of the soma of spontaneous and integrating ganglion cells. *Physiol. Zool.* **32** : 104–114.

OTTOSON, D. (1956) Analysis of the electrical activity of the olfactory epithelium. *Acta Physiol. Scand.* **35** *Suppl.* 122 : 7–83.

PALADE, G. E. (1952) The fine structure of mitochondria. *Anat. Record.* **114** : 427–451.

PALADE, G. E. (1953) An electron microscope study of the mitochondrial structure. *J. Histochem. Cytochem.* **1** : 188–211.

PLATT, J. R. (1959) Carotene-donor–acceptor complexes in photosynthesis. *Science* **129** : 372–374.

PORTER, K. R., CLAUDE, A. and FULLAM, E. F. (1945) A study of tissue culture cells by electron microscopy. *J. Exp. Med.* **81** : 233–246.

PROSSER, C. L. (1934) Responses to illumination of the eye and caudal ganglion. *J. Cell. Comp. Physiol.* **4** : 363–378.

RABINOWITCH, E. (1959) Primary photochemical and photophysical processes in photosynthesis. *Plant Physiol.* **34** : 213–218.

ROBERTIS, E. DE and LASANSKY, A. (1958) Submicroscopic organization of retinal cones of the rabbit. *J. Biophys. Biochem. Cytol.* **4** : 743.

SANDOW, A. and ISAACSON, A. (1960) Effects of methylene blue, acridine orange, and zinc on muscular contraction. *Biochem. Biophys. Research Communications.* **2** : 455–458.

SEGAL, J. R. (1958) An anodal threshold phenomenon in the squid giant axon. *Nature, Lond.* **182** : 1370.

SJÖSTRAND, F. S. (1953a) The ultra-structure of the outer segments of rods and cones of the eye as revealed by the electron microscope. *J. Cell. Comp. Physiol.* **42** : 15–44.

SJÖSTRAND, F. S. (1953b) Ultra-structure of rod-shaped mitochondria. *Nature, Lond.* **171** : 30–31.

SPYROPOULOS, C. S. (1959) Miniature responses under "voltage-clamp". *Amer. J. Physiol.* **196** : 783–790.

SPYROPOULOS, C. S. (1961) Initiation and abolition of the electric response of the nerve fiber by thermal and chemical means. *Amer. J. Physiol.*, In press.

STEINMANN, E. and SJÖSTRAND, F. S. (1955) The ultrastructure of chloroplasts. *Exp. Cell Res.* **8** : 15–22.

SVAETICHIN, G. (1956) Spectral response curves from single cones. *Acta Physiol. Scand.* **39** : 20–46.

SZENT-GYÖRGYI, A. (1941) The study of energy–level in biochemistry. *Nature, Lond.*, 148: 157–159.

SZENTAGOTHAI, J. (1961) Anatomical aspects of inhibitory pathways and synapses. This volume, p. 32.

TASAKI, I. (1959) Resting and action potentials of reversed polarity in frog nerve cells. *Nature, Lond.* **184** : 1574–1575.

TASAKI, I. and HAGIWARA, S. (1957) Demonstration of two stable potential states in the squid giant axon under tetraethylammonium chloride. *J. Gen. Physiol.* **40** : 859–885.

TASAKI, I. and SPYROPOULOS, C. S. (1958) Nonuniform response in the squid axon membrane under "voltage-clamp". *Amer. J. Physiol.* **193** : 309–317.

WALD, G. (1950) The interconversion of the retinenes and vitamins A *in vitro. Biochim. et Biophys. Acta* **4** : 215–228.

WALD, G. and BROWN, P. K. (1956) Synthesis and bleaching of rhodopsin. *Nature, Lond.* **177** : 174–176.

WALL, P. D. (1958) Excitability changes in afferent fibre terminations and their relation to slow potentials. *J. Physiol.* **142** : 1–21.

WALL, P. D. and JOHNSON, A. R. (1958) Changes associated with post-tetanic potentiation of a monosynaptic reflex. *J. Neurophysiol.* **21** : 148–158.

WATANABE, A., and BULLOCK, T. H. (1959) Modulation of activity of one neuron by subthreshold slow potentials in another. *Fed. Proc.* **18** : 167.

WIERSMA, C. A. G., FURSHPAN, E. and FLOREY, E. (1953) Physiological and pharmacological observations on muscle receptor organs of the crayfish, *Cambarus clarkii* Girard. *J. Exp. Biol.* **30** : 136–150.

WOLKEN, J. J. and PALADE, G. E. (1952) Fine structure of chloroplasts in two flagellates. *Nature, Lond.* **170** : 114–115.

ON THE ANATOMY OF THE GIANT NEURONS
OF THE VISCERAL GANGLION OF *APLYSIA*

THEODORE H. BULLOCK

Department of Zoology, University of California, Los Angeles

THE beautiful photomicrographs and electrical records shown by Arvanitaki and Chalazonitis to this meeting and the remarkable evidence of Tauc (1960) of several kinds of inhibition in the giant neurons of the visceral ganglion of *Aplysia* point to the great value of this preparation. I am sure we will be hearing much more about it.

One of the reasons for its interest is the indication of localized activity in various fractions of the membrane electrically visible to a micropipette in the soma. Besides large and small synaptic potentials, excitatory and inhibitory, Tauc has reported various sized small spike-like potentials and pacemaker potentials that are sometimes closer, sometimes farther from the recording electrode tip. Both of the French laboratories have also noted a curious synchronization of adjacent cells at times.

These and other properties attract attention to the anatomy of the ganglion and particularly of the giant cells and fibers. Arvanitaki, Cardot and Tchou (1941, 1942) have given us the little that is available beyond the gross anatomy of earlier authors (see Hoffmann, 1932–1939).

The following observations are supplementary to these and, although preliminary, may call attention to the opportunities inherent in this material. The electron microscope work was done by Dr. Elizabeth Batham of the University of Otago, while visiting in our department, and the electrical neuronography by a graduate student, Mr. Lawrence Goldman.

The visceral ganglion is seen in ordinary histological sections (Fig. 1) to be a typical molluscan ganglion in the following respects. A central core of fibrous matter is surrounded by a rind of cell bodies. Continuous with the core are the two great pleurovisceral connectives, right and left and several large peripheral nerves. The core presents two aspects—tracts consisting of fibers of passage and neuropile distinguished by its finer, more tangled texture. The rind consists of unipolar cells of widely varying sizes, numbering several hundreds, all with large nuclei poor in chromatin and with distinct cytoplasm. Few or no granule-type or globuli-type cells—very small,

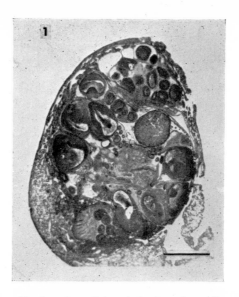

FIG. 1. Low magnification view of the whole visceral ganglion of *Aplysia californica*. Note thick connective tissue on lower left, true neuropile with giant and small fibers in center, cross section of the base of a nerve just above this, small and large ganglion cells around the outside. Fixative: Flemming's strong; stain: Masson trichrome; calibration: 0.5 mm.

chromatin-rich and plasma-poor—are present. The giant cells grade continuously into the large and intermediate sized cells (Fig. 2). The largest giant cells in *Aplysia californica* of about 20 cm relaxed length (approx. 275 g) are about 400 micra; in *A. vaccaria* of 25 cm, 800 micra. Certain ones are distinctive and usually recognizable individually by their size and position. Groupings of cells have been described by Arvanitaki and Tchou (1942). Abundant glia cells are found, especially as thick capsules around the largest cells and massive sheaths around the larger nerve fibers in the tracts, nerves and connectives. The outer connective tissue coat around the nerves and connectives is extremely thick and that around the ganglion is also in many places.

A special feature of the giant cells and fibers which I want to illustrate in particular is the enormous increase in surface area in certain places. Most of the largest cell bodies are extensively invaded by strands and trabeculae of glial cells. The appearances shown in Figs. 2, 3, 4 and 5 are no doubt equivalent to the trophospongium seen by Holmgren (1902) and other early authors in crayfish, snail and other cells. It is confined in *Aplysia* giant cells to the inner or axonal side. The cytoplasm of the axon is markedly different in texture and staining affinities from that in most of the soma and extends broadly into the

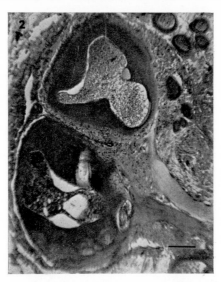

FIG. 2. Two giant nerve cells giving off axons toward the neuropile on the right, surface of the ganglion to the left. Note the difference in stain and texture between axoplasm and cytoplasm of the soma, lobulated nucleus and especially the connective tissue invasion of the axon hillock region, forming islands in the lower cell. Calibration: 100 micra.

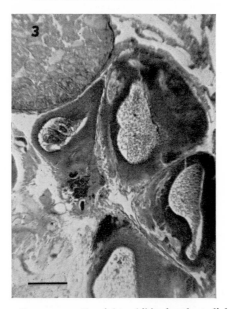

FIG. 3. The giant cell somata on the right exhibit abundant glial invasions deep in the cytoplasm—all the pale staining wisps. The cells in the center show pigment concentrations. Above, a cross section of a nerve at its origin. Giant axons in neuropile at the left. Calibration: 100 micra.

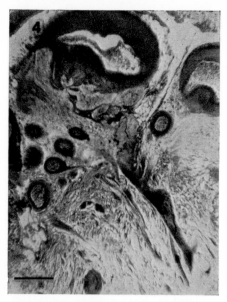

FIG. 4. The inner border of the giant cell is often difficult to trace, so complex is the glial interdigitation. The axon emerges at lower right. Calibration: 100 micra.

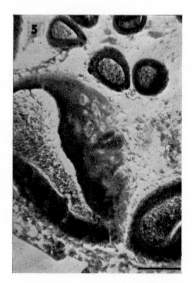

FIG. 5. Sometimes the whole inner side of the giant cell appears spongy. The increase in surface may be of the same nature as that in glial-penetrated large axons. Calibration: 100 micra.

soma on its inner side, facing the neuropile; a fairly sharp boundary separates the two (Fig. 2). The glial invasion mainly coincides with the axonal type of cytoplasm but in places goes beyond it, reaching halfway around the circumference. The surface of the cell in these regions is spongy, and not only increased in extent but produced into complex shapes. Whether or not this has any significance for local responses is unknown.

Careful study of osmic-fixed, Masson-stained ganglia and formol–acetic–alcohol-fixed, Holmes silver-stained ganglia has failed to reveal any evidence of nerve fibers ending on the cell body or the base of the axon. A large scale effort to obtain successful Golgi impregnations with the help of the late

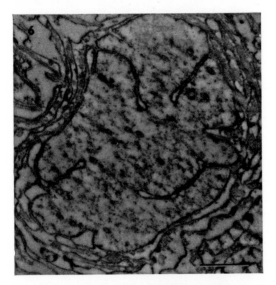

FIG. 6. Electron micrograph prepared by Dr. Elizabeth Batham showing a large (5 micra) axon in cross section in a connective; glial processes have opaque fine textured inclusions; these and glial membranes can be followed into the axonal infoldings. Calibration: one micron.

Albert E. Galigher of Berkeley gave only extremely limited pictures of occasional fibers in the neuropile. In view of the abundant experience of many workers with various invertebrate unipolar cells and the absence of evidence contradicting this in the present case, it seems best for the present to assume no synaptic endings on the soma.

With respect to cell contacts that might explain synchronization, I find little support for the idea of soma to soma intimacy. Processes connecting somata were never seen. Simple contact of two somata is impeded by the glial envelope which is general though for smaller cells often apparently missing in the light microscope. It must be concluded that the most likely anatomical basis is a connection of low electrical resistance somewhere between the processes of the cells, in the neuropile. This would resemble the connections believed to account for electrotonic communication between neurons in the lobster cardiac ganglion (Watanabe and Bullock, 1960) and in the supramedullary ganglion cell cluster of puffer fish (Bennett, 1960).

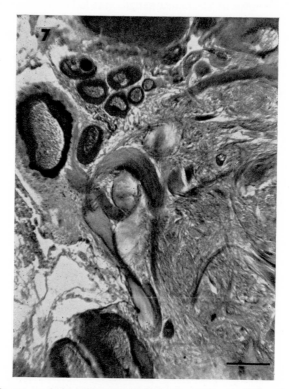

FIG. 7. Giant axons intimately entangled in the neuropile; small fibered neuropile to the right. Calibration: 100 micra.

Very little is known about the axons of the giant cells. In our preparations (Fig. 8) they measure up to 45 × 85 micra in diameter close to the ganglion in the right pleurovisceral connective (*A. californica* of *c*. 18 cm relaxed length, with largest giant nerve cells of 350 micra diameter); 35 micra is a more representative figure in the connective farther from the ganglion. Dr. Batham has prepared excellent electron micrographs of transverse sections of nerves. While the truly giant fibers were not encountered, she observed that the larger axons (5–10 micra) in the sections always exhibited a complex, infolded appearance (Fig. 6). Corresponding exactly to the findings of

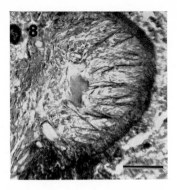

Fɪɢ. 8. Cross section of a connective showing a giant axon and the feathery aspect of the abundant glia. Calibration: 100 micra.

Schlote (1957) in *Helix*, there are four or five longitudinal ridges or deep invaginations of the axonal membrane, each occupied by sheath lamellae. These greatly increase the surface of the axon—commonly nearly doubling it. Knowing that this is a normal feature, it can readily be seen in light micrographs (Fig. 9) heretofore puzzlingly unconventional. The large fibers have a thick, loosely wound sheath of about five to twenty lamellae. Small fibers have no infoldings and fewer lamellae or none. Possibly there are systematic differences in the surface area in relation to diameter, for Mr. Goldman in my laboratory has consistently recorded a smaller, faster spike in the right connective preceding the larger, slower spike identified by Dr. Tauc, while he was with us, as that of the largest giant cell. The destination or distribution of the giant fibers is not yet known except that the largest passes anteriorly

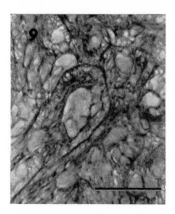

Fɪɢ. 9. Large and small nerve fibers in a region of the fibrous core of the ganglion occupied by tracts more than by neuropile; there is a high content of glial processes here, in contrast to neuropile. Calibration: 100 micra.

240 THEODORE H. BULLOCK

in the pleurovisceral connective, confined to the right side (Tauc) whereas a spike similar to the smaller one is also found in the left pleurovisceral connective (Goldman). Whether the giants end in one of the periesophageal ganglia or send branches into peripheral nerves and therefore whether they are interneurons or motoneurons is not known. The largest giant does not appear to send branches into visceral nerves.

Only one further anatomical point will be made here. The axons of several giant cells can be found to come into intimate contact in the neuropile, forming an interweaving tangle such as that shown in Fig. 7. Doubtless there are small collaterals making synaptic connections in the fine textured neuropile as is usual for large invertebrate unipolars, but we have not visualized these as yet.

These fragmentary notes may serve to emphasize the need for a thorough anatomical account of this important physiological preparation. Much could be done by electrical tracing of both afferent and efferent connections.

REFERENCES

ARVANITAKI, A. and CARDOT, H. (1941) Observations sur la constitution des ganglions et conducteurs nerveux et sur l'isolement du soma neuronique vivant chez les mollusques Gastéropodes. *Bull. Histol. Appl. Physiol. Path.* **18** : 133–144.

ARVANITAKI, A. and TCHOU, SI HO (1942) Les lois de la croissance relative individuelle des cellules nerveuses chez l'Aplysie. *Bull. Histol. Appl. Physiol. Path.* **19** : 244–256.

BENNETT, M. V. L. (1960) Electrical connections between supramedullary neurons. *Fed. Proc.* **19** : 282.

HOFFMANN, H. (1932–39) Opisthobranchia. In Bronn's *Klassen und Ordnungen des Tierreichs* 3 : 2 : 3 : 1.

HOLMGREN, E. (1902) Beiträge zur Morphologie der Zelle. I. Nervenzellen. *Anat. Hefte* **18** : 267–325.

KUNZE, H. (1921) Zur Topographie und Histologie des Centralnervensystems von *Helix pomatia* L. *Z. Wiss. Zool.* **118** : 25–203.

MERTON, H. (1907) Über den feineren Bau der Ganglienzellen aus dem Centralnervensystem von *Tethys leporina* Cuv. *Z. Wiss. Zool.* **88** : 327–357.

MOMIGLIANO, G. (1927) Sulla presenza di cellule fenestrate nei gangli di *Aplysia limacina*. *Boll. Soc. Ital. Biol. Speriment.* **2** : 230–234.

NABIAS, B. DE. (1894) Recherches histologiques et organologiques sur les centres nerveux des Gastéropodes. *Act. Soc. Linn. Bordeaux* **47** : 11–202.

SCHLOTE, F. W. (1957) Submikroskopische Morphologie von Gastropodennerven. *Z. Zellf.* **45** : 543–568.

SCHREIBER, G. (1931) Studi sol pigmento cromolipoide, l'apparato fenestrato e la respirazione di supplemento del sistema nervoso. *Pubbl. Staz. Zool. Napoli* **10** : 151–195.

TAUC, L. (1958) Processus postsynaptiques d'excitation et d'inhibition dans le soma neuronique de l'Aplysie et de l'Escargot. *Arch. Ital. Biol.* **96** : 78–110.

TAUC, L. (1960) Evidence of synaptic inhibitory actions not conveyed by inhibitory postsynaptic potentials, *Inhibition in the Nervous System and γ-Aminobutyric Acid*, (Ed. Roberts *et al.*,) Pergamon Press, Oxford.

VIGNAL, W. (1883) Recherches histologiques sur les centres nerveux de quelques invertébrés. *Arch. Zool. Exp. Gén.* (2) **1** : 267–412.

WATANABE, A. and BULLOCK, T. H. (1960) Modulation of activity of one neuron by sub: threshold slow potentials in another in lobster cardiac ganglion. *J. Gen. Physiol.* **43** : 1031–1045.

INHIBITORY INTERACTION IN THE RETINA
AND ITS SIGNIFICANCE IN VISION*

H. K. Hartline, F. Ratliff and W. H. Miller

The Rockefeller Institute, New York

The importance of nervous inhibition in sensory processes has become increasingly evident in recent years. But it was nearly one hundred years ago that Ernst Mach (1865) first recognized the possible significance of reciprocal retinal inhibition in accentuating contours and borders in the visual field. More recently, Békésy (1928) pointed out a similar possible role of inhibition as a "sharpening" mechanism in the auditory system. These speculations, based primarily on indirect evidence from psychophysical experiments have since been borne out by the direct observation of neural activity made possible by the development of modern electrophysiological techniques, especially when applied to the study of the activity of single cellular units. As a few examples of the numerous modern studies that show the diverse roles that neural inhibition plays in the physiology of sensory systems we may cite Granit's work on the interplay of excitatory and inhibitory influences in the vertebrate retina (for reviews see Granit, 1947 and 1955); the observation of inhibition in the auditory pathways by Galambos and Davis (1944), and Mountcastle and Powell's (1960) studies of inhibition in the cutaneous system.

The interaction of nervous elements and the interplay of excitatory and inhibitory influences can mold particular patterns of neural activity in specific pathways. Less specific interactions also have an important integrative action in sensory systems. Thus in the visual system, inhibitory influences exerted quite indiscriminately on one another by neighboring receptors and neurons in the retina have the effect of enhancing contrast in the visual image. If each element in the retinal mosaic inhibits the activity of its neighbors, to a degree that is greater the more strongly it is excited, then brightly lighted elements will exert a stronger suppressing action on dimly lighted neighbors than the latter will exert on the former. As a consequence, the disparity in the activities in the pathways from the two regions will be exaggerated, and brightness contrast will be enhanced. If the inhibitory interaction is stronger for near

* This work was supported by a research grant (B864) from the National Institute of Neurological Diseases and Blindness, Public Health Service, and by Contract Nonr 1442 (00) with the Office of Naval Research.

241

neighbors in the retinal mosaic than for more widely separated ones, such contrast effects will be greatest in the vicinity of sharp discontinuities in light intensity in the retinal image. That is, the outlines of objects imaged on the retina will tend to be emphasized. Thus patterns of neural activity generated by the receptor mosaic may be distorted in a useful way by inhibitory interaction in the retina; such distortions constitute an early step in the integration of nervous activity in the visual pathway.

A simple inhibitory interaction has been found to exist in the lateral eye of the horse-shoe "crab", *Limulus*. This interaction was first noticed about twenty years ago when studies of the properties of single receptor units in the *Limulus* eye showed that these elements were not, as had previously been thought, independent of one another. The analysis of this interaction has been presented in several papers in recent years and has also been reviewed elsewhere (Hartline, 1959; Ratliff *et al.*, 1958; Ratliff, 1961). This paper will give a brief description of the histology of the *Limulus* eye, and a synopsis of the experimental studies will stress the principles on which the theory of this interaction has been developed.

The lateral eye of *Limulus* is a coarsely facetted compound eye containing approximately 1000 ommatidia, each with a corneal facet approximately 0·1 mm in diameter and a crystalline cone which is the dioptric system for the sensory structure of the ommatidium. This latter structure is composed of about a dozen retinular cells and a bipolar neuron ("eccentric cell") which sends a dendritic process up the axial canal in the center of the retinular cluster (see insert Fig. 2). The contiguous inner surfaces of the retinular cells near the axis of the ommatidium are elaborated into the rhabdom. This has been shown by electron microscopy to be a "honeycomb"-like structure composed of densely packed microvillous out-pouchings of the retinular cell surfaces (Miller, 1957, 1958): the rhabdom presumably contains the visual pigment. The visual pigment of *Limulus* has recently been isolated and studied by Hubbard and Wald (1960): it is a retinine$_1$ rhodopsin whose absorption spectrum adequately accounts for the action spectrum of the ommatidium as determined from measurements of single optic nerve fiber activity by Graham and Hartline (1935). Both the retinular cells and the eccentric cell give rise to axons which, emerging from the proximal tip of the ommatidium, travel in small bundles and collect with those from the other ommatidia of the eye to form the optic nerve.

Each ommatidium of the *Limulus* eye appears to function as a single "receptor unit". Bundles of nerve fibers can be dissected from the optic nerve and subdivided until the electrical record has the characteristics of the action of a single unit. By exploring the corneal facets one by one with a small spot of light, this unit can be identified with one and only one particular ommatidium of the eye; in numerous experiments the nerve strand has been dissected free all the way up to its ommatidium of origin. The eccentric cells in individual ommatidia can sometimes be seen in living preparations; a micro-pipette thrust into one of them yields electrical records consisting of a slow "generator potential" superimposed on which are large spikes which are synchronous with the nerve impulses recorded in the strand of fibers dissected from that ommatidium (Hartline *et al.*, 1952). The uniformity of the action potential spikes in the nerve bundle, and the regularity of their discharge, are evidence that they represent impulses in just one axon, presumably that of the impaled eccentric cell. It would appear then, that the trains of impulses that are recorded in "single" fibers dissected from the optic nerve originate in the eccentric cell of the particular ommatidium from which this fiber arises. Signs of activity of the retinular cells have not been identified. Perhaps they all fire impulses in exact synchrony with the eccentric cell; perhaps the action potentials in their axons are too small to have been recognized.

For the purposes of the present paper, each ommatidium may be con-sidered a single functional unit, excited only by light entering its own corneal facet; each ommatidium, when so excited, discharges trains of impulses in one and only one optic nerve fiber. These receptor units (ommatidia) as we have said, are not independent in their action: each one may be inhibited by its near neighbors and in turn may inhibit them. Thus, the activity of any given ommatidium, while principally determined by the light shining upon its facet, may be modified by the activity generated in the neighboring omma-tidia when they are stimulated by the light falling on their facets.

The anatomical basis for this interaction of the ommatidia of the *Limulus* compound eye is a plexus of fine nerve fibers—an extensive three-dimensional network of fiber bundles immediately proximal to the layer of ommatidia. In Fig. 1, a photograph of a silver-impregnated section of the eye, axons are seen emerging from the proximal ends of the ommatidia. Several inter-connecting bundles of fibers are labeled "*B*". At higher magnification (Fig. 2) the axons of the eccentric cells (*E. ax.*) may be distinguished from those of the retinular cells (*R. ax.*) by their greater thickness and density and by the presence of a juxtaposed substance that is lacey in appearance and continuous with the interconnecting bundles (*B*). In silver-stained sections such as this the interconnections appear to be composed of small branches of the axons of the retinular and eccentric cells. Electron micrographs of these structures have proved that this is the case (Ratliff *et al.*, 1958). This is illustrated by Fig. 3 and Fig. 4, electron micrographs of a retinular cell axon and an eccen-tric cell axon in cross-section. In Fig. 3 the arrow marks the point at which a small branch is seen emerging from a retinular cell axon (*R*) and joining a small bundle of similar branches (*B*). In Fig. 4 a well defined branch (*B*) emanates from an eccentric cell axon and joins a large bundle which cor-responds to the lacey substance seen in silver-impregnated sections. In silver-impregnated sections such as Fig. 2, areas of relatively greater density (*N*) are seen within the lacey substance. The electron microscope has shown that

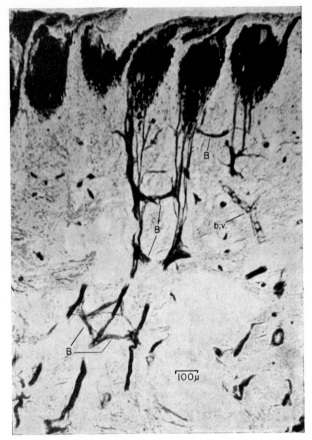

FIG. 1. Silver-impregnated section of *Limulus* compound eye. At the top of the
figure are the heavily pigmented sensory portions of the ommatidia. Bundles
containing about a dozen nerve fibers emerge from the proximal ends of the
ommatidia. Interconnecting branches, (*B*); blood vessel (*b.v.*).

the fine axonal branches in such regions contain vesicular structures similar
to those found in synaptic regions in a wide variety of animals. These knots of
neuropile are therefore assumed to be synaptic regions. Figure 5 illustrates an
eccentric cell axon (*E*) and a branch from the axon extending into a region of
neuropile (*N*). A part of the branch and neuropile are also shown in Fig. 5
at high magnification. The synaptic vesicles are seen within the eccentric cell
branch as well as other fibers comprising the neuropile. No nerve cell-bodies
have been found in the plexus.

The inhibitory interaction of the ommatidia is dependent on the integrity
of this plexus of interconnecting fibers. Cutting the plexus bundles around the
strand of nerve fibers from an ommatidium abolishes all of the inhibitory

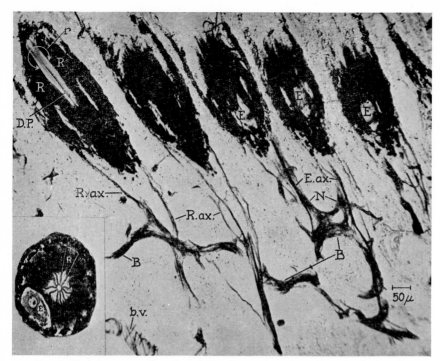

FIG. 2. Silver-impregnated section of *Limulus* compound eye. Unstained eccentric cells (*E*); pigment shrouded retinular cells (*R*); rhabdom (*r*); distal process (*D.P.*); retinular cell axons (*R. ax.*); eccentric cell axons (*E. ax.*); axonal branches (*B*); neuropile (*N*); blood vessel (*b.v.*).

(*Inset*)—Osmium-fixed ommatidium in cross-section. Eccentric cell (*E*). The border of a retinular cell (*R*) is indicated by a white line. (From Ratliff, 1961).

effects exerted on it by neighboring ommatidia. It is reasonable to suppose that the inhibitory interaction is mediated synaptically in the knots of neuropile that are located within the plexus.

Inhibition of a receptor unit by the activity of its neighbors is illustrated in Fig. 6. In the experiment from which this record was obtained a single fiber was dissected from the optic nerve and the ommatidium from which this fiber originated was located and illuminated by a small spot of light confined to its facet. After allowing a few seconds for the discharge to subside to its steady level, a region of the eye near this "test" receptor was illuminated as indicated by the signal above the time marks. This stimulation of the nearby ommatidia produced a marked slowing of the discharge of the test receptor, persisting as long as the neighboring elements were illuminated. When the illumination on them was turned off, the discharge of the test receptor rose again to its original value, with a very slight, but distinct, overshoot. There was a slight delay in the onset of the inhibitory action which can be attributed,

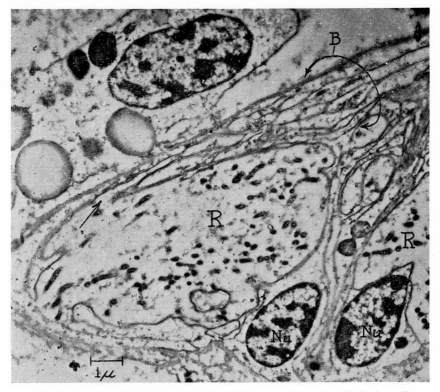

FIG. 3. Electron micrograph of retinular cell axon and branches. Retinular cell axons (*R*); axonal branch (arrow); bundle of axonal branches (*B*); nuclei of Schwann's cells (*Nu*).

in part, to the latent period of the action of light on the neighboring receptors. There was also a pronounced dip in frequency at the beginning of the period of inhibition, with partial recovery. This dip may be attributed, in part, to the strong transient outburst of impulses discharged initially when the neighboring receptors were illuminated after having been in darkness for some time.

The stronger the intensity of light on receptors that neighbor a given receptor, the greater is the depression of frequency of that receptor (Fig. 7). Similarly, the larger the area illuminated in the neighborhood of an ommatidium that is under observation, the greater is the depression of the frequency of its discharge, showing that there is spatial summation of the inhibitory influences exerted on a particular ommatidium by its neighbors. The nearer these neighbors are to a particular ommatidium, the stronger is their inhibitory effect on it; ommatidia that are widely separated in the eye interact little or not at all. A fixed degree of activity elicited in a given region of the eye

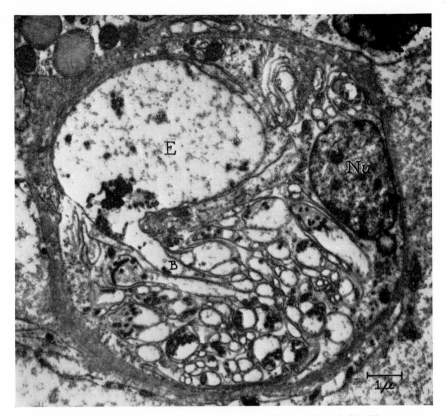

FIG. 4. Electron micrograph of eccentric cell axon (*E*) and branch (*B*). The axon and bundle of axonal branches are enclosed by a basement membrane and a thin layer of Schwann's cell cytoplasm. The nucleus of the Schwann's cell is labeled (*Nu*).

neighboring a particular ommatidium results in a fixed decrement in the frequency of discharge of that ommatidium, irrespective of its own level of excitation. These basic properties of the inhibition have been described in detail in an earlier paper (Hartline *et al.*, 1956).

Not only can inhibition be exerted by normally induced activity in the nervous pathways from regions neighboring an ommatidium, but antidromic stimulation of the optic nerve fibers from these regions also produces a slowing in the discharge rate from a test ommatidium (Tomita, 1958). The inhibition thus produced is similar in all of its aspects to that produced by the illumination of neighboring receptor units: the slowing is greater the higher the frequency of the antidromic volleys, and the larger the number of fibers recruited by submaximal shocks of increasing strength. Figure 8, showing the inhibition in response to trains of antidromic volleys, is noteworthy in showing

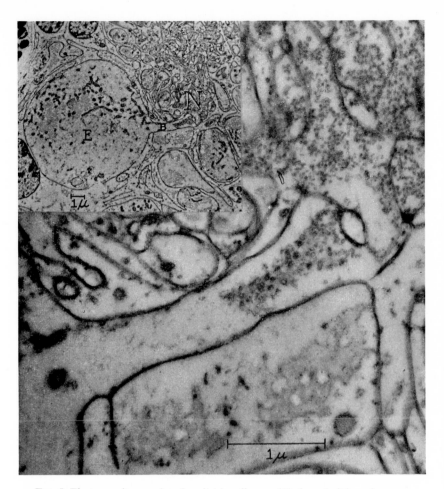

FIG. 5. Electron micrographs of eccentric cell axon (*E*), branch (*B*), and neuropile (*N*). The inset is low magnification; in the higher magnification micrograph of the same region (remainder of figure), showing part of the branch and neuropile, small dense circular outlines (synaptic vesicles) are seen. The significance of the difference in size of the vesicles is unknown.

FIG. 6. Inhibition of the activity of an ommatidium in the eye of *Limulus* produced by illumination of a nearby retinal region. Oscillogram of action potentials in a single optic nerve fiber. See text for description. Time in $\frac{1}{5}$ sec. (From Hartline *et al.*, 1953).

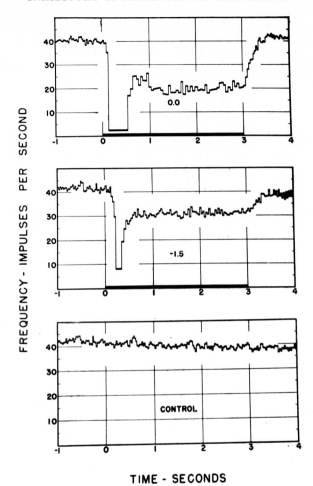

TIME - SECONDS

FIG. 7. Inhibition of the discharge of impulses from an ommatidium produced by illumination of a nearby retinal region for a period of 3 sec at a high intensity (top graph, log I inhib $= 0 \cdot 0$), and at a low intensity (middle graph, log I inhib $= - 1 \cdot 5$), with a control for comparison (bottom graph). Frequency of discharge (reciprocal of interval between successive impulses) is plotted as ordinate vs. time (sec) as abscissa. From oscillograms similar to that of Fig. 6. Throughout this paper the "magnitude of inhibition" is measured by the difference, over corresponding periods of time, between the frequency in the control and the frequency during the inhibiting illumination. (From Hartline *et al.*, 1956).

an appreciable delay in the onset of inhibitory effect. Also, a recognizable dip in frequency appears at the beginning of the period of antidromic stimulation, even though the antidromic impulses were uniformly spaced. Inhibition in the eye of *Limulus* has an appreciable lag, and shows something akin to adaptation.

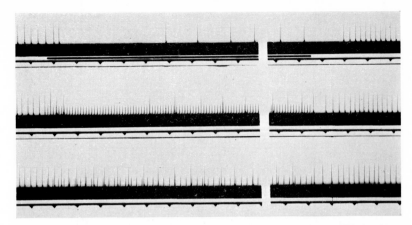

FIG. 8. Inhibition of impulse discharge in a single optic nerve fiber by illumination of nearby ommatidia and by antidromic volleys in other optic nerve fibers. (*Top record*)—During steady state of impulse discharge in fiber, elicited by illumination of its ommatidium, nearby ommatidia were illuminated for a period marked by black line. (*Middle record*)—Inhibition of activity of same fiber by antidromic volleys at 42/sec in the other optic nerve fibers. Small spikes in record were due to physical spread of action potentials of antidromic impulses in nerve trunk to lead-off electrodes; they indicate duration of antidromic stimulation. (*Bottom record*)—Antidromic volleys of 20/sec. Time in $\frac{1}{5}$ sec. (From Tomita, 1958.)

The observed slowing of the discharge of an ommatidium is not the result of interference with the access of light to its receptor mechanism, such as might result if, for example, there were some rapid migration of pigment, or other retino-motor response. This is proved by the fact that the after-discharge following intense illumination of a receptor can also be inhibited, and to the same degree as the discharge elicited during illumination (Fig. 9). Likewise the spontaneous activity that is sometimes observed in deteriorating preparations is usually inhibited in the same manner, and so is any dark discharge brought about by alteration in the ionic balance of the solutions bathing the eye. The frequency of discharge of impulses elicited by passing electric current into an eccentric cell impaled by a micropipette can also be slowed by illuminating neighboring regions of the eye.

The mechanism of the inhibition in the eye of *Limulus* is, of course, a subject of great interest. However, it has not yet been analyzed very thoroughly and we will not treat it in detail here. We have noted that the inhibitory action depends on the integrity of the nervous interconnections in the plexus and have speculated that the synaptic regions in the clumps of neuropile are sites of its mediation. It is evidently exerted at, or ahead of, the site of impulse generation within the receptor unit, for a microelectrode inserted in an ommatidium records the same slowing of the discharge as is observed more

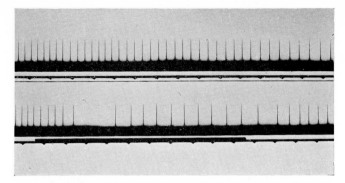

FIG. 9. After-discharge from an ommatidium inhibited by illumination of a nearby retinal region (*bottom record*); control (*top record*) for comparison. The after-discharges were elicited by intense illumination of the ommatidium for several seconds, ending just before the beginning of each record. Illumination of nearby region signalled by blackening of white band above time marks. Time in $\frac{1}{5}$ sec.

proximally in the optic nerve; hence it is not the result of a dropping out of impulses as the fibers traverse the plexus.

We have some preliminary observations on a change in membrane potential of impaled eccentric cells inhibited by illumination of adjacent ommatidia. E. F. MacNichol found, in the case of an ommatidium that was spontaneously active and unresponsive to light, that on illumination of neighboring ommatidia, the spontaneous activity was slowed concomitantly with a small hyperpolarization of the eccentric cell membrane (personal communication). We have found that preparations showing no signs of injury (no spontaneous activity and unimpaired sensitivity to light) also show hyperpolarization concomitant with a slowing of the discharge of impulses. In the record shown in Fig. 10 (obtained in collaboration with F. A. Dodge) a constant frequency of spike discharge was maintained by passing a small depolarizing current through the recording pipette. An impulse occurred just before the start of the record. At the first arrow neighboring ommatidia were illuminated, taking care to prevent scattered light from stimulating the test ommatidium. After a short latency the baseline showed a negative deflection. The illumination was discontinued at the second arrow, whereupon the membrane potential returned to the firing level and the spike discharge was resumed. The fact that, during inhibition of slightly depolarized cells, the membrane potential tended towards the resting potential would seem to indicate a synaptic inhibitory mechanism similar to that of other preparations which have been analyzed more extensively (Fatt and Katz, 1953; Brock *et al.*, 1952; Kuffler and Eyzaguirre, 1955).

Even though we do not have a clear understanding of the cellular mechanisms of the inhibitory interaction, it is still possible to understand its consequences as a basis of an integrative mechanism in the eye. We begin our dis-

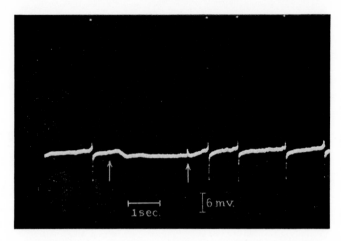

FIG. 10. Oscillograms of electric potential changes recorded by a micropipette electrode in an eccentric cell showing slight hyperpolarization (downward displacement of base-line) concomitant with inhibition of spike discharge, caused by illumination of nearby ommatidia during period between arrows (small switch artifact at second arrow). Tops of spikes marked by white dots. See text.

cussion with the consideration of the mutual action of the receptor units on one another.

A survey of single optic nerve fibers sampled successively from any one eye has shown that any ommatidium one picks can be inhibited at least to some degree by illumination of any retinal area within a few millimeters of it. More specifically, it has been shown by recording from two optic nerve fibers simultaneously that any two individual ommatidia, sufficiently close to one another in the retinal mosaic, inhibit one another by direct mutual action (Fig. 11). Often the inhibitory action is unequal in the two directions; occasionally it is quite one-sided, but it is safe to say that as a rule any ommatidium is inhibited by its neighbors and, being a neighbor of its neighbors, inhibits them in turn. This mutual interaction gives special interest to the phenomenon of inhibition in the eye of *Limulus*.

The first step in the quantitative analysis of this inhibitory interaction reveals a crucial point. The strength of the inhibitory influences exerted by a given ommatidium on other ommatidia in its neighborhood has been shown to depend not just on the stimulus to it, but rather on the net level of its activity. This level is the resultant of the excitation this ommatidium receives from light shining on its facet, diminished by whatever inhibitory influences are exerted on it by its neighbors. Now, the strength of those inhibitory influences from the neighbors depends in turn on the level of their activity, which is partially determined by the inhibition that the ommatidium in question exerts on them. Since these statements apply simultaneously to each

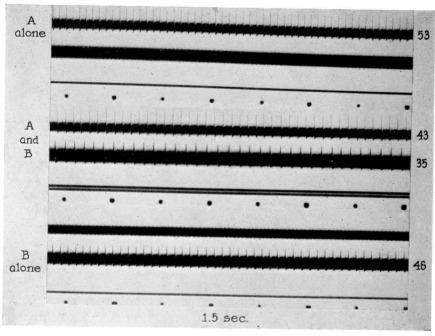

Fig. 11. Oscillograms of action potentials recorded simultaneously from two optic nerve fibers, showing the discharge of nerve impulses when the respective ommatidia in which these fibers arose were illuminated separately and together. The numbers on the right give the total number of impulses discharged in the period of 1·5 sec, for the respective cases. The inhibitory effect on A, 53–43, is to be associated with the concurrent frequency of B, 35; likewise the effect on B, 46–35, is to be associated with the concurrent frequency of A, 43 (see text). Time in $\frac{1}{5}$ sec. (From Hartline and Ratliff, 1957.)

ommatidium in the interacting set, it is evident that a closely-knit interdependence characterizes the activity of receptor units in this eye.

This crucial feature of the inhibitory interaction was unrecognized by us in the early years of our work. We were puzzled by confusing and seemingly contradictory results: spatial summation of inhibitory influences seemed to depend unpredictably on the location of the retinal regions with respect to one another and to the receptor on which the summating action was being tested; inhibitory effects could not be consistently related to intensities of retinal illumination. Only when we recognized that the inhibition exerted by a receptor depended on the level of its activity rather than on the level of its stimulation, could we make sense out of our results. When we recorded from two interacting ommatidia simultaneously, using different intensities on them, in various combinations, it became apparent that the decrement of

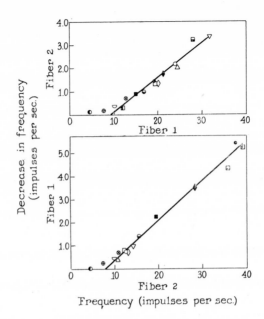

FIG. 12. Mutual inhibition of two receptor units. In each graph the magnitude of the inhibitory action (decrease in frequency of impulse discharge) exerted on one of the ommatidia is plotted (ordinate) as a function of the degree of concurrent activity (frequency) of the other (abscissa). See legend, Fig. 11. The different points were obtained by using various intensities of illumination on ommatidia 1 and 2, in various combinations. The data for points designated by the same symbol were obtained simultaneously. (From Hartline and Ratliff, 1957.)

frequency of each was an unambiguous function only of the *response* of the other (Fig. 12).

A more direct experimental proof that the inhibition exerted by receptors depends quantitatively on the level of their activity comes from experiments demonstrating "disinhibition". A region of the eye too far distant from a test receptor to affect it by direct action can nevertheless influence its response indirectly. If a nearer region of the eye, properly chosen in a position between the test receptor and the distant region, is illuminated at a fixed intensity, it will inhibit the discharge of the test receptor. If now the more distant region is illuminated, it will by its direct action on the receptors in the intermediate region inhibit their activity and as a consequence release the test receptor from the inhibition they exert on it (Fig. 13). Quantitatively, the degree of release is just that which could be produced by lowering the intensity on the intermediate receptors (in the absence of illumination on the distant region) by the amount necessary to reduce the frequency of their discharge to the level they had when illuminated at full intensity but inhibited by the distant region.

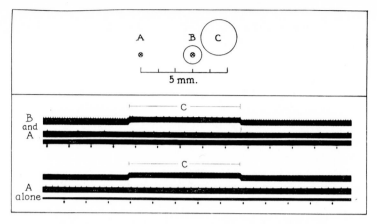

FIG. 13. Oscillograms of the electrical activity of two optic nerve fibers, showing disinhibition. In each record the lower oscillographic trace records the discharge of impulses from ommatidium A, stimulated by a spot of light confined to its facet. The upper trace records the activity of ommatidium B, stimulated by a spot of light centered on its facet, but which also illuminated approximately eight or ten ommatidia in addition to B. A third spot of light, C, was directed on to a region of the eye more distant from A than from B (the geometrical configuration of the pattern of illumination is sketched above). Exposure of C was signalled by the upward offset of the upper trace. (*Lower record*)—Activity of ommatidium A in the absence of illumination on B, showing that illumination of C had no perceptible effect under this condition. Upper record: activity of ommatidia A and B together, showing (i) lower frequency of discharge of A (as compared with lower record) resulting from activity of B, and (ii) effect of illumination of C, causing a drop in frequency of discharge of B and comitantly an increase in the frequency of discharge of A, as A was partially released from the inhibition exerted by B. Time in $\frac{1}{5}$ sec. The black band above the time marks is the signal of the illumination of A and B, thin when A was shining alone, thick when A and B were shining together. (From Hartline and Ratliff, 1957.)

These quantitative measurements compel us to accept the principle of mutual interdependence of receptor responses. Thus it appears that while the strength of the inhibitory influence generated by any receptor is determined by its output, the locus at which this influence is exerted on a neighboring receptor is at, or ahead of, the point at which the neighbor's output is determined. The inhibitory influences are transmitted reciprocally and in a sense recurrently over the plexus pathways. In this respect the inhibition in the *Limulus* eye is reminiscent of the recurrent (Renshaw) inhibition familiar in the physiology of spinal reflexes and discussed elsewhere in this symposium by Professor Granit. We note in this connection that it has been suggested that recurrent facilitation is a disinhibition which enhances reflex discharge by the removal of tonic inhibitory activity (Wilson *et al.*, 1960).

In the eye of *Limulus*, the quantitative expressions describing the essential properties of the inhibitory interaction have been found to be comparatively

18

simple, once the principle of mutual interdependence of the receptor unit responses is recognized. This makes it possible to construct a useful formal theory describing the inhibitory interaction succinctly.

The value of such a theoretical formulation lies in the compactness with which a number of experimental observations are described, and the insight it gives into the understanding of relationships that, while inherently simple, sometimes yield phenomena of considerable complexity. It has predicted several experimental results. With the addition of simplifying assumptions, it furnishes a semiquantitative explanation of experimental phenomena associated with patterns of retinal illumination on the eye of *Limulus*. Applied with caution, it may be useful as a basis for hypothetical explanations of such phenomena as brightness contrast and sensitivity to moving patterns in human vision.

Perhaps the aspect of greatest interest for this symposium is the value this theory may have in furnishing a prototype for the construction of theories of more complex interacting systems. For highly organized nervous centers, basic principles may be difficult to establish by direct experiment, and patterns of interaction may be extremely complex. In such cases it may be of value to start with a simple model—one which possesses the merit that it describes fairly faithfully an interacting system that actually exists in at least one living organism.

We have based the theory of the inhibitory interaction in the eye of *Limulus* on postulates that have been derived inductively from certain empirical experimental observations. It would be much more desirable, of course, to have a complete knowledge of the underlying mechanism of the receptor unit and of the inhibitory process, and a complete description of the histological and functional interconnections of the interacting units. Undoubtedly, such knowledge would permit the derivation of fundamental postulates on which could be based an exact and rigorous theory of the interaction. In the absence of such basic knowledge, the postulates can only be worked out empirically, step by step, and of necessity still incompletely.

The construction of the theory must begin with a search for a parameter which, taken as the measure of the response of a receptor unit, yields a useful measure of the degree of its inhibition. It is no surprise to physiologists that the frequency of discharge, which seems a natural measure of a neuron's response, should turn out to be the required parameter. However, this should not necessarily be regarded as a consequence of any *a priori* considerations. Some other aspect of the discharge might have been more useful in the construction of an empirical theory of interaction: the magnitude of the time interval between successive impulses, for example, or the logarithm of the frequency. Less obvious is the experimental finding that it is the absolute decrease in frequency, independent of its absolute level, that is the most useful measure of the degree of inhibition exerted on a "test" receptor by a fixed inhibitory influence from neighboring receptors. This, too, is not the consequence of any *a priori* speculation. It could well be imagined that, for example, the relative decrease (percentage reduction in frequency) might have turned out to provide a more useful theoretical structure. For the *Limulus* eye, however, it is the fact that no matter what the level of activity of a particular ommatidium whose nerve fiber is on the recording electrodes, the absolute decrease in frequency produced by a fixed inhibitory influence from neighboring elements is always the same.

We can express this experimental fact in the equation:

$$r = e - i \tag{1}$$

In this equation the term r stands for the response of the ommatidium under observation, measured by the steady frequency of its discharge of nerve impulses while it is being subjected to inhibition from its steadily illuminated neighbors. The term e represents the magnitude of the external excitation supplied by the stimulating light of given intensity. It is to be measured by the frequency of discharge that the receptor would have in the absence of any inhibitory illumination, that is, when that ommatidium alone is illuminated at the given intensity. The term i represents the inhibitory influence exerted on the ommatidium by its neighbors; it is some function, as yet to be specified, of the activity of those elements.

Implicit in our use of this notation is the understanding of several restrictions: r and e, being frequencies cannot be negative; the quantity i likewise is to be restricted to positive values, since we are dealing with a purely inhibitory interaction. In defining a notation for some other system, however, one might not wish to be bound by these particular restrictions. For example, the mechanoreceptors of lateral line organs and of vestibular ampullae discharge impulses "spontaneously" and one might wish to consider levels of activity both above and below the resting discharge. For the *Limulus* eye, however, these restrictions apply. For the present, moreover, we will restrict our consideration to the steady conditions of response, after all of the transients have subsided that are associated with turning on the stimulating light and establishing the inhibitory interactions. Later in this paper we will describe briefly some preliminary experiments on transient effects.

In the equation (1) the term i, representing the total inhibitory influence exerted by the combined action of all the neighboring elements that are activated by a given pattern of retinal illumination, is to be expressed as a set of "partial" terms, each representing the action of some one neighbor on the ommatidium under consideration, all combined in an appropriate manner as yet to be specified. Each partial inhibitory term is to be written as a function of the response r of the particular neighbor whose action it represents; this expresses the experimentally established principle of mutual interdependence of receptor responses, discussed above. As a consequence, the activity of each ommatidium in an interacting set will be described by an equation of the form of equation (1) expressing its response r in terms of its excitation e and an i which is a function of the r's of all the other ommatidia in the set. The resulting set of equations, one for each receptor, must be solved simultaneously to determine the values of any of the r's in terms of the e's (that is, in terms of a distribution of light over the retinal mosaic). It is the "recurrent" mutual interaction of the receptor units in the eye of *Limulus* that requires description by such sets of simultaneous equations.

Before we can give explicit form to the equations we have proposed, two pieces of information are required: we must know the form of the functions describing the partial inhibitory terms and we must know how these partial terms are to be combined to make up the function describing the total inhibition on a given receptor unit. Experiments provide the empirical answers to these two questions.

The form of the function that may be taken to describe the relation between the frequency of a given receptor and the amount of inhibitory influence it exerts on a particular neighbor is suggested by the graphs of Fig. 12. It is evident that, above a certain threshold, a linear relation describes the data satisfactorily. For example, the inhibitory action ($i_{1, 2}$) exerted by ommatidium 2 on ommatidium 1 is proportional to the amount by which 2's frequency of discharge (r_2) exceeds the threshold $r^0_{1, 2}$ for its action on 1:

$$i_{1, 2} = K_{1, 2}(r_2 - r^0_{1, 2}). \qquad (2)$$

A similar expression holds, of course, for 1's action on 2:

$$i_{2, 1} = K_{2, 1}(r_1 - r^0_{2, 1}). \qquad (2a)$$

These statements are true for any arbitrarily selected pair of ommatidia in a set of interacting receptor units—an inference from the fact that we have always observed this relationship in every experiment we have performed. Thus the partial inhibitory terms making up i in equation (1) are each of the form given by equation (2) with appropriate subscript labels to identify the pair of elements involved and the direction of the action that is being considered.

The law of combination of inhibitory influences also turns out to be a simple one; the partial inhibitory terms are merely *added* to express the total inhibition exerted on a given receptor. Thus for ommatidium 1 the total inhibition exerted by all of its neighbors (all of the *other* ommatidia in a group of n interacting units) is expressed by:

$$i_1 = i_{1, 2} + i_{1, 3} + \ \cdots \ i_{1, n} \qquad (3)$$

This law of "spatial summation" of inhibitory influences is not an *a priori* assumption; it has been derived from experimental findings. Two patches of light were projected on to regions on either side of a test receptor, close enough to it to inhibit it but far enough from each other that they did not interact. The decrement in frequency of the test receptor's discharge when both regions were illuminated together was found to be equal to the sum of the frequency decrements produced by illumination of each separately (Fig. 14). This was true with considerable accuracy for a wide range of intensities on the two patches in various combinations. This is the basic fact on which the law of summation is based.

When, in an experiment similar to that just described, two patches of light

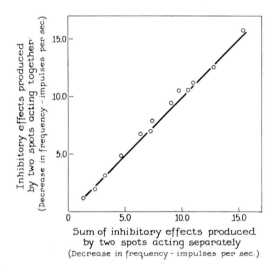

FIG. 14. The summation of inhibitory effects produced by steady illumination, at various intensities, of two widely separated groups of receptors. The sum of the inhibitory effects on a test receptor (steadily illuminated at a fixed intensity) produced by each group acting separately is plotted as abscissa; the effect produced by the two groups of receptors acting simultaneously is plotted as ordinate. (From Hartline and Ratliff, 1958.)

were put close together, their combined effect in inhibiting the test receptor became considerably less than the sum of their separate effects (Fig. 15). We attribute this to the interaction of the two groups of receptors illuminated, for we know that each group must have inhibited the activity of the other and that this must have reduced the net inhibition exerted on the test receptor. We now make the *assumption* that the law of spatial summation of inhibitory effects stated above can be extended to this case of interacting elements. According to this assumption, the reduction in intensity of inhibitory action is *quantitatively* accounted for solely by the reduction in activity of the two receptor groups (due to their mutual inhibition). In the formal description the partial inhibitory terms representing the influences exerted on the test receptor by the two regions will each be reduced by mutual action, but are

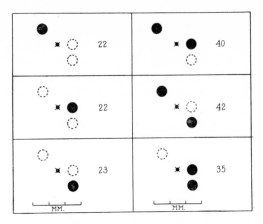

Fig. 15. The summation of inhibitory influences exerted by two widely separated groups of receptors and by two groups of receptors close together. Each panel in the figure is a map of the same small portion of the eye. The test receptor, location indicated by the symbol X, was illuminated steadily by a small spot of light confined to its facet. Larger spots of light were placed singly in one of three locations, as shown in the three panels on the left side of the figure, and in pairs, as shown in the three panels on the right. The filled circles indicate the spots illuminated in each case; the other locations (not illuminated) are indicated in dotted outline merely for purposes of orientation. The number of impulses discharged from the test receptor in a period of 8 sec was decreased upon illumination of the neighbouring spot or spots by the amount shown at the right in each panel. (From Hartline and Ratliff, 1958.)

still to be combined by simple addition to describe quantitatively the net inhibitory effect. An experiment served to establish the law of summation for a special case (no interaction); the assumption serves to extend it to the general case. The validity of this assumption will be demonstrated below, where we will present experimental evidence based on measurements of the simultaneous activity of three interacting ommatidia.

We can now write explicitly the set of n simultaneous linear equations describing the interaction of a set of n interacting receptor units:

$$r_p = e_p - \sum_{j}^{n} K_{pj}(r_j - r^0_{pj}) \qquad p = 1, 2, \ldots n \qquad (4)$$

(n equations)   Restrictions:

$$\text{all } r, e, K \not< 0$$
$$\text{all } r_j \not< r^0_{pj}$$
$$j \neq p$$

These equations can be solved by conventional methods, expressing all the r's as functions of the e's (distribution of light on the retinal mosaic), and of the K's and r^0's (parameters of the inhibitory interaction). All of these, in principle at least, can be measured by direct experiment.

The restrictions require comment. We have explained why only positive values of r, e and K are considered in this particular formalism. The second restriction, that no partial inhibitory term may be admitted for which the r is less than the r^0 with which it appears in that term, reflects experimental fact. Without exception, a receptor that affects a neighboring receptor has been found to do so only if its frequency of discharge exceeds a certain threshold value characteristic of the pair and of the direction of the action. No "subliminal" inhibitory effects have ever been observed: if an ommatidium is caused to discharge at a frequency below the threshold of its action on another ommatidium, it does not add anything to the inhibition exerted on that second one by other ommatidia in the neighborhood. (The absence of any subliminal effects that might sum to produce appreciable inhibition from large dimly lighted regions has an important practical bearing on this experimental work. It assures us that the halo of scattered light, so difficult to avoid entirely in any experiment, contributes nothing to the interaction, at least for moderate levels of "focal" illumination.) The restriction of equations (4) to r's that are suprathreshold for all partial inhibitory terms implies that the equations as written hold only for those values of the e's for which solutions meet this requirement. In any other case, the equations may be solved tentatively, the solutions inspected, and those partial terms for which $r < r^0$ set equal to zero. The resulting set of equations may then be solved, and the process repeated as often as necessary, until solutions have been found that meet the requirement for all terms.

The requirement $j \neq p$ in any of the summations is meant to express an unwillingness to consider the possibility of "self-inhibition" in this formal treatment (cf. equation 3). Now, there is no *a priori* reason to deny the existence of "self-inhibition"—it may well occur in the eye of *Limulus*, where the ommatidia are themselves complex cellular entities, or in other interacting systems that we might wish to consider. "Self-inhibition" might conceivably be demonstrated by the use of some pharmacological agent, for example, which could abolish all inhibition without otherwise affecting the neural elements. But "self-inhibition" really concerns the intimate mechanism of the ommatidium itself as a functional unit and therefore is properly excluded from a theory of *inter*action.

We choose to avoid the entire question of self-inhibition for the present by the following treatment. Suppose the receptor units did inhibit themselves by the same mechanism by which they inhibit each other; call the frequency with which a unit responds in the absence of *all* inhibitory influences e'; call its inhibitory coefficients K'. $K'_{p,\,j}$ will be the "actual" coefficient representing the inhibitory action of the jth receptor on the pth and, by admitting $j = p$, $K'_{p,\,p}$ appears as the "coefficient of self-inhibition" (with $r^0{}_{p,\,p}$ the threshold of the "self-inhibition"). Then in a set of equations (4') (not written here) where the primed letters replace the unprimed in (4), collect terms and divide by $1 + K'_{p,\,p}$ in each equation. This yields a set of equations of the same form as (4), in which the quantity $(e'_p + K'_{p,\,p} r^0{}_{p,\,p})/(1 + K'_{p,\,p})$ appears in place of e_p (unprimed) and $K'_{p,\,j}/(1 + K'_{p,\,p})$ appears in place of $K_{p,\,j}$, and in which the restriction $j \neq p$ must be restored in the summations. It is evident that these quantities are in fact the e's and K's (unprimed) of equation (4), according to the operational definition of these observable quantities (e_p is the frequency of discharge of ommatidium p, observed when it is illuminated by itself, $K_{p,\,q}$ is the coefficient of the inhibitory action of ommatidium q on ommatidium p, calculated from measurements of the responses of p and q when illuminated together at different intensities). It is also clear that "self-inhibition" cannot, indeed, be detected by the kind of experiments we have described in which optic nerve fiber activity is recorded under various conditions of retinal illumination. These considerations permit us to proceed without committing ourselves as to the presence or absence of "self-inhibition"; they indicate how the formal theory would have to be amended in case it became desirable to consider such self-action in an interacting system.

The theory so far developed has been subjected to test in a series of experiments in each of which three optic nerve fibers were isolated, coming from ommatidia close to one another in the eye. The ommatidia were illuminated independently, at various intensities in various combinations. The e's were determined, for the various intensities used, by illuminating the ommatidia separately and measuring the discharge frequency of each over a fixed interval of time, beginning at a fixed time after turning the light on (to permit the steady level of discharge to be attained). By pairwise illumination and measurement, the K's and r^0's were determined (from plots similar to Fig. 12). The responses (steady frequencies) in all three optic nerve fibers were then measured when all three ommatidia were illuminated together. The test of the theory was the comparison of these observed responses with values calculated from the solutions of a set of three simultaneous equations (equations (4), $n = 3$) using the measured values of the e's, K's and r^0's. The agreement has been satisfactory in all of the experiments done so far within the limits of the methods. An example is shown in Table 1. The different

TABLE 1. INHIBITORY EFFECTS (DEFICIT IN NUMBER OF IMPULSES OVER A 10 SEC PERIOD) OBSERVED IN THREE RECEPTOR UNITS ILLUMINATED SIMULTANEOUSLY, COMPARED WITH EFFECTS CALCULATED BY SOLUTION OF SIMULTANEOUS EQUATIONS (SEE TEXT)

Effect exerted on	Units illuminated pair-wise			Three units illuminated simultaneously	
	Separate effects produced by:			Observed effect	Calculated effect
	A	B	C		
A	—	27·1	14·8	36·2	35·0
B	6·8	—	11·1	14·0	13·5
C	6·0	18·9	—	20·4	22·0

experiments furnish a variety of combinations of interaction effects, all instructive but not all equally crucial as a test of the theory. The more interesting ones are those in which the interactions are strong between all three units in all directions but preferably unequal, to display instructive asymmetries in the actions. The satisfactory agreement between calculated values and observed measurements suggests that the theory has been properly constructed and the assumption extending the law of spatial summation to the general case of interacting receptors is valid under the conditions of our experiments.

It would be possible in principle to extend these experiments to larger numbers of interacting elements measured individually. However, this would be difficult in the *Limulus* preparation; the three fiber experiments are difficult enough and it is doubtful whether much more would be learned. It is instructive, however, to consider the interactions of groups of ommatidia.

By illuminating large enough regions of the eye (spots of light 1–2 mm in diameter) to include a moderate number of ommatidia (from 10 to 40) strong inhibitory effects can be elicited. A test receptor in the neighborhood of such groups can be used to analyze the properties of the inhibitory interaction as we have done in experiments on disinhibition and spatial summation. Effects of large groups on a test receptor are large; effects of a single test receptor, exerted back on to large groups are relatively small (though often recognizable) and the analysis is simplified. A more detailed analysis is provided by choosing one of the receptors within a group as a representative of the group. This is useful but not without its drawbacks, for individual receptor units differ appreciably in their individual properties and in their interactions with others.

The theoretical treatment of group interaction may be approached by considering idealized situations. We will assume that within small compact groups the receptor units have identical properties, that each receptor inhibits equally all others in the group and that each one of the group inhibits and is inhibited by any one receptor unit outside the group to the same degree. We know that actual receptor groups depart from these idealizations, often considerably, but the theory may be developed for the simpler ideal case and the results used to give understanding of the more complex actual ones.

Starting with the consideration of a single group of n receptor units, our assumptions state that all the e's, K's and r^0's are equal; the r's must then also be equal. Just one of the set of n equations suffices and the subscripts may be dropped:

$$r = e - (n - 1) K(r - r^0) \qquad (5)$$

or

$$r = \frac{e + (n - 1) Kr^0}{1 + (n - 1) K}$$

If the group is of a fixed size and is illuminated at various intensities, the frequency of any one of the units (r) will vary more slowly with the stimulus intensity than if it were illuminated alone (e), by the factor $1/\{1 + (n - 1) K\}$ (a slight displacement, due to the constant term, might be noticeable). Figure 16 shows that this expectation is borne out to a fair approximation. For large

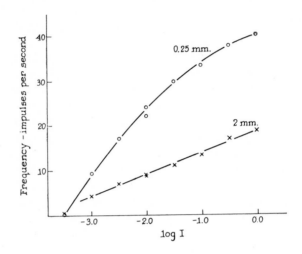

FIG. 16. Relations between intensity of light (log I, abscissae) and frequency of discharge (ordinates) of a single ommatidium when illuminated alone (upper curve, 0·25 mm spot of light centered on its facet), and when illuminated together with a large number (approx. 40) of neighboring ommatidia surrounding it (lower curve, 2·0 mm spot of light centered on its facet).

areas of retinal illumination, the activity of the individual receptors is reduced proportionately at each intensity. One of the consequences that this must have is that the range of intensities capable of being covered by the visual receptors is increased before a possible physiological limit to the frequency of the receptors is reached.

The relation between r and n for fixed e is hyperbolic, since (5) may be written

$$(r - r^0) \left(n + \frac{1}{K} - 1\right) = \frac{e - r^0}{K} \tag{5a}$$

If one of the receptors is considered a "test" receptor, the difference $(e - r)$ in the frequency of its response when illuminated alone and when illuminated with the rest of the n members of the group, measures the inhibition exerted by the group on each of its members. As a function of n this will increase along a hyperbolic curve from zero at $n = 1$ to $(e - r^0)$ at large values of n (in (5a) write $r - r^0$ as $(e - r^0) - (e - r)$). This is shown in the experiment reported in Fig. 6 of the paper by Hartline *et al.* (1956). The curve drawn in that figure is theoretical, based on equation (5a), but neglecting r^θ. Too much weight must not be given to the exact form of the fitted curve, for the larger areas were great enough in linear extent that the falling off in inhibitory action between widely separated receptors undoubtedly contributed to the flattening of the upper part of the curve.

Experiments on the effect of area necessarily depart from the idealized situation, but the principle involved can usually be illustrated to a good approximation: as area is increased, receptors recruited in each new increment are subjected to increased inhibition from receptors in the rest of the area and so themselves add less and less to the total inhibition. We have shown this effect directly in the following experiment. A small fixed area was used as an "increment" to a contiguous area, the size of which was varied. The contribution of this fixed increment of area to the total inhibition exerted on a test receptor became less and less as the area of the contiguous region was increased (Fig. 17).

We now turn to the consideration of two groups of receptors, idealized by the assumption that all the receptors in any group have uniform properties, interact equally with one another in that group and also interact equally with

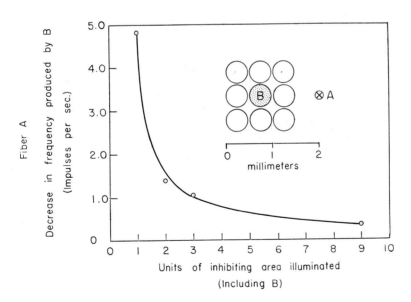

FIG. 17. Increment in the inhibitory effect on a test receptor (A) produced by adding a small retinal region (B, stippled) to various numbers of other small regions (arranged around B, as diagrammed). The decrease in A's frequency produced by the region B in combination with various other regions minus the decrease produced by those other regions alone is plotted (ordinate) as a function of the total number of regions illuminated (abscissa).

each receptor in the other group. In each group the r's of the receptors are equal and two simultaneous equations suffice:

$$r_A = e_A - [(n_A - 1) K_{AA}(r_A - r^0_{AA}) + n_B K_{AB}(r_B - r^0_{AB})] \qquad (6)$$

$$r_B = e_B - [n_A K_{BA}(r_A - r^0_{BA}) + (n_B - 1) K_{BB}(r_B - r^0_{BB})]$$

The validity of these equations is established by solving the entire set of $n_A + n_B$ equations (4), subject to the idealized assumptions. The notation used in these equations has the following meaning: the two groups are designated A and B, containing n_A and n_B receptor units, respectively. They are illuminated at intensities such that any single receptor in group A if illuminated by itself would have a frequency e_A; in group B, e_B. When the two groups are illuminated together, each receptor in group A responds at a frequency r_A; in group B, at r_B. K_{AA} is the coefficient of the inhibitory action between any two receptors in group A, and r^0_{AA} is the threshold of that action. Likewise K_{BB} and r^0_{BB} are the inhibitory parameters for the interaction within group B. K_{AB} is the coefficient of the inhibiting action (r^0_{AB} its threshold) exerted by each unit in B on each unit in A; K_{BA} and r^0_{BA} are the parameters of the action exerted by receptors in A on receptors in B. Collecting terms and dividing the first equation by $1 + (n^A - 1) K_{AA}$ and the second by $1 + (n_B - 1) K_{BB}$ we have

$$r_A = \bar{e}_A - \bar{K}_{AB}(r_B - r^0_{AB}) \qquad (6a)$$

$$r_B = \bar{e}_B - \bar{K}_{BA}(r_A - r^0_{BA})$$

where we define

$$\bar{e}_A \equiv \frac{e_A + (n_A - 1) K_{AA} r^0_{AA}}{1 + (n_A - 1) K_{AA}} \; ; \; \bar{e}_B \text{ likewise} \qquad (6D)$$

$$\bar{K}_{AB} \equiv \frac{n_B K_{AB}}{1 + (n_A - 1) K_{AA}} \; ; \; \bar{K}_{BA} \text{ likewise}$$

We note (cf. equation (5)) that $\bar{e}_A$ is the frequency we would obtain from each unit in A by illumination of the entire group A alone, at an intensity that would yield e_A if restricted to any one of the units in the group; likewise $\bar{e}_B$. The parameters $\bar{K}_{AB}$ and $\bar{K}_{BA}$ may be considered coefficients of group interactions (respectively, group B on group A, and group A on group B). Thus the two groups may be treated as units, each with a certain amount of self-inhibition, acting on each other with coefficients that depend on the numbers of ommatidia involved.

The variation of group inhibitory coefficients with group size has been examined experimentally. Figure 18 shows that enlarging a group increases

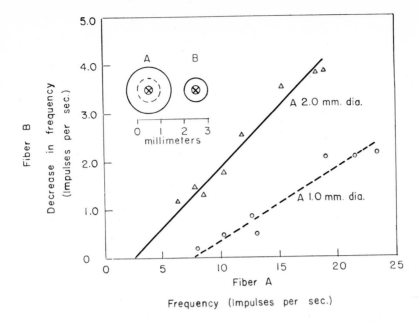

F<small>IG</small>. 18. Effect of size of group on the inhibition it exerts on a nearby ommatidium. Decrease in frequency of a receptor B (one of a small group of fixed size) produced by illumination of a nearby group, A, is plotted (ordinate) as a function of the frequency (abscissa) of one of the receptors in A. For the lower plot the diameter of the spot of light on A was 1·0 mm. For the upper plot the group A was enlarged by using a spot of light 2·0 mm in diameter, and the slope of the line (K_{BA}) was increased, as predicted by theory (the change in threshold is not expected according to the theory of *idealized* group action).

the coefficient of its inhibitory action on a nearby group of fixed size. It also decreases the coefficient of action of that fixed group on it (not shown). This is as predicted by the definitions (6D), for an idealized situation. Exact quantitative prediction cannot be made because of the departure of the actual groups from the ideal uniformity in receptor properties and interactions, required in the derivation of (6) and (6D).

Especially noteworthy is the case in which one of the groups is reduced to just one ommatidium (a "test receptor"). Then the coefficient of the other group (n receptors) on it is n times the coefficient of one of that group's receptors acting on the test receptor, while the action of the test receptor back on the receptors comprising the other group is diminished by the factor $1/\{1 + (n - 1) K'\}$. Here K' is used to designate the internal self-inhibition of the group—for a compact group perhaps of the order of 0·1 to 0·2. Hence for a large group, the test receptor's "back effect" might be substantially diminished compared with the effect it would have on any one of the receptors of the group by itself.

It is clear that this treatment may be extended to any number of groups. We will consider the case of three groups, but will have no occasion to go beyond this number. Our experiments have been confined to special cases concerning the separate and combined effects of two retinal regions on a third, from one of whose receptors we recorded optic nerve activity. Our results have been analyzed and published (Hartline and Ratliff, 1958). The coefficients required in the analysis are group coefficients, but only certain combinations are observable experimentally. The experimental results in all cases are interpretable in terms of the theory developed for three idealized groups of receptor units.

In most of these experiments, we illuminated independently two moderately large (1–2 mm in diameter) retinal regions, A and B together with a third small region X. One of the ommatidia in the region X served as a "test" receptor; its optic nerve fiber was isolated and the discharge of impulses in it recorded. Unless otherwise noted, we attempted to confine the spot of light to the ommatidium of the test receptor alone; when we wished to accentuate the effects of this third group in the interaction we then enlarged the spot of light to include the immediate neighbors of the test receptor. In some cases we also recorded from the optic nerve fiber of an ommatidium in one of the other regions. We will summarize our main results briefly.

When A and B were separated by 5 mm or more, and were on opposite sides of X, they interacted little if at all. As we have said earlier in this paper (cf. Fig. 14), their combined effect in lowering the frequency of X was then equal to the sum of the effects they produced separately

$$(\bar{K}_{XA}, \bar{K}_{XB} > 0; \quad \bar{K}_{AB}, K_{BA} = 0).$$

However, if A and B were close together ($\bar{K}_{AB}, \bar{K}_{BA} > 0$), their combined effect was less than the sum of their separate effects, because of their mutual inhibition (cf. Fig. 15). To extend this latter experiment, we held constant the intensity on one, B, and varied the illumination on A; the combined effect on X of A and B together then increased as a linear function of the effect of A alone on X. This was true, of course, only in that range of intensities for which A was strongly enough excited to respond, in the presence of B, at a level that exceeded its threshold of action on X and on B. Examples of results obtained for various configurations of A, B and X are shown in Fig. 19. For A and B close together and at approximately the same distance from X, the slope of this linear function was always positive, but less than 1, being smaller the closer together we placed A and B. If A was placed farther from X than B, so as to inhibit X only slightly while still affecting B strongly, the action of the combination was principally determined by A's inhibition of B producing an indirect effect on X to release it from the inhibition exerted by B. The slope of the function was then negative. This is the case of disinhibition described earlier in this paper. If we placed B farther from X than A

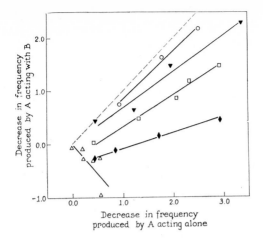

Decrease in frequency
produced by A acting with B

Decrease in frequency
produced by A acting alone

FIG. 19. Summation of inhibitory influences exerted on a test receptor (X) by two groups of receptors (A and B) at various distances from one another and from X. Each of the graphs was obtained from an experiment on a different preparation. In each case B refers to a group which was illuminated at a fixed intensity, A to a group illuminated at various intensities. (X was always illuminated at a fixed intensity.) As abscissa is plotted the magnitude of the inhibition (decreases in frequency of the discharge of X) resulting from illumination of A alone. As ordinate is plotted the change in frequency produced by A when it acted with B; that is, the decrease in frequency produced by A and B together less the decrease produced by B alone.

In the upper graph A and B were on opposite sides of X; in the others they were on the same side, in various configurations, the lowest being a case showing disinhibition. (From Hartline and Ratliff, 1958.)

(not shown in Fig. 19) then as the illumination on A was increased, it tended to release itself from B's inhibition (cf. Hartline and Ratliff, 1957, Fig. 7). Therefore the slope of the function was positive and in one experiment was as high as 1·0 (theoretically, the slope could be greater than 1). In all of these cases, the combined action of A and B was always less than the sum of their separate actions.

Returning to the case in which A and B were widely separated on either side of X, we note that a number of the individual observations in Fig. 14 showed the combined effect of A and B slightly to exceed the sum of their separate effects. This is a real phenomenon, greater than the scatter attributable to experimental error. It is readily understood, for in our first approximation we neglected the inhibition exerted by the test receptor itself back on A and B. When A and B were both illuminated they, of course, reduced the activity of X more than when only one of them was active, hence X inhibited each of them to a smaller degree when they were both active and in turn their individual contributions to the inhibition of X were greater when acting together than when acting separately. That this is indeed the correct interpretation was readily shown by enlarging the spot of light illuminating the test receptor so as to include several of its neighbors. Then the combined effect of A and B together was clearly greater than the sum of their separate effects (Fig. 4 in Hartline and Ratliff, 1958). Of course, the interaction of the group X, even when it consisted of the test ommatidium only, was of necessity present in all of the other experiments we have described. It is never possible in these simple experiments to provide an entirely unambiguous evaluation of the various inhibitory effects. The formulas for the combined and separate effects involve combinations of the inhibitory parameters of the several groups, and measurement of the activity in just one receptor does not provide enough information to calculate the parameters individually. Nevertheless, the theoretical formulas are useful in providing insight into the properties of the interacting system which can sometimes be unexpectedly complex even for relatively simple configurations of retinal illumination.

We need not reproduce here the analytic expressions derived theoretically to describe these experiments, but will show instead theoretical solutions plotted by an analog computer (Fig. 20). The examples chosen show all of the features found in actual experiments, and a few others not yet observed.

We will now turn to an aspect of the inhibitory interaction that has a special significance in visual physiology. In the foregoing analysis, we have treated the inhibitory interaction as determined by parameters r^0 and K whose numerical values were specified without inquiring how different values could arise. We will now discuss the principal factor that determines the values of these parameters. This is the distance separating any two ommatidia in the retinal mosaic (Ratliff and Hartline, 1959). Inhibitory influences are exerted more strongly, on the average, between near neighbors in the mosaic of retinal receptors than between widely separated ones. For example, Fig. 21 shows an instance in which the action of a group of receptors (A) on a nearby receptor (B) had a low threshold ($r^0_{BA} = 5$ impulses/sec) and a high coefficient of inhibition ($K_{BA} = 0.17$); on a more distant ommatidium (C) the threshold of A's inhibitory action was higher ($r^0_{CA} = 18$ impulses/sec) and its coefficient lower ($K_{CA} = 0.07$). C was approximately 3 mm from A; ommatidia separated by more than 5 mm rarely exert any observable influence on one another. The explanation of this dependence of inhibitory interaction on retinal separation is unknown. Perhaps inhibitory influences are conducted decrementally over the fine nerve branches of the plexus; perhaps there are merely less profuse connections between ommatidia that are widely separated than there are between near neighbors. More complete knowledge of the inhibitory mechanism and of the histology of the plexus is required.

The rule we stated above for the diminution of the inhibitory influence with distance, while true on the average, often fails in specific instances when applied to the interaction of individual ommatidia. The interaction of pairs of ommatidia of equal separation may vary considerably even in the same

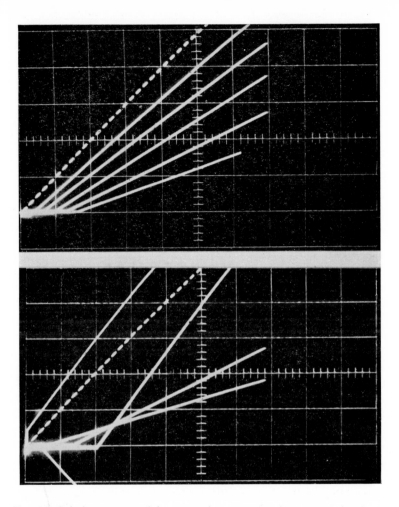

FIG. 20. Solutions generated by an analog computer (constructed by C. C. Yang) imitating the responses of three interacting receptor groups. The traces are analogous to the experimental plots of Fig. 19. The decrease in response of a test element (X) inhibited by two interacting elements, A and B, in combination minus the decrease produced by B alone is traced (ordinate) as a function of the decrease in response of X when inhibited by A alone (abscissa). In the upper figure, A and B were caused to inhibit one another to varying degrees (increasing from top to bottom). In the lower figure, various degrees of interaction between A and B are portrayed. The lowest trace (negative slope) illustrates disinhibition. The topmost trace is the only one for which X was caused to inhibit A and B. In this latter case A and B did not interact: this illustrates how their combined effect can sometimes exceed the sum of their separate effects, as in the points above the line in Fig. 14. In both figures the dotted line represents the case for equality of the combined and separate effects of A and B (solid line of Fig. 14).

19

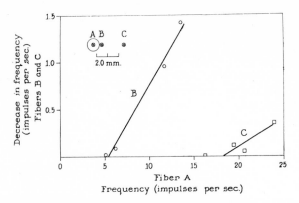

FIG. 21. The dependence of the magnitude of inhibition on distance. The inhibition exerted by a small group of receptors (A) on two other receptors (B and C) is plotted as ordinate. As abscissa is plotted the concurrent frequency of the discharge of impulses of one of the receptors in the group A. The geometrical configuration of the pattern of illumination on the eye is shown in the insert. The locations of the facets of the receptors whose discharges were recorded are indicated by the symbol ⊗. The receptor A was at the center of a group of six or seven receptors illuminated by a spot of light 1 mm in diameter. The illumination on B and C was provided by spots of light 0·2 mm in diameter and of fixed intensity. The effects of the group A on B and C were determined separately. (From Ratliff and Hartline, 1959).

region of the eye. Sometimes a near neighbor of an ommatidium will exert a much weaker influence on it than will its more distant neighbors. Furthermore, the correlation between the threshold and the coefficients of the inhibitory action is not perfect. We have even seen a few cases in which it is the reverse of that shown in Fig. 21. We have already noted that the strength of the inhibitory influences between two receptor units is not necessarily equal for the two directions of action, as it was, approximately, for the pair represented in Fig. 12. Sometimes, but rarely, the inequality is considerable: an ommatidium may effect a particular neighbor quite strongly but be only slightly affected by it. However, when we measure the interactions of moderately sized, compact groups of receptors we find greater regularity and the rule we have stated is followed in the manner illustrated in Fig. 21.

It is evident that any law relating the strength of the mutual inhibitory interaction of any two individual ommatidia in the retinal mosaic to the distance by which they are separated must take a statistical form. At the present we do not have enough data to formulate such a law quantitatively. Nevertheless, the broad rule we have stated is significant. The fact that the inhibitory parameters are strongly dependent, albeit statistically, on retinal separation, introduces a topographic factor into the inhibitory interaction which gives it special significance in pattern vision.

We have alluded to the possible role of retinal inhibition in explaining the enhancement of visual contrast at borders or steep intensity gradients in the retinal image. Consider two contiguous regions of different retinal illumination with a sharp transition between them. A receptor that is within the region of high illumination but close to the transition will receive less inhibition than a receptor that is well inside that region, where all of the closely neighboring receptors are brightly lighted. Consequently, the receptors near the transition will respond more vigorously than those well inside the region and the bright area will appear a little brighter near its border. Conversely, the dimly lighted region will appear a little dimmer near the border where it adjoins the bright region. These bands of greater and lesser brightness, flanking and accentuating a transition between two areas of unequal illumination, are Mach's bands. They are specially noticeable if the transition is not perfectly sharp but is an extended though fairly steep gradation in intensity. The penumbra of a shadow formed by a small extended source usually shows Mach's bands clearly. A double shadow cast by an object illuminated by two point sources of light usually shows striking variations in apparent brightness across its double edge—variations that have no counterpart in the actual distribution of light but are entirely the result of "border contrast" in the eye.

We have demonstrated the physiological counterpart of Mach's bands in the eye of *Limulus*, recording from a single receptor unit as the eye was caused to scan, slowly, a pattern consisting of two regions of different brightness separated by a transitional gradient (Ratliff and Hartline, 1959). When the eye was masked so that only the one receptor from which we were recording viewed the pattern, then the frequency of optic nerve impulse discharge mapped faithfully the distribution of physical brightness in the pattern. But when the mask was removed, so that the entire eye viewed the pattern, then as the pattern was scanned the receptor from which activity was being recorded showed maxima and minima of discharge rates correlated with those regions of the pattern where a human observer saw Mach's bands (Fig. 22, upper graph). Even more pronounced border contrast effects were recorded when the intensity step was abrupt (Fig. 22, lower graph). In the *Limulus* eye, this phenomenon is the inevitable consequence of mutual inhibitory interaction; for the human observer, a similar inhibitory interaction in the visual system may be postulated to explain this and related subjective phenomena of simultaneous "brightness contrast". Indeed, an inhibitory *Wechselwirkung* of adjacent retinal regions is precisely what Mach postulated to explain his now well known bands.

An exact theoretical treatment of "border contrast" cannot be given as yet for the eye of *Limulus* or for any other visual system because the exact law relating the magnitude of the inhibitory parameters to retinal distance between receptors is not known. We have, however, considered theoretically an idealized system—a uniform, fine-grained mosaic of large extent with respect to the range of inhibitory interaction. We postulated convenient plausible

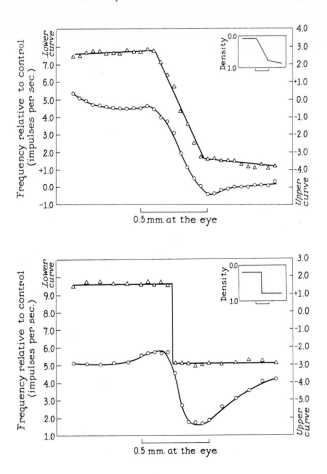

FIG. 22. The discharge of impulses from a single receptor unit in response to simple patterns of illumination in various positions on the retinal mosaic. Upper figure: the so-called "Mach pattern" (a simple gradient of intensity). The demagnified image of a photographic plate was projected on the surface of the eye. The insert shows the relative density of the plate along its length as measured, prior to the experiment, by means of a photomultiplier tube in the image plane where the eye was to be placed. The density of the plate was uniform across its entire width at every point. The upper (rectilinear) graph shows the frequency of discharge of the test receptor, when the illumination was occluded from the rest of the eye by a mask with a small aperture, minus the frequency of discharge elicited by a small control spot of light of constant intensity also confined to the facet of the test receptor. Scale of ordinate on the right. The lower (curvilinear) graph is the frequency of discharge from the same test receptor when the mask was removed and the entire pattern of illumination was projected on the eye in various positions, minus the frequency of discharge elicited by a small control spot of constant intensity confined to the facet of the receptor. Scale of ordinate on the left. Lower figure: a simple "step pattern" of illumination. Same procedure as in upper figure. (From Ratliff and Hartline, 1959).

guesses as to the quantitative form of the spatial function of interaction (we have considered only K, neglecting, for the present, the thresholds). This function should be symmetric, falling off equally in opposite directions from any given receptor. For simplicity, it should be isotropic in the retinal mosaic although this may not be the case in actuality (in *Limulus*, the inhibitory influences fall off more rapidly in the dorsoventral direction from any given receptor than in the anteroposterior direction). We have explored several forms of functional relation: one in which the inhibition had a constant non-zero value up to a given distance and was zero beyond; one in which it decayed exponentially in all directions with a given space constant. For one numerical solution, we chose a function which had the form of a Gaussian error curve (used by Fry (1948) in a similar treatment of "border contrast"). We have considered only patterns in which the intensity varied along one co-ordinate, and have dealt mostly with a simple step in intensity from a low value on one side of the step to a higher one on the other. Numerical solutions of equations (4) were obtained by an iterative method of successive approximations, as is sometimes done when dealing with integral equations. Indeed, a Fredholm integral equation of the second type may be considered an approximation to the present set of simultaneous equations representing the interaction of discrete elements. The first step in the computation is to substitute the e's in place of the r's under the summation (integration) sign; this yields an approximate solution which is next substituted, and the process is repeated as often as necessary. If the total inhibition on any element, $\sum_{j} K_{pj}$, is less than unity, as it must be in any actual retina, the successive approximations converge to a solution in which maxima and minima of r flank the intensity step on the high and low sides, respectively. We may note that Fry (1948) has made a somewhat similar calculation to explain Mach's bands in human vision. His treatment, however, does not involve a mutual interaction of the "recurrent" type demonstrated in the *Limulus* eye; the inhibition was assumed to depend only on the intensity of the stimulating light rather than on the activity of the receptors. This assumption is equivalent to using the e's in place of the r's under the summation sign in our equation (4) and is, indeed, the first step in our approximation procedure. Fry's model generates "Mach bands"; computation with it is much easier than with ours, of course, and for many purposes it may be useful in explaining contrast effects in human vision even though some evidence has been presented favoring "recurrent" inhibition in the human visual system (Alpern and David, 1959).

The form of the curves we obtained by our numerical solution differs very little from that obtained by Fry; there are, however, very weak minima and maxima flanking the main maxima and minima of the Mach bands—second-order Mach bands, so to speak. They could not be present, of course, in Fry's curves but are so weak in the particular case we have computed, that there would be little chance of detecting them in an effort to decide between the two models for human vision. In *Limulus*, they must be present and perhaps could be demonstrated.

These exercises with idealized models are perhaps instructive but they are so speculative at present that we will not give any numerical results here.

Up to this point our analysis of the inhibitory interaction in the eye of *Limulus* has been confined to the "steady state", in which light was allowed to shine steadily on the eye for a long enough time to permit sensory adaptation of the receptors to take place and to permit the inhibiting influences to take effect and come to a mutual equilibrium. Whenever the pattern of illumination on the eye is changed, transient changes in receptor activity take place and readjustments of the inhibitory influences follow. These transient changes are no less interesting than the steady-state interaction, and are of equal or greater significance in visual physiology.

Transient inhibitory effects are demonstrated in an experiment in which the responses of two ommatidia were observed (Fig. 23). To begin with, the receptors were steadily illuminated; then the light intensity on one of them was increased for a period of several seconds. An isolated receptor similarly stimulated responds to the increment of intensity, after brief latency, with a sharp peak in frequency; as the receptor adapts the frequency soon subsides to a steady level, higher than the value it had before the increment was applied. When the increment is turned off, there is again a short delay and then a sharp dip in the frequency of discharge which reaches a minimum and then returns to a value close to the initial level (MacNichol and Hartline, 1948). The upper curve of Fig. 23 illustrates these phenomena in the experiment under consideration; these frequency changes were determined primarily by the response of the first receptor to the stimulus increment that was applied to it. The second receptor, whose responses are plotted in the lower curve, was steadily illuminated throughout the entire period. Its frequency changes mirrored those of the first, with maxima and minima inverted with respect to those of the first fiber. Evidently the inhibition exerted by the first receptor varied with its discharge rate and these variations were followed with some fidelity by the frequency of the second. It must now be recognized that the variations in the frequency of the second receptor must also have produced changes in the inhibition it exerted back on the first so that the responses of the two receptors, being mutually interdependent, must have affected one another so as to modify each other's transient responses reciprocally. Since there are time delays in the exertion of inhibitory actions, and since the inhibitory process may itself exhibit transient changes in magnitude, it is evident that the temporal interactions of a group of receptors may become quite complex.

We have begun the analysis of the temporal aspects of the inhibitory inter-

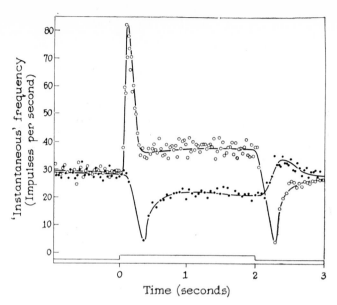

FIG. 23. Graph showing simultaneous excitatory and inhibitory transients in two adjacent receptor units. One ommatidium, black filled circles, was illuminated steadily throughout the period shown in the graph. The other unit, open circles, was illuminated steadily until time 0 when the illumination on it was increased abruptly to a new steady level at which it remained for 2 sec, then was decreased abruptly to the original level. The added illumination produced a large transient increase in frequency of that receptor which subsided quickly to a steady rate of responding ; the subsequent decrease in illumination to the original level produced a large transient decrement in the frequency of response after which the frequency returned to approximately the level it had prior to these changes. Accompanying these marked excitatory transients are large transient inhibitory effects in the adjacent, steadily illuminated receptor unit. A large decrease in frequency is produced by the inhibitory effect resulting from the large excitatory transient; during the steady illumination the inhibitory effect is still present but less marked; and finally, accompanying the decrement in the frequency of response of the ommatidium on which the level of excitation was decreased, there is a marked release from inhibition. (From Ratliff, 1961.)

action by studying the effects of short flashes of light applied to one receptor while a second receptor was illuminated steadily. Figure 24 shows the brief burst of impulses elicited by a short flash applied to one receptor and the brief transient dip in frequency elicited by this burst of impulses in the response of the second. The delay in the action is noteworthy: the dip in frequency did not begin until about 0·13 sec after the onset of the burst of impulses in the first receptor's fiber (0·20 sec after the flash of light). Indeed, we chose this record to show that if the burst of impulses is short, the inhibitory effect may not begin until the burst is nearly all over.

We can measure the total inhibitory effect produced by a burst of impulses in one fiber by counting the number of impulses discharged in the second fiber over a period containing the entire transient dip in frequency, and comparing this with the number discharged in a comparable control period of equal length. The deficit measures the integrated inhibition; it may be correlated with the integrated activity of the inhibiting receptor, that is, with the total number of impulses discharged in the first fiber in response to the flash. When this was done in an experiment in which various flash intensities were used, the relation was found to be a linear one similar to that shown for the steady state (Fig. 12). The slope of the plot may be taken as an inhibitory coefficient and the intercept with the axis of abscissae suggests a threshold for the action of the flash. We are therefore led to hope that the linearity found to hold for the steady-state interaction may also find a useful extension in the analysis of the transient phenomena. Our work on this phase of the problem, however, is still at its beginning.

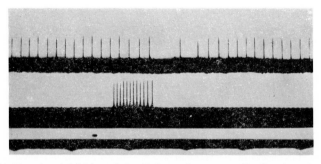

FIG. 24. Transient inhibition of the discharge from a steadily illuminated ommatidium (upper trace) by a burst of impulses discharged by a second ommatidium nearby (bottom trace) in response to a $0 \cdot 01$ sec flash of light (signalled by the black dot in the white band above the time marks). Time in $\frac{1}{5}$ sec.

The spatial summation of transient inhibitory effects exerted on a test receptor when brief flashes were applied to two regions of the eye in its neighborhood has been examined briefly. The experiments reveal a point of some interest. Since the bursts of impulses from such regions in response to short flashes of moderate intensity may be completed before the beginning of inhibitory effects they produce (as in Fig. 24), two regions that can be shown to interact under conditions of steady illumination may give no evidence of affecting one another when their inhibitory actions on a test receptor are produced by sufficiently short flashes. This is illustrated in Table 2, where the inhibitory effects of two regions, A and B, on a test receptor X are shown for these two conditions. When the frequencies of X were measured during steady illumination of A and B separately and in combination, the combined effect of A and B illuminated together (measured by the decrement produced in X's steady frequency), was less than the sum of their separate effects—the consequence of their mutual inhibition, as we have explained in the earlier

TABLE 2. SUMMATION OF INHIBITORY EFFECTS IN A TEST RECEPTOR (DEFICIT IN NUMBER OF IMPULSES OVER A 1 SEC PERIOD) PRODUCED BY TWO CLOSELY SPACED RETINAL REGIONS (A AND B) WHEN ILLUMINATED STEADILY, COMPARED WITH THE SUMMATION OF THEIR EFFECTS WHEN ILLUMINATED BY BRIEF FLASHES

Illumination	Separate inhibitory effects produced by		Sum of separate effects	Combined effect produced by A and B together
	A	B		
Steady	4·5	4·7	9·2	6·0
Flash	4·7	2·2	6·9	7·0

part of this paper. But when short flashes were used, the deficits in X's discharges showed no evidence of interaction between A and B: the combined effect equalled the sum of the separate effects. This we interpret to mean that the mutually exerted inhibitory interaction of A and B on each other did not have time to act before the bursts of impulses from them had been completed. Evidently, the process of combining the effects from the two receptor groups is able to operate linearly for short flashes as well as for steady illumination. Our assumption is strengthened, that the combination of inhibitory influences always takes place by simple addition and one need only take into account mutual interaction to explain all the effects observed under both the steady and the transient conditions.

Complex transient effects are to be expected when a receptor's activity lasts for a long enough time to be affected in turn by the modifications it produces in the activity of its neighbors. The principles, however, can be demonstrated in a rather simple experiment. The response of an ommatidium to turning on a small spot of light confined to its facet was compared with that obtained when the stimulus spot was enlarged to include a number of near neighbors. Figure 25 illustrates the difference. When the receptor was illuminated alone, the initial peak in its discharge was followed, as the receptor adapted, by a monotonic decrease in frequency to a lower level which was then maintained steadily. When a larger area was illuminated, surrounding and including this same ommatidium, the initial part of the discharge was the same, but just after the peak there was a sudden drop in frequency—a "silent period"—after which the discharge was resumed, but at a lower level than when the light was confined to a single receptor. We are familiar with the lowering of the steady level of a receptor's response when it is one of a large group of interacting units. The "silent period" in this experiment we interpret as the result of the transient in the inhibitory influences from the neighboring elements, reflecting the initial peak in their responses, acting, after a delay, on the receptor unit whose activity we were observing. It is no different from

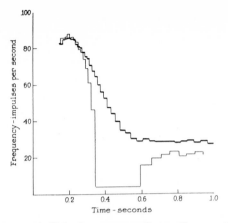

FIG. 25. The "silent period" in the response of an optic nerve fiber. The upper heavy line shows the frequency of discharge of impulses from an ommatidium illuminated alone. The lower curve shows the frequency of discharge in the same fiber when the area of illumination (same intensity as before) was enlarged so that neighboring ommatidia were also stimulated. The time delay of their inhibitory action on the test receptor was long enough that the initial peak of the discharge was unaffected; it was complete before the inhibitory influences affected the test receptor. Soon after, however, the inhibitory influences affected the test receptor and its response dropped abruptly. Since the inhibition is mutual, similar effects were produced on the neighboring receptors themselves, the inhibition they exerted became smaller, and the response of the test receptor increased somewhat.

the deep minimum observed in the response of a steadily illuminated test receptor when a neighboring group of units is suddenly illuminated (Fig. 7).

One can readily understand how several groups of receptors, under suitable conditions, might respond to sudden changes of intensity with rather complex transient oscillations, as the groups interact with time delays. An actual experimental example is given in Fig. 26. It is easy to simulate such oscillations in the output of a pair of interacting amplifiers, connected through an electrical delay network (Fig. 27). However, the detailed quantitative analysis of these complex transient effects in the eye of *Limulus* must wait for a more thorough experimental study of the temporal features of the inhibitory interaction.

Vigorous and complex transient responses to sudden changes in light intensity are familiar to students of visual physiology. "Charpentier's bands", for example, are oscillations in brightness perceived by a human subject under suitable stimulus configurations. Of much greater importance is the pronounced sensitivity of animals to movements in their visual fields. A physiological basis for this sensitivity is found in the "on" and "off" bursts of impulses characteristic of the responses of certain ganglion cells of the vertebrate retina, and in the visual pathways of many invertebrates as well. Such elements are often extremely sensitive to slight changes in intensity of

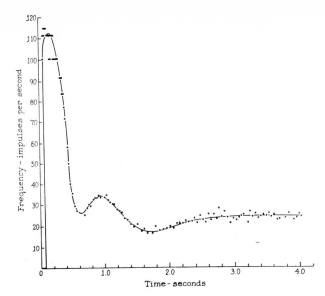

Fig. 26. Plot of the time-course of the frequency of discharge of an ommatidium suddenly illuminated together with several nearby receptors, showing oscillations resulting from the time delay in the action of the mutual inhibitory influences.

retinal illumination, and also respond to minute movements of a spot of light or a shadow across their receptive fields (Hartline, 1940). Similarly, as the eye itself moves—even minutely—neural responses occur. That minute motions

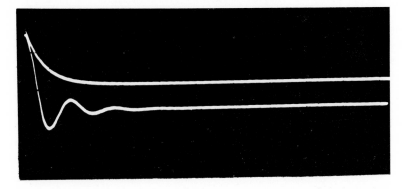

Fig. 27. Oscillations in the output of one of a pair of interacting amplifiers connected to "inhibit" one another through electrical delay circuits, to imitate the receptor responses shown in Figs. 25 and 26. The amplifiers were "excited" by a wave form imitating approximately the response (frequency of discharge) of an ommatidium when suddenly illuminated and showing the usual sensory adaptation. Upper trace shows the response of just one amplifier excited alone; lower trace the output of the same amplifier when interconnected through the delay circuits with the second amplifier (similarly excited).

of the eye actually play an important role in human vision has been shown in experiments in which an optical device is used to cancel all the effects of eye movements. When a retinal image is formed that is stationary with respect to the retinal mosaic, all contours and discontinuities gradually fade out, and within a few seconds the visual field appears uniform, although the image is physically unchanged on the retina (Riggs, Ratliff, Cornsweet and Cornsweet, 1953; for a review of work by Ditchburn and his associates see Ditchburn, 1955).

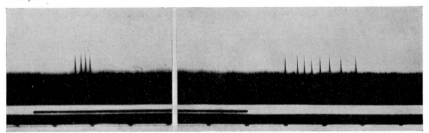

FIG. 28. Oscillogram of a "synthetic" on–off discharge in a single fiber of *Limulus* optic nerve. The typical response to steady illumination of a single receptor is a sustained discharge. In the record shown, the receptor was illuminated simultaneously with other nearby receptors which exerted inhibition on it. By properly balancing the excitatory and inhibitory influences against one another transient burst of impulses at the onset and cessation of illumination were obtained. A section 0·8 sec long (no impulses) was cut from the center of the record (cf. Ratliff and Mueller, 1957).

Responses to movement are but one instance of a retinal action that serves as a step in the integration of sensory information; the wide diversity of response characteristics of the ganglion cells of the vertebrate retina undoubtedly subserve other integrative processes that have their beginnings in the sense organ itself. Receptive fields of retinal ganglion cells have an elaborate functional organization (Kuffler, 1953; Barlow, 1953). The full significance of this organization is one of the important problems of visual physiology; in some animals, antagonistic actions within the receptive fields of single ganglion cells are "color-coded" (Wagner *et al.*, 1960). The neural mechanisms involved in these various phenomena are not fully understood, but it is clear that they are based on an interplay of excitatory and inhibitory influences, and on the interactions of retinal receptors and neurons (Granit, 1955). In the simpler eye of *Limulus*, these mechanisms are not elaborated, but a simple integrative process is nevertheless present in the form of the inhibitory interaction.

Although "on–off" and "off" responses are never observed in the optic nerve fibers of *Limulus* under ordinary conditions of stimulation, such response patterns can be "synthesized" by careful balancing of the excitation furnished directly by illumination on an ommatidium and the inhibition from its neighbors (Ratliff and Mueller, 1957). An example is shown in Fig. 28, where the strengths of the excitatory and inhibitory influences, their transients and their relative time delays were favorable to the development of an "on–off" response. This shows that an interplay of excitatory and inhibitory influences can indeed generate complex response patterns, that may resemble those produced in the vertebrate retina where neural interactions are more elaborate.

The eye of *Limulus* has provided a useful object for the study of neural interaction in a form that is complex enough to have general interest, and yet simple enough to permit quantitative analysis and the development of a formal theory for its concise representation. This analysis has been successful for the steady-state condition, and offers promise of useful extension to the transients. Its significance to visual physiology has been indicated, and its extension to other sensory systems should be useful. It is hoped that it may have general value in the analysis of the complex interactions that characterize the action of all nervous centers.

REFERENCES

ALPERN, M. and DAVID, H. (1959) The additivity of contrast in the human eye. *J. Gen. Physiol.* 43 : 109–127.

BARLOW, H. B. (1953) Summation and inhibition in the frog's retina. *J. Physiol.* (*London*) 119 : 69–88.

BÉKÉSY, G. VON (1928) Zur Theorie des Hörens; Die Schwingungsform der Basilarmembran. *Physik. Z.* 29 : 793–810.

BROCK, L. G., COOMBS, J. S. and ECCLES, J. C. (1952) The recording of potentials from motoneurones with an intracellular electrode. *J. Physiol.* (*London*) 117 : 431–460.

DITCHBURN, R. W. (1955) Eye movements in relation to retinal action. *Optica Acta* (*Paris*) 4 : 171–176.

FATT, P. and KATZ, B. (1953) The effect of inhibitory nerve impulses on a crustacean muscle fiber. *J. Physiol.* (*London*) 121 : 374–389.

FRY, G. A. (1948) Mechanisms subserving simultaneous brightness contrast. *Am. J. Optom. and Arch. Am. Acad. Optom.* 25 : 162–178.

GALAMBOS, R. and DAVIS, H. (1944) Inhibition of activity in single auditory nerve fibers by acoustic stimulation. *J. Neurophysiol.* 7 : 287–304.

GRAHAM, C. H. and HARTLINE, H. K. (1935) The response of single visual sense cells to lights of different wave-lengths. *J. Gen. Physiol.* 18 : 917–931.

GRANIT, R. (1947) *Sensory Mechanisms of the Retina.* Oxford University Press, London.

GRANIT, R. (1955) *Receptors and Sensory Perception.* Yale University Press, New Haven.

HARTLINE, H. K. (1940) The receptive fields of optic nerve fibers. *Am. J. Physiol.* 130 : 690–699.

HARTLINE, H. K. (1959) Receptor mechanisms and the integration of sensory information in the eye. *Rev. Mod. Phys.* 31 : 515–523.

HARTLINE, H. K. and RATLIFF, F. (1957) Inhibitory interaction of receptor units in the eye of *Limulus*. *J. Gen. Physiol.* 40 : 357–376.

HARTLINE, H. K. and RATLIFF, F. (1958) Spatial summation of inhibitory influences in the eye of *Limulus*, and the mutual interaction of receptor units. *J. Gen. Physiol.* 41 : 1049–1066.

HARTLINE, H. K., WAGNER, H. G. and MACNICHOL, E. F., JR. (1952) The peripheral origin of nervous activity in the visual system. *Cold Spring Harbor Symposia Quant. Biol.* 17 : 125–141.

HARTLINE, H. K., WAGNER, H. G. and RATLIFF, F. (1956) Inhibition in the eye of *Limulus*. *J. Gen. Physiol.* 39 : 651–673.

HUBBARD, R. and WALD, G. (1960) Visual pigment of the horseshoe crab, *Limulus polyphemus*. *Nature* **186** : 212–215.

KUFFLER, S. W. (1953) Discharge patterns and functional organization of mammalian retina. *J. Neurophysiol.* **16** : 37–68.

KUFFLER, S. W. and EYZAGUIRRE, C. (1955) Synaptic inhibition in an isolated nerve cell. *J. Gen. Physiol.* **39** : 155–184.

MACH, E. (1865) Über die Wirkung der räumlichen Vertheilung des Lichtreizes auf die Netzhaut—I. *Sitzber. Akad. Wiss. Wien Math. naturw. Kl.* II, **52** : 303–322.

MACNICHOL, E. F. and HARTLINE, H. K. (1948) Responses to small changes of light intensity by the light-adapted photoreceptor. *Federation Proc.* **7** : 76.

MILLER, W. H. (1957) Morphology of the ommitidia of the compound eye of *Limulus*. *J. Biophys. Biochem. Cytol.* **3** : 421–428.

MILLER, W. H. (1958) Fine structure of some invertebrate photoreceptors. *Ann. N.Y. Acad. Sci.* **74** : 204–209.

MOUNTCASTLE, V. B. and POWELL, P. S. (1960) Neural mechanisms subserving cutaneous sensibility, with special reference to the role of afferent inhibition in sensory perception and discrimination. *Bull. Johns Hopkins Hosp.* **105** : 201–232.

RATLIFF, F. (1961) Inhibitory interaction and the detection and enhancement of contours. *Sensory Communication* (ed. by ROSENBLITH, W. A.) Chap. 11. Technology Press, Cambridge, and John Wiley, New York.

RATLIFF, F. and HARTLINE, H. K. (1959) The responses of *Limulus* optic nerve fibers to patterns of illumination on the receptor mosaic. *J. Gen. Physiol.* **42** : 1241–1255.

RATLIFF, F., MILLER, W. H. and HARTLINE, H. K. (1958) Neural interaction in the eye and the integration of receptor activity. *Ann. N.Y. Acad. Sci.* **74** : 210–222.

RATLIFF, F. and MUELLER, C. G. (1957) Synthesis of "on-off" and "off" responses in a visual-neural system. *Science* **126** : 840–841.

RIGGS, L. A., RATLIFF, F., CORNSWEET, J. C. and CORNSWEET, T. N. (1953) The disappearance of steadily fixated test objects. *J. Opt. Soc. Am.* **43** : 491–501.

TOMITA, T. (1958) Mechanism of lateral inhibition in the eye of *Limulus*. *J. Neurophysiol.* **21** : 419–429.

WAGNER, H. G., MACNICHOL, E. F., JR. and WOLBARSHT, M. L. (1960) The response properties of single ganglion cells in the goldfish retina. *J. Gen. Physiol.* **43**, pt. 2 : 45–62.

WILSON, V. J., DIECKE, F. P. J. and TALBOT, W. H. (1960) Action of tetanus toxin on conditioning of spinal motoneurons. *J. Neurophysiol.* **23** : 659–666.

EXCITATORY AND INHIBITORY PROCESSES IN CRUSTACEAN SENSORY NERVE CELLS*

C. EYZAGUIRRE

Department of Physiology, University of Utah College of Medicine,
Salt Lake City, Utah

SINCE Alexandrowicz's original description (1951, 1952), a number of papers have dealt with the properties of sensory nerve cells located in the abdomen and in the thorax of lobsters and crayfish. In addition, this subject has been reviewed recently by Kuffler (1958, 1960) and Edwards (1960); see also Eccles (1957).

The purpose of this paper is to review once more, from a rather personal point of view, some of the functional properties of these crustacean nerve cells. Whenever possible, an effort has been made to avoid overlap with material already covered by other reviewers.

A. THE CRUSTACEAN SENSORY NERVE CELLS

In general these cells have their soma near receptor muscle elements; their dendrites approach the muscles and become embedded in their mass. The axon emerges from the pole opposite to that facing the receptor muscle and, following a relatively long trajectory, reaches the ventral cord. This view of these neurons is valid only for the more commonly occurring "receptor organs" of Alexandrowicz. In fact, other receptor cells (N-cells) also occur in these animals (Alexandrowicz, 1952) and are quite different. They are very small, with long and intricate dendritic processes which reach ordinary muscles. Some of these dendrites emerge from the axon at some distance from the soma. The function of the N-cells has been investigated only recently (Pilgrim and Wiersma, 1960); most of the attention has been focused on the larger "receptor organ" cells.

From the start one is faced with the question of describing the cell in accordance to the classical components, axon, soma and dendrites. In morphological terms the soma is usually defined as a prominent region containing the nucleus while dendrites are non-axonal processes emerging from the cell. In crustacean sensory nerve cells the region containing the

* Supported by a Senior Research Fellowship (SF-260) from the U.S. Public Health Service and by grant NSF G-9952 from the National Science Foundation.

A

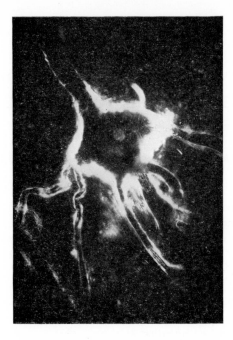

B

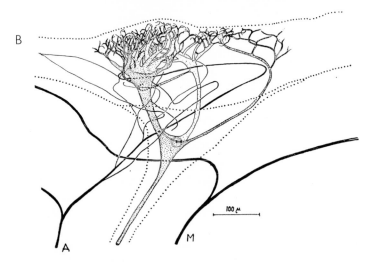

FIG. 1. A. Unstained lobster slow receptor cell under dark field illumination. Six large dendrites emerge from the cell body (nucleus a little off center to right) with their distal portions invisible, embedded in the tissue of the receptor muscle strand. The axon is seen on the opposite side from the dendrites. (From Ezyaguirre and Kuffler, *J. Gen. Physiol.* **39** : 87–119, 1955a). B. Drawing of a silver stained preparation of a fast crayfish receptor cell. *M*, motor axon. *A*, accessory fiber. (From Florey and Florey, *J. Gen. Physiol.* **39** : 69–85, 1955.)

nucleus is not always the largest or most prominent part of the cell. As shown by Florey and Florey (1955), some dendrites are the most conspicuous part of the soma–dendrite complex. The axonal segment, formed by that portion which connects the soma–dendrite complex with the ventral cord, is less difficult to define. The axon hillock region is sometimes not distinct (Fig. 1). From a functional point of view this classification may be quite arbitrary. It has been suggested that the soma–dendrite complex differs from neighboring axonal regions in that the soma membrane has a larger resistance (cf. Edwards and Ottoson, 1958). Also, intracellular potentials (evoked by antidromic stimulation) and recorded in the soma, have a different recovery time course than simple axonal potentials evoked in a similar manner (Eyzaguirre and Kuffler, 1955b). However, the situation becomes complicated if one tries to separate functionally the soma and the dendrites. The larger dendritic trunks behave functionally as the soma while the distal and very fine dendritic portions have different properties with regard to excitation and conduction properties. Indeed, dendritic terminals are depolarized by stretch and they do not seem able to conduct propagated impulses (see later). The length of the terminal dendritic membrane presenting such properties is not known. This picture is complicated even more since inhibitory synaptic endings seem to occur over a fairly large dendritic area (Kuffler and Edwards, 1958). This innervated area includes dendritic portions which respond actively to stretch excitation, but it may include also other parts of the dendrites.

The Dendritic Endings on the Receptor Muscle

The manner by which the dendritic processes terminate on the receptor muscles varies in different species and also depends on the type of cell that is being studied. In addition, the muscle receptor organ of lobsters loses its striation somewhere around its middle and the dendrites are embedded in this apparently non-contractile tissue whereas in crayfish the striations continue across the region where the dendrites are embedded.

In the crayfish one type of neuron (RM 1) has a dendritic system which consists mainly of three parts: (1) a long dendrite extending rostrally rather parallel to the muscle receptor; (2) a stout or rather short dendrite whose main direction is perpendicular to the extension of the muscle fibers; and (3) a system of from one to four thin dendrites which leave the cell body at the opposite side from the first long dendrite. Furthermore, silver staining has revealed that these dendrites send their final endings to different muscle fibers and that branches from one dendritic system run toward the main area of branching of another dendritic system. When the dendritic branches reach their designated muscle fiber they bifurcate in a characteristic T-shape, the ends running in opposite directions along the muscle fiber. If further bifurca-

20

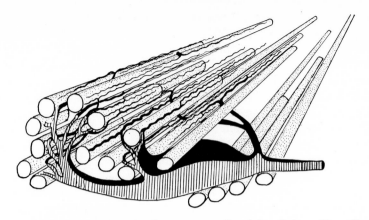

FIG. 2. Schematic drawing of a slow receptor cell and the relation of its endings to the muscle fibers. (From Florey and Florey, *J. Gen. Physiol.* **39** : 69–85.)

tions occur, the new branch leaves perpendicular to the region of ending which continues its course and it may bifurcate again in a T fashion at the same muscle fiber. The nerve cells of *RM* 2 present a somewhat different picture with regard to the dendritic terminals. The dendrites leave the cell body all in about the same direction. There are three to four dendrites, one of them being rather stout. They end in a brush-like manner, their terminations being short. They do not seem to be oriented in the direction of the muscle fiber (Figs. 1B and 2). This morphological arrangement could be of importance in understanding some of the basic processes of the phenomena of adaptation (for anatomical details consult Florey and Florey, 1955).

One feature of these neurons is that the cell body as a whole is completely devoid of terminal nerve endings and the only known efferent connections from the central nervous system terminate around the dendrites forming axodendritic synapses. These synapses, supplied by the "accessory fibers" of Alexandrowicz, have been shown to be of an inhibitory nature (Kuffler and Eyzaguirre, 1955; Burgen and Kuffler, 1957). This particular type of innervation differs from that of many neurons in the central nervous system of vertebrates where the cell body is covered by a number of "boutons terminaux". Unfortunately, no information is available with regard to the fine structure of the crustacean nerve-cell synapses since no electron microscope studies of these structures have appeared.*

B. THE EXCITATION PROCESS

Wiersma *et al.* (1953) first showed the sensory nature of the organs described by Alexandrowicz; tension applied at both ends of the muscular portion of these structures produced repetitive discharges which could be recorded from

* See note on page 316.

the axon of this preparation. Furthermore, sustained stretch produced continuous firing of the *RM* 1 receptor while the same type of stimulus applied to the *RM* 2 receptor produced only a short burst of discharges. This shows that *RM* 1 is a slowly adapting receptor while *RM* 2 is of a fast-adapting type. These observations have been extended in a series of papers by Kuffler (1954), Eyzaguirre and Kuffler (1955a, b), Kuffler and Eyzaguirre (1955). From these studies several facts have emerged: (i) that stretch deformation is capable of depolarizing that portion of the dendrites which is in close contact with the muscle, and (ii) that a series of intermediate processes lead to the initiation of conducted sensory impulses.

Stretch Deformation of the Dendrites

The dendrites are deeply embedded in the muscle mass, and stretch produces deformation of the dendritic endings with consequent changes in sensory frequency. The depolarization produced by deformation seems to be restricted to the terminal dendritic filaments because bending of thick dendritic trunks, the cell soma or the axon does not produce any changes in the frequency of sensory impulses.

Stretch-deformation of the dendrites can be accomplished also by stimulation of motor nerve fibers which innervate the muscular portion of the receptor. These fibers were described histologically by Alexandrowicz (1951, 1952), and by Florey and Florey (1955). Upon stimulation of the motor axons the muscle contracts visibly and tension can be recorded by a sensitive transducer. The muscle of *RM* 1 contracts in a fashion similar to "slow" crustacean muscles; only junctional potentials, similar in appearance to end-plate potentials of vertebrates, are recorded by means of intracellular microelectrodes. On the other hand, stimulation of the motor fibers innervating *RM* 2 produces a fast, twitch-like contraction and intracellular recording from the muscle fibers reveals propagated action potentials superimposed on local junctional potentials. Contraction of the receptor muscle element pulls on the dendrites and the ultimate effect is qualitatively similar to that of externally applied stretch (cf. Kuffler, 1954; Eyzaguirre and Kuffler, 1955a).

Little is known about the basic processes underlying stretch-excitation in dendrites since it is not known to what extent the dendrites are deformed by stretch and what structural changes occur while the organ is being pulled. Electron microscope studies of receptors fixed at different degrees of stretch might yield some pertinent information concerning the relation between stretch-deformation and the production of the generator potential (but, see later).

The dendrites of *RM* 1 are thin and long; such an arrangement might permit effective and sustained deformation during stretch and might explain the fact that this receptor is slowly adapting. On the other hand, *RM* 2 has

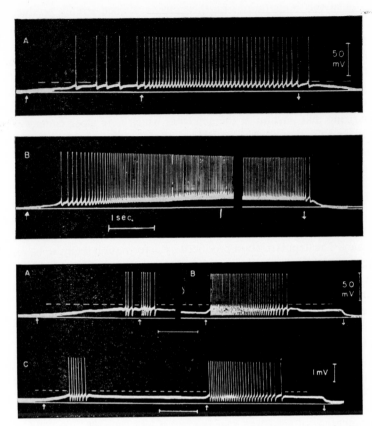

FIG. 3. (*Upper portion*)—A. Slow cell impaled and stretched just above threshold
setting up five irregular discharges at a depolarization threshold of 12 mV. At
second arrow additional stretch increases discharge rate to from 12 to 14/sec.
Firing level marked by broken line remains almost constant while rate of pre-
potential rise increases. B. Same cell. Stretch is gradually increased over 4 sec
between first arrow and straight line and then held constant. Note rise in firing level
as frequency increases while spike declines by several millivolts. The discharge is
regular (30/sec) during maintained stretch. Several seconds of rhythmic discharge
not shown (dark gap). Relaxation is followed by small transient phase of hyperpolarization.

(*Lower portion*)—A. Adaptation of impaled fast cell, during maintained stretch.
Slow stretch for about 2 sec sets up three impulses at a depolarization threshold
near 22 mV. At second arrow additional stretch given and maintained for from
4 to 5 sec. As depolarization drops below 20 mV discharges stop. B. depolarization
fell to 7 mV when at the third arrow additional stretch was given and maintained.
Once more the cell discharges at the previous membrane level. C. Fast cell. Extracellular recording, small monophasic potentials. Between first and second arrows
stretch applied and further extension added and maintained between second and
third arrows. Dotted line drawn slightly above the firing levels. Note in both cells
the decline of the generator potential below threshold during steady stretch.
Time, 1 sec.(From Eyzaguirre and Kuffler, *J. Gen. Physiol.* **39**, 87–119, 1955a).

short, brush-like, endings which might undergo less well sustained deformation during stretch, thus accounting for the more rapid adaptation of this receptor (Fig. 3).* In this case a mechanical effect might be largely responsible for the striking differences in adaptation rate. However, one cannot assume that differences in adaptation are produced only by mechanical factors. No comparative studies concerned with the role of applied currents on the discharges of the slowly and the rapidly adapting receptors have yet appeared. Terzuolo and Bullock (1956), and Hagiwara *et al.* (1960) studied the effects of applied current on the slowly adapting receptor only.

Processes Leading to the Production of Conducted Axonal Impulses

By appropriate placement of external leads or by insertion of a micro-electrode into the soma, it is possible to record a fairly well maintained depolarization which occurs whenever the preparation is stretched. Applying a weak tension one is able to record this type of potential only, or, by using small doses of novocaine one can block the propagated nerve impulses and study only this slow response under greater degrees of stretch (Fig. 4). Similar potentials have been recorded from other receptor organs such as the mammalian Pacinian corpuscle (Alvarez-Buylla and Ramirez de Arellano, 1953; Gray and Sato, 1953; cf. also, Loewenstein, 1959), the frog muscle spindle (Katz, 1950), the retina of some invertebrates (cf. Hartline *et al.*, 1952) and from olfactory receptors (Ottoson, 1956). In line with a suggestion by Granit (1947) this potential has been called the *generator potential*. In the crustacean stretch receptor it is produced at the end of the dendrites; it is non-propagated, graded and spreads electrotonically over the rest of the system. In normal preparations, propagated potentials are set up if the generator potential reaches a critical level of about 10 mV in slowly adapting cells (Fig. 5) and of about 20 mV in fast-adapting neurons. The actual magnitude of the generator potential produced at the dendritic terminals is unknown since it has been recorded only at some distance from its site of origin. Consequently, it must have been attenuated considerably, although it is difficult to estimate the degree of attenuation since the space constant of dendrites is unknown.

In slowly adapting cells the generator potential seems to be better maintained than in rapidly adapting neurons where a rather conspicuous decay occurs during constant stretch. This phenomenon might explain the fact that rapidly adapting neurons discharge only for a very short period of time since the generator rapidly declines to values below threshold at the region responsible for setting up propagated impulses.

* The term pre-potential as used in the illustration and subsequently refers to a slowly increasing depolarization that precedes the spike. Consequently, the pre-potential is smaller immediately after the previous orthodromic discharge and increases by several millivolts until the next orthodromic discharge appears (cf. Eyzaguirre and Kuffler, 1955a).

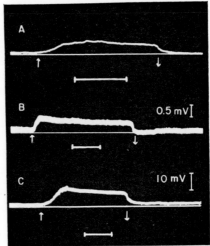

FIG. 4. Membrane potential changes during stretch in the absence of sensory discharges. A. Intracellular record from the cell body of a slowly adapting cell. Stretch and relaxation marked by arrows. Resting potential of 75 mV reduced by from 6 to 7 mV for the duration of stretch. B. Stretch applied to slow cell for almost 4 sec during conduction block with 0·1% novocaine. Extracellular recording. Note similarity to A (slower camera speed). C. Impaled fast adapting cell stretched for 3 sec. Potential calibrations same for A and C. Time calibration 1 sec in all records. Note the decline of the potentials during maintained stretch.
(From Eyzaguirre and Kuffler, *J. Gen. Physiol.* **39** : 87–119, 1955a.)

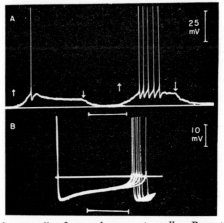

FIG. 5. Intracellular recording from a slow receptor cell. A. Receptor stretched and relaxed twice in succession. First stretch setting up one conducted soma impulse while second stretch causes five discharges after an initial depolarization of 12 mV. Impulse peaks 80 mV. Time, 1 sec. B. Slow cell discharging at about 5/sec each triggered by a sensory impulse thereby superimposing the succeeding prepotentials. Higher amplification—only lower portions of impulses are seen. The difference between impulse intervals reflects fluctuations in frequency. Second beam set near firing level of cell. Time, 0·1 sec. (From Eyzaguirre and and Kuffler, *J. Gen. Physiol.* **39** : 87–119, 1955a.)

The mechanisms underlying the production of the generator potential are, to a large extent, unknown. It is possible that conditions present in other receptor organs may also occur in crayfish and lobster stretch receptors. Thus, an inward flux of Na^+ ions may occur during stretch and this ionic movement might be responsible for setting up the generator potential. Gray and Sato (1953) have been able to obtain changes in the magnitude of the generator potential in Pacinian corpuscles by altering the sodium content of the bathing solution. Similar studies in the crustacean preparation are lacking.

The problem of how rhythmic activity is initiated in these receptors was thoroughly studied by Eyzaguirre and Kuffler (1955a). This aspect of the problem has been extensively reviewed by a number of authors (Eccles, 1957; Kuffler, 1958, 1960; Edwards, 1960; Grundfest, 1956, 1957, 1959). Consequently, it is felt that further writing on this subject is, at present, unnecessary.

The Origin of the Conducted Nerve Impulse

Eyzaguirre and Kuffler (1955a, b), recording intracellularly from the cell soma, showed that the slowly adapting neuron discharged impulses if its resting potential was reduced by about 8 to 12 mV. Rapidly adapting cells, on the other hand, needed a reduction in resting potential of about 18 to 22 mV before firing occurred. With this evidence it was concluded that the low firing level presented by the slowly adapting cells indicated that impulses arose at some distance from the recording lead, presumably somewhere along the dendrites or near the dendrite–soma junction. Similarly the high firing level presented by rapidly adapting cells seemed to indicate that the nerve impulses arose near the recording lead, that is at the soma. This view seemed to be consistent with the finding that antidromic impulses blocked at or near the axon hillock were capable of eliciting a local response in the cell which, if it attained a magnitude of about 20 mV, was capable of eliciting propagated action potentials in the soma.

A different view has been proposed by Edwards and Ottoson (1958) working with the slowly adapting neuron of the lobster. These authors recorded the sensory discharges by means of extracellular microelectrodes, the preparation being immersed in a large volume of fluid. With this system they were able to localize a region in the axon where the nerve impulses apparently originated several hundred microns from the center of the neuron soma (Fig. 6).

The method employed by Edwards and Ottoson yields more accurate information, when trying to localize the origin of the nerve impulse, than that employed by Eyzaguirre and Kuffler (1955a, b). However, it is felt that more work is needed in order to locate accurately the site of initiation of the sensory impulses for the following reasons: (1) it is not known whether the site of origin is constant throughout a wide range of stretch or whether

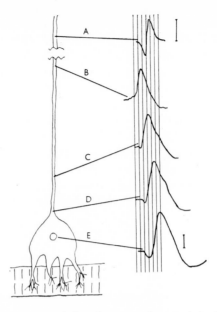

FIG. 6. Tracings of orthodromic impulses set up by stretch in the lobster stretch receptor recorded with external leads at the various indicated points on the nerve cell. One electrode was kept fixed on the cell at *E* while the other was pulled to the other positions. Point *A* was about 1·3 mm from the cell body axon boundary. *B* was about 500 μ distant. Time intervals are 0·1 msec. Scale = 0·5 mV. Negativity is recorded upwards. (From Edwards and Ottoson, *J. Physiol.* (*London*) **143** : 138–148, 1958.)

this point shifts depending on the intensity of the generator potential. It is probable, however, that during moderate stretch the point of origin does not shift appreciably judged by the relative constancy of the firing level. Nevertheless, when strong stretch is applied the firing level changes (Fig. 3); this might indicate that the point of origin might be shifted appreciably. (2) It is not known whether or not the site of origin of the nerve impulses in rapidly adapting receptors is similar to that of slowly adapting organs. The available evidence seems to indicate that in rapidly adapting cells the site of origin is closer to the soma than is the case with the slowly adapting receptor. (3) No studies of this kind have been performed in crayfish since the only evidence available refers to the slowly adapting receptor of lobster.

The fact that nerve impulses can start in the axon at some distance from the soma means that the cell body has a higher threshold, probably due to a larger membrane resistance. Differences in the intrinsic properties of the soma membrane and of the fiber have been postulated by Edwards and Ottoson (1958). There is no doubt, however, that the cell soma of the crustacean stretch receptor produces propagated spikes once its threshold is reached (Fig. 7). This possibility has been questioned in the case of mammalian motoneurons.

Another factor that must be taken into consideration when analyzing the site of origin of the nerve impulses in these cells is that the configuration of the neurons varies greatly not only from one species to another, but within one species in different animals (see Alexandrowicz, 1951, 1952; Florey and Florey, 1955). It is conceivable, therefore, that the site of origin of nerve impulses might not be constant and that it would be closely dependent on cell geometry, diameter and length of the dendrites, and on the morphology of that portion of the axon closer to the cell soma.

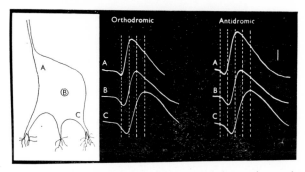

FIG. 7. Orthodromic and antidromic impulses recorded at various points on the cell body. Time intervals 0·1 msec. Scale 0·5 mV. (From Edwards and Ottoson, *J. Physiol. (London)* **143** : 138–148, 1958.)

Some Characteristics of Antidromically Evoked Potentials

Further information on the behavior of the crayfish stretch receptor neuron has been obtained by stimulating the axon and recording potential changes intracellularly from the cell body. These potentials have been analyzed and compared with propagated activity produced by stretch-deformation of the dendrites.

When a receptor muscle is not stretched, the sensory neurons do not discharge, and they generally show membrane potentials between 70 and 80 mV. Antidromic impulses set up centrally in the axon cause in the cell soma an action potential which rises to its peak in about 0·6 msec. This potential overshoots the zero baseline level by about 20 mV. The recovery process consists of a rapid falling phase followed by a slower, gradually decaying component which has a total duration of 10–20 msec. This slow repolarization has been called *after-negativity* since it is not known to what extent it can be related to other well known after-potentials. The situation is different if a cell is stretched and its membrane potential is reduced to a new level. An antidromic soma–dendrite impulse then acquires a "positive"

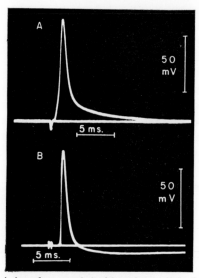

FIG. 8. A. Antidromic impulse recorded with an intracellular lead from soma of a slowly adapting receptor cell. Cell was relaxed with a resting potential of 70 mV. Spike peak 90 mV, the after-negativity disappearing within about 13 msec. No after-positivity seen. Short axon–soma delay responsible for slight inflection or rising phase. B. Slow cell under light stretch. Resting potential reduced by about 10 mV. Antidromic impulse followed by after-positivity of 6 mV. (From Eyzaguirre and Kuffler, *J. Gen. Physiol.* **39** : 121–153, 1955b.)

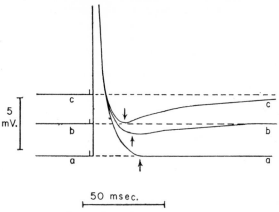

FIG. 9. Slow receptor cell. Tracings of three antidromic impulses at high amplification superimposed to compare changes in time course of repolarization phase at three levels of stretch. Spike peaks (not seen in these tracings) remain unchanged during stretch but impulses start from different displaced (depolarized) resting levels. Repolarization phase of impulses in stretched cells undershoots the new resting level (dotted lines), creating the after-positivity. End of repolarization marked by arrows showing progressive shortening of that portion of the cycle by stretch. (From Eyzaguirre and Kuffler, *J. Gen. Physiol.* **39** : 121–153, 1955b.)

phase; i.e. the cell interior becomes transiently more negative in relation to the outside in the post-spike period (Fig. 8) and the spike recovery phase becomes progressively shorter. This is better shown in Fig. 9 where the arrows indicate the turning point when the generator action takes over, working in the opposite direction to the recovery phase, again depolarizing the cell soma to the level determined by the extent of stretch. In addition, during stretch the levels of repolarization, as referred to the relaxed resting potential, become less complete.

The *after-positivity* seen in these experiments is a hyperpolarization relative to the reduced membrane potential maintained by a persisting generator action during stretch. Actually, during the recovery phase of the action potential the generator action is considerably reduced although it is not completely wiped out since the recovery phase does not return to the full resting potential level. Therefore, it seems legitimate to assume that this axon-type of impulse does not propagate through the distal dendrite portions. Also, progressive reduction in the extent of repolarization following an impulse as stretch is increased suggests that the impulses penetrate less and less distally as the dendrites become more depolarized. More direct evidence of a persisting generator action during antidromic invasion of the dendrites by all-or-none impulses will be shown later on. In fact, inhibitory impulses during the peak of antidromic after-positivity may further repolarize the cell (see Fig. 18).

Sometimes an axon impulse does not reach the soma but is blocked somewhere along the axon, presumably near the axon hillock. This phenomenon occurs almost exclusively in relaxed preparations. In such case the axon impulse is detected by an intracellular lead recording from the soma as a small potential of short duration which has spread electrotonically. In other instances these blocked antidromic impulses set up a local response in the soma which is distinguishable from a merely electrotonically conducted impulse because of its amplitude and time course. It is, generally, considerably slower and it may attain magnitudes of about 20 mV. If a second impulse is sent through the axon it adds to the potential of the first and at a critical level of about 20–25 mV a full soma impulse may arise.

The converse picture is obtained in the same cell if its dendrites are depolarized by a small steady stretch reducing the resting potential by several millivolts. In this case, an antidromic impulse is capable of invading the soma and it shows a small after-positivity. However if two antidromic impulses are brought close together the second impulse disappears, leaving only a local response. This observation shows that axon–soma transmission can be greatly influenced by changing the membrane potential. Axon–soma delays are longest when soma invasion is critical. Whenever such a delay occurs it may be reduced or made to disappear by stretch. Some of these delay times measured from the first inflection of the potential to the spike peak are, occasionally, quite long (see Fig. 10).

The phenomenon just described appears both in slowly and rapidly adapting cells. In some instances, however, an antidromic axon impulse invades the soma–dendrite complex. However, due to various reasons like "fatigue", subnormality, or cell geometry, the magnitude of potential gradients becomes critical for adequate impulse conduction. Thus, when a cell is relaxed it may have a resting potential similar to that of the axon. When the dendrites become depolarized, the soma region can be brought

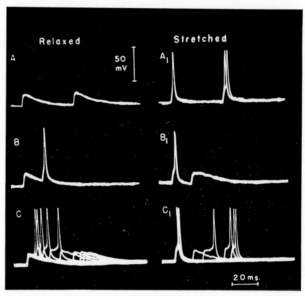

Fig. 10. Axon–soma invasion and membrane potential in slowly adapting cell. Left portion, relaxed cell has resting potential of 70 mV. A. Two axon impulses (a1, a2) at 40 msec fail to invade cell soma. B. At 13 msec interval a2 invades. C. a2 is moved closer to a1 during exposure and at 20 msec it propagates into cell soma. The axon–soma delay becomes progressively shorter at small intervals. Right portion, cell slightly stretched, resting potential reduced by several millivolts. A1. Both axon impulses invade cell soma. B1. Second antidromic now blocked at 16 msec interval. C1. a2 is moved closer to a1 and is blocked during after-positivity. Axon–soma delay becomes progressively longer at shorter intervals. After-positivity not well seen at this amplification and stretch.
(From Eyzaguirre and Kuffler, *J. Gen. Physiol.* **39** : 121–153, 1955b.)

quite near to its firing range by light stretch, and readily triggered by an axonal impulse which failed to do so in the unstretched preparation. The subthreshold excitatory depolarization of the soma should sum with the advancing front of the axon impulse, the latter being speeded up, as shown by shortened axon–soma delay. The failure of invasion by a second axon impulse when the cell is stretched cannot be due entirely to refractoriness of the cell because this occurs at intervals much longer than those associated with refractoriness. It is more likely that during the positive repolarization phase of the first impulse the membrane potential transiently returns toward its "relaxed" equilibrium state. During that period, therefore, the generator effect is decreased and the axon impulse may not produce the adequate depolarization which normally constitutes the discharge threshold for anti-dromic excitation of the cell soma.

Effect of Antidromic Impulses on Discharge Frequency

If an antidromic impulse arrives at the cell soma when an orthodromic discharge is just about to fire it will have little effect on the timing of the subsequent response and the rhythm of discharge is not appreciably disrupted. If, however, the antidromic impulse arrives during the after-positivity of the orthodromic discharge it delays the next orthodromic impulse and at the same time the prepotential rise after the antidromic impulse is slowed. It is assumed that the antidromic impulse, by having spread into the dendrites, delays re-excitation by interfering with the generator action. The depressant action of antidromic stimuli, as measured by the reduction of afferent activity, is best seen during low-frequency discharge under weak stretch. Thus, a train of antidromic impulses may stop a sensory discharge for a second or more while its effect on high-frequency rhythmic activity may be relatively small. The different results obtained during weak and strong stretch may be expected if the antidromic impulses either depress the generator itself or attenuate the electrotonic spread from dendrites to the cell soma. At near threshold stretch a diminution of the barely adequate generator potential would therefore be more readily detected.

Grouped Discharges

A number of slowly adapting cells are capable of producing spontaneous and grouped discharges when they are completely relaxed or slightly stretched. These discharges are short high-frequency bursts which are followed by a pause. Besides occurring "spontaneously" an orthodromic train from the receptor cell may be elicited by a single antidromic impulse. These discharges have been recorded by means of an intracellular microelectrode in the cell soma and by placing recording electrodes on the sensory axon. Therefore, all the discharges going in as well as those leaving the soma–dendrite region could be monitored and correlated. It is of some interest that changing the tension applied to the receptor muscle influences the number of impulses within each high-frequency burst. Applied stretch is capable of abolishing this type of response. In a naturally occurring impulse burst, recorded intra-cellularly, the first orthodromic volley shows part of the usual pre-potential which is absent in subsequent smaller components. When the action potentials are recorded from the axon several conducted impulses are detected. An essentially similar picture is obtained when this burst is produced by antidromic impulse, but in this case the first antidromically occurring impulse does not have the initial pre-potential phase (Fig. 11).

The absence of pre-potentials preceding each member of such group discharges and the high frequencies (up to 500/sec) clearly distinguish this type of activity from the usual stretch-evoked impulse. Moreover, the fact that stretch actually reduces the grouped discharge or abolishes it indicates that the impulses are not set up by the normal generator mechanism.

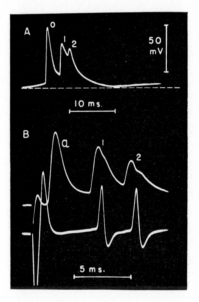

FIG. 11. Grouped discharges from a slow cell. A. Intracellular lead from cell soma of a lightly extended cell. No antidromic stimulation. The complex potential was accompanied by three sensory axon impulses (not shown). A pre-potential precedes the first large deflection (O). B. Same cell with simultaneous extra-cellular axon impulses on the lower beam. First deflection set up by antidromic stimulus (a). Components 1 and 2 were always associated with afferent impulses recorded in the axon. (From Eyzaguirre and Kuffler, *J. Gen. Physiol.* **39** : 121–153, 1955b.)

Eyzaguirre and Kuffler (1955b) interpreted this observation in the following way: The first fully grown impulse in the cell soma resulting from antidromic invasion or from orthodromic excitation invades one or more dendrites with some delay. During this delay period the soma impulse reaches its recovery phase; when the dendrite impulses occur they propagate towards the soma as well as toward the terminal region. Since the soma is still refractory; for instance, 0·5 to 2·0 msec after the spike peak, only a local response could be added. This local response may be too small and may die out (like the soma deflections not correlated with afferent activity) or it may spread into the axon. Since the axon has a briefer refractory period it may have recovered sufficiently to conduct an impulse. In this manner if several dendrites are invaded at different times, each dendrite impulse could add its distinct effect to the partially recovered soma and thereby excite the more fully recovered axon. This interpretation has been questioned by Bullock (1957) on the basis that similar phenomena occur in the giant fiber of the earthworm. In fact, when a spike, traveling some distance along the giant fiber, arrives at a locus of partial or complete anodal block it hesitates before proceeding or it may die out. After several milliseconds a burst of impulses at high frequency is originated at that point or near to it (Bullock and Turner, 1950). Bullock's objection indicates that this phenomenon does not depend on a particular anatomical arrangement such as that present in the crayfish stretch receptor

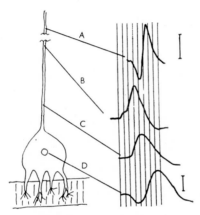

FIG. 12. Tracings of orthodromic impulses set up by antidromic impulse recorded at various indicated points on the same nerve cell. Time intervals, 0·1 msec; scale 0·5 mV. (From Edwards and Ottoson, *J. Physiol.* (*London*) **143** : 138–148, 1958.)

cell. It does not dispose, however, of the possibility that partial blocks in some portions of the crayfish dendrites might occur.

Edwards and Ottoson (1958) have offered a different interpretation with regard to the origin of the grouped discharges which occur either spontaneously or provoked by antidromic stimuli. These authors have shown that these discharges originate in the axon at some distance from the soma (Fig. 12). It is their contention that grouped discharges start nearer to the soma than those occurring normally. Once the grouped discharges are originated the impulse travels both in an orthodromic direction and backwards into the cell soma. Whether the findings reported by Eyzaguirre and Kuffler (1955b) and by Edwards and Ottoson (1958) can be interpreted only according to the latter's explanation is doubtful. Many factors could play a role in the onset of grouped discharges, especially since this phenomenon seems to appear in abnormally functioning cells. Consequently, cell geometry, changes of excitability of the cells, or slight injury produced during manipulation of the receptors might determine the appearance of an abnormal "pacemaker". It is possible that this new "pacemaker" might coincide with the normally occurring one, it might be close to it, or it might occur at some distance. Also, it might shift from one site to another during prolonged experimentation. In conclusion, the experiments of Edwards and Ottoson (1958) seem to offer a better explanation of grouped discharges than that offered by Eyzaguirre and Kuffler (1955b). But it is felt that more work is needed in order to take into account a number of variables which may occur in different preparations.

C. THE INHIBITORY PROCESS

Synaptic inhibition has been studied both in slowly adapting and in rapidly adapting sensory neuron of crayfish and lobster. Kuffler and Eyzaguirre (1955) were able to stimulate in the crayfish the "accessory" nerve described by Florey and Florey (1955). Stimulation of this nerve was capable of impeding the onset of sensory discharges or stopping discharges already occurring. Burgen and Kuffler (1957) studied these effects in lobster stretch receptors and were able to find the presence of two inhibitory nerves which corresponded to the "thick" and "thin" accessory nerves described by Alexandrowicz (1951, 1952). The effects produced by independent stimulation of these nerves are similar. In general, the thick nerve has a more pronounced inhibitory effect on the sensory neurons than that obtained by stimulation of the thin accessory nerve. Also, the latter has to be stimulated at higher frequency to obtain the desired results.

At present there is little information concerning the role of the thin accessory nerve on postsynaptic inhibition, and since results obtained by stimulation of both types of inhibitory fibers in the lobster seem to differ only quantitatively we shall describe only those effects produced by stimulation of inhibitory axons in the crayfish. As said before, the inhibitory synapses supplied by the accessory nerves are mainly located in the dendrites of the receptor cells forming, therefore, an axo-dendritic synapse.

Inhibitory phenomena occurring in the crayfish stretch receptor cells are not necessarily identical to well known inhibitory processes occurring in other structures. However, inhibition in crustacean stretch receptors resembles not only similar processes occurring in neurons of the central nervous system of vertebrates (cf. Eccles, 1957), but also inhibition obtained at the crustacean neuromuscular junction (Fatt and Katz, 1953) and in the heart of frogs and turtles (Hutter and Trautwein, 1956).

Inhibition of Sensory Discharges

While a slowly adapting receptor is stretched, rhythmic discharges occur which may be recorded from the cell soma by means of intracellular micro-electrodes. If during stretch the inhibitory nerves are stimulated at a certain frequency, sensory discharges stop immediately and this effect remains for the duration of inhibitory stimulation (see Fig. 13). In most cases a small hyperpolarization occurs in an apparent effort to bring the membrane potential back to its resting level. In other instances inhibition is accomplished although inhibitory stimulation results in a small depolarization which, if maintained below the firing level, accomplishes essentially similar results. During inhibitory stimulation even strong stretch is incapable of making the receptor fire. The effectiveness of the inhibitory impulses in stopping sensory activity depends on the relationship between afferent discharge rate and efferent inhibitory frequency. An inhibitory impulse arriving at a dendrite just after the cell soma has conducted will delay the subsequent discharge only a little but if it arrives when the prepotential has already developed and the cell is ready to fire it will cause an appreciable delay because the prepotential will have then to develop anew.

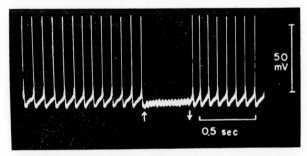

Fig. 13. Intracellular recording from a slowly adapting receptor cell. The regular train of afferent discharges (11/sec) set up by maintained stretch is interrupted by stimulation of the inhibitory axon between arrows, at 34/sec. Small deflections are inhibitory potentials. (From Kuffler and Eyzaguirre, *J. Gen. Physiol.* **39** : 155–184, 1955.)

Membrane Potential Changes during Inhibition

The potential changes produced by inhibitory stimulation on the receptor cell membrane have been observed both in rapidly and in slowly adapting cells. In general, when the receptor cell membrane potential decreases during progressive depolarization by stretch, inhibitory stimulation produces a repolarization and the magnitude of this repolarization is dependent on the magnitude of the membrane potential level obtained during stretch. This has been clearly seen in rapidly adapting neurons since once adaptation occurs no sensory discharges appear which could obliterate the smaller inhibitory potential. In Fig. 14 (upper portion) a relaxed fast-adapting cell had a resting potential of about 60–70 mV. By appropriate stretch this potential was reduced by 16·5 mV to a new maintained level when the inhibitory nerve fiber was excited at 20/sec. Each inhibitory impulse, in this illustration, caused a repolarization of 9·7 mV which was rapidly attained and then decayed almost entirely within 50 msec. If a cell was held under less stretch, and therefore was less depolarized, the inhibitory potential became progressively smaller. When the cell was relaxed to about 6 mV above its own membrane potential each inhibitory impulse set up a small initial depolarization followed by a polarization phase. Figure 14 (upper portion) shows the

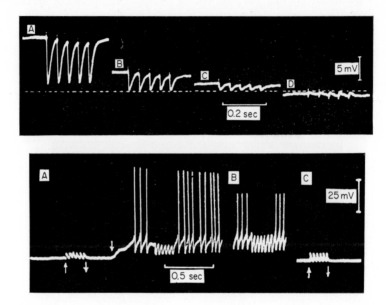

Fig. 14. (*Upper portion*)—Effect of inhibitory impulses at different membrane potential levels, intracellular leading. Fast receptor cell of second abdominal segment. Trains of inhibitory impulses at 20/sec. A. Cell stretched causing initial maintained depolarization of 16·5 mV. Inhibitory impulse repolarization peaks 9·7 mV. B and C. During progressively lower stretch and higher membrane potential levels the same train of impulses sets up smaller inhibitory potentials of 4 and 1 mV. D. Still further relaxation of stretch. Inhibitory impulse sign reverses. Initial depolarization follows each inhibitory stimulus. (*Lower portion*)—Inhibitory potentials at different levels of stretch. Fast cell. Intracellular records. A. Receptor almost completely relaxed, six inhibitory impulses at 30/sec caused depolarization potentials (arrows). At third arrow stretch causes about 20 mV depolarization and three discharges followed by inhibitory train setting up repolarization potentials. Further continued increasing stretch results in afferent impulses which gradually decline in height. At gap 10 sec of record cut out. In B, same inhibitory train; the repolarization potential reaching 12 mV. C. During complete relaxation of cell 6·5 mV inhibitory depolarization peaks are seen (From Kuffler and Eyzaguirre, *J. Gen. Physiol.* **39** : 155–184, 1955.)

level of membrane potential at which the inhibitory potentials reverse their polarity and this indicates the inhibitory "equilibrium level" or "reversal potential". In other words, the inhibitory action tends to restore the membrane potential if it is displaced in either direction by stretch. A similar picture, but this time complicated by normally occurring sensory discharges, has been obtained from rapidly adapting receptors (Fig. 14, lower portion) and from slowly adapting cells (not illustrated).

Hagiwara *et al.* (1960) have studied the effects of changing the resting membrane potential of slowly adapting cells by means of applied currents and observed a linear relationship between the magnitude of the membrane potential change and the amplitude of the inhibitory postsynaptic potentials. The findings of these authors, using applied currents, are similar to those obtained by Kuffler and Eyzaguirre (1955) although the former displaced the membrane potential to a greater extent, since the latter only used stretch and relaxation as means of changing the magnitude of the membrane potential (Fig. 15).

These experiments demonstrate that the membrane effect produced by inhibitory impulses depends on the state of the sensory receptor cell and this is true both for the fast and the slowly adapting cells. At certain membrane

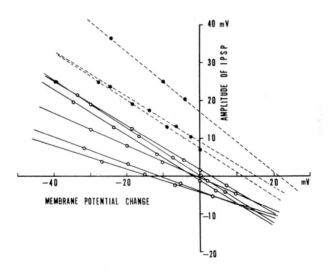

FIG. 15. Relations between the amplitude of the inhibitory junctional potential (on the Y-axis) and the change of membrane potential (on the X-axis) by applied current from the resting potential level. The amplitude of the depolarizing junctional potential or the depolarization of the resting membrane potential is positive on each axis. Open circles and full circles were obtained from the recording with K₂SO₄ filled and KCl filled internal electrodes respectively. (From Hagiwara, Kusano and Saito, *J. Neurophysiol.* **23** : 505–515, 1960.)

potential levels inhibition causes no electrical changes, or only small ones; if the cell is displaced from this "inhibitory equilibrium level" in either direction the inhibitory action tends to restore this equilibrium by either polarizing or depolarizing the structure. Since inhibitory potentials of both polarities may be obtained with extracellular as well as with intracellular leads depolarizing inhibitory potentials are not necessarily caused by recording artefacts or by injury resulting from impalement of nerve cells.

Usually, inhibitory potentials are not uniform and therefore a rigid description is difficult. It seems that during intracellular recording of these nerve cells a number of variables appear which might change some characteristics of these potentials, their amplitude, polarity, or time course. However, in general, one inhibitory impulse produces a large enough potential change that a second impulse set up shortly afterwards does not add to the amplitude of the first potential; a ceiling effect occurs and this effect has been shown to be present regardless of the polarity of the inhibitory potential. This ceiling effect is not present in all cells. In some preparations during repetitive stimulation these potentials frequently sum building up to twice or more the peak value of individual inhibitory potentials.

Inhibitory After-effects

In most preparations an inhibitory impulse train is capable of blocking the sensory discharges abruptly, but, as soon as inhibition is stopped discharges come back immediately to baseline levels. In a number of preparations, however, two types of inhibitory after-effects have been observed: (a) a post-inhibitory depression and (b) a post-inhibitory facilitation.

(a) *Post-inhibitory depression.* A short burst of inhibitory impulses may be able to clamp the membrane below the firing level. In this case inhibition occurs and the only detectable membrane potential changes are those produced by the inhibitory train. However, in a number of cases, after applying the inhibitory train, a hyperpolarization may be observed both with microelectrodes inserted into the cell soma and by means of extracellular electrodes recording from the vicinity of the cell. The magnitude and the time course of this post-inhibitory hyperpolarization is dependent upon the frequency of the inhibitory impulses and on the duration of the train of these pulses (Fig. 16). Not all cells react in a similar manner; for instance, this phenomenon may not appear even after a few seconds of stimulation at 50/sec while on occasions an indication of post-inhibitory depression appears even after a single inhibitory stimulus suggested by a double phase during the inhibitory potential decay. This post-inhibitory hyperpolarization prolongs inhibition effectively and it may, perhaps, be an active process since it appears in opposition to depolarization produced by stretch.

(b) *Post-inhibitory facilitation.* An opposite phenomenon has been observed

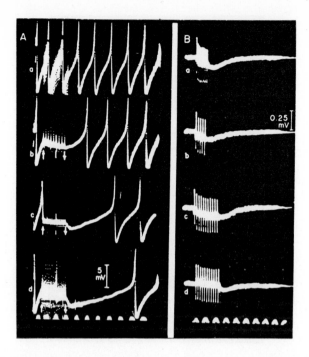

Fig. 16. Post-inhibitory polarization. A (a). Stretched slow receptor cells discharge at 7/sec. Intracellular records. A (b). Inhibitory impulse train at 45/sec
inhibits discharge. A (c). Inhibitory impulse train at 150/sec causes longer
inhibitory period. End of inhibition potential is followed by a delayed polarization phase. A (d). Inhibitory train at 200/sec. A delayed polarization potential is
further increased. B (a). Extracellular records. Another slow receptor cell under
light stretch. Inhibitory train at 100/sec sets up repolarization during stimulation
followed by additional delayed polarization. B (b). Stimulation at 50/sec causes
polarization and little post-inhibitory effect. B (c). Longer inhibitory train at
50/sec sets up marked post-inhibitory polarization phase. B (d). Less stretch
on cell. Inhibitory impulses at 50/sec set up smaller polarization potential during
train. Time, 10 c/s. (From Kuffler and Eyzaguirre, *J. Gen. Physiol.* **39** : 155–184,
1955.)

in a number of preparations. After inhibition has been withdrawn the rate
of rise of the pre-potential increases and the discharge rate may be transiently
accelerated in some slow receptors. This phenomenon is particularly well
seen in rapidly adapting neurons which have been stretched near to their
firing level. A short burst of inhibitory impulses may initiate one or more
afferent discharges in a quiescent receptor cell (see Fig. 17). This is probably
a post-inhibitory rebound phenomenon since inhibition removes effectively
the depolarization produced by stretch. If the transmitter effect produced by
inhibitory impulses is suddenly removed, this will be equivalent to applying
stretch very quickly.

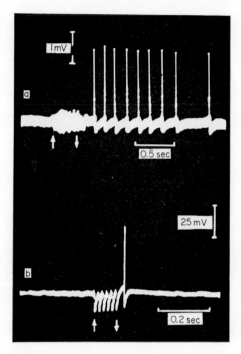

FIG. 17. Post-inhibitory excitation. Fast receptor cell stretched to near firing
level. (a) Extracellular recording. Between arrows inhibitory stimuli at 23/sec
are followed by afferent discharge. (b). Intracellular record. Six inhibitory impulses
are followed by one conducted impulse. (From Kuffler and Eyzaguirre, *J. Gen.
Physiol.* **39** : 155–184, 1955.)

Interaction of Antidromic and Inhibitory Activity

Antidromic impulses normally invade the soma–dendrite complex. Their
repolarizing phase has been analyzed and compared with inhibitory potentials
set up either independently or during this repolarization phase. With this
type of experiment, information has been obtained as to the extent of
dendritic invasion by an antidromic impulse.

If the preparation is stretched, orthodromic discharges are initiated. The
repolarization phase of the orthodromic impulses brings the membrane
potential back to less than several millivolts from the resting potential of
the relaxed cell. If an antidromic impulse invades one of these cells its
repolarization phase is similar to that of the orthodromic impulse. However,
in a cell which has its membrane potential reduced by stretch, stimulation of
an inhibitory fiber hyperpolarizes the cell to levels below those obtained
following orthodromic or antidromic impulses (Fig. 18). This indicates very
clearly the following: (1) Since inhibitory impulses may repolarize cells
further than the recovery stage of antidromic or orthodromic impulses it is

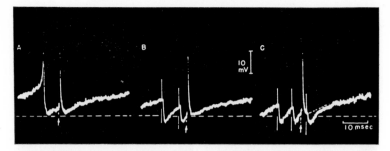

FIG. 18. Persistence of generator potential during antidromic impulse. Intra-cellular records from a stretched slow receptor. Lower portion only of a large impulse is seen. A. An antidromic impulse at arrow sent into the cell shortly after an orthodromic discharge. The repolarization phase of both impulses reaches the same level. B. Two inhibitory impulses precede the antidromic. C. During peak of antidromic repolarization phase a third inhibitory impulse further polarized, indicating that distal dendrite portions were still depolarized. Dotted line drawn through membrane level to which antidromic impulse repolarized. (From Kuffler and Eyzaguirre, *J. Gen. Physiol.* **39** : 155-184, 1955.)

clear that the generator potential is not completely wiped out during the repolarization phase of the orthodromic discharge or of the antidromic impulse. (2) The inhibitory potential effectively abolishes the remaining generator potential.

The phenomenon just described does not occur always and is strictly dependent on the equilibrium level of the inhibitory potential. In fact, if the inhibitory equilibrium potential is at a value significantly less than the resting potential, the repolarization phase of an orthodromic or an antidromic discharge will bring the membrane potential to values greater than those of the reversal potential for inhibitory action. In such a case inhibitory stimulation during the peak of repolarization of an antidromic or orthodromic spike may produce a small depolarization since the inhibitory action tends to drive the membrane toward the inhibitory equilibrium level.

The more commonly occurring effects of inhibitory activity on antidromic invasion of the soma dendrite complex are changes affecting the after-positivity of an antidromic spike set up during an inhibitory train. For instance, if a cell is depolarized by stretch and an antidromic spike is sent through, a prominent after-positivity is recorded. However, if this antidromic spike arrives at the soma during an inhibitory train (which by itself produces a hyperpolarization) the after-positivity of the antidromic spike is completely wiped out. If, on the other hand, the cell is relaxed, the antidromic spike shows only a small or short after-negativity. If the antidromic spike is sent through and falls in the middle of the depolarization produced by inhibitory activity, the repolarizing phase of the antidromic potential is blocked (Fig. 19). Under normal circumstances an antidromic volley sent through at a

310 C. EYZAGUIRRE

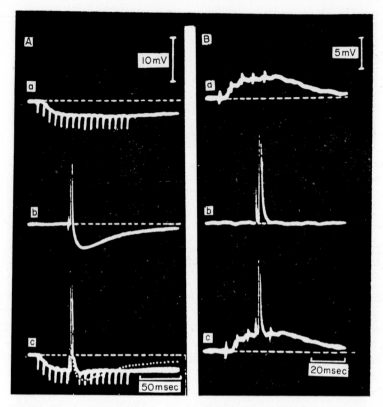

FIG. 19. Slow receptor cell. Resting potential 70 mV (unstretched). A (a). Cell under stretch, train of inhibitory impulses at 130/sec polarizes. A (b). Antidromic impulse (a) alone. A (c). (a) invades cell during inhibitory train which prevents development of complete after-positivity. Dotted line indicates expected time course. B (a). Cell relaxed, train of five inhibitory impulses at 200/sec depolarizes. B (b). (a) alone shows no after-positivity. B (c). (a) during inhibition is not appreciably changed. (From Kuffler and Eyzaguirre, *J. Gen. Physiol.* **39** : 155–184, 1955.)

depolarization level similar to that produced by the inhibitory potentials would produce an after positivity (this possibility is illustrated in the left column of Fig. 19). This observation indicates clearly that the generator potential is turned off during inhibition and mainly those parts of the antidromic impulse which are linked with excitation spread into the dendrites are modified.

When the antidromic invasion of a cell is unobstructed the overshoot of the action potential is not changed by inhibitory stimulation. If for some reason a partially blocked antidromic impulse reaches the cell, inhibitory activity exerts a very profound effect on the amplitude of the antidromic impulse. This is especially noticeable when the antidromic impulse has been

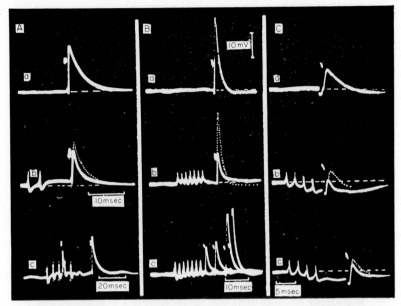

FIG. 20. The effect of inhibition on blocked antidromic impulses. Fast cell. Resting potential 70 mV (unstretched). Intracellular electrodes filled with 0·6 M K₂SO₄. A (a). Antidromic impulse (a) alone (17 mV) blocked at the axon–soma boundary region. A (b). Two inhibitory impulses set up depolarization in relaxed cell. (a) is reduced and its time course accelerated. Dotted line indicates control. A (c). Two antidromic impulses. (a1) during inhibitory train more reduced than (a2) after cessation of inhibitory stimulation. Note slower sweep. B (a) and B (b). Preparation lightly stretched. (a) impulse again greatly reduced by preceding train of seven inhibitory impulses at 500/sec. No appreciable potential change was set up by inhibitory train alone. B (c). Antidromic impulses placed at different times after inhibitory train revealed time course of inhibitory effect. C (a) and C (b). Cell stretched, inhibitory impulse polarizes in C (b) and again reduces the antidromic impulse. C (c). (a) moved later is less affected. Voltage calibration same for all records. Large dots preceding antidromic impulses are artefacts. (From Kuffler and Eyzaguirre, *J. Gen. Physiol.* **39** : 155–185, 1955.)

blocked somewhere along the axon and its electronic spread is recorded at the cell soma. The size of this electrotonically conducted impulse is markedly reduced and its repolarization phase is accelerated. This effect seems to be completely independent of any electric potential changes which might be produced by the inhibitory impulses (Fig. 20).

In order to explain this phenomenon one might think that inhibitory action may change the properties of the soma–dendrite complex by increasing its conductance and thereby changing the conditions for current flow. It is possible that current flowing from the dendrites toward the blocked axonal region is necessary either to propagate the impulse actively or to set up a fairly large local response. The inhibitory action would tend to divert part of

312   C. EYZAGUIRRE

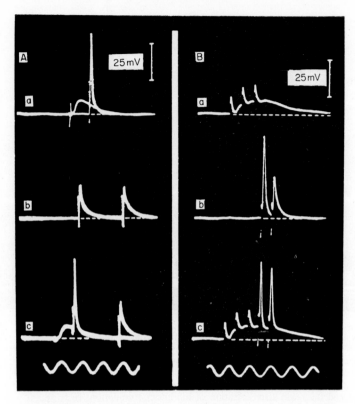

Fig. 21. Facilitation of antidromic invasion by inhibitory action. Same cell as in
Fig. 20. A (a). Single inhibitory and antidromic (a1) potential on same sweep (not
stimulated together). A (b). (a1), (a2) at 20 msec interval, sweep repetition rate
of 5/sec. Full invasion of soma is blocked. A (c). Inhibitory impulse facilitates soma
invasion by (a1). B (a). Three inhibitory impulses alone. B (b). (a1), (a2) at 5 msec
interval, single sweep. (a2) is blocked. B (c). Inhibitory stimulation facilitates invasion by previously blocked (a2). Time, 100 c/s. (From Kuffler and Eyzaguirre, *J.
Gen. Physiol.* **39** : 155–184, 1955.)

this current flow (if there are conductance changes in the dendrites) in such
a way that part of this current will not reach the soma or that zone of the
axon where the impulse has been blocked. This, in itself, will diminish the
chances for local, partially conducted impulse activity and it is a good indication that synaptic endings occur over a sizable portion of the dendrites (cf.
Kuffler and Edwards, 1958).

When an inhibitory potential is capable of setting up a *depolarization*,
partial axon–soma transmission block can actually be relieved by inhibitory
activity. This is shown in Fig. 21. It may be seen in the illustration that when
the inhibitory potentials set up a depolarization and when the antidromic
impulse is riding on top of that depolarization, an actual facilitation of axon-

soma transmission occurs. This effect depends on the depolarizing effect produced by the inhibitory impulses.

In short, one may have either blocking or enhancing of axon–soma transmission during inhibitory activity. The end result depends on a delicate balance between two factors: (1) conductance changes produced at the dendrites by inhibition which will tend to block axo-somatic transmission; and (2) membrane potential changes which the inhibitory impulses are capable of setting up. If the membrane potential change is a depolarization then antidromic invasion will actually be enhanced. This effect is consequently similar to the facilitation of axo-somatic transmission produced by stretch-depolarization of the dendrites (see Fig. 10).

A difference between facilitation of axo-somatic transmission produced by stretch-depolarization and by inhibitory depolarization is well seen when two antidromic impulses are sent in in close succession. In the first case the first impulse may be fully propagated while the second, riding on top of the after-positivity of the first, is usually blocked (Fig. 10). During inhibitory depolarization a different picture occurs since the after-positivity of the first impulse is wiped out and both antidromic impulses are capable of invading the cell.

The Ionic Mechanisms Involved in the Inhibitory Process

In contrast to inhibitory phenomena studied in other structures relatively little information is available concerning the role of different ions in the inhibitory process of crayfish and lobster stretch receptors.

Fatt and Katz (1953) suggested that inhibition produces appreciable conductance changes on the postsynaptic membrane determined by an increase in permeability to K^+ and/or Cl^- across the membrane of the crustacean neuromuscular junction. Boistel and Fatt (1958) later presented evidence indicating that the action of the inhibitory transmitter on crustacean neuromuscular junction is largely dependent on an increase in the permeability of Cl^- ions. In spinal motoneurons Coombs et al. (1955) have been able to alter the inhibitory equilibrium level by injections of K^+, Cl^-, Br^-, NO^-_3, and SCN^- ions. In the heart, Harris and Hutter (1956) have been able to show, by the use of K^{42}, that permeability to this ion is greatly increased during application of acetylcholine and Trautwein and Dudel (1958) have shown that, in the presence of acetylcholine, the equilibrium potential is dependent on the external K^+ concentration.

Evidence for K^+ movements during inhibition in the crustacean nerve cells has been reported by Kuffler and Edwards (1958) and by Edwards and Hagiwara (1959). These authors studied the inhibitory potential while changing the K^+ content of the bathing solution. They recorded potential changes by means of extracellular electrodes connected to a d.c. amplifier.

314   C. EYZAGUIRRE

Judging by the repolarization level of orthodromic discharge and by the
magnitude of the inhibitory potential they concluded that the resting potential
increased during the application of a K⁺-free solution, and that the inhibitory
potentials increased even more (Fig. 22). Since, in the absence of K⁺ the
resting membrane potential is much farther from the potassium equilibrium
potential than in its presence, an increase in the difference between the
membrane potential level and the inhibitory equilibrium level in the absence
of potassium is consistent with the assumption that the membrane potential
during the inhibitory process is more dependent upon K⁺ distribution than
at rest.

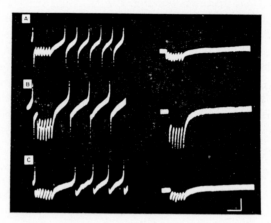

FIG. 22. Effect of K⁺ deficiency on the inhibitory potential in the relaxed preparation and during stretch. Extracellular d.c. recording A and C. Inhibition in
normal solution. B. Inhibition in K⁺-free solution showing the increase in size
of the inhibitory potentials in the absence of K⁺ ion. Voltage calibration 0·1 mV.
Time, 0·1 sec. (From Edwards and Hagiwara, *J. Gen. Physiol.* **43** : 315–321, 1959.)

Very recent work has shown that Cl⁻ ions are also involved in the inhibitory
process of crustacean sensory nerve cells, as was suggested earlier by Kuffler
and Eyzaguirre (1955). In fact, Hagiwara *et al.* (1960) have been able to
show that replacing glutamate for Cl⁻ in the bathing solution produces a
shift of the inhibitory reversal potential in a depolarizing direction. This shift
is not accompanied by resting membrane potential changes as shown in
Fig. 23. The change in baseline is only produced by a diffusion potential
between normal and glutamate saline. These recent experiments bring into
focus a former observation reported by Kuffler and Eyzaguirre (1955) who
observed a reversal of the inhibitory potential while a cell was impaled with
a KCl-filled microelectrode. In this case the inhibitory potential grew progressively in a depolarizing direction which eventually produced a propagated
action potential. Apparently Cl⁻ ions leaked from the electrode thus loading
the cell with this particular anion. Furthermore, Hagiwara *et al.* (1960) have

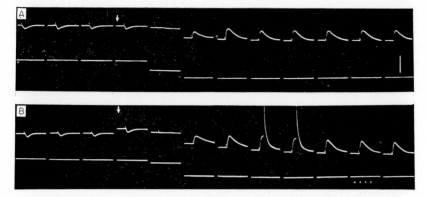

FIG. 23. Two series (A and B) of records of inhibitory junctional potentials obtained during the exchange of external NaCl by Na-glutamate. K_2SO_4-filled internal electrodes were used. Arrows indicate the start of the exchange. Successive records were obtained at 2 sec intervals. The upper trace shows the intracellular potential change obtained with a K_2SO_4-filled electrode while the lower trace showed the potential just outside the cell recorded by a KCl-filled microelectrode. Voltage calibration, 10 mV. Time calibration 20 msec. (From Hagiwara, Kusano and Saito, *J. Neurophysiol.* **23** : 505–515, 1960.)

found that the inhibitory reversal potential is very near the resting membrane potential level when K_2SO_4 filled electrodes are used. KCl electrodes seem to displace this value.

In summary, the available evidence obtained in the crustacean stretch receptors indicates the following: (1) inhibitory stimulation may produce a postsynaptic potential which accompanies postsynaptic conductance changes; (2) these changes are determined by an increased permeability to K^+ and to Cl^- ions. Whether a decrease of Na^+ permeability also occurs is unknown, although at present this possibility seems unlikely since Kuffler and Eyzaguirre (1955) have shown that inhibition is accompanied by increased conductance of the stretch receptor cell (see Fig. 20).

The Inhibitory Transmitter

In recent years an effort has been made to find a transmitter responsible for inhibitory processes. While in the heart acetylcholine release is responsible for inhibition, in other structures the nature of the inhibitory transmitter is unknown. Several amino acids have been explored in the crustacean nerve–muscle junction and in sensory nerve cells; of these, γ-aminobutyric acid (GABA) has been found to be a very potent inhibitor. However, the available evidence does not point in the direction of this compound as a possible inhibitory transmitter in the crustacean stretch receptor (cf. Kuffler and Edwards, 1958; Edwards and Kuffler, 1959).

316 C. EYZAGUIRRE

Problems related to inhibitory transmitters will not be treated in the present paper since this subject is discussed elsewhere in this symposium. In addition, an extensive survey on inhibitory transmitters is available (cf. *Conference on Inhibition in the Nervous System and Gamma-aminobutyric acid (GABA)*. Pergamon Press, 1960).

Note added in proof: Since this paper was written, P. Peterson (private communication) has shown that nerve fibres, presumably inhibitory, may end on the soma of these cells, as seen with the electronmicroscope.

REFERENCES

ALEXANDROWICZ, J. S. (1951) Muscle receptor organs in the abdomen of *Homarus vulgaris* and *Palinurus vulgaris. Quart. J. Microscop. Sci.* **92** : 163–199.

ALEXANDROWICZ, J. S. (1952) Receptor elements in the thoracic muscles of *Homarus vulgaris* and *Palinurus vulgaris. Quart. J. Microscop. Sci.* **93** : 315–346.

ALVAREZ-BUYLLA, R. and RAMIREZ DE ARELLANO, J. (1953) Local responses in Pacinian corpuscles. *Am. J. Physiol.* **172** : 237–250.

BOISTEL, J. and FATT, P. (1958) Membrane permeability change during inhibitory transmitter action in crustacean muscle. *J. Physiol. (London)* **144** : 176–191.

BULLOCK, T. H. (1957) Neuronal integrative mechanisms. In *Recent Advances in Invertebrate Physiology.* University of Oregon Publ.

BULLOCK, T. H. and TURNER, R. S. (1950) Events associated with conduction failure in nerve fibers. *J. Cellular Comp. Physiol.* **36** : 59–82.

BURGEN, A. S. V. and KUFFLER, S. W. (1957) Two inhibitory fibers forming synapses with a single nerve cell in lobster. *Nature* **118** : 1490–1491.

COOMBS, J. S., ECCLES, J. C. and FATT, P. (1955) The specific ionic conductances and the ionic movements across the motoneuronal membrane that produce the inhibitory postsynaptic potential. *J. Physiol. (London)* **130** : 326–373.

ECCLES, J. C. (1957) *The Physiology of Nerve Cells.* Johns Hopkins Press, Baltimore.

EDWARDS, C. (1960) Physiology and pharmacology of the crayfish stretch receptor. In *Conference on Inhibition in the Nervous System and Gamma Aminobutyric Acid (GABA).* Pergamon Press, London.

EDWARDS, C. and HAGIWARA, S. (1959) Potassium ions and the inhibitory process in the crayfish stretch receptor. *J. Gen. Physiol.* **43** : 315–321.

EDWARDS, C. and KUFFLER, S. W. (1959) The blocking effect of γ-aminobutyric acid and the action of related compounds on single nerve cells. *J. Neurochem.* **4** : 19–30.

EDWARDS, C. and OTTOSON, D. (1958) The site of impulse initiation in a nerve cell of a crustacean stretch receptor. *J. Physiol. (London)* **143** : 138–148.

EYZAGUIRRE, C. and KUFFLER, S. W. (1955a) Processes of excitation in the dendrites and in the soma of single isolated sensory nerve cells of the lobster and crayfish. *J. Gen. Physiol.* **39** : 87–119.

EYZAGUIRRE, C. and KUFFLER, S. W. (1955b) Further study of soma, dendrite and axon excitation in single neurons. *J. Gen. Physiol.* **39** : 121–153.

FATT, P. and KATZ, B. (1953) The effect of inhibitory nerve impulses on a crustacean muscle fiber. *J. Physiol. (London)* **121** : 374–389.

FLOREY, E. and FLOREY, E. (1955) Microanatomy of the abdominal stretch receptors of the crayfish (*Astacus fluviatilis* L.). *J. Gen. Physiol.* **39** : 69–85.

GRANIT, R. (1947) *Sensory Mechanisms of the Retina.* Oxford University Press, London.

GRAY, J. A. B. and SATO, M. (1953) Properties of the receptor potential in Pacinian corpuscles. *J. Physiol. (London)* **122** : 610–636.

GRUNDFEST, H. (1956) Excitation triggers in post-junctional cells. In *Physiological Triggers* pp. 119–151. American Physiological Society, Washington, D.C.

GRUNDFEST, H. (1957) Electrical inexcitability of synapses and some consequences in the central nervous system. *Physiol. Revs.* **37** : 337–361.

GRUNDFEST, H. (1959) Evolution of conduction in the nervous system. In *Evolution of Nervous Control* pp. 43–86. American Association for the Advancement of Science.

HAGIWARA, S., KUSANO, K. and SAITO, S. (1960) Membrane changes in crayfish stretch receptor neuron during synaptic inhibition and under the action of gamma aminobutyric acid. *J. Neurophysiol.* **23** : 505–515.

HARRIS, E. J. and HUTTER, O. F. (1956) The action of acetylcholine on the movements of potassium ions in the sinus venosus of the heart. *J. Physiol. (London)* **133** : 58–59 P.

HARTLINE, H. K., WAGNER, H. G. and McNICHOL, E. F. (1952) The peripheral origin of nervous activity in the visual system. *Cold Spring Harbour Symposia Quant. Biol.* **17** : 125–141.

HUTTER, O. F. and TRAUTWEIN, W. (1956) Vagal and sympathetic effects on the pacemaker fibers in the sinus venosus of the heart. *J. Gen. Physiol.* **39** : 715–733.

KATZ, B. (1950) Depolarization of sensory terminals and the initiation of impulses in the muscle spindle. *J. Physiol. (London)* **111** : 261–282.

KUFFLER, S. W. (1954) Mechanisms of activation and motor control of stretch receptors in lobster and crayfish. *J. Neurophysiol.* **17** : 558–574.

KUFFLER, S. W. (1958) Synaptic inhibitory mechanisms. Properties of dendrites and problems of excitation in isolated sensory nerve cells. *Exptl. Cell Research*, Suppl. **5** : 493–519.

KUFFLER, S. W. (1960) Excitation and inhibition in single nerve cells. *Harvey Lectures* **54** : 176–218.

KUFFLER, S. W. and EDWARDS, C. (1958) Mechanisms of gamma aminobutyric acid (GABA) action and its relation to synaptic inhibition. *J. Neurophysiol.* **21** : 589–610.

KUFFLER, S. W. and EYZAGUIRRE, C. (1955) Synaptic inhibition in an isolated nerve cell. *J. Gen. Physiol.* **39** : 155–184.

LOEWENSTEIN, W. R. (1959) The generation of electric activity in a nerve ending. *Ann. N.Y. Acad. Sci.* **81** : 367–387.

OTTOSON, D. (1956) Analysis of the electrical activity of the olfactory epithelium. *Acta Physiol. Scand.* **35** : suppl. 122, 1–82.

PILGRIM, R. L. C. and WIERSMA, C. A. G. (1960) Thoracic stretch receptors in the crayfish. *Federation Proc.* **19** : 300.

TERZUOLO, C. A. and BULLOCK, T. H. (1956) Measurement of imposed voltage gradient adequate to modulate neuronal firing. *Proc. Nat. Acad. Sci. U.S.* **42** : 687–694.

TRAUTWEIN, W. and DUDEL, J. (1958) Zum Mechanismus der Membranwirkung des Acetylcholin an der Herzmuskelfaser. *Arch. ges. Physiol. Pflüger's* **266** : 324–334.

WIERSMA, C. A. G., FURSHPAN, E. and FLOREY, E. (1953) Physiological and pharmacological observations on muscle receptor organs of the crayfish *Cambarus Clarkii* Girard. *J. Exptl. Biol.* **30** : 136–150.

EXCITATION, INHIBITION
AND THE CONCEPT OF THE STIMULUS

ERNST FLOREY

Department of Zoology, University of Washington, Seattle 5, Washington

INHIBITION is not confined to the central nervous system and to the peripheral innervation of cardiac and striated muscle (crustacea) but occurs also with sensory receptor neurons. Here the phenomenon of inhibition can have two causes: (1) the action of efferent inhibitory neurons, and (2) the "rebound" (silent period) which immediately follows the cessation of excitatory stimulation to which the neuron has accommodated. Efferent inhibitory neurons and inhibitory agents can produce two effects on the receptor neurons: (1) temporary depression or inhibition of excitability during the direct action of the inhibitory agent (neuron); and (2) "rebound" excitation which occurs when the inhibitory action suddenly ceases. It is the second effect of inhibitory agents to which I wish to draw attention, because this appears to be a functionally most important mechanism which does not depend on inhibitory neurons or synaptic inhibition. Although the phenomenon can best be studied in sensory receptor neurons it is likely to play a major role in the functioning of central neurons.

I could not resist to show once more the famous figure (Fig. 1) of Eyzaguirre and Kuffler (1955) which demonstrates that in the crayfish stretch receptor neuron stretch causes depolarization and that the frequency of firing of the neuron is proportional to the amount of membrane depolarization. The record shown in this figure, furthermore, shows that during maintained stretch the impulse frequency falls off (*adaptation*) and that simultaneously the membrane depolarization is diminished (*accommodation*). It can also be seen that at the end of stretch stimulation, that is at the moment when the muscle element is allowed to relax to its original length, there occurs a momentary hyperpolarization: the membrane potential becomes for a moment larger than the equilibrium potential which corresponds to the particular resting tension of the receptor muscle. The exact opposite happens when the tension of the receptor muscle is lowered for a period of time and then suddenly raised to its original value. In this case the rise in tension causes the membrane potential to swing temporarily below the equilibrium potential. This transient depolarization can be sufficient to set off one or a

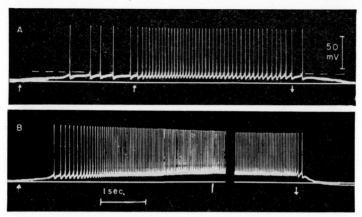

FIG. 1. Intracellular record from slow adapting stretch receptor neuron of crayfish. A. Between first two arrows, the receptor muscles are stretched just enough to set up irregular discharges. At second arrow stretch is increased and maintained almost constant: note decline of overall depolarization (accommodation) and decline in impulse frequency (adaptation). B. Between first arrow and the vertical line the receptor muscle is gradually stretched and then held at constant length until the second arrow. Note increasing depolarization and impulse frequency with increasing stretch. Note silent period and hyperpolarization as receptor muscle is allowed to relax to previous length. (From Eyzaguirre and Kuffler, 1955; with the permission of *J. Gen. Physiol.*)

few conducted spike potentials. An abstraction of the behavior of the receptor neuron is shown in Fig. 2.

It is of great importance that the same type of response can be elicited by other modes of stimulation: electric current (Turzuelo and Bullock, 1956), temperature and chemicals. Figure 3 gives an example of the changes in the frequency of firing of a crayfish stretch receptor neuron in response to three different stretch stimulations. It can be seen that the times required to reach a steady rate of firing after the onset of stimulation is the same regardless of the amount of tension applied to the muscle and in spite of the fact that the overall frequency increase is larger with larger tensions; it can also be recognized that the duration of the silent period and the time course of the recovery are proportional to the amount of previously applied tension. (For a detailed description of the experiments see Florey, 1956, 1957).

If a certain concentration of acetylcholine is applied to the neuron and maintained, the frequency of firing instantly changes to a higher value and then declines exponentially to a steady state. Removal of the stimulating drug causes the typical silent period. Again the adaptation times are equal regardless of the amount of acetylcholine applied but the duration of the silent period is proportional to the amount of acetylcholine previously applied and removed. Furthermore, the adaptation times are of the same magnitude as those observed as a result of mechanical stimulation. Similar observations were made with temperature changes: lowering of the temperature acts as

22

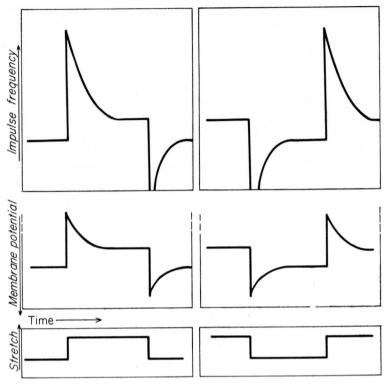

FIG. 2. Abstraction of behavior of slow-adapting neuron of crayfish stretch receptor neuron in response to sudden changes in tension applied to the muscle element of the receptor organ. All scales are linear, the units are arbitrary.

excitatory stimulation. Responses opposite to those obtained with acetyl-choline are caused by application and removal of Substance I, the inhibitory substance isolated from crustacean inhibitory neurons. If the receptor neuron is "set" to fire at a moderate rate, application of the inhibitory substance causes an immediate cessation of the discharge. After a certain time the neuron starts to fire again: the curve of the frequency change is identical with that obtained during recovery after a silent period induced by removal of excitatory stimulation (stretch, acetylcholine). The duration of the silent period is proportional to the concentration of inhibitory substance applied, and if enough is given, no recovery takes place. We may assume that accom-modation to the inhibitory action proceeds but that the membrane potential does not reach the firing level. When the inhibitory substance is removed, the neuron responds with momentary excitation and behaves as if it had received an excitatory stimulus. This response is indistinguishable from that induced by instant return to the original muscle tension from a period of

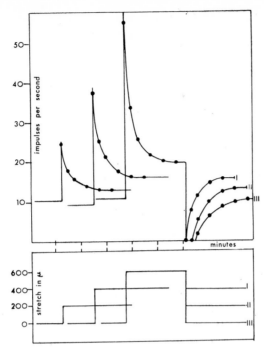

FIG. 3. *Cambarus virilis*. Changes in impulse frequency of slow-adapting stretch receptor neuron induced by sudden changes in the amount of tension (stretch) applied to the muscle element of the stretch receptor organ. (From Florey, 1957; with the permission of *J. Gen. Physiol.*)

mechanical relaxation, and from that caused by application of maintained stretch or acetylcholine.

From the similarity of the responses to the different modes of stimulation one may conclude that the stimuli affect the same primary receptor structure and that accommodation is the reaction to this alteration. It is impossible to tell from the frequency responses of the neuron which parameter of the environment has been changed since the effects of any one of them simply add or subtract, as the case may be. An example of the results of interaction of chemical and mechanical stimulation is shown in Fig. 4.

The results of experiments with chemical stimulation are of particular interest because the substances involved are assumed to function as transmitter substances. We may thus assume that neurons can accommodate and adapt to the action of transmitters and that responses seen in stretch receptors are common to chemically activated and inactivated neurons, whether they are sensory, motor- or inter-neurons.

Stimulation of a neuron by repetitive release of excitatory transmitter from presynaptic nerve endings can be expected to give rise to accommoda-

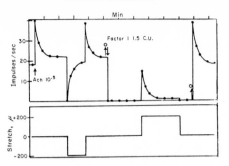

FIG. 4. Interaction of changes in mechanical and chemical conditions of the environment on slow adapting stretch receptor neuron of *Cambarus virilis*. *o* indicates washing with saline medium. The acetylcholine (ACh) concentration is given in g/ml, that of the inhibitory Factor I in crayfish units (*c.u.*) which correspond each to the inhibitory action of about 2 μg of GABA/ml. (From Florey, 1957; with permission of *J. Gen. Physiol.*)

tion and adaptation in the postsynaptic neuron, and inhibition caused by repetitive release of inhibitory transmitter can likewise induce accommodation. And, if the transmitter is suddenly removed "rebound" phenomena should occur which produce states of inhibition when excitatory agents are removed, and excitation when inhibitory agents are removed. Thus, one and the same transmitter should be able to produce both excitation and inhibition. The degree of the "rebound" phenomenon would depend on the speed with which the transmitter is removed. The situation is explained in the diagram of Fig. 5.

Assuming rapid removal (enzymatic inactivation, diffusion, absorption, etc.) of released transmitter one can state: removal of excitatory stimulation has the same effect as application of an inhibitory agent and conversely, removal of an inhibitory agent acts like application of excitatory stimulation.

The consequences of this scheme of events is illustrated in Fig. 6. In a chain of neurons where the transmission of information is the important feature, events which cause temporary excitation of the first neuron are more or less faithfully transmitted to the last neuron in the chain, even if transmission is not one-to-one but simply causes depolarization in the postsynaptic neuron which in turn sets up a corresponding frequency of firing. At the cessation of stimulation of the first neuron rebound inhibition of the first cell takes place and the same happens in all the following neurons as soon as presynaptic stimulation ceases. But since information is carried in the form of spike potentials, these inhibitory states are without information value. The situation is quite different if one of the neurons in the chain (the first one in Fig. 6, 2) is an inhibitory neuron (which presumably acts by hyperpolarizing the postsynaptic cell). Excitation will cause the repeated release of inhibitory transmitter (one quantum per impulse) but the action of the transmitter will have no information value since it does not lead to the formation of conducted

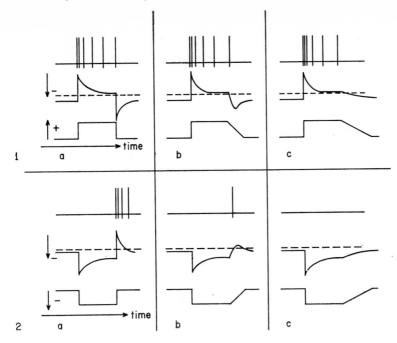

FIG. 5. Hypothetical responses of a neuron to excitatory (sequence 1) and inhibitory (sequence 2) transmitter and to the active or passive removal of the transmitter. The first line in each diagram represents the nerve action potentials, the second line the changes in membrane potential and the third line represents appearance and disappearance of the time course of appearance and disappearance of transmitter. The arrows point in the direction of increasing membrane potential and increasing amount of transmitter, respectively. *a, b* and *c* represent increasing time courses of disappearance of transmitter. Rebound excitation (2) and rebound inhibition (1) diminish with increasing time course. It is assumed that the transmitters are released by presynaptic stimulation. The amounts represented in the diagram are taken as the average concentrations maintained between the individual releases of transmitter quanta, assuming a decay time greater than the interval between presynaptic impulses.

spikes. As soon as the stimulation which gives rise to the inhibitory transmitter, and as soon as the action of this transmitter stops, rebound excitation results and the end of stimulation is signaled along the chain of excitatory neurons in the form of information-carrying conducted spikes. Using the terminology of receptor physiology we can call the first-mentioned response type an "on"-response and the second type an "off"-response. The advantage of the off-response lies in the fact that it is effective regardless of accommodation and adaptation that may have set in in the presynaptic element(s). Immediately obvious examples for the significance of such a system are the photoreceptors which give rise to the shadow reflexes in many animals. There are animals which show no response to an increase in light intensity but

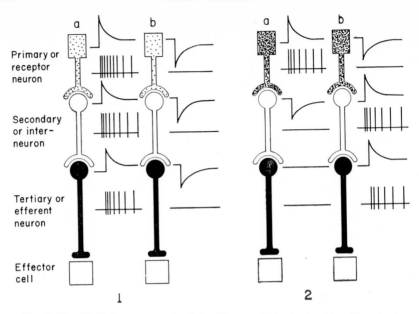

FIG. 6. Hypothetical responses of a chain of neurons to beginning (a) and termination (b) of stimulation of the first neuron. In sequence 1 the first neuron, as well as all the others, is excitatory; in sequence 2; it is inhibitory. The change in somatodendritic membrane potential and the sequence of resulting action potentials are shown for each neuron, the former as they appear with intracellular recording, the latter as they appear with extracellular recording. Sequence 1 represents the behavior of a typical "on" element, sequence 2, that of a typical "off" element.

which, even after hours of exposure to light, respond instantly (by flight, withdrawal into a shell or burrow) to a shadow (the approaching enemy). This negative vision is easily understood if we assume that one of the neurons (possibly the receptor neuron) is an inhibitory neuron (see Fig. 6b). Dr. Hartline has given us beautiful examples of the interactions of sensory neurons in the eyes of *Limulus* and comparable situations are known from the vertebrate eyes (Kuffler, 1953). Such interactions lead to an exaggeration of the information value of spatial and temporal contrasts of light and dark.

What applied to patterns of stimulation in eyes may well apply also to patterns of activation (and inhibition) of neurons within the central nervous system. Here too, inhibitory fibers may have decisive functions not only in the suppression of activity in other neurons, but in the production of excitation (information) whenever there is abrupt termination of inhibitory action. And, conversely, we may expect that excitatory neurons can induce temporary inhibition in postsynaptic cells whenever their prolonged activity ceases abruptly. Such inhibition, however, would only assume information-value and functional significance if it lowers the rate of firing of an already active neuron or if it prevents or diminishes its activation from another pathway.

When it is recognized that excitatory agents (or neurons) can cause inhibition as soon as their influence is removed, and that inhibitory agents (neurons) can cause excitation as soon as their action is terminated, it becomes an important matter of definition what one is to call a "stimulus". If the muscle element of a stretch receptor organ is stretched, we can call that a stimulus; and if we remove an inhibitory substance from an inhibited cell, we can call this also a stimulus.

A stimulus can thus be something that is applied or something that is removed. The common denominator between these two types of events is the change in environmental conditions (mechanical, chemical, thermal or electrical). The direction of the change determines whether inhibition or excitation results from the change.

In the previous discussion I was careful to avoid the term "stimulus" and to use instead the term "stimulation". I would like to suggest to reserve the term "stimulus" for any change in environmental conditions from a state A to a state B, which leads to either excitation or inhibition in the responding cell. The term "stimulation" should be used for the whole complex of events which includes the change from state A to state B, and the maintenance of state B for a certain length of time (thus permitting accommodation). If repetitive stimuli result in a shift of membrane potential which is maintained even during the intervals between stimuli, the series of stimuli should be referred to as stimulation.

With this terminology two things are achieved: (1) Recognition is given to the fact that the term stimulus implies the reaction of a cell to an environmental change and that it is not a substitute name for the agent applied. (2) It is possible to describe physiological phenomena in unambiguous terms. For instance, it is possible clearly to differentiate the meaning of "duration of stimulation" and "duration of the stimulus". One can now make the statement: the end of inhibitory stimulation can act as an excitatory stimulus provided the duration of the stimulation was long enough to permit accommodation of the responding cell.

REFERENCES

EYZAGUIRRE, C. and KUFFLER, S. W. (1955) Process of excitation in the dendrites and in the soma of single isolated nerve cells of the lobster and crayfish. *J. Gen. Physiol.* **39** : 87–119.

FLOREY, E. (1956) Adaptationserscheinungen in den sensiblen Neuronen der Streckreceptoren des Flusskrebses. *Z. Naturforsch.* **11b** : 504–513.

FLOREY, E. (1957) Chemical transmission and adaptation. *J. Gen. Physiol.* **40** : 533–545.

KUFFLER, S. W. (1953) Discharge patterns and functional organization of mammalian retina. *J. Neurophysiol.* **16** : 37–68.

TERZUOLO, C. A. and BULLOCK, T. H. (1956) Measurement of imposed voltage gradient adequate to modulate neuronal firing. *Proc. Nat. Acad. Sci. U.S.* **42** : 687–694.

EXCITATION BY HYPERPOLARIZING POTENTIALS.
A GENERAL THEORY OF RECEPTOR ACTIVITIES*

HARRY GRUNDFEST

Department of Neurology, College of Physicians and Surgeons,
Columbia University, New York

STUDIES on sense organs which have been classically designated as "primary sense cells" (cf. Autrum, 1959) are exemplified by the analysis of the mechano-receptors of muscle spindles (Katz, 1950; Paintal, 1959), the Pacinian corpuscles (Alvarez-Buylla and Ramirez de Arellano, 1953; Gray, 1959; Loewenstein, 1959), and the crayfish stretch receptor (Eyzaguirre and Kuffler, 1955). The latter cell is the only primary receptor neuron thus far studied with intracellular recording (Fig. 1). It produces a graded depolarizing "generator potential" (Bernhardt and Granit, 1946) which may be sustained as long as the stimulus is applied. Spikes are evoked in the axon (Edwards and Ottoson, 1958) and are conducted centripetally as a frequency-number coded message of all-or-none pulses.

The eccentric cell of *Limulus* eye, strictly speaking, should not be considered as a primary receptor neuron (Grundfest, 1961) since the photosensory process probably takes place in the retinular cells or their rhabdomes (cf. Fuortes, 1959). However, it, too, produces a depolarizing potential in its dendrite which may be recorded in the soma (Hartline *et al.*, 1952; Tomita, 1956; Fuortes, 1959). This potential is graded with the intensity of the light and lasts as long as the stimulus does.

The data obtained by studies with intracellular techniques confirm the deductions of earlier work (Adrian, 1932; Hartline, 1942; Bernhardt, 1942; Katz, 1950), on the linkage between the stimulus and message formation through the intermediate of the generator potential. Conceptually, they raise two questions: (1) How is it that one and the same cell can produce two different kinds of potentials—one a graded sustained depolarization, the other a sequence of pulses? (2) What happens in receptor systems of the secondary kind in which receptor cells without axons are involved and precede a neuron which may be regarded as the final common path for the centripetal sensory message?

* The researches at the author's laboratory were supported in part by funds from the following sources: Muscular Dystrophy Associations of America, National Institutes of Health, National Science Foundation and United Cerebral Palsy Research and Educational Association.

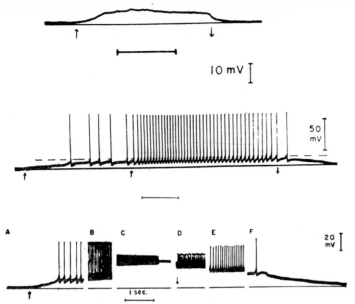

FIG. 1. Depolarizing electrogenesis of crayfish mechanoreceptor sense organ and the effects it evokes in the electrically excitable portion of the cell. (*Top*)—A weak stretch stimulus (↑) caused a depolarization of about 7 mV across the membrane of the cell body. This was maintained until the stretch was released (↓). (*Middle*)—Records at lower amplification. A weak stimulus produced a low-frequency discharge of spikes. Increased stretch (second arrow) caused a higher frequency discharge which continued with some slowing as long as the stimulus was applied. The spikes generated during the depolarization develop a hyperpolarizing undershoot which is absent when the response is evoked by a single electrical stimulus. (*Bottom*)—Three increasingly larger stimulations are shown in A–C. The spikes produced at a high frequency by the strongest stimulus (C) were diminished in amplitude and at the end were no longer evoked, while the receptor continued to respond with its sustained depolarization. D–F. The return of responsiveness of the electrically excitable membrane after its inactivation. Note that the average level of the depolarization produced by the mechanoreceptor dendrites is graded with the degree of the stimulus. (From Eyzaguirre and Kuffler, 1955.)

SPIKE GENERATING SENSORY CELLS

The two different electrogenic components that are found in the primary sensory neurons and in the final path neuron of secondary receptors behave quite differently to applied currents. The long-lasting depolarizing generator potential decreases with depolarizing current and increases when hyper-polarizing currents are applied (Fig. 2). The centripetal messages of spikes, however, increase in number and frequency with depolarizing currents and decrease with hyperpolarizing. These differences are, of course, explicable as manifestations of two fundamentally different activities: one, in an electrically

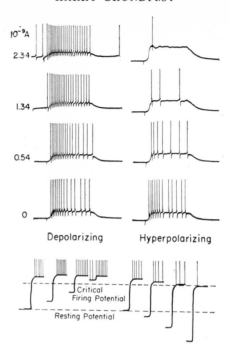

FIG. 2. Interaction of generator potential and polarizing voltages on electrically excitable membrane. Eccentric cell of *Limulus* eye was impaled with a microelectrode, used both for recording and for polarizing the cell. Magnitude of the applied currents are given on left. During polarization a constant light intensity was also delivered for about 1·5 sec. This stimulus gave rise to a depolarizing generator potential. The latter decreased with increasing depolarization (*left*) while the spike frequency increased. The strongest depolarization itself evoked spikes which recommenced after a silent period following the light stimulus. With increasing hyperpolarization of the cell (*right*) the generator potential increased, but the spike frequency decreased. The diagram indicates how these interactive effects occur. The smaller generator potential during depolarization was carried higher above the critical firing level. For the strongest hyperpolarizing current the generator potential barely attained the critical firing level. The changes in membrane potential from the resting level produced by the polarizing currents are drawn proportional to the applied currents, but the amplitudes of the generator potential exaggerated. (Modified from Fuortes, 1958; full spike traces lost in original figure have been retouched. They were about 50 mV high and probably were generated not in the cell body, but in the axon.)

inexcitable input membrane and the other in an electrically excitable conductile membrane (Grundfest, 1957b, c, 1959a, c). Wherever this has been studied it is now fairly general knowledge that the input element does not "support spikes" and that the potential which it does produce is local and non-propagating (cf. Edwards and Ottoson, 1958; Eyzaguirre and Kuffler, 1955; Gray, 1959; Loewenstein, 1959; Paintal, 1959). Direct evidence that this membrane component of the *Limulus* eccentric cell does not react to electrical

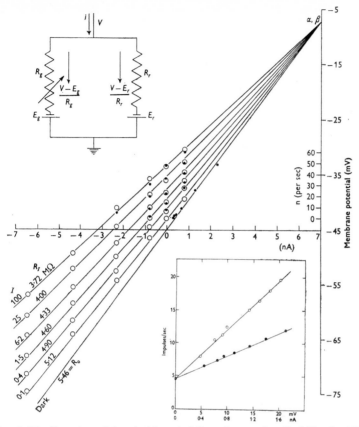

FIG. 3. Manifestation of electrical inexcitability of eccentric cell of *Limulus*. The frequency of discharges in the axon was increased by depolarizing the cell with an intracellularly applied current (dots, lower inset figure; abscissa in nA = 10^{-9} A) or by lights which produced depolarizing generator potentials of different amplitudes (circles; abscissa in mV of generator potential). (*Main graph*)—Another experiment. The effects of the applied currents on the frequency are plotted as the dots fitted by the "dark" curve. The circles of the other curves show the generator potential produced by different intensities of light (I = 0·1–100 units) at various values of polarizing current. The dots show the frequencies of the discharges in the axon under the same condition. The change in the slopes of the straight lines shows that the membrane resistance of the "dark" cell is decreased progressively by brighter illuminations. (*Upper inset*)—Equivalent circuit of the electrically inexcitable *Limulus* eccentric cell. *Er* and *Eg* are the sources of the resting potential. One is in unreactive membrane whose resistance (*Rr*) is unaffected by either illumination or polarization. The other is the generator membrane whose resistance (*Rg*) is diminished by light, but not by applied current (*i*). The voltage (*V*) resulting from the combined effects of current and illumination, is the effective potential which determines the frequencies of the discharges and may be calculated from the equivalent circuit. The calculated lines for different illuminations and currents agree quite well with the frequencies (dots) and generator potentials (circles) in main graph. (Figures combined from Fuortes, 1959 and Rushton, 1959.)

stimuli has been provided recently (Fuortes, 1959; Rushton, 1959). Under the combined effects of polarizing currents and illumination the observed changes in the frequency of the impulses of the *Limulus* final path neuron can be described quantitatively (Fig. 3). The system has an equivalent circuit of two parallel membrane components. The resistance of only one decreases and only with light, not by depolarization of the membrane, i.e. it is electrically inexcitable.

Thus, the functional organization of a primary receptor cell, like the crayfish stretch receptor, or of a final common path sensory neuron, like the *Limulus* eccentric cell, is the same as that of a generalized neuron (Fig. 4).

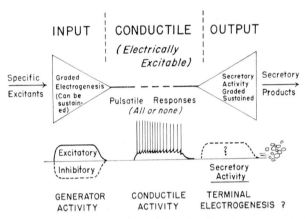

FIG. 4. Diagrammatic representation of functional components and electrical responses of a receptor cell or neuron. The electrically inexcitable input produces electrogenesis graded in proportion to its specific stimulus and sustained as long as the latter is applied. The possibility of hyperpolarizing electrogenesis is shown but is not further considered. The depolarization at the input, operating upon the conductile electrically excitable component, can evoke spikes in the latter coded in number and frequency in proportion to the depolarization. These signals, propagated to the output, there command secretory activity, roughly proportional to the information encoded in their message and sustained as long as the message demands. The transmitter released at the output can initiate a synaptic transfer by operating upon the depolarizing input of another cell. The possibility of a special output electrogenesis is indicated but is not further considered. (From Grundfest, 1957b.)

A specifically sensitive membrane at the input responds with a depolarizing electrogenesis which is graded and produces coded messages of spikes. The input membrane in most receptors is probably electrically inexcitable (Grundfest, 1956, 1957b, c, d). Thus, the conclusion that the olfactory epithelium in vertebrates is electrically inexcitable (Grundfest, 1957b) has recently been confirmed (Ottoson, 1959). Parenthetically, it may be noted that this is the only primary receptor type among the cranial special senses of the vertebrates. However, at least one type of receptor ought to respond to electrical stimuli (Grundfest, 1958a). This is the presumed receptor for the electrical guidance systems of fishes (Coates *et al.*, 1954; Grundfest, 1957a; Bennett and Grundfest, 1959; Lissmann, 1958). Indeed, the sensitivity of these receptors for changes in the electric current must be very high (Coates *et al.*, 1954). In one form detection of a gradient of about $0.02 \, \mu V/cm$ has been reported (Lissmann, 1958). These receptors may therefore be truly "specific" for electricity.

ELECTROPHYSIOLOGICAL PROCESSES IN SECONDARY RECEPTOR SYSTEMS

Secondary receptors are said to be confined to vertebrates (cf. Autrum, 1959), but as noted above, the *Limulus* lateral eye is probably a secondary receptor system. The vertebrate organs of special senses, vision, taste, hearing and equilibrium and the lateral-line organs of fishes have specialized receptor cells which act on other cells. In all but vision, the receptor cells make contact with a nerve cell. The latter therefore is the final common path. In the eye the rods and cones play upon horizontal and bipolar cells which in turn impinge on neurons of the ganglion cell layer. The horizontal and bipolar cells do not produce spikes (MacNichol and Svaetichin, 1958; Tomita *et al.*, 1959; Brown and Wiesel, 1959) and they may be regarded as operating in a manner similar to that of the receptor cells. They may be all considered as elements in which the conductile component of the generalized neuron is missing (Grundfest, 1958a). They should be electrically inexcitable (cf. Watanabe *et al.*, 1960) and might with propriety be regarded as neurosecretory cells (Grundfest, 1958b, 1961).

The vertebrate taste buds, which are secondary receptor cells, generate sustained depolarizing potentials without spikes (Fig. 5). The various cells respond to different degrees to standard stimuli, and this indicates that the specific sensations of taste arise out of differential patterns of many kinds of cells. Presumably the cells excite activity of the common path neurons, but whether by ephaptic means (cf. Grundfest, 1959a) or by release of a secretory transmitter cannot be decided at present.

In the case of the fish and cat retina, however, ephaptic transmission is ruled out. No potentials have been recorded in conjunction with the activity of the rods and cones. The absence of electrical sign may be due to some experimental artifact since these receptor elements are small. However, an artifact seems unlikely, since a number of investigators have looked for responses in rods and cones without success. Perhaps, therefore, the photochemical activity can excite the next cell (horizontal or bipolar) without itself producing a potential. Certainly in the absence of potentials in the sensory receptors ephaptic transmission to the neural element must be ruled out. Transmission between the photochemical receptors and the intermediate

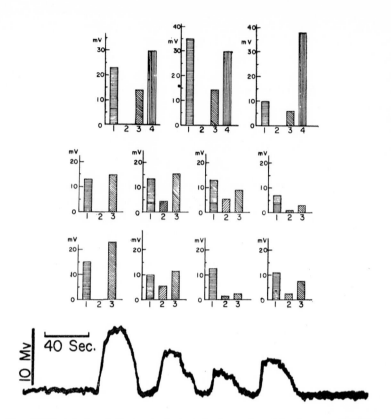

FIG. 5. Electrical activity in single taste buds produced by four standardized stimuli: (1) salt, (2) sweet, (3) bitter and (4) acid. (*Below*)—Records of potentials evoked by the four substances acting on a single taste bud. (*Above*)—Different patterns of responses in 11 different cells. (Unpublished data, courtesy of Beidler and Kimura.)

cells is probably chemical. The intermediate cells generate only graded, sustained hyperpolarizing potentials (Fig. 6), or both hyperpolarizing and depolarizing activity depending on the cell and the wavelength of the stimulating light (Fig. 7). Hyperpolarization certainly cannot produce ephaptic excitation of ganglion neurons, yet the hyperpolarization clearly causes depolarizing generator potentials and spikes in the neuron (Fig. 6).

At the time Svaetichin first described the hyperpolarizing potentials, Granit (cf. 1955) stated the then generally held opinion: ". . . it is . . . impossible to accept the idea that hyperpolarization causes a discharge" because of the "unequivocal . . . correlation between excitation and depolarization, and between hyperpolarization and inhibition" (p. 32). When Svaetichin (1956) reported his data in full he noted that hyperpolarization which causes activity

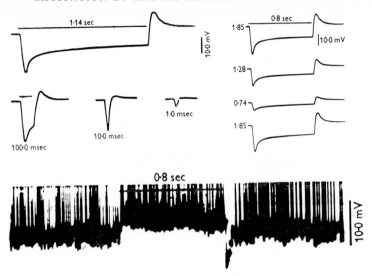

Fig. 6. Hyperpolarizing potentials developed in intermediate cells of cat retina and depolarizing generator potential and spikes from a ganglion cell. (*Upper left*)—Hyperpolarizations graded in duration and amplitude resulting from flashes of constant intensity but varying in duration from 1·0 msec to 1·14 sec. (*Upper right*)—Gradation of the response by changing the intensity of a light flash of 0·8 sec duration. (*Below*)—Intracellular recording from a retinal ganglion neuron, showing depolarizing generator potential and augmented spike activity during a light flash of 0·8 sec. (From Brown and Wiesel, 1959.)

of neurons is "a somewhat unexpected finding which is not compatible with present neurophysiological views" (p. 34).

The possibility that sense organs might involve electrically inexcitable activity had already been proposed at that time, however (Grundfest, 1956, 1957c, d). The evolutionary relation of the secretory output of neurons, the neurosecretory cells, and glands had also been noted (Grundfest, 1957b, 1959b). Indeed, glands may produce hyperpolarizing activity, a fact that was known to Garten (1910) and which was recently confirmed by Lundberg (1956) with intracellular recording (Fig. 8). Garten had likened the electrosalivogram to the electroretinogram, but apparently chiefly because of the long durations of the potentials.*

An explanation lies in the clarification of the functions which the receptors and intermediate cells are called upon to perform. These cells receive speci-

* Garten (1910) also explained the deviation from Pacini's rule (Grundfest, 1957a) of the responses of *Malapterurus* electroplaques as a sign of hyperpolarizing electrogenesis due to the supposed origin of the electroplaques from gland cells (Fritsch, 1887). In view of the data on salivary gland hyperpolarization this explanation was accepted until recently (Grundfest, 1957a). Subsequent work, however, showed that the electroplaques respond directly to electrical stimuli and produce all-or-none spikes overshooting to internal positivity as do other electrically excitable, conductile cells (cf. Keynes *et al.*, 1961).

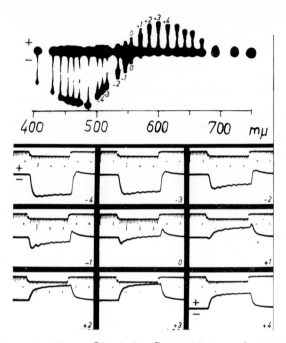

FIG. 7. Hyperpolarizing and depolarizing potentials from a cell in fish retina excited by illumination of different wave lengths, but of constant energy. (*Above*)—Action spectrum by scanning method. (*Below*)—The responses numbered on the upper traces are individually shown swept out on a time base. Note that the hyperpolarizing and depolarizing potentials appear to counterbalance at the record marked 0, except for a brief initial negative deflection and a terminal positive one. Durations of light flashes, monitored on upper trace, were 0·3 sec. (From MacNichol and Svaetichin, 1958.)

alized information from some outside source, transform or transduce it into information digestible by the organism and pass it on to the latter. The other essential feature is that they pass on the information to nearby cells and thus do not need a conductile component. Since the input of the cell next in line is electrically inexcitable the receptor cells must secrete some transmitter agent. Thus, their activity need not be and probably is not electrically excitable. The cell may generate no potential at all (Grundfest, 1957d), it could generate depolarizing potentials as in the taste buds, or hyperpolarizing potentials, or both kinds. Basically therefore these cells function in their capacity as secretory cells, the electrical activity being secondary, and probably contingent upon the type of secretory activity.

In order to distinguish between the generator potentials in primary neurons which are always depolarizing and associated with spikes and potentials that are produced in sensory receptor cells without production of spikes, Davis has recently suggested (1960) that the latter should be called receptor

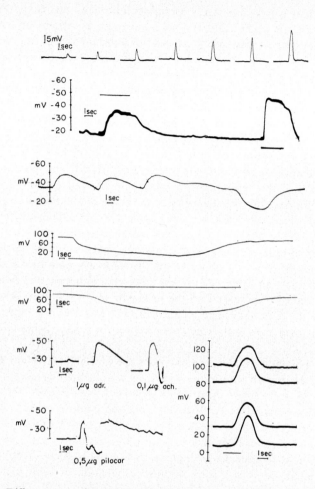

Fig. 8. Different types of electrical activity in cat salivary gland cells. Depolarization shown as downward deflection in these records. A. Type I cells produce hyperpolarizing p.s.p.'s which are graded with strength of the stimulus. Single shocks to chorda tympani evoke p.s.p.'s which last about 1 sec. B. Type I cells produce only hyperpolarizing p.s.p.'s to excitation of the sympathetic (*upper* signal) or parasympathetic (*lower signal*) nerves. However, the latencies and magnitudes of the p.s.p.'s differ somewhat. C. Type II cells develop hyperpolarizing p.s.p.'s on stimulating the chorda tympani and depolarizing p.s.p.'s through their sympathetic innervation. D. Type III cells (which may be myoepithelial elements of the ducts) respond only with depolarizing p.s.p.'s to parasympathetic (*above*) or sympathetic (*below*) stimulation. The resting potential, about − 80 mV, is large in comparison with that of Type I or II cells and resembles that of muscle fibers. E. Type I cells respond with hyperpolarization to epinephrine, acetylcholine and pilocarpine. (From Lundberg, 1955.) F. The hyperpolarizing p.s.p. of the gland cell is remarkably insensitive to changes of the membrane potential. The resting potential was 30 mV. (From Lundberg, 1956.)

potentials. This is only a partially useful definition and justifiable only if the definition also recognizes that the potentials may be absent or may be of either sign and that in any case they need have nothing to do with the process of transmission of the information which is analogous to neurosecretory activity.

Information about the functioning of auditory receptors and equilibrium receptors of vertebrates and, indeed, of sensory receptors in most forms of vertebrates and invertebrates is at present known only indirectly from the recording of the impulses in the nerves. However, there is now ample evidence that the relatively simple receptor systems like that of the *Limulus* eye have complex excitatory and inhibitory interactions (Ratliff and Hartline, 1959) and this is probably even more elaborate in the vertebrate systems (cf. Kuffler, 1953). Accordingly, the views on the mode of function of the auditory and vestibular receptors are as yet speculative. Davis (1959) considers that the hair cells of the auditory receptors are mechanosensory transducers which change their resistance during rarefaction and condensation of the air. There is a potential difference of about 80 mV between the scala media and scala tympani. If the hair cells act as resistance microphones they might thus impress a change of potential on the terminals of the auditory nerve fibers. In that case the terminals ought to be electrically excitable and might perhaps be related in evolution to the electrical receptors in electric fishes (Grundfest, 1961).

Another possibility is that the hair cells are in reality secretory cells producing and emitting a transmitter agent. At first glance this seems unlikely. The cells and nerve fibers must follow relatively high-frequency changes in pressure. However, with the discovery that the continuous high-frequency discharges of electric fish are mediated by synaptic means (Bennett and Grundfest, 1961, and unpublished), this is no longer a stumbling block. Some of the fish discharge at frequencies as high as 1600/sec (Lissmann, 1958), while in the mammalian nervous system impulse production at such high rates is possible for only a brief time (Gasser and Grundfest, 1939; Grundfest and Campbell, 1942). The frequencies of the discharges are remarkably constant in many gymnotids and are set by a command nucleus (Szabo, 1961; Bennett and Grundfest, 1961, and unpublished). Every discharge of the organ is associated with a discharge of a spinal neuron (Fig. 9). That discharge is initiated by synaptic excitation which accordingly must arise from a spike and a pulse of secretory activity in the nerve fibers descending from the nucleus. As noted above, auditory nerve fibers probably do not conduct impulses at rates higher than 1000–1500/sec. Thus, it is entirely possible that the auditory receptors are also secretory cells converting mechanical to chemical energy. The same considerations apply to the vestibular receptors.

The frankly neurosecretory cells which are found in lower forms as well as higher (cf. Scharrer and Scharrer, 1954; Ortmann, 1960) provide a link between the sensory receptor cells and neurons and gland cells. Some of the neurosecretory cells respond to external stimuli such as changes in luminous or thermal radiant energy, others to changes in various chemical components, osmotic pressure and temperature of body fluids. Still others are probably activated only by specific excitatory innervation. Thus, the line between sense organs and neurosecretory cells appears to be tenuous.

A discussion of the evolutionary implications of these concepts will be found elsewhere (Grundfest, 1961). At this point, however, it may be appropriate to point to possible relations between secretory and neurosecretory

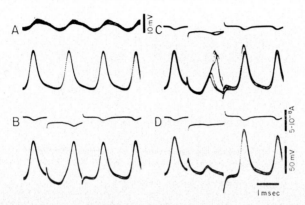

Fig. 9. Postsynaptic potentials and spikes in spinal cord electromotor neuron of *Sternarchus albifrons*. A. Activity of single neuron (*lower trace*) is synchronous with organ discharge at about 620/sec (upper trace). B–D. Upper trace is monitor for hyperpolarizing currents applied to the neuron. Current of organ discharges also appear in this trace. B. Weak hyperpolarization delayed the spike somewhat. C. Superimposed traces show variation in response with stronger hyperpolarization. D. Still stronger hyperpolarization eliminated spikes, leaving p.s.p. behind as evidence that each neuronal spike arises by activation through a descending bulbo-spinal tract system (Bennett and Grundfest, unpublished data).

cells on the one hand and various receptors and neurons on the other. One may expect to find six types of cells (Fig. 10) arranged in two general groups that are differentiated by the presence or absence of an innervation. Simple epitheliocytes without innervation (Ia) might be gland cells or sensory receptor elements of exteroceptive or enteroceptive function. The same cells with innervation (IIa) would represent the simple epithelial gland cells. A more complicated pair of cell types (Ib, IIb) would be secretory or neurosecretory cells with direct processes which might or might not develop spikes. Other neurosecretory cells might fall into the third group (Ic, IIc), the ducts being axons which produce spikes and secretion being confined to the terminal. One neurosectory cell type which probably generates spikes is known at present, that of *Lophius* (Potter and Loewenstein, 1955).

Cells of type IIc in which secretory activity is concentrated at the terminus of the axon is also a neuron, while cell type Ic is a primary receptor neuron. Combinations of Ia and Ic; Ib and Ic; or of all three cell types would then represent secondary and tertiary receptor systems. Some neurosecretory cells of types Ic and/or IIc have both synaptic vesicles and neurosecretory granules, the two differing markedly in size. This may indicate existence of a double mechanism, the nerve impulses releasing "transmitter agent" from the vesicles, and the substance then exciting the secretory activity of an effector membrane (DeRobertis, 1961).

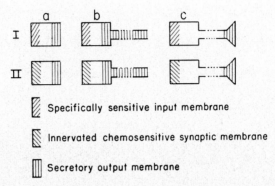

FIG. 10. Diagrammatic representation of six possible types of related secretory, neurosecretory, receptor and neuron cells. *Group I:* Cells which receive excitation from external or internal specific stimuli. *Group II:* Cells that are excited by innervation. (a) Simple columnar cells which might be glands, neurosecretory cells, or receptor cells. (b) Neurosecretory or receptor cells. (c) Neurosecretory, receptor, and correlational neurons. Further explanation in text.

The conductile properties of the nervous system are essential for all but the smallest of the co-ordinated Metazoa. Accordingly, electrical excitability and spikes are already found in the nervous system of coelenterates (Horridge, 1954) and have been studied with intracellular recording in earthworm (Kao and Grundfest, 1957). Both coelenterates and worms exhibit complex central integrative patterns. Perhaps, the Porifora may still yield examples of primitive electrically inexcitable receptor–effector cells (Grundfest, 1959b). However, it seems rather more likely that closer study of various types of gland and neuroserectory cells might be more rewarding in establishing evolutionary relations.

REFERENCES

ADRIAN, E. A. (1932) *The Mechanisms of Nervous Action: Electrical Studies of the Neurone.* University of Pennsylvania Press.

ALVAREZ-BUYLLA, R. and RAMIREZ DE ARELLANO, J. (1953) Local responses in Pacinian corpuscles. *Am. J. Physiol.* **172** : 237–244.

AUTRUM, H. (1959) Nonphotic receptors in lower forms. Chap. XVI in *Handbook of Physiology* Vol. I. *Neurophysiology*. American Physiological Society, Washington, D.C.

BENNETT, M. V. L. and GRUNDFEST, H. (1959) Electrophysiology of electric organ in *Gymnotus carapo. J. Gen. Physiol.* **42** : 1067–1104.

BENNETT, M. V. L. and GRUNDFEST, H. (1961) Studies on morphology and electrophysiology of electric organs—III. Electrophysiology of electric organs in Mormyrids. In *Bioelectrogenesis*. Amsterdam, Elsevier. In press.

BERNHARD, C. G. (1942) Isolation of retinal and optic ganglion response in the eye of *Dytiscus. J. Neurophysiol.* **5** : 32–48.

BERNHARD, C. G. and GRANIT, R. (1946) Nerve as model temperature end organ. *J. Gen. Physiol.* **29** : 257–265.

BROWN, K. T. and WIESEL, T. N. (1959) Intraretinal recording with micropipette electrodes in the intact cat eye. *J. Physiol. (London)* **149** : 537–562.

COATES, C. W., ALTAMIRANO, M. and GRUNDFEST, H. (1954) Activity in electrogenic organs of Knifefishes. *Science* **120** : 845–846.

DAVIS, H. (1959) Excitation of auditory mechanism. Chapter XXIII in *Handbook of Physiology* Vol. I. *Neurophysiology*. American Physiological Society, Washington, D.C.

DAVIS, H. (1960) Electrophysiology of the sense organs. *Federation Proc.* **19** : 740.

DEROBERTIS, E. (1961) Morphological bases of synaptic processes and neurosecretion. In *The Regional Chemistry, Physiology and Pharmacology of the Nervous System*. Pergamon Press, Oxford. In press.

EDWARDS, C. and OTTOSON, D. (1958) The site of impulse initiation in a nerve cell of a crustacean stretch receptor. *J. Physiol. (London)* **143** : 138–148.

EYZAGUIRRE, C. and KUFFLER, S. W. (1955) Processes of excitation in the dendrites and in the soma of single isolated nerve cells of the lobster and crayfish. *J. Gen. Physiol.* **39** : 87–119.

FRITSCH, G. (1887) *Die elektrischen Fische* Vol. I. *Malapterurus electricus*. Veit, Leipzig.

FUORTES, M. G. F. (1958) Discussion in: Electrophysiology of the visual system. *Am. J. Ophthalmol.* **46** : 13–16.

FUORTES, M. G. F. (1959) Initiation of impulses in visual cells of *Limulus. J. Physiol. (London)* **148** : 14–28.

GARTEN, S. (1910) Die Produktion von Elektrizität. *Winterstein's Hdbuch. d. vergl. Physiol.* Vol. 3, pt. 2, pp. 105–224. Fischer, Jena.

GASSER, H. S. and GRUNDFEST, H. (1939) Axon diameters in relation to the spike dimensions and conduction velocity in mammalian A fibers. *Am. J. Physiol.* **127** : 393–414.

GRANIT, R. (1955) *Receptors and Sensory Perception*. Yale University Press, New Haven.

GRAY, J. A. B. (1959) Initiation of impulses at receptors. Chap. IV in *Handbook of Physiology* Vol. I. *Neurophysiology*. American Physiological Society, Washington, D.C.

GRUNDFEST, H. (1956) Electric field effects and synaptic potentials in the functioning of the nervous system. In *Problems of Modern Physiology of the Nerve and Muscle Systems* pp. 81–97. Academy of Sciences, Georgian S.S.R., Tbilisi.

GRUNDFEST, H. (1957a) The mechanisms of discharge of the electric organ in relation to general and comparative electrophysiology. In *Progress in Biophysics* Vol. 7, pp. 1–85. Pergamon Press, London.

GRUNDFEST, H. (1957b) Electrical inexcitability of synapses and some of its consequences in the central nervous system. *Physiol. Revs.* **37** : 337–361.

GRUNDFEST, H. (1957c) Excitation triggers in post-junctional cells. In *Physiological Triggers* pp. 119–151. American Physiological Society, Washington, D.C.

GRUNDFEST, H. (1957d) General problems of drug action on bioelectric phenomena. *Ann. N. Y. Acad. Sci.* **66** : 537–591.

GRUNDFEST, H. (1958a) An electrophysiological basis for cone vision in fish. *Arch. ital. biol.* **96** : 135–144.

GRUNDFEST, H. (1958b) Discussion in: Electrophysiology of the visual system. *Am. J. Ophthalmol.* **46** : pt. 2.

GRUNDFEST, H. (1959a). Synaptic and ephaptic transmission. Chap. V in *Handbook of Physiology* Vol. I. *Neurophysiology*. American Physiological Society, Washington, D.C.

GRUNDFEST, H. (1959b) Evolution of conduction in the nervous system. In *Evolution of Nervous Control* pp. 43–86. American Association for the Advancement of Science, Publ. 52.

GRUNDFEST, H. (1959c) General physiology and pharmacology of synapses and some implications for the mammalian central nervous system. *J. Nervous Mental Disease* **128** : 473–496.

GRUNDFEST, H. (1961) Evolution of electrophysiological varieties among sensory receptor systems. In *Evolution of Physiological Processes*. Academy of Sciences, U.S.S.R., Moscow. In press.

GRUNDFEST, H. and CAMPBELL, B. (1942) Origin, conduction and termination of impulses in the dorsal spino-cerebellar tract of cats. *J. Neurophysiol.* **5** : 275–294.

HARTLINE, H. K. (1942) The neural mechanisms of vision. *Harvey Lectures* **37** : 39–68.

HARTLINE, H. K., WAGNER, H. G. and MacNICHOL, E. F., JR. (1952) The peripheral origin of nervous activity in the visual system. *Cold Spring Harbor Symposia Quant. Biol.* **27** : 125–141.

HORRIDGE, G. A. (1954) The nerves and muscles of Medusae—I. Conduction in the nervous system of *Aurellia aurita* Lamarck. *J. Exptl. Biol.* **31** : 594–600.

KAO, C. Y. and GRUNDFEST, H. (1957) Postsynaptic electrogenesis in septate giant axons—I. Earthworm median giant axon. *J. Neurophysiol.* **20** : 553–573.

KATZ, B. (1950) Depolarization of sensory terminals and the initiation of impulses in the muscle spindle. *J. Physiol.* (*London*) **111** : 261–282.

KEYNES, R. D., BENNETT, M. V. L. and GRUNDFEST, H. (1961) Studies on morphology and electrophysiology of electric organs—II. Electrophysiology of electric organs of *Malapterurus electricus*. In *Bioelectrogenesis*. Elsevier, Amsterdam. In press.

KUFFLER, S. W. (1953) Discharge patterns and functional organization of mammalian retina. *J. Neurophysiol.* **16** : 37–68.

LISSMANN, H. W. (1958) On the function and evolution of electric organs in fish. *J. Exptl. Biol.* **35** : 156–191.

LOEWENSTEIN, W. R. (1959) The generation of electric activity in a nerve ending. *Ann. N. Y. Acad. Sci.* **81** : 367–387.

LUNDBERG, A. (1955) The electrophysiology of the submaxillary gland of the cat. *Acta. Physiol. Scand.* **35** : 1–25.

LUNDBERG, A. (1956) Secretory potentials and secretion in the sublingual gland of the cat. *Nature* **177** : 1080–1081.

MacNICHOL, E. J., JR. and SVAETICHIN, G. (1958) Electric responses from the isolated retinas of fishes. *Am. J. Ophthalmol.* **46** : 26–46.

ORTMANN, R. (1960) Neurosecretion. Chap. XL in *Handbook of Physiology* Vol. II. *Neurophysiology*. American Physiological Society, Washington, D.C.

OTTOSON, D. (1959) Olfactory bulb potentials induced by electrical stimulation of the nasal mucosa in the frog. *Acta Physiol. Scand.* **47** : 160–172.

PAINTAL, A. S. (1959) Intramuscular propagation of sensory impulses. *J. Physiol.* (*London*) **148** : 240–251.

POTTER, D. D. and LOEWENSTEIN, W. R. (1955) Electrical activity of neurosecretory cells. *Am. J. Physiol.* **183** : 652.

RATLIFF, F. and HARTLINE, H. K. (1959) The responses of *Limulus* optic nerve fibers to patterns of illumination of the receptor mosaic. *J. Gen. Physiol.* **42** : 1241–1245.

RUSHTON, W. A. H. (1959) A theoretical treatment of Fuortes' observations upon eccentric cell activity in *Limulus*. *J. Physiol.* (*London*) **148** : 29–38.

SCHARRER, E. and SCHARRER, B. (1954) Neurosekretion. In *Handbuch der Mikroskopischen Anatomie des Menschen* pp. 953–1066. Springer, Berlin.

SVAETICHIN, G. (1956) Spectral response curves from single cones. *Acta Physiol. Scand.* **39** : Suppl. No. 134, 17–112.

SZABO, T. (1961) Histologie des organes électriques de quelques Mormyrides. In *Bioelectrogenesis*. Elsevier, Amsterdam. In press.

TOMITA, T. (1956) The nature of action potentials in the lateral eye of the horseshoe crab as revealed by simultaneous intra- and extracellular recording. *Japan J. Physiol.* **6** : 327–340.

TOMITA, T., MURAKAMI, M., SATO, Y. and HASHIMOTO, Y. (1959) Further study of the origin of the so-called cone action potential (S-Potential). Its histological determination. *Japan. J. Physiol.* **9** : 63–68.

WATANABE, K., TOSAKA K. and YOKOTA, T. (1960) Effects of extrinsic electric current on the cyprinid fish EIRG (S-Potential). *Japan. J. Physiol.* **10** : 132–141.

THE IDENTIFICATION OF
MAMMALIAN INHIBITORY TRANSMITTERS

David R. Curtis

Departments of Physiology, The Australian National University, Canberra, and
Downstate Medical Center, State University of New York, Brooklyn, New York

THE purpose of this communication is to discuss the methods by which inhibitory transmitters of the mammalian central nervous system may be identified. It will be assumed that apart from the depression of neuron excitability which occurs during the refractory period following a spike, the modifications of this excitability are normally purely synaptic processes and that synaptic inhibition is the consequence of an increase in the permeability of specialized areas of the postsynaptic membrane following the production of an inhibitory transmitter–receptor complex (Eccles, 1957, 1959; Grundfest, 1959). Inhibitory substances therefore differ from a series of compounds, classified as depressants, which lower the excitability of neurons in the absence of such a specific permeability increase.

The criteria, all of which must be satisfied before a substance can be established as a transmitter, are based upon the methods by which acetylcholine was shown to be a transmitter at the neuromuscular junction and in autonomic ganglia (Feldberg, 1951; del Castillo and Katz, 1956; Eccles, 1957; Elkes, 1957; Crossland, 1957; Paton, 1958; Koelle, 1959; Curtis and Watkins, 1960a). It is proposed to discuss these individually in terms of the special conditions imposed by the location of neurons within the nervous system. The order in which these points will be treated has been determined mainly by the practicability of establishing methods by means of which the various criteria can be tested. The use of relatively simple neurophysiological techniques may help to limit the number of substances to which the rather more difficult chemical and assay procedures need be applied, assuming, however, that the substance being investigated has been selected as a possible transmitter because of either its presence or the presence of a structurally similar compound in brain extracts or because of pharmacological observations of its action upon the activity of neurons.

A. THE ACTION OF THE SUBSTANCE UPON NEURONS MUST BE IDENTICAL WITH THAT OF THE INHIBITORY TRANSMITTER ACTING UPON THESE CELLS

Many chemical agents are capable of diminishing the responses of neurons to excitatory synaptic action but the process of inhibition is associated with a

342

particular mode of depression. It has been established for spinal motoneurons (Coombs *et al.*, 1955) that the alteration in the permeability of the receptor membrane produced by the interaction between the inhibitory transmitter and the specialized subsynaptic receptors involves both potassium and chloride ions. For the motoneuron, the resultant redistribution of these ions results in a flow of current through this membrane which hyperpolarizes the rest of the postsynaptic membrane (cf. Eccles, 1957, 1959). This hyperpolarization or inhibitory postsynaptic potential (i.p.s.p.) has been detected by intracellular recording not only from motoneurons but also from cells of Clarke's column (Curtis *et al.*, 1958) and from neurons of the cerebral cortex (Albe-Fessard and Buser, 1955; Phillips, 1956). The transient increase in membrane conductance produced by the transmitter–receptor complex, in association with the longer lasting hyperpolarization, accounts satisfactorily for the depression of the activity of neurons by inhibitory synaptic action (cf. Eccles, 1957).

Therefore, in order that a substance be considered as an inhibitory transmitter, it must also interact with these specialized transmitter–receptors to produce the same permeability change as does the naturally occurring transmitter. The importance of the method of applying the substance to neurons then becomes apparent since methods depending upon administration via the blood stream or by surface application to neuronal tissue may fail to produce an adequate concentration of the substance at its site of presumed action. Not only may the agent fail to penetrate the blood–brain or cerebro-spinal fluid–brain barriers but it may be partially inactivated by enzymic action during its passage through the blood stream or nervous tissue. In addition, even though observations may be made of the behavior of a single cell, it may be impossible to determine whether the administered compound is depressing the excitability of this cell by a direct action upon its membrane or by an indirect action due to the stimulation of cells or sensory receptors having inhibitory synaptic connections with the cell under observation.

The necessity for recording intracellularly from the observed neuron is also obvious since extracellular recording may not be adequate to distinguish between depression in the absence of a membrane potential change and inhibition associated with an hyperpolarization. The requirements for applying suspected transmitter agents to neurons and recording the effects upon the membrane are most conveniently satisfied by the use of co-axial electrodes (Curtis *et al.*, 1959) since the location of these cells precludes the use of the separate recording and drug-applying electrodes which have been used in investigations of the neuromuscular junction (Nastuk, 1953; del Castillo and Katz, 1955). These electrodes consist of two glass microelectrodes, the inner, of tip diameter approximately 0.5μ, projecting 40–60μ beyond the 10–12μ orifice of the outer barrel with which it is co-axial. It is usually possible to penetrate the surface membrane of a motoneuron with the inner barrel, the orifice of the outer barrel remaining in the extracellular position, so that chemical substances can be applied into this extracellular space iontophoretically (cf. Curtis and Eccles, 1958; Curtis et al., 1960a; Curtis and Watkins, 1960b). The use of such an electrode therefore enables the resting potential of the impaled cell to be measured, the membrane conductance to be evaluated and the presence and magnitude of postsynaptic and spike potentials to be determined. These studies can be performed before, during and after the application of the chemical agent and if a hyperpolarization is so produced, the similarity between the responsible membrane permeability alteration and that producing the i.p.s.p. can be assessed. The membrane potential of the cell can be varied by applying current through the intra-cellular electrode and also the ionic concentrations of the intracellular medium can be modified by iontophoretic injections of ions from this electrode. Such techniques established that the equilibrium potential of the ions that diffuse across the receptor membrane to produce the i.p.s.p. is approximately 10 mV more hyperpolarized than the resting potential of motoneurons (-70 mV) and that the responsible ions are probably K^+ and Cl^- (Coombs et al., 1955). If the equilibrium potential of the change in membrane potential produced by the applied chemical agent is the same as that of the i.p.s.p., the possibility that it is a transmitter would be very strong and would be further strengthened by the finding that the membrane con-ductance of K^+ and Cl^- ions was also increased.

It must be assumed that excitatory and inhibitory transmitter substances are not identical (Grundfest, 1957) and that the permeability changes at the respective synapses are specific to the type of synapse not only because of the type of receptor involved but also because of the nature of the chemical transmitter liberated. If this were not so, diffuse application of a transmitter to the neuron, although producing an increase in membrane conductance, may fail to change the membrane potential if approximately equal numbers of excitatory and inhibitory synapses were activated. It would then be necessary to apply the substance to the immediate environment of the subsynaptic receptors of one synapse. Such a technique is clearly impossible and is rendered unnecessary by the evidence to be discussed below, that excitatory and inhibitory transmitters, at least in the spinal cord, are different substances.

Several substances which have been investigated by these methods have failed to alter the resting membrane potential of motoneurons although the excitability of these cells has been modified. Thus γ-amino-n-butyric acid, β-alanine and some related monocarboxylic amino acids (Curtis et al., 1959; Curtis and Watkins, 1960b), although increasing the membrane conductance of motoneurons, fail to produce a membrane hyperpolarization and have therefore been rejected as possible inhibitory transmitters. The application of a high concentration of certain dicarboxylic amino acids also depresses spinal neurons (Curtis *et al.*, 1960b) whilst lower concentrations effectively excite these cells by producing a membrane depolarization. It is probably that the depolarization produced by the high concentrations of these acids is sufficient to inactivate the processes responsible for the rising phase of the spike potential. Procaine and atropine also depress spinal neurons, probably in the absence of a change in membrane conductance. These substances stabilize the electrically excitable component of the neuronal membrane and so reduce the effectiveness with which depolarization initiates a spike potential (Curtis and Phillis, 1960).

B. DEMONSTRATION OF THE PRESENCE OF THE SUBSTANCE WITHIN THE APPROPRIATE PRESYNAPTIC TERMINALS

Although the identification of a substance, which has satisfied criterion (A), within extracts of nervous tissue strengthens further its possible function as a transmitter, mere presence is insufficient evidence in the absence of precise anatomical localization. If the substance had been tested upon a variety of neurons and was found to be present in extracts only of those areas of the nervous system in which cells were inhibited by it or in those areas containing cell bodies of fibers having inhibitory synaptic connections with these neurons, the inference that the tested agent was indeed the inhibitory transmitter would be reasonable. The possibility that transmitters are stored in synaptic vesicles of the presynaptic terminals has been proposed (Robertson, 1956; del Castillo and Katz, 1956; Eccles, 1957; Eccles and Jaeger, 1957; Palay, 1958; de Robertis, 1958) and attempts are being made to identify such vesicles in homogenates of brain tissue (Hebb and Whittaker, 1958; Whittaker, 1959). It has been shown that, in extracts of nervous tissue, transmitters exist not only in "bound" form, perhaps contained in vesicles, but also in the free state, the proportions of the two forms depending upon the manner in which the extracts are prepared. Thus procedures aimed at destroying the membrane of the vesicles would be expected to increase the amount of free transmitter extracted (cf. Whittaker, 1959).

However, the identification of particles in brain homogenates is exceedingly difficult and in spite of any variations that may be observed in the amounts of a particular substance so extracted from particular anatomical regions, such methods do not necessarily indicate that the agent was originally present in inhibitory neurons and their terminals. The anatomical localization within these sites can only be determined by histochemical methods which, to the present time, have not been refined sufficiently to deal with particles of the vesicle type. In addition to the chemical problems involved in these techniques, a difficulty arises in determining whether a particular synapse is inhibitory in nature. Some attempts have been made in this direction

346 DAVID R. CURTIS

(Szentagothai, 1958, 1961) and progress in these fields may be rapid in the near future.

C. DEMONSTRATION OF THE PRESENCE OF ENZYMES ASSOCIATED WITH THE SYNTHESIS AND INACTIVATION OF THE SUBSTANCE

Feldberg's proposals of the role of acetylcholine as a transmitter substance within the central nervous system were based not only upon the distribution of acetylcholine but also upon that of choline acetylase (cf. Feldberg, 1957). If a substance be a synaptic transmitter it is reasonable to consider that components responsible for its synthesis would be present both at the terminations where release occurs and at the parent cell body (cf. Birks and MacIntosh, 1957). The problems of detecting the presence of an enzyme responsible for the synthesis of a transmitter substance are the same as those discussed in reference to detection of the transmitter itself, but it is possible that inhibitors of such an enzyme, by blocking the synthesis of the transmitter, may be useful in determining its chemical nature.

The role of enzymes responsible for the inactivation of transmitter substances is not so clear. The distribution of acetylcholine esterase has been determined histochemically (Koelle, 1959) and its presence near the post-synaptic receptors at certain sites, together with the prolongation of the acetylcholine transmitter action which follows the administration of acetylcholine esterase inhibitors, suggests that the enzyme is at least partly responsible for the inactivation of synaptically released acetylcholine (cf. del Castillo and Katz, 1956). However, other factors may also contribute to the removal of transmitters (cf. Blaschko, 1956). Analysis of the ionic currents responsible for the postsynaptic potentials of spinal motoneurons (Curtis and Eccles, 1959) indicate that the alterations in the permeability of the subsynaptic receptor membrane which produces these currents are of brief duration. It is reasonable to assume that the time course of these changes in permeability are identical with the period of activity of the particular transmitter–receptor complex and the further assumption that such complexes are of low stability allows the conclusion that the calculated time course of the currents reflects the concentration of transmitter within the synaptic cleft. On the basis of this conclusion and the dimensions of synaptic clefts, it has been calculated (Eccles and Jaeger, 1957) that for these central synapses, the process of diffusion is adequate to account for the brief transmitter time of action observed.

The assumptions of this argument, however, are such that enzymic inactivation of transmitters cannot be fully excluded, and, although analogies based upon events at cholinergic synapses are not necessarily applicable to central synapses, the possibility that enzymes might exist for this purpose must not be disregarded. Again, the detection of these enzymes is a histochemical problem but the use of enzyme inhibitors, by prolonging the action of both synaptically released transmitter and iontophoretically applied agents, would indicate a similarity between these substances.

D. DEMONSTRATION OF THE RELEASE OF THE TRANSMITTER SUBSTANCE FOLLOWING STIMULATION OF THE APPROPRIATE NERVE FIBERS

Because of the difficulty of stimulating a particular inhibitory pathway in isolation and also of collecting a suitable effluent from the region where the transmitter is released, the requirements for satisfying this criterion are formidable. In addition, if enzymes are present for the inactivation of the transmitter, inhibition of these may be necessary before detectable amounts of the substance could be collected. In the spinal cord it appears that inhibitory neurons have short axons (cf. Eccles, 1957) and consequently it is unlikely that such cells could be excited without prior activation of excitatory neurons having synaptic terminals upon them. Consequently, in the event of a perfusate or an effluent being collected, presumably from veins or possibly from the surface of the tissue, any method of assay would have to distinguish between excitatory and inhibitory transmitters.

E. DEMONSTRATION THAT THE PHARMACOLOGY OF THE SYNAPTIC INHIBITORY PROCESS WAS IDENTICAL WITH THAT OF THE APPLIED SUBSTANCE

The possibility that the inhibition of enzymes responsible for the destruction of transmitter substances might aid in the identification of the chemical nature of these agents has been mentioned above. The identification of acetylcholine as the transmitter at a particular synapse is indicated by the ability of D-tubocurarine to block transmission at the junction. As yet, little is known about the pharmacology of central synaptic transmission and, apart from acetylcholine, an excitatory transmitter or Renshaw cells, no other central transmitter has been identified. When administered intravenously, strychnine depresses all forms of synaptic inhibition within the spinal cord (Eccles, 1957; Curtis, 1959) without affecting excitatory synaptic action. It has been assumed that strychnine hinders the access of the inhibitory transmitter to the specialized subsynaptic receptors and in so doing has an action similar to that of curare at cholinoceptive synaptic receptors (cf. Eccles, 1957, 1959). However, the alternative explanation that strychnine prevents the release of the inhibitory transmitter, although unlikely, has not been disproved. If strychnine has a postsynaptic site of action, the blockage of the inhibitory effect of an applied chemical substance would indicate certain structural similarities between this substance and the inhibitory transmitter. In addition, if the manner by which the strychnine molecule interacts with the inhibitory receptors can be determined, the structure of these receptors may be elucidated and this in turn may give some indication of the molecular structure of the inhibitory transmitter itself.

CONCLUSION

Although it must be agreed with Paton (1958) that all of the foregoing criteria must be satisfied by a substance before it can be fully classified as an inhibitory transmitter, the finding of a chemical substance in brain extracts, which, when applied to neurons in the same areas from which the extracts were made, produces a membrane hyperpolarization due to an increase in the membrane conductance of K^+ and Cl^- ions, would be strong evidence that the substance was an inhibitory transmitter. If in addition this action was blocked by strychnine, the failure to satisfy fully the other criteria discussed above, because of technical difficulties, need not prevent the provisional acceptance of the substance as an inhibitory transmitter.

REFERENCES

ALBE-FESSARD, D. and BUSER, P. (1955) Activités intracellulaires recueillies dans le cortex sigmoide du chat: participation des neurones pyramidaux au 'potentiel evoqué' somésthésique. *J. Physiol.* (*Paris*) **47** : 67–69.
BIRKS, R. I. and MACINTOSH, F. C. (1957) Acetylcholine metabolism at nerve-endings. *Brit. Med. Bull.* **13** : 157–161.
BLASCHKO, H. (1956) *Hypotensive Drugs* (ed. by HARRINGTON, M.) Pergamon Press, London.
DEL CASTILLO, J. and KATZ, B. (1955) On the localization of acetylcholine receptors. *J. Physiol.* (*London*) **128** : 157–181.
DEL CASTILLO, J. and KATZ, B. (1956) Biophysical aspects of neuro-muscular transmission. *Progr. in Biophys. and Biophys. Chem.* **6** : 121–170.
COOMBS, J. S., ECCLES, J. C. and FATT, P. (1955) The specific ionic conductances and the ionic movements across the motoneuronal membrane that produce the inhibitory post-synaptic potential. *J. Physiol.* (*London*) **130** : 326–373.
CROSSLAND, J. (1957) *Metabolism of the Nervous System* (ed. by RICHTER, D.) Pergamon Press, London.
CURTIS, D. R. (1959) Pharmacological investigations upon inhibition of spinal motoneurones. *J. Physiol.* (*London*) **145** : 175–192.
CURTIS, D. R. and ECCLES, R. M. (1958) The excitation of Renshaw cells by pharmacological agents applied electrophoretically. *J. Physiol.* (*London*) **141** : 435–445.
CURTIS, D. R. and ECCLES, J. C. (1959) The time courses of excitatory and inhibitory synaptic actions. *J. Physiol.* (*London*) **145** : 529–546.
CURTIS, D. R. and PHILLIS, J. W. (1960) The action of procaine and atropine on spinal neurones. *J. Physiol.* (*London*). **153** : 17–34.
CURTIS, D. R. and WATKINS, J. C. (1960a) In *Conference on Inhibition in the Nervous System and γ-Aminobutyric Acid.* Pergamon Press, London.
CURTIS, D. R. and WATKINS, J. C. (1960b) The excitation and depression of spinal neurones by structurally related amino acids. *J. Neurochem.* **6** : 117–141.

CURTIS, D. R., ECCLES, J. C. and LUNDBERG, A. (1958). Intracellular recording from cells in Clarke's column. *Acta. Physiol. Scand.* **43** : 303–314.

CURTIS, D. R., PERRIN, D. D. and WATKINS, J. C. (1960a). The excitation of spinal neurones by the iontophoretic application of agents which chelate calcium. *J. Neurochem.* **6** : 1–20.

CURTIS, D. R., PHILLIS, J. W. and WATKINS, J. C. (1959) The depression of spinal neurones by γ-amino-*n*-butyric acid and β-alanine. *J. Physiol. (London)* **146** : 185–203.

CURTIS, D. R., PHILLIS, J. W. and WATKINS, J. C. (1960b) The chemical excitation of spinal neurones by certain acidic amino acids. *J. Physiol. (London)* **150** : 656–682.

ECCLES, J. C. (1957) *The Physiology of Nerve Cells.* Johns Hopkins Press, Baltimore.

ECCLES, J. C. (1959) *Handbook of Physiology* Vol. I. *Neurophysiology* (ed. by FIELD, J.). American Physiological Society, Washington, D.C.

ECCLES, J. C. and JAEGER, J. C. (1957) The relationship between the mode of operation and the dimensions of the junctional regions at synapses and motor end-organs. *Proc. Roy. Soc. (London)* B **148** : 38–56.

ELKES, J. (1957) *Neuropharmacology* Vol. III (ed. by ABRAMSON, H. A.) Josiah Macy Foundation, New York.

FELDBERG, W. (1951) Some aspects in pharmacology of central synaptic transmission. *Arch. intern. physiol.* **59** : 544–560.

FELDBERG, W. (1957) *Metabolism of the Nervous System* (ed. by RICHTER, D.). Pergamon Press, London.

GRUNDFEST, H. (1957). Electrical inexcitability of synapses and some consequences in the central nervous system. *Physiol. Revs.* **37** : 337–361.

GRUNDFEST, H. (1959) *Handbook of Physiology* Vol. I. *Neurophysiology* (ed. by FIELD, J.). American Physiological Society, Washington, D.C.

HEBB, C. O. and WHITTAKER, V. P. (1958) Intracellular distributions of acetylcholine and choline acetylase. *J. Physiol. (London)* **142** : 187–196.

KOELLE, G. B. (1959) *Evolution of Nervous Control from Primitive Organisms to Man* (ed. by BASS, A. D.). American Association for the Advancement of Science, Washington, D.C.

NASTUK, W. L. (1953) Membrane potential changes at a single muscle end-plate produced by transitory application of acetylcholine with an electrically controlled microjet. *Federation Proc.* **12** : 102.

PALAY, S. L. (1958) The morphology of synapses in the central nervous system. *Exptl. Cell Research Suppl.* **5** : 275–293.

PATON, W. D. M. (1958) Central and synaptic transmission in the nervous system (pharmacological aspects). *Ann. Rev. Physiol.* **20** : 431–470.

PHILLIPS, C. G. (1956) Intracellular recording from Betz cells in the cat. *Quart. J. Exptl. Physiol.* **41** : 58–69.

DE ROBERTIS, E. (1958) Submicroscopic morphology and function of the synapse. *Exptl. Cell Research Suppl.* **5** : 347–369.

ROBERTSON, J. D. (1956) The ultrastructure of a reptilian myoneural junction. *J. Biochem. Biophys. Cytol.* **2** : 381–394.

SZENTAGOTHAI, J. (1958) The anatomical basis of synaptic transmission of excitation and inhibition in motoneurones. *Acta. Morphol. Acad. Sci. Hung.* **8**, 287–309.

SZENTAGOTHAI, J. (1961) Anatomical aspects of inhibitory pathways and synapses. This volume, p. 32.

WHITTAKER, V. P. (1959) The isolation and characterization of acetylcholine-containing particles from brain. *Biochem. J.* **72** : 694–706.

INHIBITORY TRANSMITTERS—A REVIEW*

H. McLennan

Department of Physiology, University of British Columbia, Vancouver

The concept of the transmission of excitation at synapses within the nervous system, or at the junctions between neurons and effector organs, by means of the release of a substance from the endings of the pre-junctional side is now almost universally accepted. The same type of mechanism has logically been invoked for synapses, activation of which gives rise to inhibition or depression of the postsynaptic structure. It is the purpose of this paper to consider some of the evidence which has been produced in support of certain substances as possible mediators of transmission at these inhibitory synapses. I shall consider first of all the situation pertaining to the vertebrate central nervous system, and thereafter mention some peripheral inhibitory processes which occur in vertebrates and in other animal species.

The work of Eccles and his colleagues in Australia has provided the ultimate criteria for assessment of any given compound as a possible transmitter released at mammalian inhibitory synapses. From their work on the neurons of the spinal cord, especially motor neurons, has emerged a picture of the electrical changes brought about in a postsynaptic cell by activation of an inhibitory pathway, and of the ionic mechanisms underlying these electrical phenomena. It is worthwhile to summarize the findings at this point.

When a spinal cord motor neuron is penetrated by a suitable microelectrode, a steady potential difference appears between the electrode tip and that of an indifferent lead in contact with the extracellular fluid. When the cell is at rest the magnitude of this potential difference is about 70 mV, inside negative. Stimulation of an afferent pathway which functionally results in inhibition of the motor neuron gives rise to a potential change superimposed on the resting potential, and the amplitude of this transient potential increases as the intensity of the afferent stimulation is raised. Typical potentials of this type recorded from a motor neuron, and which Coombs et al. (1955c) have named inhibitory postsynaptic potentials (i.p.s.p.) are shown in Fig. 1. The effect of stimulation of an inhibitory pathway then, is transiently to render the inside of the cell more negative than is the case during rest. It has been shown that the equilibrium potential for the i.p.s.p. is in the neighborhood

* Aided by grants from the National Research Council of Canada and the Leon and Thea Koerner Foundation.

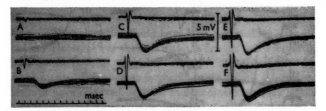

FIG. 1. Inhibitory postsynaptic potentials recorded from a biceps–semitendinosus motor neuron (*lower trace*) elicited by increasing strength of stimulation of quadriceps nerve (*upper trace*). Downward deflexion in the motor neuron records indicates membrane hyperpolarization (Coombs *et al.*, 1955c). (Courtesy of Sir John Eccles and the *Journal of Physiology*.)

of -80 mV, and that the current responsible for it is carried by an inward movement of chloride and, less importantly, by an outward movement of potassium ions, these fluxes taking place through the membrane underlying the synaptic endings (Coombs *et al.*, 1955a).

The equilibrium potential for the i.p.s.p. was estimated in experiments wherein the resting potential of the cell was artificially altered by the passage of a steady background current, and the effect upon an evoked i.p.s.p. observed. A typical series of records is shown in Fig. 2. When the resting potential was set at 82 mV, the i.p.s.p. almost disappeared. If the resting potential was less than this, the i.p.s.p. was an hyperpolarizing response; if the resting potential was greater than 80 mV the i.p.s.p. was depolarizing, and in both cases the farther the resting potential was from 80 mV the greater the amplitude of the evoked change (Coombs *et al.*, 1955a).

The i.p.s.p. upon which I have concentrated here is to be contrasted with the analogous potential change brought about in the cell by stimulation of an excitatory pathway. In this case the transient potential reduces the resting potential of the cell, and if the reduction is large enough will cause an all-or-nothing spike discharge to occur. It has been named an excitatory postsynaptic potential (e.p.s.p.): its amplitude again depends upon the strength of afferent stimulation, its equilibrium potential is about 0 mV and its time course is similar to that of the i.p.s.p.'s shown in Fig. 1 (Coombs *et al.*, 1955b). The arithmetic sum of the depolarizations produced by e.p.s.p.'s and the hyperpolarizations of the i.p.s.p.'s will determine the state of excitability of the postsynaptic cell. It can be presumed that essentially similar processes underlie the excitation and inhibition of other types of neurons within the central nervous system, and that the effects which I have described are not mechanisms peculiar to motor neurons.

From these observations, then, criteria for the action of an inhibitory transmitter substance can be set up (Curtis *et al.*, 1959). (1) If a substance be artificially applied to a postsynaptic cell it must mimic the action of stimulation of an afferent pathway which, if the pathway is an inhibitory one must

24

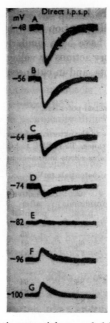

FIG. 2. Inhibitory postsynaptic potentials recorded from a biceps–semitendinosus motor neuron in response to stimulation of quadriceps nerve. A double-barrelled microelectrode was employed, and a steady background current was passed through one barrel to pre-set the membrane potential, while the voltage change due to nerve stimulation was recorded through the other. In the absence of applied current the membrane potential was −74 mV. A depolarizing current increased the amplitude of the i.p.s.p., while an hyperpolarizing current caused a reversal of its polarity at a membrane potential level near −82 mV. (Coombs et al., 1955a). (Courtesy of Sir John Eccles and the *Journal of Physiology*.)

lead to a transient hyperpolarization. The level of the resting potential of the cell under observation should therefore be raised. (2) An increased polarization results in a decrease in amplitude of an evoked i.p.s.p. (see Fig. 2), and this effect also should be observable upon "artificial" administration of the postulated transmitter. (3) There should be an observable change in the amplitude of an evoked e.p.s.p. Hyperpolarization of the cell removes its resting potential farther from the equilibrium potential of the e.p.s.p. (0 mV), and it might be expected from this that the amplitude of an evoked e.p.s.p. would be greater (by analogy with the changes in i.p.s.p.'s shown in Fig. 2). However, Curtis et al. (1959) have argued that the increased permeability to small ions brought about by activation of the inhibitory subsynaptic membrane would, by reason of the increased membrane conductance, reduce the effectiveness of the current produced by the action of the excitatory transmitter, and would thus lead to a smaller observed e.p.s.p. In summary, one would expect that application of a solution containing inhibitory transmitter to a postsynaptic cell would (1) increase the resting potential; (2) reduce or abolish an i.p.s.p.; and (3) reduce the size of an e.p.s.p.

There are of course other conditions which must be met by any substance which is postulated for the role of transmitter. These have often been summarized, most recently perhaps by Florey (1960), and some are: (4) the substance must occur in detectable quantities in the neurons whose action it transmits and must be synthesized there; (5) the postsynaptic structure should contain an enzyme system for the inactivation of the transmitter; (6) during stimulation of the neuron the substance should be detectable in the extracellular fluid in the vicinity of the synapse, if necessary after inhibition of the inactivating enzyme; and (7) drugs which potentiate or block the action of the neuron should similarly affect the action of the applied substance.

Before considering to what extent known substances or extracts of unknown constitution fulfil these various requirements, it should be noted that other possibilities for depression of neuronal function exist. It will have been noted that no mention has been made of blocking of the spike discharge of the postsynaptic neuron. This of course will occur if sufficient afferent inhibitory influence of the type just described is brought to bear upon the cell under observation, but it is possible also that such abolition of discharge can occur from other causes. One such cause is the inhibition of a cell with an associated reduction in amplitude of the e.p.s.p., but without the development of an hyperpolarization resulting from inhibitory stimulation alone. This phenomenon Frank and Fuortes (1959) have called "remote inhibition" in contrast to the "direct" inhibitory process described above. Eccles (1961), however, has shown that this inhibition is brought about by block of presynaptic action as a consequence of excitation in adjacent neurons, and an inhibitory transmitter is therefore not involved. Another possible cause of inhibition of cell discharge is by the action of what may be called "depressor" substances, whose effect will be to reduce the excitability of the cell as a whole. Such substances released into or artificially added to the extracellular fluid may prevent the discharge of a cell under study without having an effect on the resting potential. Both e.p.s.p.'s and i.p.s.p.'s evoked in a cell while under the influence of such a depressor would be expected to be reduced in size.

With these thoughts as background we will examine the qualifications of various substances as possible inhibitory transmitters in the mammalian central nervous system. In 1953, and in more detail in 1954, Florey reported some of the actions of extracts of mammalian brain which had striking inhibitory properties on the slow-adapting neuron of the abdominal stretch receptors of crayfish. These extracts were said to contain Factor I, and some of their actions in Crustacea will be further considered below. Florey and McLennan (1955a, b) studied the effects of Factor I in the mammalian nervous system and some of the pertinent observations may be presented here. Factor I can be extracted from the central nervous system and from no other structure; it is not present in peripheral nerve or spinal roots. A more detailed study of its distribution was made by Florey and Florey (1958), who showed that it was largely concentrated in the grey matter of the extrapyramidal centres, with little in white matter other than the superior cerebellar peduncle, optic tract and crus cerebri: however, their conclusion was that "it is not possible to establish a definite correlation between location and function of Factor I". The results were not inconsistent with the role of Factor I as an inhibitory transmitter, although Florey and Florey considered that at some sites it might have excitatory actions as well.

Topical application of Factor I solutions to the exposed spinal cord results in a prompt and complete inhibition of monosynaptic tendon jerk reflexes (Florey and McLennan, 1955b). This effect is prevented by the administration to the animal of small doses of strychnine (Fig. 3), which Curtis (1959) has

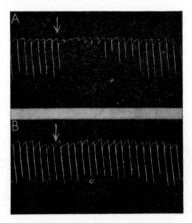

FIG. 3. Records of the movements of the lower leg of a decerebrate cat in response to tapping the patellar tendon. At the arrows Factor I solution was applied to the exposed spinal cord; A before, B 5 min after the intravenous administration of 0·08 mg/kg strychnine. (Florey and McLennan, 1955b.) (Courtesy of the *Journal of Physiology*.)

shown to prevent the action of afferent inhibitory stimulation on the neurons of the cord. Here then is a more direct connection between Factor I and inhibitory synaptic action, since a drug which affects the action of the physiological pathway similarly affects the action of the applied extract. Factor I also blocks synapses in sensory pathways (Honour and McLennan, 1960); but a more disquieting note is introduced by the finding that it likewise prevents the discharge of postganglionic cells in some sympathetic ganglia (Florey and McLennan, 1955a), and in this last instance there is no indication for the presence of a physiological inhibitory nerve supply. It would seem then that Factor I may have properties similar to those of the inhibitory transmitter at motor neurons, but is perhaps acting as a "depressor" at other sites.

Of the numbered conditions listed above then, Factor I seems to satisfy nos. 4 and 7. Florey (1954) reported the inactivation of Factor I by homogenates of brain (point no. 6), and Florey and McLennan (1955a) showed that Factor I activity appeared in an exudate from cerebral cortex (point no. 5), although they did not show an increase in its appearance during inhibitory stimulation.

Recently McLennan (unpublished observations) has attempted to assess the degree to which Factor I can also satisfy the three criteria for an inhibitory transmitter detailed by Curtis *et al.* (1959). Intracellular records were made from motor neurons of the cat's spinal cord, and subjected to the action of Factor I by topical application of the material to the cord. As expected, orthodromic action potentials recorded from the cells were blocked; the effect of the Factor I could be reversed by washing or was sometimes spontaneously reversed. Concomitant with the disappearance of action potentials the membrane potential of the cell was raised by 2–5 mV and i.p.s.p.'s reduced or, rarely, entirely abolished (Fig. 4). E.p.s.p.'s showed relatively little change

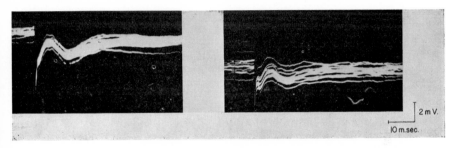

FIG. 4. Inhibitory postsynaptic potentials recorded from a quadriceps motor neurone in response to dorsal root stimulation. Factor I solution was applied to the exposed spinal cord between the two records. Note the increased polarization of the membrane (displacement downwards) and reduced amplitude of the i.p.s.p. (McLennan, unpublished observations).

except when the alteration of the membrane potential was comparatively large, in which event the e.p.s.p.'s were somewhat reduced (Fig. 5). These actions on the membrane potential and on evoked postsynaptic potentials are in accord with the requirements for the action of an inhibitory transmitter set out above.

Considerable work has been devoted to attempts to isolate the active ingredients in Factor I-containing extracts. Using the original definition of Factor I activity (see above) as the basis for their assay, Bazemore *et al.* (1957) isolated from the extracts γ-aminobutyric acid (GABA) which they

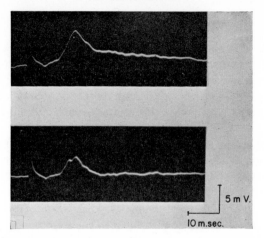

FIG. 5. Excitatory postsynaptic potentials recorded from a quadriceps motor neuron in response to dorsal root stimulation. Upper record before, lower after application of Factor I solution to the spinal cord. (McLennan, unpublished observations.)

showed to have a potent blocking action on the crayfish stretch receptor neuron.

GABA was compared with Factor I in a number of situations where the latter is active (McLennan, 1957; Florey and McLennan, 1959; Honour and McLennan, 1960) and found not to have precisely similar effects. In particular it had no action on monosynaptic reflexes even when applied in high concentration to the spinal cord. The substance has been applied to the cerebral cortex by a number of workers with results which have been interpreted by some as an indication of specific blocking of excitatory synaptic processes (Grundfest, 1958). However, Curtis *et al.* (1959) have now provided convincing evidence that the action of GABA is as a "depressor" on spinal neurons, inasmuch as after local application to the vicinity of a cell it reduced both e.p.s.p.'s and i.p.s.p.'s without any alteration in the resting potential. Strychnine furthermore was without effect on these actions. It seems apparent then that GABA cannot be the inhibitory transmitter of the mammalian central nervous system.

It is moreover possible to prepare active Factor I solutions which contain little or no GABA (McLennan, 1958). There are a number of other related compounds whose actions on the crayfish neuron (Edwards and Kuffler, 1959) and spinal neurons (Curtis *et al.*, 1959) are similar to those of GABA. Such are β-alanine, δ-aminovaleric acid, β-guanidinopropionic and γ-guanidinobutyric acids, γ-amino-β-hydroxybutyric acid, etc. All of these are possible constituents of the brain extracts: all, like GABA, fail to duplicate entirely the actions of Factor I. McLennan (1960) has recently divided Factor I into two active fractions whose biological actions are very similar but whose behaviour on paper chromatograms is markedly different. One of these fractions was purified to the point that its specific activity towards the cray-fish neuron was three times higher than that of GABA, but the material was not further characterized. The constituent of Factor I extracts active on the motor neurons of the mammalian spinal cord remains to be identified; it should perhaps be added that it is not identical with any of the other commonly considered compounds likely to be present in an extract of brain acetyl-choline, histamine, 5-hydroxytryptamine, adrenaline, etc.

Other substances known to occur and to be metabolized in the brain have been reported to have effects which may possibly be on synaptic structures, or have depressant actions on neurons similar to those described above for GABA. A brief discussion only of these other potential candidates will there-fore be made.

Sympathin (Adrenaline and Noradrenaline)

Vogt (1954) has published figures showing the distribution of noradrenaline within the central nervous system which indicate its widespread occurrence, and markedly higher concentration in the hypothalamus and area postrema. Rather variable effects of adrenaline on cord reflexes have been reported in the past, with depressant actions predominating. Recently Cranmer et al. (1959) have shown that inhibition of spinal reflexes brought about by stimu-lation of the bulbar reticular formation can likewise be induced by adrenaline, which observation may therefore serve to explain the results of earlier workers. The "anaesthetic" effect of adrenaline administered through the carotid artery or into the cerebrospinal fluid has long been known, and Feldberg (1958) has argued that the result points to a neuronal inhibition as the cause. The fact, however, that Curtis et al. (1957) found no electrical effects which could be interpreted as due to synaptic action suggest that the results which have been described may be due to "depressor" effects or are even secondary to vascular changes.

5-Hydroxytryptamine

The statements made above respecting sympathin are to a considerable extent repeatable for 5-hydroxytryptamine (5HT). Its distribution in the brain is similar to that of sympathin, being highest in the hypothalamus and area postrema, but as much may be extracted also from the mesencephalic grey matter (Amin et al., 1954). It can be shown to be released from the frog's spinal cord (Angelucci, 1956) and the amount is increased by reflex excitation. Intraventricular administration of the substance again leads to a lethargic or stuporous reaction of the animal which, as in the case of nor-adrenaline above, may well be due to neuronal depression. Evidence for an inhibitory synaptic action of 5HT is, however, completely lacking.

Substance P

The third substance which should briefly be mentioned here is the poly-peptide substance P. Its occurrence and distribution in the brain have been studied by Kopera and Lazarini (1953) and by Amin *et al.* (1954). In general its distribution resembles that of 5HT, with the addition that significant amounts are to be found in the first neuron of the posterior columns of the spinal cord.

The effect of intraventricular administration of substance P is not striking. Changes in the rate and depth of respiration have been reported, as well as slight behavioural changes described as "a general inhibition of spontaneity" (von Euler and Pernow, 1956). Zetler (1956) has reported also that substance P caused sedation in mice, and that it antagonized the "central stimulating effects" of strychnine and picrotoxin. His conclusion was that substance P could play a physiological role as a transmitter substance of inhibitory neurons, but the evidence is slight and indirect.

To summarize: the distributions in the central nervous system of the three substances here considered is very similar, as is also their action upon appli-cation to the brain. The distribution pattern itself would tend perhaps to cast doubt upon the likelihood of their partaking in synaptic events, for many areas of the brain appear to be completely lacking in them while the activity of inhibitory neurons is most probably a generalized one. For none of these compounds, however, have studies been made to elucidate their effects upon the electrical responses of single neurons when they are introduced into the extracellular space, and until that is done no definitive answers can be given. At the moment I should tentatively assign to them all actions as "depressors" rather than as transmitters. The fact that sympathin certainly, and the other two possibly, can function as transmitters of excitation under certain circum-stances of course does not rule out their possible role as inhibitors at other sites.

γ-Aminobutyrylcholine

The existence of this compound in the brain was demonstrated by Kuriaki *et al.* (1958). It has been reported to have actions antagonistic to those of acetylcholine in a number of situations—on the isolated mammalian intestine (Kuriaki *et al.*, 1958); on the isolated sea urchin oesophagus (Florey and McLennan, 1959); and at the mammalian neuromuscular junction (Asano *et al.*, 1960). It has also been reported that γ-aminobutyrylcholine acted to reduce evoked potentials in the cerebral cortex (Takahashi *et al.*, 1958); however, this effect could not be confirmed by Honour and McLennan (1960), and Curtis and Watkins (1960) have found the compound without action on the neurons of the spinal cord. It seems unlikely therefore that it can have a role to play as an inhibitory transmitter.

Mention should also be made of extracts of brain which have been made by two other groups of workers (Pataky and Pfeifer, 1955; Pfeifer and Pataky, 1955; Lissák and Endröczi, 1956; Lissák *et al.*, 1957) and which have some similarities to and some differences from Factor I. Some of the properties described for these various extracts are summarized in Table 1.

It seems quite possible that both Pfeifer and Pataky, and Lissák and Endröczi are in fact dealing with extracts which contain Factor I. Two principal differences between Factor I and Lissák and Endröczi's material are: (a) that the latter is described as soluble in organic solvents, whereas Factor I is not; and (b) that relatively very large amounts of brain had to be used by Lissák and Endröczi for an active extract to be obtained. A small

TABLE 1. SOME PROPERTIES OF BRAIN EXTRACTS EXHIBITING INHIBITORY ACTIONS

	Factor I	Extract of Lissák and Endröczi	Extract of Pataky and Pfeifer
Solubility	Soluble in water, insoluble in organic solvents	Soluble in water, alcohol and chloroform	Soluble in water, insoluble in organic solvents
Stability	Stable to boiling, stable in the blood	"Some actions" lost by boiling, inactivated in the blood	Stable in boiling alkali, inactivated in acid
Acetylcholine contractions of isolated intestine	Ileum: inhibited at pH < 7	Ileum: inhibited at pH < 7	Ascending colon; inhibited
Transmission through superior cervical ganglion	No action	Inhibited	—
Neuromuscular transmission	No action	Inhibited	—
Strychnine convulsions	Prevented	Prevented	—
Monosynaptic spinal reflexes	Inhibited	Inhibited	—

amount of water contained in the organic solvents used by Lissák and Endröczi might have been sufficient to extract some Factor I from the brain. However, the fact that their extract caused block of transmission in the superior cervical ganglion and at neuromuscular junctions while Factor I does not, may reflect real differences in the composition of the active material.

Two other workers have described evidence for inhibitory agents produced by the brain, i.e. Kornmüller (1958), and Wasserman (1954). The relationship, if any, between these and the materials discussed above cannot at present be determined.

Thus far mention has been made only of possible mediators at inhibitory synapses in the vertebrate central nervous system. Some aspects of peripheral inhibition, largely in invertebrate animals, will be given in the pages which follow.

HEART

The vertebrate heart provided the object for the classical experiments in the field of synaptic transmission, i.e. the studies of Loewi. As is universally known, he demonstrated the liberation of a substance into the perfusion fluid in response to stimulation of the vagus, which upon application to a second heart mimicked the effect of vagal stimulation. The substance was later identified as acetylcholine. It is worthwhile to remember that the earliest demonstration of chemical transmission was an inhibitory process, and further that the mediator there involved has excitatory functions at other synapses. The obvious conclusion is that the inhibitory materials which were discussed above may also be excitatory under certain circumstances, and indeed such was indicated for Factor I by Florey (1956) and by Florey and McLennan (1955b). The excitatory actions of Factor I could not be separated chemically from the inhibitory ones.

The membrane potential changes in the fibres of the sinus venosus of the frog heart are characteristic of those found in spontaneously excitable structures. Thus during diastole a slow depolarization (the pacemaker potential) develops, at the peak of whose amplitude (13–15 mV) an action potential is initiated. If the vagi are stimulated during the phase which follows the action potential the repolarization process is speeded, and continued until the membrane potential is more negative than the point reached in previous cycles. The next beat is delayed because the slope of the pacemaker potential is reduced (Hutter and Trautwein, 1956). Stronger vagal stimulation gives rise to an hyperpolarization averaging 10 mV and the heart is stopped. On cessation of stimulation the pacemaker potential slowly builds up again.

The events in the fibres of the sinus then are analagous to those described above as occurring at motor neurons. The inhibitory action of the vagus is abolished by atropine, as is the effect of applied acetylcholine, and there can be little doubt that in this instance acetylcholine is acting as the mediator of the inhibitory synaptic action.

The hearts of Crustacea are likewise inhibited by peripheral nerve stimulation although in this case the effects are upon the neurons of a heart ganglion. Stimulation of the inhibitory fibres results in a diastolic arrest of the heart during which an occasional normal beat may occur. The effect is duplicated in every way by the application to the heart (either in a perfusion fluid or added to a bath) of Factor I solutions (Florey, 1954), extracts of crustacean peripheral nerve prepared in the same way as Factor I extracts (Florey, 1956), or GABA (Florey, 1957). Furthermore the actions both of applied materials and of inhibitory nerve stimulation are prevented by picrotoxin, which there is reason to believe acts in these animals in much the same way as do low concentrations of strychnine in the vertebrates (Florey, 1951). The suggestion is strong then that the active material of Factor I (and the material in the crustacean nerve extracts) acts as an inhibitor of synaptic processes in the heart ganglion. The question of its possible identity with GABA will be further discussed below.

CRUSTACEAN STRETCH RECEPTORS

The thoracic and abdominal stretch receptor organs of crayfish, the detailed anatomy of which has been described by Florey and Florey (1955), have been extensively used as assay preparations in the work on Factor I, but have also been important in the study of the inhibitory process itself. The sensory neurons of the stretch receptors receive a direct peripheral inhibitory innervation, and the effects of stimulation of this fibre can be recorded from the two neurons of each organ.

The electrical events associated with this inhibitory process have been studied by Kuffler and his colleagues. They have shown that the discharge of the neuron is preceded by slow depolarization of the cell soma (the generator potential) which must achieve a critical level for the spike discharge to occur (Eyzaguirre and Kuffler, 1955). Stimulation of the inhibitory fibre brings about a repolarization of the membrane such that the generator potential is abolished and the cell prevented from firing (Kuffler and Eyzaguirre, 1955). Alteration of the membrane potential demonstrates that the inhibitory potential can be reversed in polarity, as was described above for i.p.s.p.'s at motor neurons. An increased permeability to potassium ions, but apparently not to chloride, is involved (Edwards and Hagiwara, 1959).

The application of Factor I solutions to the stretch receptor neuron results in cessation of their discharge (Florey, 1954) and this finding led to the use of these organs as test and assay preparations in studies of Factor I. It was through the use of this method that GABA was originally suggested as the active constituent of Factor I (Bazemore et al., 1957) and it has in fact been shown that the effect of GABA closely mimics the action of stimulation of the inhibitory axon (Kuffler and Edwards, 1958). The application of GABA results in an hyperpolarization of the cell, prevents the production of the sensory discharge, and, as is shown in Fig. 6, reduces the size of an evoked inhibitory potential. The significance of this last observation has been considered above in relation to the i.p.s.p. The suggestion that GABA is the transmitter substance released on stimulation of these inhibitory axons is thus very strong, yet as will be indicated later there is good reason for believing

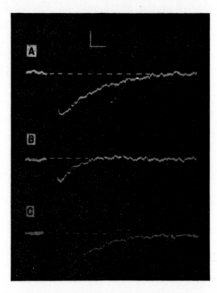

Fɪɢ. 6. Effect of γ-aminobutyric acid on the inhibitory potential evoked in a crayfish stretch receptor neurone—A before, B after 5 × 10⁻⁵ mole/l GABA, c after recovery. Calibration, 10 msec and 100 μV. Note that the amplitude and half-time of decay of the potential are reduced in the presence of GABA. (Kuffler and Edwards, 1958.) (Courtesy Dr. S. W. Kuffler and the *Journal of Neurophysiology*.)

that such is not in fact the case. It is worth noting that other related compounds have effects similar to those which have been described for GABA. These include guanidinoacetic acid, β-guanidinopropionic acid, β-alanine, δ-aminovaleric acid, β-guanidinobutyric acid and agmatine (γ-guanidinobutylamine), although all but the first two are very much less potent than is GABA (Edwards and Kuffler, 1959). As in the case of the crayfish heart, picrotoxin prevents the actions of Factor I, GABA and inhibitory nerve stimulation.

CRUSTACEAN NEUROMUSCULAR TRANSMISSION

The electrical events associated with stimulation of a peripheral axon whose action is to inhibit the contraction of a crustacean muscle have been studied by a number of workers. Some of the inhibitory processes show similarities to those discussed above for other structures, while others apparently differ.

Marmont and Wiersma (1938) and Kuffler and Katz (1946) demonstrated that inhibition of contraction could be accompanied by a reduction in amplitude of the excitatory junctional potentials evoked by motor nerve stimulation ("supplemented", or α-inhibition); or that there could be inhibition without

TABLE 2. COMPARISON OF THE EFFECTS OF ACETYLCHOLINE WITH THOSE OF INHIBITORY EXTRACTS

	Factor I	Substance I	Extract of Lissák and Endröczi	Extract of Pataky and Pfeifer
yfish stretch eptor	ACh stimulation blocked (Florey, 1954)	As Factor I		
yfish intestine	ACh stimulation blocked (Florey, 1954)	As Factor I		
urchin oesophagus	ACh stimulation blocked (Florey and McLennan, 1959)			
id rectum	Stimulating effect blocked by ACh (Florey, 1956)			
halopod hearts	Inhibitory effect of ACh mimicked (Florey, 1956)	As Factor I		
g heart	Inhibitory effect of ACh mimicked (Romanowski et al., 1957)			Prevents inhibitory effect of ACh (Pfeifer and Pataky, 1955)
mmalian intestine	ACh stimulation blocked (Florey and McLennan, 1959)		ACh stimulation blocked (Lissák and Endröczi, 1956)	ACh stimulation blocked (Pfeifer and Pataky, 1955)
od pressure	No action (Florey and McLennan, 1955a)			Prevents depressor effect of ACh (Pfeifer and Pataky, 1955)
nsmission in sympathetic ganglia	No action in superior cervical ganglion. Others blocked (Florey and McLennan, 1955a)		Blocked in superior cervical ganglion (Lissák and Endröczi, 1956)	
mmalian neuromuscular transmision	No action (Florey and McLennan, 1955a)		Blocked (Lissák and Endröczi, 1956)	
poglossal nucleus	Stimulating effect of ACh mimicked (Florey and McLennan, 1955b)			

a change in the excitatory potentials ("simple", or β-inhibition). The two processes have been studied further by Fatt and Katz (1953) and by Hoyle and Wiersma (1958).

Fatt and Katz observed little or no effect upon the level of polarization of the muscle membrane produced by inhibitory nerve stimulation alone; however, if the membrane potential were altered by passage of current, inhibitory potentials appeared which apparently had equilibrium potentials near -75 mV. They observed also that, whether or not an inhibitory potential was produced, there was a change in permeability of the membrane leading to a more rapid decay of the excitatory junctional potentials. This resulted in a diminished total depolarization during inhibitory action. Boistel and Fatt (1958) concluded that an increased permeability to chloride ions occurred in crayfish muscle during inhibitory action.

Hoyle and Wiersma reported that stimulation of inhibitory fibres in crayfish, crabs and lobsters could lead to either depolarization or hyperpolarization of the cell (the equilibrium potential for the process in crayfish was about -58 mV) but that more often β-inhibition was observed.

Factor I solutions perfused through a crayfish claw prevent muscular contraction on stimulation of the motor nerve (Florey, 1954). The effect has been claimed to be duplicated by GABA (McLennan, 1957; Robbins, 1959) and suitable administration of picrotoxin could prevent the GABA effect (van der Kloot and Robbins, 1959). Boistel and Fatt (1958) and van der Kloot and Robbins (1959) both concluded that GABA mimicked the action of inhibitory nerve stimulation, when the stimulation gave rise to α-inhibition. On the other hand Hoyle and Wiersma (1958) reported that the substance failed to produce an increase in membrane potential in cases where inhibitory nerve stimulation had this effect, and in no case caused mechanical inhibition.

On the basis of the evidence presented in the foregoing sections there was reason to believe that GABA was in fact the transmitter substance involved in several inhibitory processes in Crustacea; and, as mentioned above, their similarity of action on the crayfish stretch receptor neuron led to the suggestion that GABA and Factor I were identical. It is therefore the more surprising that Florey and Biederman (1960) have shown that inhibitory axons in the legs of crabs and lobsters do not contain any detectable GABA, and the same is apparently true also for the cardio-inhibitory fibres of crayfish (Florey, 1960). Florey has suggested the term Substance I for the active crustacean material to differentiate it from the mammalian Factor I. The actions of Substance I, the transmitter released on activation of peripheral inhibitory axons in Crustacea are thus duplicated by GABA, but the two materials are not chemically identical. The chemical nature of Substance I, like that of Factor I remains unknown.

Thus the preparations which appear most likely to contain an inhibitory transmitter, namely Factor I extracts for the mammalian central nervous system and Substance I for crustacean inhibitory neurons, are uncharacterized as yet. It seems to me possible, however, that some chemical relationship to acetylcholine may be a feature of the active ingredient of either or both materials, for it is striking in how many situations the actions of these extracts either antagonize or mimic the effects of applied acetylcholine. This point is brought out by the data of Table 2, in which the interactions of Factor I and of the extracts studied by Pfeifer and Pataky and by Lissák and Endröczi, with acetylcholine are set forth.

The implication that the "I's" and acetylcholine are competing for the same receptor sites in these various tissues, sometimes with parallel and sometimes with antagonistic effects, is very strong, and the corollary is that some structural relationship between them may exist. As mentioned earlier the distinction between Factor I and Substance I is one of definition only at present and it may be that the active component of each is identical. The extracts prepared by Lissák and Endröczi and by Pfeifer and Pataky have been less studied but it is evident that they too show anti-acetylcholine properties.

In conclusion, it is obvious that the search for inhibitory transmitter substances is far from over. The electrical events associated with activation of inhibitory synapses have now been well described for a number of organs, both in vertebrates and in invertebrates, and show considerable similarities in the situations studied. The characteristic change is a transient increase in the polarization of the cell membrane, due to an increased membrane permeability to potassium and/or to chloride ions. These effects are mimicked by Factor I at mammalian motor neurons, by Substance I for peripheral inhibition in Crustacea and by acetylcholine for the vertebrate heart. There is some evidence for believing that the "I" extracts may owe their activity to a compound related structurally to acetylcholine. It is reasonable to assume that the two nervous tissue extracts, which may or may not owe their activity to the same chemical substance, in fact contain a transmitter substance active at inhibitory synapses.

REFERENCES

AMIN, A. H., CRAWFORD, T. B. B. and GADDUM, J. H. (1954) The distribution of Substance P and 5-hydroxytryptamine in the central nervous system of the dog. *J. Physiol. (London)* **126** : 596–618.

ANGELUCCI, L. (1956) Experiments with perfused frog's spinal cord. *Brit. J. Pharmacol.* **11** : 161–170.

ASANO, M., NORO, T. and KURIAKI, K. (1960) Inhibitory actions of γ-aminobutyrylcholine. *Nature* **185** : 848–849.

BAZEMORE, A. W., ELLIOTT, K. A. C. and FLOREY, E. (1957) Isolation of Factor I. *J. Neurochem.* **1** : 334–339.

BOISTEL, J. and FATT, P. (1958) Membrane permeability change during inhibitory transmitter action in crustacean muscle. *J. Physiol. (London)* **144** : 176–191.

COOMBS, J. S., ECCLES, J. C. and FATT, P. (1955a). The specific ionic conductances and the ionic movements across the motoneuronal membrane that produce the inhibitory post-synaptic potential. *J. Physiol. (London)* **130** : 326–373.

COOMBS, J. S., ECCLES, J. C. and FATT, P. (1955b). Excitatory synaptic action in motoneurones. *J. Physiol. (London)* **130** : 374–395.

COOMBS, J. S., ECCLES, J. C. and FATT, P. (1955c). The inhibitory suppression of reflex discharges from motoneurones. *J. Physiol. (London)* **130** : 396–413.

CRANMER, J. I., BRANN, A. W. and BACH, L. M. N. (1959) An adrenergic basis for bulbar inhibition. *Am. J. Physiol.* **197** : 835–838.

CURTIS, D. R. (1959) Pharmacological investigations upon inhibition of spinal motoneurones. *J. Physiol. (London)* **145** : 175–192.

CURTIS, D. R., ECCLES, J. C. and ECCLES, R. M. (1957) Pharmacological studies on spinal reflexes. *J. Physiol. (London)* **136** : 420–434.

CURTIS, D. R., PHILLIS, J. W. and WATKINS, J. C. (1959). The depression of spinal neurones by γ-amino-n-butyric acid and β-alanine. *J. Physiol. (London)* **146** : 185–203.

CURTIS, D. R. and WATKINS, J. C. (1960). The excitation and depression of spinal neurones by structurally related amino acids. *J. Neurochem.* **6** : 117–141.

ECCLES, J. C. (1961) Inhibitory pathways to motoneurons. This volume, p. 47.

EDWARDS, C. and HAGIWARA, S. (1959) Potassium ions and the inhibitory process in the crayfish stretch receptor. *J. Gen. Physiol.* **43** : 315–321.

EDWARDS, C. and KUFFLER, S. W. (1959) The blocking effect of γ-aminobutyric acid (GABA) and the action of related compounds on single nerve cells. *J. Neurochem.* **4** : 19–30.

EYZAGUIRRE, C. and KUFFLER, S. W. (1955) Processes of excitation in dendrites and in the soma of single isolated sensory nerve cells of the lobster and crayfish. *J. Gen. Physiol.* **39** : 87–119.

FATT, P. and KATZ, B. (1953) The effect of inhibitory nerve impulses on a crustacean muscle fibre. *J. Physiol. London* **121** : 374–389.

FELDBERG, W. (1958) Pattern of excitation and inhibition produced by injection of substances into the cerebral ventricle of the conscious cat. *Acta Physiol. et Pharmacol. Neerl.* **7** : 425–440.

FLOREY, E. (1951) Vorkommen und Funktion sensibler Erregungssubstanzen und die abbauenden Fermente im Tierreich. *Z. vergleich. Physiol.* **33** : 327–377.

FLOREY, E. (1953) Über einen nervösen Hemmungsfaktor in Gehirn und Rückenmark. *Naturwissenschaften* **40** : 295–296.

FLOREY, E. (1954) An excitatory and an inhibitory factor of mammalian central nervous system, and their action on a single sensory neuron. *Arch. intern. Physiol.* **62** : 33–53.

FLOREY, E. (1956) The action of Factor I on certain invertebrate organs. *Can. J. Biochem. and Physiol.* **34** : 669–681.

FLOREY, E. (1957) Further evidence for the transmitter function of Factor I. *Naturwissenschaften* **44** : 424–425.

FLOREY, E. (1960) Physiological evidence for naturally occurring inhibitory substances. *Proceedings of the Conference on Inhibition in the Nervous System and γ-Aminobutyric Acid.* pp. 72–84. Pergamon Press, Oxford.

FLOREY, E. and BIEDERMAN, M. A. (1960). Studies on the distribution of Factor I and acetylcholine in crustacean peripheral nerve. *J. Gen. Physiol.* **43** : 509–522.

FLOREY, E. and FLOREY, E. (1955) Microanatomy of the abdominal stretch receptors of the crayfish (*Astacus fluviatilis* L.) *J. Gen. Physiol.* **39** : 69–85.

FLOREY, E. and FLOREY, E. (1958) Studies on the distribution of Factor I in mammalian brain. *J. Physiol. (London)* **144** : 220–228.

FLOREY, E. and MCLENNAN, H. (1955a) The release of an inhibitory substance from mammalian brain, and its effect on peripheral synaptic transmission. *J. Physiol. (London)* **129** : 384–392.

FLOREY, E. and MCLENNAN, H. (1955b) Effects of an inhibitory factor (Factor I) from brain on central synaptic transmission. *J. Physiol. (London)* **130** : 446–455.

FLOREY, E. and MCLENNAN, H. (1959) The effects of Factor I and of gamma-aminobutyric acid on smooth muscle preparations. *J. Physiol. (London)* **145** : 66–76.

FRANK, K. and FUORTES, M. G. F. (1959) Quoted in Paton, W. D. M. Mechanisms of transmission in the central nervous system. *Anaesthesia* 14 : 3–27.

GRUNDFEST, H. (1958) An electrophysiological basis for neuropharmacology. *Federation Proc.* 17 : 1006–1018.

HONOUR, A. J. and MCLENNAN, H. (1960) The effects of γ-aminobutyric acid and other compounds on structures of the mammalian nervous system which are inhibited by Factor I. *J. Physiol. (London)* 150 : 306–318.

HOYLE, G. and WIERSMA, C. A. G. (1958) Inhibition at neuromuscular junctions in crustacea. *J. Physiol. (London)* 143 : 426–440.

HUTTER, O. F. and TRAUTWEIN, W. (1956) Vagal and sympathetic effects on the pacemaker fibres in the sinus venosus of the heart. *J. Gen. Physiol.* 39 : 715–733.

KOPERA, H. and LAZARINI, W. (1953) Zur Frage der zentralen Übertragung afferenter Impulse—IV. Die Verteilung der Substanz P in Zentralnervensystem. *Arch. Exptl. Path. Pharmakol.* 219 : 214–222.

KORNMÜLLER, A. E. (1958) Ein inhibitorisch wirkender Hirn-Extrakt. *Arzneimittel-Forsch.* 8 : 675–676.

KUFFLER, S. W. and EDWARDS, C. (1958) Mechanism of gamma aminobutyric acid (GABA) action and its relation to synaptic inhibition. *J. Neurophysiol.* 21 : 589–610.

KUFFLER, S. W. and EYZAGUIRRE, C. (1955) Synaptic inhibition in an isolated nerve cell. *J. Gen. Physiol.* 39 : 155–184.

KUFFLER, S. W. and KATZ, B. (1946) Inhibition at the nerve-muscle junction in crustacea. *J. Neurophysiol.* 9 : 337–346.

KURIAKI, K., YAKUSHIJI, T., NORO, T., SHIMIZU, T. and SAJI, SH. (1958) Gamma-amino-butyrylcholine. *Nature* 181 : 1336–1337.

LISSÁK, K. and ENDRÖCZI, E. (1956) Presence in nerve tissue of substances inhibiting nervous function and blocking the action of chemical mediators. *Acta Physiol. Acad. Sci. Hung.* 9 : 111–121.

LISSÁK, K., ENDRÖCZI, E. and FÁBIÁN, I. (1957) Further studies on the effect of the humoral inhibitory factor. *Acta Physiol. Acad. Sci. Hung.* 11 : 376–383.

MARMONT, G. and WIERSMA, C. A. G. (1938) On the mechanism of inhibition and excitation of crayfish muscle. *J. Physiol. (London)* 93 : 173–193.

MCLENNAN, H. (1957) A comparison of some physiological properties of an inhibitory factor from brain (Factor I) and of γ-aminobutyric acid and related compounds. *J. Physiol. (London)* 139 : 79–86.

MCLENNAN, H. (1958) Absence of γ-aminobutyric acid from brain extracts containing Factor I. *Nature* 181 : 1807.

MCLENNAN, H. (1960) The fractionation and purification of Factor I. *J. Physiol. (London)* 151 : 31–39.

PATAKY, I. and PFEIFER, A. K. (1955) Physiological significance of the acetylcholine blocking agent in the central nervous system. *Acta Physiol. Acad. Sci. Hung.* 8 : 221–229.

PFEIFER, A. K. and PATAKY, I. (1955) Acetylcholine blocking agent in the central nervous system. *Acta Physiol. Acad. Sci. Hung.* 8 : 209–219.

ROBBINS, J. (1959) The excitation and inhibition of crustacean muscle by amino acids. *J. Physiol. (London)* 148 : 39–50.

ROMANOWSKI, W., LENARTOWICZ, P. and JANCZARSKI, I. (1957) Examination of the effect on the heart activity of a brain extract obtained by the Florey method. *Bull. acad. polon. sci.* 5 : 271–276.

TAKAHASHI, H., NAGASHIMA, A. and KOSHINO, C. (1958). Effect of γ-aminobutyrylcholine upon the electrical activity of the cerebral cortex. *Nature* 182 : 1443–1444.

VAN DER KLOOT, W. G. and ROBBINS, J. (1959) The effects of γ-aminobutyric acid and picrotoxin on the junctional potential and the contraction of crayfish muscle. *Experentia* 15 : 35.

VOGT, M. (1954) The concentration of sympathin in different parts of the central nervous system under normal conditions and after administration of drugs. *J. Physiol. (London)* 123 : 451–481.

VON EULER, U. S. and PERNOW, B. (1956) Neurotropic effects of Substance P. *Acta Physiol. Scand.* 36 : 265–275.

WASSERMAN, I. (1954) Über einen Hemmungsfaktor in der Zerebrospinalflüssigkeit. *Przeglad Lekarski* No. 9.

ZETLER, G. (1956) Substanz P, ein Polypeptid aus Darm und Gehirn mit depressiven, hyperalgetischen und Morphin-antagonischen Wirkungen auf das Zentralnervensystem. *Arch. exp. Pathol. Pharmakol.* **228** : 513–538.

FURTHER OBSERVATIONS CONCERNING THE INHIBITORY SUBSTANCE EXTRACTED FROM BRAIN

K. LISSÁK, E. ENDRÖCZI AND E. VINCZE

Physiological Institute, University of Pécs, Hungary

ONE of the characteristics of neurophysiological research work in the past decade has been the great interest in inhibitory processes, functional as well as morphological, in which the recognition of direct inhibiting synaptic mechanisms, i.e. that of an inhibitory transmitter substance of such character, constitutes the central question. Without going into the exceedingly increased number of publications on the subject, we wish to refer to some of the characteristic data in the literature pertinent to the chemical mediator assumed to play a role in the inhibitory process.

It was more than a decade ago that we first examined in our laboratory the question whether or not the brain tissue contained a substance, or substances, which were able to inhibit the effect of stimulating chemical mediators on peripheral receptors—thus on isolated cat's ileum and uterus, on frog's heart—and further, if applied locally, it could inhibit the excitability of the spinal cord and decrease the electrical excitability of the motor cortex (Lissák and Endröczi, 1949, 1955, 1956a, b, 1957).

Almost simultaneously with these investigations, but independently of them, observations were published by Florey (1953, 1956), Florey and McLennan (1956), Bazemore et al. (1956) according to whom the brain tissue contained an I (inhibitor) factor which could produce inhibition on receptors of Crustacea as well as on those of the central nervous system of mammals. Starting with considerations of a different kind, Hayashi and Nagai (1956) suggested that the inhibitory factor might be identical with γ-amino-β-hydroxybutyric acid, considerable quantities of which were present in the brain tissue. Bazemore et al. (1956) ascribed the inhibitory effect of the brain extract studied by them to the action of γ-aminobutyric acid alone. However, McLennan (1957, 1958) and, on the basis of our own observations made in the past years, we also have stated that GABA alone cannot be responsible for the biological effects. Similarly, γ-amino-β-hydroxybutyric acid may not be regarded as a factor which would be able to simulate the effect of the natural inhibitory extract from the brain (Lissák et al., 1959).

369

In the present lecture I wish to present a picture of our results obtained last year with an extract from brain tissue and γ-aminobutyric acid, and with the biological effects of γ-amino-β-hydroxybutyric acid. The extract was prepared partly from dog's brain and partly from ox brain with the method used by us in earlier experiments. One volume of 96% ethanol having been added to it, the freshly removed tissue was homogenized and then, after the addition of one more volume of ethanol and one volume of colloidal aluminium hydroxide, centrifuged. The transparent supernatant, slightly yellow in colour, was concentrated *in vacuo* to one-tenth of its original volume, clarified with active carbon, concentrated, then filtered, and the filtrate evaporated *in vacuo*. The residue was redissolved in from 10 to 50 ml aqueous ethanol (1 : 1 v/v) and after the repeated addition of active carbon filtered and again evaporated *in vacuo*. Depending on the initial amount of the substance, the residue was dissolved in from 1 to 10 ml 50% ethanol, and then run on Whatman No. 4 paper partly with a mixture of phenol–water and partly with one of butanol–glacial acetic acid–water (4 : 1 : 1 by volume). In the case of descending chromatography, different amounts of GABA and GABOB were run for testing and demonstrated with the ninhydrin reaction. After the ninhydrin reaction, and then dissolution in ethanol: 0·1 N NaOH (4 : 1 v/v), estimation of the GABA content in the brain tissue was done photometrically with standard GABA. It should be mentioned here that a series of qualitative chemical reactions were carried out on the paper chromatograms of the brain tissue. Of these the formation of picrate obtained in alkaline milieu deserves to be mentioned. As can be seen in Fig. 1, the picrate-positive area in the system butanol–acetic acid–water shows a position similar to that of GABA. I wish to mention here that in a different chromatographic system, thus in one of phenol–water too, the ninhydrin positive GABA was situated similarly to the picrate positive substances in the brain tissue. The importance to be ascribed to this observation cannot be decided as yet. However, it was the same area that, in the course of biological testing, proved active with regard to inhibition.

I shall now pass on to the description of results suggesting that the brain extract contains an inhibitory factor, but GABA or GABOB can only partly be responsible for the inhibitory effect.

(a) According to observations on isolated cat ileum, the extract eluated from the paper chromatogram is able to inhibit acetylcholine contraction at or below pH 7, while, at the same time, in the case of GABA or GABOB even several hundred micrograms are ineffective. The GABA content in the brain extract that proved effective hardly exceeded 10–15 μg, which shows that GABA or its derivative cannot be responsible for the inhibition.

(b) When examining on the motor cortex of the cat the electrical threshold stimulus for the motor reaction of a foreleg, we found that while local application of an amount of brain extract obtained from one-third of a dog's

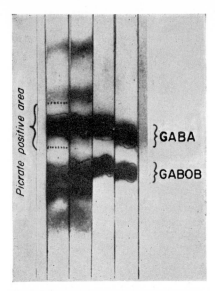

FIG. 1. Paper chromatogram of the brain extract. Left stripes indicate the GABA and picrate positive area, right ones the position of standard GABA and GABOB.

brain resulted in marked decrease of excitability, the same effect could not be obtained with GABA or GABOB.

(c) By means of recording the electrical activity of the cat's cortex, we examined the effects of local and systemic administration of the brain extract, and those of GABA and GABOB on strychnine and metrazol convulsions. The recordings were made under barbiturate (Evipan-Na) or ether anaesthesia, or in succinylcholine paralysis with artificial respiration in the waking state. Our observations may be summarized as follows.

(1) Under barbiturate anaesthesia not even high concentrations of the brain extract, GABA or GABOB, administered either locally or intravenously, resulted in a noteworthy effect on the electrical activity of the somatomotor cortex, recorded with bipolar "ball-electrodes" of silver. Under superficial ether anaesthesia, or in succinylcholine paralysis in the waking state, local as well as intravenous administration of the extract from one-third to a half of a dog's brain tissue, resulted in decreased frequency and increased amplitude, which, however, was of a transitory nature. Even larger doses of GABA or GABOB failed to produce an effect worth mentioning. During metrazol convulsion produced by the intravenous administration of Tetracor, convulsive activity was considerably decreased, or in the case of smaller doses of Metrazol, inhibited by the extract from a half to one dog's brain given a few seconds before Tetracor.

On the basis of Figs. 2 and 3 it can be seen that during or immediately

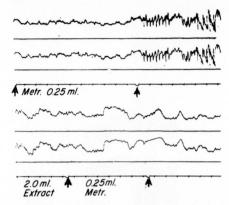

FIG. 2. Metrazol convulsion under the influence of previously administered brain extract. (*Upper channels*)—Convulsive activity without brain extract. (*Lower channels*)—Blocking of the convulsive activity after the intravenous administration of brain extract (at arrow).

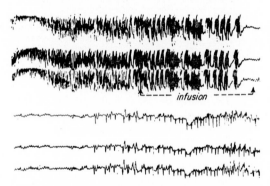

FIG. 3. The blocking effect of the brain extract on convulsions induced by metrazol in the cat. Bipolar leads from the somatomotor cortex. The arrows indicate the administration of brain extract (intravenous).

before convulsive activity, the intravenous administration of the extract results in a transitory inhibitory effect. An attempt to produce inhibition of a similar nature by the administration of 50–200 mg/kg GABA or GABOB failed. Local application proved to be less effective. However, when it was used the activity due to metrazol convulsion was often replaced by a regular synchronized activity of a frequency of from 2 to 3/sec, which, without the use of the extract, could only be observed very rarely and for a very short time. Even local application of GABA or GABOB failed to influence metrazol activity.

In the following part of our experiment we examined the effects of GABA, GABOB and the brain extract by recording the superficial negative convulsive activity produced by strychnine. The monopolar leads were recorded in succinylcholine paralysis, in the waking state. The amplitude of the negative discharges produced by the local application of a 1·0% strychnine solution was decreased by locally administered GABA or GABOB of 1 mg/ml concentration, which confirmed earlier observations on the subject by Purpura *et al.* (1958). A similar result was obtained when the brain extract was applied. Intravenously administered GABA or GABOB did not influence the depolarizing dendritic potentials, while the intravenous administration of the brain extract not only prevented the depolarizing activity, but also had a transitory hyperpolarizing effect. Similar phenomena were also reported by Iwama and Jasper (1957) further by Purpura and his co-workers (1958), although it was only in the case of a blood–brain barrier destroyed by methanol–chloroform and after the administration of large quantities of GABA that those authors observed a similar effect. From the data in Fig. 4

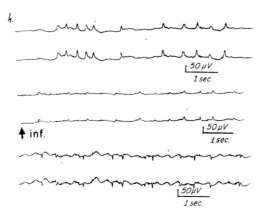

FIG. 4. Electrical activity produced by topical application of strychnine to the cat's brain. Monopolar recording: different silver-ball electrode on the motor cortex, indifferent electrode on the frontal bone. At arrow surface negative activity was reversed by the intravenous administration of the brain extract.

it may be seen that the brain extract can turn the initial depolarizing activity into hyperpolarization. The development of the mechanism is unknown; however, it is highly probable that in this experiment abolition of the inhibitory effect of strychnine on axo-dendritic hyperpolarization plays an important role.

The action of the brain extract and that of GABA on subcortical structures were studied on the conditional reflex activity of dogs with chronically implanted microcannulas. The cannula was implanted, with the methods we usually employ, after the establishment of a conditioned alimentary motor reflex. In each of the four experimental animals the cannula was localized in

374 K. LISSÁK, E. ENDRÖCZI AND E. VINCZE

the reticular formation and the amount of fluid introduced varied between 0·01 and 0·05 ml. It was observed that the brain extract strengthened the labile processes of differentiation, and shortened the duration of latency. GABA or GABOB, even in concentrations of 1–10 mg/0·1 ml, failed to produce changes in the conditional reflex processes.

In summary it may be stated that the brain tissue contains a substance whose physicochemical properties, as revealed by paper chromatography, resemble those of GABA. However, the two substances differ in their effects. On the one hand, the natural inhibitory substance is more pronounced in its effects; on the other, it will act on receptors on which even high concentrations of GABA are ineffective. The basis of this disparity may be an essential difference in structure. Or the natural inhibitory substance might represent a more complex compound of GABA, which differs in permeability or has a more pronounced biologic action.

In order to be able to form a final view of the mediation of inhibition it would be necessary to have a more definite knowledge of the essential properties of the inhibitory factor and the morphologic substrate through which it acts.

REFERENCES

BAZEMORE, A., ELLIOTT, K. A. C. and FLOREY, E. (1956) Factor I and γ-aminobutyric acid. *Nature* **178** : 1052–1053.
FLOREY, E. (1953) Über einen nervösen Hemmungsfaktor in Gehirn und Rückenmark. *Naturwissenschaften* **40** : 295–296.
FLOREY, E. (1956) The action of Factor I on certain invertebrate organs. *Can. J. Biochem. and Physiol.* **34** : 669–681.
FLOREY, E. and MCLENNAN, H. (1956) Effects of an inhibitory factor (Factor I) from brain on central synaptic transmission. *J. Physiol.* (*London*) **130** : 446–455.
HAYASHI, F. and NAGAI, K. (1956) Action of γ-amino acids on the motor cortex of higher animals, especially γ-amino-β-oxybutyric acid as the real inhibitory principle in brain. *XX Int. Physiol. Cong.* p. 410.
IWAMA, K. and JASPER, H. (1957) The action of gamma aminobutyric acid upon corticol electrical activity in the cat. *J. Physiol.* (*London*) **138** : 365–380.
LISSÁK, K. and ENDRÖCZI, E. (1949) Adrenalin hatást gátló kivonat különbözö idegele-mekböl. *Kisérletes Orvostudomány* **1** : 3.
LISSÁK, K. and ENDRÖCZI, E. (1955) An inhibitory substance in neural tissue. *Naturwissenschaften* **42** : 630.
LISSÁK, K. and ENDRÖCZI, E. (1956a) Presence in nerve tissue of substances inhibiting nervous function and blocking the action of chemical mediators. *Acta Physiol. Acad. Sci. Hung.* **9** : 111–121.
LISSÁK, K. and ENDRÖCZI, E. (1956b) Neural inhibitory substance. *XX Congrès International de Physiologie, Bruxelles.*
LISSÁK, K. and ENDRÖCZI, E. (1957) Further studies on the effect of the humoral inhibitory factor. *Acta Physiol. Acad. Sci. Hung.* **11** : 377–383.
LISSÁK, K., ENDRÖCZI, E. and VINCZE, E. (1959) Weitere Untersuchungen über den Hemmungsfaktor des Hirngewebes. *Ann. Meeting of the Hung. Physiol. Soc., Szeged.*
MCLENNAN, H. (1957) A comparison of some physiological properties on an inhibitory factor from brain (Factor I) and of γ-amino-butyric acid and related compounds. *J. Physiol.* (*London*) **139** : 79–86.

MCLENNAN, H. (1958) Absence of γ-aminobutyric acid from brain extracts containing Factor I. *Nature* **181** : 1807.

PURPURA, D. P., GIRADO, M., SMITH, T. G. and GOMEZ, J. A. (1958) Effects of systemically administered γ-amino and guanidino acids on spontaneous and evoked cortical activity in regions of blood-brain barrier destruction. *Electroencephalog. and Clin. Neurophysiol.* **10** : 677–685.

EXTRACTION OF AN EXCITATORY SUBSTANCE FROM DOG'S BRAIN

TAKASHI HAYASHI,* KAZUO NAGAI† AND KEISABURO MIYATA†

* Department of Physiology, School of Medicine, Keio University, Tokyo, and
† Department of Physiology, School of Dental Surgery, Nihon University, Tokyo

WHEN an electrical stimulation was applied to the exposed surface of the motor cortex, or an electric-shock current applied through the skull of the dogs, generalized seizures appeared. These continued 60–180 sec after cessation of the stimulation. During these convulsions, an excitatory substance was released from the motor cells which rapidly diffused into the cerebrospinal fluid and which could be collected. For this purpose, a small metal syringe was inserted into a lateral ventricle, the electric current applied through the skull and 2·0 ml of the c.s.f. was taken during the lapse of the seizure of the donor dog. The fluid taken was introduced into the c.s.f. of another dog. The experiment showed that it produced clonic convulsions with a latent period of 5–18 sec in the receiver dog. We constructed a special dog holder so that the procedure could be rapidly accomplished. There were, however, a few difficulties with these experiments (Hayashi, 1959). One, the time relation of the appearance of the exciting substance: the c.s.f. of the donor dogs did not contain the effective substance 3–4 min after the cessation of the seizure, in other words, the exciting factor was very unstable. Second, success of the experiments was not confirmed in every case and out of twelve experiments we could get the effective substance only in one or two cases. It was uncertain whether this came from the instability of the substance or other reasons.

Experiments were conducted in order to determine whether the reactive substance is destroyed by some enzyme contained in the cerebrospinal fluid or whether the substance released would re-combine and re-enter the brain.

DEPROTEINIZATION

If the cerebral spinal fluid was collected during the seizure into a syringe filled with 10% sublimate or with alcohol, the fluid, after centrifugation of the precipitated proteins, had no convulsive action if introduced into a receiver dog. Deproteinization of the cerebrospinal fluid by treatment in a water bath at 100°C for 5 min likewise resulted in inactivity. The effective substance could, however, be extracted in the following way: the small metal syringe was filled with 10 ml of absolute methyl alcohol so as to mix with 5 ml of the cerebrospinal fluid collected during the seizure. After centrifugation, the fluid was reduced by evaporation on a 50°C water bath to 48% of the original volume. This fluid produced a seizure when it was introduced into the ventricles of the receiver dog. The extracted fluid was dried to a yellow-brown mass and kept for 2 weeks at room temperature of 15°C. After this period the fluid was taken up to the original volume with water. Two millilitres were introduced into the receiver dog's ventricle. Violent seizures, especially clonic convulsions, were produced with a latent period of 5–10 sec and they continued for 160–180 sec. Thus we obtained a crude excitatory substance from central nervous system which is active at least in the motor system of dogs.

ANALYSIS OF THE CRUDE EXCITATORY SUBSTANCE

For the sake of convenience we named the effective component of the extract "excitine". This excitine was found to be rather unstable at temperatures above 40°C, that is its activity was reduced during the process of 30–60 sec of evaporation.

The methanol-extracted fluid lost 50% of its effectiveness during 2 weeks of storage at room temperature (15°C during the day and 3–7°C at night). When it was kept in a dry state, however, its effectiveness was not absolutely lost. If the extracted fluid was kept at a pH of 2–3 for 6–10 hr, its effectiveness was reduced by one-half. The active agent was highly unstable in an oxygen atmosphere. If one bubbled pure oxygen through the fluid it became quite ineffective within 60 sec. When the fluid was kept in open air the excitatory action was abolished during 1 or 2 weeks. On the other hand, when the fluid was kept in contact with nitrogen the activity was maintained for over 3 weeks.

Further analysis is now going on in our laboratory which makes us believe that it seems difficult but not hopeless to obtain purification and identification of the substance.

REFERENCE

HAYASHI, T. (1959) *Neurophysiology and Neurochemistry of Convulsion.* Dainihon-Tosho, Tokyo.

COMMENTS ON THE
EXCITINE–INHIBITINE HYPOTHESIS

TAKASHI HAYASHI

Department of Physiology, School of Medicine, Keio University, Tokyo

DURING and after the second world war, we began to study the mechanism of excitation of muscle and nerve from the standpoint of chemical physiology. The fundamental idea of the mechanism of excitation which we arrived at, was a statement expressed in the following equation:

$$\text{excitine-inhibitine} \underset{\leftarrow}{\rightarrow} \text{excitine} + \text{inhibitine} \qquad (1)$$
$$\text{(rest)} \qquad\qquad \text{(excitation)}$$

The idea was based on our experiments on the "salt contraction"—the long continued spontaneous twitches of an excised skeletal muscle bathed in isotonic sodium chloride solution (Hayashi, 1956).

The equation (1) means that the excitation of muscle is due to a sudden dissociation of a certain chemical agent at the site of the excitable tissue. The two components of this agent are called "excitine" and "inhibitine".

In the early phase of our study, we identified the excitine as carnosine (β-alanyl-L-histidine) and the inhibitine as carnitine (betaine of γ-amino-β hydroxybutyric acid). Since then we succeeded in synthesizing DL-carnitine as well as L-carnosine, and on repeating the early experiments once ascertained that these substances do not have exciting or inhibiting actions by themselves, but that they cause excitation or inhibition if they are mixed with each other at certain ratios (Hayashi, 1960). But now we have to revise it. Carnitine corresponds to excitine, carnosine to inhibitine. If the two combinations are mixed, their actions are neutralized and they have no affect on excised muscle.

The following experimental results were obtained:

(1) If DL-carnitine in Ringer's solution (0·066–0·147%) is dropped on to an excised sartorius muscle of toad a sequence of twitches result. If small amounts of glutamic acid, aspartic acid, taurine, cysteine or acetylcholine are added to the carnitine solution, concentrations of 0·0066–0·0147% of this compound are sufficient to induce muscle contractions. The substances which potentiate the action of DL-carnitine are normal constituents of ordinary vertebrate skeletal muscles. Their concentrations in this tissue are indicated in Table 1. It should be mentioned that they do not cause muscle contractions by themselves.

TABLE 1. EXISTENCE OF CERTAIN SUBSTANCES IN VERTEBRATE MUSCLE OR BRAIN (%)

Substance	Muscle	Brain	Authors
Carnitine	$0 \cdot 045 \sim 0 \cdot 017$		Guggenheim (1951)
Glutamic acid		$0 \cdot 13 \sim 18$	Folch-Pi and Le Baron (1957)
Aspartic acid		$0 \cdot 0297$	Folch-Pi and Le Baron (1957)
Taurine		$0 \cdot 024$	Folch-Pi and Le Baron (1957)
Cysteine		$0 \cdot 001$	Folch-Pi and Le Baron (1957)
Acetylcholine		$1 \cdot 25 \sim 3 \cdot 45 \times 10^{-4}$	Feldberg (1957)
Carnosine	$0 \cdot 26$		Dubuisson (1954)

(2) L-Carnosine in isotonic sodium chloride solution (0·30%) stops the muscle contractions occurring in an isolated toad's sartorius muscle bathed in isotonic sodium chloride solution. This inhibitory action of L-carnosine is not enhanced by addition of glutamic acid, aspartic acid or cysteine, but it is definitely enhanced by the addition of taurine (0·075%) and acetylcholine (0·000025%). The concentrations necessary to enhance the inhibitory action of L-carnosine are less than those in which these substances are normally present in muscle.

(3) If 0·0147% carnitine is combined with 0·25% carnosine in the presence of 0·075% taurine, the mixture is completely ineffective if applied to an excised muscle.

We conclude that the true excitine is carnitine in combination with taurine and that the true inhibitine is carnosine in combination with taurine.

It is possible to separate the excitine from the inhibitine by the application of electric current as indicated in Fig. 1. The current from a 2 V dry cell applied for 5 sec is sufficient to cause the appearance of excitine in the anodal fluid (as tested on a freshly excised toad sartorius muscle) and the appearance of inhibitine in the cathodal fluid (as shown by the ability of this fluid to inhibit the contractions of a muscle subjected to isotonic sodium chloride solution).

These facts permit the conclusion that electric current which stimulates a live muscle can dissociate the excitine–inhibitine complex and explains why a contraction should occur at the cathode of the stimulating electrodes.

THE INHIBITINE (NC) AND EXCITINE (NC) OF
THE CENTRAL MOTOR SYSTEM

Carnitine as well as carnosine was found to have no effect on excised nerves of toads and frogs. However, when part of the nerve was desheathed or when isolated single nerve fibres were prepared, carnitine (0·005 M) in combination with taurine (0·005 M) caused excitation which was recognized by the resulting muscle contractions. Carnosine in combination with taurine (both 0·005 M) had no detectable effect. We tried these and related substances on the central nervous system, especially on the motor cortex.

Elliott and Florey (1956) identified Factor I extracted from vertebrate brain as γ-aminobutyric acid (GABA) and in the same year Hayashi and Nagai declared that the inhibitine of the central motor system is γ-amino-β-hydroxybutyric acid (GABOB). We tested both substances for their excitatory and inhibitory action on the motor cortex. We did find that GABA as well as GABOB has a strong inhibiting action on electrically induced seizures if they are introduced into the cerebrospinal fluid or if they are rapidly introduced through the carotid artery. We also found that GABOB was a constituent of mammalian brain (Hayashi, 1958).

We found that GABA could produce seizures in higher concentrations and that it inhibited seizures if applied in lower concentrations. We furthermore found that GABA produced seizures in all cases when it was accompanied by vitamin B_{12} and B_1; and we showed that it always produced inhibition if accompanied by vitamin B_6. We, therefore, believed that GABA might be the mother substance of excitatory as well as inhibitory transmitter (Hayashi, 1959). Although the structure of the former is not yet elucidated, the latter is definitely GABOB.

Previously we have used synthetic DL-GABOB, but recently we have used L-GABOB and found that the inhibitory actions of the two compounds are related as one to three; that is, L-GABOB is a stronger inhibitor than DL-GABOB.

The extraction of excitine from the brain of vertebrates has been tried by many authors, but the results were dubious since it was not known that the substance exists in free form in the normal condition of the brain. Several years ago we succeeded in extracting it from cerebral spinal fluid of dogs during electrically induced seizures. For convenience, we named the active principle "excitine NC". Generalized seizures were produced by direct electrical stimulation of the exposed surface of the motor cortex or by application of electro-shock current applied through the scalp of dogs. The induced seizures lasted from 60 to 180 sec after the cessation of stimulation. When 1–3 ml of cerebral spinal fluid were taken during the seizure and introduced into the cerebrospinal fluid of another dog, a generalized seizure occurred in the receiver dog.

If the fluid was taken 3–4 min after cessation of the seizures, no seizures were produced if such fluid was transferred to another dog. In fact, the excitatory substance seems to be quite labile since out of twelve cases we could obtain the substance in only one or two cases.

We have attempted to discover the reason for the rapid disappearance of the excitatory principle. We found that heating of the cerebrospinal fluid caused the disappearance of the active substance and the same could be achieved by de-proteinization with sublimate and ethyl alcohol.

When 3 ml of the cerebral spinal fluid collected during seizure were mixed with 9 ml of absolute methanol the activity was maintained. After centrifugation the supernatant was reduced to half its original volume and when it was injected into the ventricle of another dog it produced seizures.

It was found that the effective agent cannot withstand temperatures above 40°C, and that it is unstable in acid media (pH 2–3) and in alkaline media of pH 8–9. The substance is very unstable in pure oxygen and disappears within 1 min; during exposure to open air it loses its activity in 1 or 2 weeks.

Further analysis of the constitution of the excitatory agent is now going on. At present we call the effective fluid "crude excitine".

When a dose of "crude excitine" which is effective to produce seizures was mixed with 2 ml of 0·2 M GABOB and introduced into the cerebral spinal fluid of a dog it did not produce seizure. If such a mixture was subjected to the flow of an electric current in the apparatus shown in Fig. 1, excitatory activity could be found in the cathodal as well as in the anodal fluid.

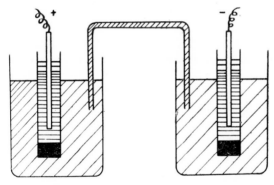

Fig. 1. Experimental set-up for the electrophoretic separation of excitine and inhibitine (see text).

We therefore feel that the excitine–inhibitine hypothesis can be applied to the central nervous system.

DISCUSSION

I have named released chemical agents "excitine" and "inhibitine" on some occasions, and "chemical transmitters" on others. Are they the same things? In the peripheral nervous system they are not the same. For instance, in a motor nerve in skeletal muscle there are three patterns of tissue:

(1) The nerve fibre.

(2) Nerve endings and motor end-plate.

(3) The muscle fibre.

Of these, the muscle fibre has a special "excitine" and "inhibitine" and the motor nerve fibre also has a special "excitine (N)" and "inhibitine (N)". The chemical structure of excitine (N) and inhibitine (N) is not yet known, but factors extracted from muscle are quite effective on the desheathed nerve as shown by the following experiment:

A sartorius muscle was prepared with its nerve. The nerve was de-sheathed and bathed with Ringer's solution. Application of excitine (carnitine plus taurine) to the nerve caused a sequence of muscle contractions. If the nerve was exposed to an isotonic sodium chloride solution, muscle contractions resulted also and when inhibitine (carnosine plus taurine) was applied to the nerve, contractions ceased at once.

In contrast to tissues (1) and (3) in which excitation is produced in a similar manner, the tissue (2) produces acetylcholine as transmitter and an end-plate potential as a generator potential.

The question is now: is there a system in the central nervous system corresponding to the above two, that is a tissue producing acetylcholine and "end-plate potential"?

(1) When an appropriate concentration of metrazol is applied directly to the grey matter of the motor cortex of the brain of dogs, a seizure occurs. If, however, this drug is applied to the white matter, seizures do not occur. The same was found for any other convulsants. On the other hand, it is known that electrical stimulation is effective in both the grey matter as well as the white matter. We have, therefore, believed that a chemical stimulation acts only on soma and dendrite but not on the pathways of the central nervous system.

(2) Soma and dendrite are characterized by "excitine (NC)" and "inhibitine (NC)" as shown before. How about the pathway? On the basis of experiments in which we applied carnitine with taurine as well as carnosine with taurine, crude excitine and GABOB to the motor cortex and to the cerebral spinal fluid in various combinations, we conclude that soma and dendrite have an "excitine" and "inhibitine" different from that which is active in the nerve fibres (the pathway). The results of the experiments follow.

We would like to call the excitine and inhibitine of pathways excitine (P) and inhibitine (P). It can be seen that the effect of crude excitine (NC) could not be inhibited by carnosine (the peripheral inhibitine (N)) and that carnitine (the peripheral excitine (N)) had an effect on central nerve tissue. The excitine (NC) is neutralized only by GABOB while the carnitine–taurine complex is neutralized only by carnosine–taurine. GABOB does not neutralize carnitine–taurine, and carnosine–taurine does not neutralize excitine (NC). We, therefore, have a special excitine–inhibitine system for soma and dendrites and another one for the pathway.

(3) The next question is: do soma and dendrite have a special receptor tissue which corresponds to that of the motor end-plate; in other words, is there acetylcholine and end-plate type tissue in the grey matter? This does indeed seem to be the case. When acetylcholine is applied to the grey matter from the outside only high concentrations cause convulsions. If acetylcholine is applied in a concentration of 0·5–2·0 M a seizure occurs with a latency of 5–30 sec. However, when it is accompanied by B_1, acetylcholine in a concentration in which it alone does not produce seizures, promotes the generation of excitine and results in a seizure with a latency of 10–20 min. Acetylcholine has, however, a dual action, for it is antagonistic to the effect of vitamin B_6; it enhances the action of isonicotinic acid hydrazide (INH) in preventing production of inhibitine at soma and dendrites of central nerve cells (see Table 2).

TABLE 2. MOTOR EFFECTS OF VARIOUS SUBSTANCES ON THE GREY MATTERS OF DOGS

Substances	Concentration	Motor effects	Remarks
ACh	0·5 ～ 2·0 M	Seizure	Short latency (5–30 sec)
D-tubocurarine	0·1 ～ 0·5 M	Seizure	Long latency (10–30 min)
ACh + B_1	0·01 ～ 0·001 M + 0·02 ～ 0·03 M	Seizure	Producing "excitine"
ACh + INH	0·01 ～ 0·001 M + 0·1 ～ 0·2 M	Seizure	Inhibiting the genesis of "inhibitine"

(4) The last question must be then: are excitine (NC) and the assumed excitatory transmitter the same substances, and is inhibitine (NC) the same as the inhibitory transmitter in the central motor system? The answer must be yes. We conclude that the endings of the excitatory fibres attached to the soma of the second cells secrete the excitine (NC) and that this affects the soma in such a way as to produce excitation which travels over the pathway which has its special excitine (P) and inhibitine (P). Likewise, the endings of the inhibitory fibres liberate inhibitine (NC). This substance affects the second cell to neutralize the excitine which the second cell has, produces, or has received from another fibre.

REFERENCES

DUBUISSON, M. (1954) *Muscular Contraction*. Charles C. Thomas, Springfield, Illinois.

26

ELLIOTT, K. A. C. and FLOREY, E. (1956) Assay and properties of an inhibitory factor from the brain. *Communication of XX International Physiological Congress*, Brussels.

FELDBERG, W. (1957) Acetylcholine. *The Metabolism of the Nervous System* (ed. by RICHTER, D.) p. 493. Pergamon Press, London.

FOLCH-PI, J. and LE BARON, F. N. (1957) Chemical composition of the mammalian nervous system. *The Metabolism of the Nervous System* (ed. by RICHTER, D.) p. 67. Pergamon Press, London.

GUGGENHEIM, M. (1951) *Die biogene Amine* (4te. Auf.). S. Kanger, Basel.

HAYASHI, T. and NAGAI, K. (1956) Action of ω-amino acids on the motor cortex of higher animals, especially γ-amino-β-hydroxybutyric acid as the real inhibitory principle in the brain. *Communication of XX International Physiological Congress*, Brussels.

HAYASHI, T. (1956) *Chemical Physiology of Excitation of Muscle and Nerve* (1st Ed.). (2nd Ed. 1958). Nakayama-Shoten, Tokyo.

HAYASHI, T. (1958) Inhibition and excitation due to gamma-aminobutyric acid in the central nervous system. *Nature* **182** : 1076.

HAYASHI, T. (1959) *Neurophysiology and Neurochemistry of Convulsion.* Dainihon-Tosho, Tokyo.

HAYASHI, T. (1960) Action of carnitine on excitable tissues of vertebrates. In *Proteides of the Biological Fluids.* Proceedings of the Seventh Colloquium, Elsevier, Amsterdam, 1959.

PHYSIOLOGICAL MECHANISM OF PRODUCING EXCITATORY TRANSMITTER IN THE BRAIN OF DOGS

TAKASHI HAYASHI

Department of Physiology, School of Medicine, Keio University, Tokyo

WHEN metrazol and sodium glutamate were introduced into the ventricle of dogs they produced generalized seizures as shown in Table 1 with latent

TABLE 1. THE CRITICAL DOSAGE TO PRODUCE SEIZURE IN DOGS

Substances	Introduced into c.s.f.		Latent period	Seizure
Metrazol	0·0377 M	1·0 ml	10 ~ 15 sec	+
Sodium glutamate	0·1 M	1·0 ml	15 ~ 30 sec	+
I NH	0·1 M	1·0 ml	40·3 min	+
O MP	0·1 M	1·0 ml	15·5 min	+
D-Tubocurarine	0·04 M	1·0 ml	11·5 min	+
Vitamin B₁	0·1 M	1·0 ml	15·0 min	+
Folic acid	0·0003 M	1·0 ml	24·0 min	+

periods of 15–30 sec. In contrast, isonicotinic acid hydrazide (INH), oxymethyl pyrimidine (OMP), as well as D-tubocurarine produced seizures with latencies of 600–2400 sec (10–40 min), that is about 30–200 times longer than those of the former substances. To our surprise, vitamin B₁ as well as folic acid produced seizure if given in appropriate concentration and the latency belongs to the second group. To our further surprise, all convulsants were found to fall into these two categories.

The most simple interpretation of this phenomenon would be that convulsants of shorter latent periods acted by direct action of their own, while convulsants with longer latent periods acted not directly but by secondary and indirect actions which could be, for example, as follows:

(1) the substance undergoes some change in its chemical structure to become the real excitatory transmitter; or

(2) the substance accelerates the production of the real excitatory transmitter; or

(3) it inhibits the production of the anti-substance of the excitatory transmitter in the brain.

As for INH, OMP and curare, as well as semicarbazide and hydroxylamine they were found to belong to the last category mentioned above (3). We found the convulsants which belonged to the above category (2) to be guanidine or methylene blue, while GABA was found to belong to category (1). As shown in Table 2, when GABA was introduced into the ventricle of dogs,

TABLE 2. THE CRITICAL DOSAGE TO PRODUCE SEIZURE
IN DOGS

Substances	Introduced into c.s.f.	Seizure	Remarks
GABA	0·002 M, 1·0 ml	—	
Vitamin B_{12}	0·0002%, 1·0 ml	—	
ATP	0·002%, 1·0 ml	—	
GABA + Vitamin B_{12}	0·002 M, 1·0 ml + 0·0002%, 1·0 ml	—	
ATP + Vitamin B_{12}	0·002%, 1·0 ml + 0·0002%, 1·0 ml	—	
GABA + Vitamin B_{12} + ATP	0·002 M, 1·0 ml + 0·0002%, 1·0 ml + 0·002%, 1·0 ml	+	Latent period 12 min

it produced a seizure in one case out of twenty experiments. But we found that when vitamins B_{12} and B_1 accompanied GABA it produced seizures in twenty cases out of twenty. Here GABA was changed into some unknown factor which acted to produce generalized seizure. The normal brain contains GABA in the concentration of 0·031% and it has been argued that GABA might be the mother substance of both the excitatory and the inhibitory transmitter in higher animals (Hayashi, 1959).

AN EXPERIMENTAL METHOD CONCERNING THE GENESIS OF AN EXCITATORY TRANSMITTER

The method we used was to introduce a substance into the cerebrospinal fluid of a dog and, at the same time, to introduce a coenzyme in order to transform the substance into the excitatory transmitter. As in the experiment described in Table 2, we took folic acid instead of vitamin B_{12} in a concentration which by itself caused no motor effects. When combined with GABA and ATP it produced strong seizures. Vitamin B_1 could be used instead of ATP in this case and the result indicated that it acts as energy liberator in the reaction.

The method hitherto used to detect enzymatic actions in tissues consisted in the artificial addition of substrate to homogenates or slices of brain *in vitro* and one obtained the expected substances from the incubation fluid or used the output of CO_2 as an indicator. This was essentially the procedure in biochemistry. But here we found a method of neurochemistry whereby the substrate is introduced *in vivo* into the cerebrospinal fluid of a dog so that it can contact the cells of the brain that contain the enzymatic systems whose substrate was increased by the artificial addition. It was assumed that if this excess of substrate drives the reaction in the direction of synthesis of a new substance at a rate which is greater than that of the normal state, this resulting substance should be detectable by any indicator, in our case, the production of a seizure. From the experiments just mentioned we could formulate the reaction that produces the excitatory chemical transmitter in central nervous system (at least in the motor system).

$$\text{GABA plus vitamin } B_{12} \text{ plus } B_1 \rightarrow cc^* \qquad (1)$$

$$\text{GABA plus folic acid plus } B_1 \quad \rightarrow cc^*$$

Instead of vitamin B_{12} we tested vitamin B_2, biotin, lipoic acid and vitamin C, but these substances did not accelerate the reaction. Pantothenic acid was, however, found to produce clonic convulsions according to the following reaction:

$$\text{GABA plus pantothenic acid plus } B_1 \rightarrow cc \qquad (2)$$

It was now a question of whether the reaction of formulae (1) and (2) represented the same sequence (that is, whether pantothenic acid had the same action as B_{12} or folic acid), or if there were quite different reactions leading to two different substances.

When GABA, vitamin B_{12}, pantothenic acid and vitamin B_1 were combined, the seizure was delayed or the concentration of each substance needed to be increased in order to produce a seizure. In other words, the reactions of vitamin B_{12} on the one hand and the reaction of pantothenic acid on the other

* cc = clonic convulsions.

are quite different and it is likely that they both represent stages in the same direction so that reaction (1) produced reaction (2) or vice versa. At any rate, the excitatory transmitter substance was produced from GABA with the aid of a coenzyme and energy in that certain sequence of reactions (1) and (2).

A tentative structure of the excitatory chemical transmitter substance of the motor system. The reaction (1) suggests that a methylation process is involved in the course of reconversion of GABA into the chemical transmission. We therefore tried the action of several methylated derivatives of GABA on the motor system, for example:

(1) dimethylaminoethanol;
(2) γ-aminobutyrobetaine;
(3) acetyl-γ-aminobutyrylbetaine.

All these compounds did not produce any seizure when they were introduced into the cerebrospinal fluid of dogs.

From the reaction (2) we might expect that GABA was at first combined with coenzyme A and that GABA-coenzyme A was converted into GABA-choline. Accordingly, one would expect that GABA-choline should cause seizures, but it was found to have no such action as indicated in Table 3. We

TABLE 3

Substances	Dose administered into c.s.f.		Seizure
Dimethylaminoethanol	$0 \cdot 01 – 1 \cdot 0$ M	1 ml	None
γ-aminobutyrobetaine	$0 \cdot 01 – 1 \cdot 0$ M	1 ml	None
γ-acetoaminobutyric acid ethyl ester	$0 \cdot 01 – 1 \cdot 0$ M	1 ml	None
γ-aminobutyrycholine	$0 \cdot 01 – 1 \cdot 0$ M	1 ml	None
γ-aminobutyrycholine	$0 \cdot 02$ M		
+			
Folic acid	$0 \cdot 0002$ M		Seizure
+			
Vitamin B$_1$	$0 \cdot 02$ M		

Derivatives of GABA and their action on the motor system of dogs.

then tried to give the methylated compounds together with vitamins B$_{12}$ and B$_1$. We found the first three did not produce seizures but γ-aminobutyryl-choline with vitamins B$_{12}$ and B$_1$ produced seizures with a latent period of 15–60 min. This suggests that the methylation of γ-aminobutyrylcholine, that is, dimethyl-γ-butyrylcholine, might not yet be the real transmitter for excitation in the central motor system.

REFERENCE

HAYASHI, T. (1959) *Neurophysiology and Neurochemistry of Convulsion.* Dainihon-Tosho, Tokyo.

COMPLETE CURE OF NATURAL EPILEPSY OF DOGS BY β-HYDROXY-γ-AMINOBUTYRIC ACID INTRODUCED INTO THEIR VENTRICLES

Takashi Hayashi* and Kazuo Nagai†

* Department of Physiology, School of Medicine, Keio University, Tokyo, and

† Department of Physiology, School of Dental Surgery,
Nihon University, Tokyo

MEDICATION *PER OS* TO HUMAN EPILEPTICS

THE lethal dose of β-hydroxy-γ-aminobutyric acid (GABOB) in mice was found to be 13 mg/g. Small doses were tried on human adults, but medication *per os* of 6 g/day (2·0 g/day) caused no change in subjective as well as objective observations.

A clinic in a certain medical school in Tokyo examined 70 epileptic patients and treated them with GABOB. The results of a 12 months' study follow.

TABLE 1. CASE DESCRIPTION OF A TREATMENT OF AN EPILEPTIC DOG WITH GABOB INTRODUCED INTO THE CEREBROSPINAL FLUID

Day	Hour	Minute	Dog B, wt. = 8·2 kg, Idiopathic epilepsy
1	13	00	Cisternal injection of 1·0 ml of 0·2 M GABOB
	15	21	A generalized seizure occurred, and recurrently continued for 2 hr 31 min
	24	00	No seizure
2	13	00	Second cisternal injection of 1·0 ml of 0·2 M GABOB
	20	18	A generalized seizure occurred and recurrently continued for 50 min
	24	00	No seizure
3	13	00	No seizure
	24	00	No seizure
After 1 month			5 attacks
After 2 months			No seizure
After 3 months			No seizure
After 4 months			No seizure

Seventy patients were chosen which suffered an attack at least once a month, as follows: 1–2 attacks, 42 cases; 3–4, 8 cases; 5–6, 9 cases; 7–8, 2 cases; 9–10, 2 cases; more than 11, 5 cases. The medication taken was alleviatin (diphenyl-hydantoin) 33 cases, alleviatin and phenobarbital in 23 cases, and other anti-convulsants, for example comital and diamox in 13 cases.

The above selection consisted of 53 cases of idiopathics and 17 cases of symptomatics. The age distribution of the first attack was as follows: 1–9 year old, 21 cases; 10–19, 35; 20–29, 10; and over 30 years old, 4 cases. Each patient received 0·5 g/day of DL-GABOB. Half of them were medicated with DL-GABOB plus alleviatin at the beginning, then the latter was gradually reduced.

The results must be discussed in two sections. One, concerned with the effect of the medication on the convulsive fit, the other, with the effect of the other combined symptoms.

(1). Out of 45 cases with grand mal attack, 16 cases (29·1 %) were completely cured, i.e. no attacks occurred for 12 months after a weeks medication. Among the improved cases, 27 (49·1 %) showed the attacks decreased to under one-half, and in two cases (3·6 %) the grand mal fits changed into petit mal.

(2) Of 15 cases which had grand mal and petit mal at the same time, 5 were completely cured, 9 improved, and in 1 case (7·7 %) petit mal remained. All included, the distribution of the effects was as follows: total cases 70, complete cure 22 (30·4 %), improved 39 (55·7 %), unchanged 10 (14·3 %). Headache or vomiting after the attacks was completely cured in 12 cases out of 40 (30·0 %), improved in 9 (22·5 %), and unchanged in 19 cases (47·5 %). Long sleep after the attack was completely cured in 11 cases out of 47 (67·1 %), improved in 10 (14·3 %), and unchanged in 28 (57·2 %). Stiff shoulder was completely cured in 15 cases of 20 (54·1 %), improved in 5 (25·0 %), and unchanged in 3 cases (15·0 %). Personality behaviour characterized by lack of consideration for others or marked centring of attention upon themselves was cured completely in 20 cases out of 37(54·5 %), improved in 8 (21·6 %), and unchanged in 9 cases (24·5 %).

In summary, the symptoms of 70 epileptics were cured in 61·9%, improved in 20·3%, and remained unchanged in 26·5% of the cases during the medication.

STUDIES ON EPILEPTIC DOGS

For 20 years we have used dogs exclusively in our experiments in our physiological institutes in Japan. The dogs for medical use are obtained from several animal dealers; according to our information, half of them are bred and raised until maturity, the other half are collected by a round-up of stray dogs by the permission of the authorities. We could not find any epileptic dogs among them since the dealers do not by choice keep such dogs and if one happens to have a fit, the dog will be destroyed.

On one occasion we told a dealer that we wanted epileptic dogs for the physiological study of epilepsy and were told that there are many owners of dogs which have fits lasting over several years. We listed the names of the owners and called on them one by one and learned that the dogs were very valuable ornamental ones of noble pedigree, sometimes very highly priced, for example, one million yen or over. A partial list of 39 epileptic dogs shows that 17 had 1–5 attacks per month, 7 had 6–15, 9 had 16–50, and 6 dogs had over 30 attacks during a month.

We were able to collect over 60 epileptic dogs. A few of them were treated with GABOB *per os* 0·5–2·0 g/day. The results were exactly the same as those obtained with human epileptics. The principal result was that the continuous application of the drug could depress the attacks but if the drug was discontinued the attacks occurred again.

DIRECT APPLICATION OF GABOB INTO THE BRAIN OF EPILEPTIC DOGS

The 39 dogs mentioned above could be divided according to their symptoms into 9 dogs with idiopathic epilepsy and 27 with symptomatic epilepsy. A dose of 1·0 ml 0·2 M GABOB was introduced into the ventricle or cysterna cerebellomedullaris of these dogs. A case history is given in Table 1. Other cases are shown in Table 2. Each injection of GABOB precipitated several

TABLE 2. INJECTION OF GABOB INTO DOG CEREBROSPINAL FLUID AND THE PRECIPITATION OF SEIZURES

Injection (days)	Cases	Cases of precipitation of seizure		Latent period (min)
1	38	14	(36·8%)	30 ~ 79
2	22	5	(22·7%)	120 ~ 600
3	8	0	—	—
4	3	0	—	—

seizures in 36·8% of the dogs. This had never been observed in normal dogs after the injection of GABOB. The meaning of these induced seizures will be discussed in a later section. The results of these injections as given in Tables 2 and 3 were remarkable. In several cases, complete cure resulted. This means that the dogs had no attacks since the last injection of GABOB in the case of the longest observation over 5 years and in the case of the shortest period of observation for 6 months. The first dog treated is still alive after 5 years and

TABLE 3. SIX MONTHS' OBSERVATION OF THE RESULTS OF GABOB INJECTION
INTO CEREBROSPINAL FLUID OF EPILEPTIC DOGS (THIRTY-SIX CASES)

Injection (days)	Completely cured	Improved	Unchanged	Changed for worse
1	5	5	3	0
2	3	4	5	2
3	0	2	1	3
4	0	2	0	0
5	0	0	0	0
6	0	1	0	0
Cases	8 (22·2%)	14 (38·9%)	9 (25·0%)	5 (13·9%)

2 months, and this is the first successful case unexpected at first, of complete cure in a dog. Figures 1, 2 and 3 show this remarkable specimen which is a pure-bred dog of Japanese Akita-blood. Figure 2 gives a picture of the epileptic attack. Figure 3 is a photograph taken after the treatment. Compared with the previous photograph of Fig. 1, the outward appearance, especially the facial expression has become quite different. The former aspect shows

FIG. 1. For explanation see text.

FIG. 2. For explanation see text.

FIG. 3. For explanation see text.

exophthalmos and tonic emotions, while the latter shows a calm and quiet expression. This dog has had no seizures during the 5 years of observation; during this time the observer slept beside the dog at night, and though a bell was attached to the dog, the observer was not once awakened by it. If we include the improved cases, the treatment was effective in 61·1% of the cases while 38·9% remained unchanged or died. These results are quite different from those obtained with medication *per os*. .

The above facts tell us that the direct application of GABOB to the brain can completely cure epilepsy of dogs in certain cases, but that it can induce status epilepticus in a few cases. The important questions are:

(1) Why and by what mechanism does directly applied GABOB cure epileptics?

(2) Why does it in a few cases cause status epilepticus resulting in death?

(3) Why does it have no complete action when applied indirectly *per os* or intravenously?

To the first question it can be stated that the completely cured cases were found in the list diagnosed as having idiopathic epilepsy, and not symptomatic epilepsy. We examined the electroencephalogram of those dogs which were chosen from the list, four cases of the completely cured and four cases of the unchanged dogs. The results were as follows: The encephalograms of the unchanged animals showed focal or multi-focal disturbances, but almost all of the cured animals showed no abnormalities. Unfortunately, we have no records from the time before the GABOB was introduced so that we do not know whether the treatment is responsible for the absence of electrical focal disturbances.

The conclusion can be drawn, however, that symptomatic epileptic dogs cannot be cured by the treatment while dogs with idiopathic epilepsy can. The cure through GABOB succeeded only in the case of weak metabolic changes in nerve cells which lead to diffuse multiple foci but not in cases of a strong localized focus which was caused by traumatic local lesion or a cicatrix of infectious adhesion.

Concerning the second question: Since in most cases after the first treatment with an excessive dose of GABOB introduced into the brain, epileptic attacks were precipitated (although sometimes they were delayed by weeks), it must be concluded that the mechanism of complete cure will not be attained suddenly but that it takes several days. The fact that GABOB must be given in rather large doses and that the mechanism for cure requires a certain lapse of time leads us to believe that an enzyme which produces a substance that causes epileptic attacks is not only inhibited but transformed or modified into an inactive state by the excessive dose of ω-amino acid. If this is the case, GABOB must be adsorbed by the enzyme, probably by its protein. The question of the precipitation of attacks by introduction of concentrated solutions of GABOB into the cerebrospinal fluid is probably related to the fact that a small percentage of the dogs got worse after the injections. This problem must be studied in the future.

THE ORGANIZATION OF THE PRIMITIVE CENTRAL NERVOUS SYSTEM AS SUGGESTED BY EXAMPLES OF INHIBITION AND THE STRUCTURE OF NEUROPILE

G. Adrian Horridge

Gatty Marine Laboratory and Dept. of Zoology, University of St. Andrews, Scotland

In 1957 I laid out an explanation of the transmission of excitation in the nerve nets of various types of corals, and, by implication, of all coelenterates, in terms of a model which was a network of connected units, each unit representing a neuron or through-conducting group of neurons. The essential feature of this model of this special type of nervous system was that the effective connexions between units of the model were randomly distributed, and at the time I suggested that random connexions may make up some part of the organization of other nervous systems. The present considerations are an exploration of this line of thought as applied to some other invertebrate central nervous systems. A number of examples will be presented to show that diffuse and widely ramifying neurons having a general activating or inhibitory effect occur commonly in invertebrates and it is suggested that an explanation of their action does not require a set of specific connexions. Alongside them, and interacting with them, are neurons which are more limited regionally and could have more specific connexions. As part of this problem, therefore, it is essential to consider the formation of specific connexions. Finally, it is suggested that there has been a progressive evolution away from random connexions towards a greater individuality and specificity of the interrelationships between neurons.

The complexity of a model of a nervous system depends on the number of specifications which must be laid out in order to determine the formal pattern of connexions of the model. A simpler model is therefore one with fewer such specifications. Here lies the reason for considering the connexions within the model to be random until evidence is available from the animal to prove that patterns exist in the structure. This is essentially the application of the null-hypothesis of statistics to the connexions of a model of the nervous system which is based on a combination of anatomical and physiological data. Order is not assumed, in general, in the study of relationships in any natural phenomenon; it is looked for and then, at a certain level of significance, is demonstrated to be present.

On the other hand we are familiar with the attitude that the nervous system is a biological structure which by virtue of patterns of growth is presumably to some extent ordered, and only as an unfavoured alternative are theories developed to show how a random set of connexions can provide, in a formal way, and with economy in number of assumptions, an adequate model of some aspects of the structure. This is understandable but abandoned in the present article for two reasons. Firstly, it is the least complex explanation of both the structure and its behaviour which is sought, and the degree of complexity is judged by the number of specifications required to formulate the model which takes account of both aspects. Secondly, it appears to the writer that the increase in complexity of the invertebrate nervous system, especially at the lower end of a series from coelenterates up to arthropods, can be profitably considered as a progressive but incomplete development away from a random structure towards a physiologically or anatomically more ordered structure. If this is so, then the process has necessarily been accompanied by a differentiation of the neurons into distinct classes and in many instances, especially on the efferent side, into unique individual neurons. However, as will be shown, specific anatomical contacts between potentially recognizable distinct neurons are only one method of achieving this differentiation of specific interrelationships.

Together with definitions of some of the terms which I shall use, it is helpful to consider the anatomical form of a neuron by analogy with the path taken by a letter during the delivery of mail. Letters which are addressed to a single recipient may take a circuitous path to their destination and similarly addressed letters from the same source may go by different paths. Similarly, a recognizable neuron, when found again in a different segment or a different animal, need not have exactly the same anatomical form but may nevertheless be in part "anatomically addressed" in so far as it makes particular contacts with other recognizable neurons. The recognizable and therefore regularly discernible structural relationships of a neuron with the others which it excites are defined as *anatomically addressed*. In the anatomically addressed mailing system the individual letters need not necessarily have any content, and information can be transmitted by the frequency of arrival of empty envelopes.

In a different but not necessarily mutually exclusive system, letters do not bear individual addresses but are distributed with various degrees of approximation as to the area of their destination, as when leaflets are scattered from the air, but with definable shapes and extents of the area covered. This situation is similar to that of a branching neuron which makes contact with any other neuron it happens to meet in the area of its terminations. As in the case of the models of the coelenterate nerve net, the leaflet in the mail analogy can be a blank sheet which by its arrival merely triggers a response, and, as in the anemone nerve net, in particular, the frequency of arrival of such blanks can convey information to the effectors. Such a system, with the pattern of excitation in time as its only parameter, is *non-addressed*. Far from being necessarily random, all degrees of anatomical pattern may be found in such a system, but the physiologically significant connexions cannot be divided into recognizable classes. Neurons in a coelenterate nerve net may meet with a characteristic number of others, or have a regular pattern, but there is no discrimination between one individual neuron and another. Each can act vicariously for any of the others in the net and we have no anatomical or physiological means of distinguishing an individual neuron when it recurs in different animals. As conceived here, in a simple nerve net, the neurons themselves do not distinguish.

There is a third possible type of system which, until ruled out by experiment, must be considered as a possibility in the interpretation of neuron-to-neuron transmission in a system which is more complex than a single nerve net. This depends on the differential sensitivity of the efferent neurons to different transmitter substances produced from thereby distinguishable afferent neurons and interneurons. If we imagine a primitive ganglion with different classes of afferent neurons having distinct transmitter substances and only a few classes of efferent neurons, then it can be readily seen that differential sensitivity of the efferents, to the transmitters which have access to them, can account for their differential responses to various types and combinations of afferent excitation. From points of observation on the efferent side there is no way of distinguishing such a system from one which is fully anatomically addressed although it need contain no anatomically addressed connexions at all. Such a system, called *chemically addressed*, is one of a class of systems which are *physiologically addressed*. Other physiologically addressed systems can be imagined; they could, for example, have codes based upon the proportion of afferents which are active, or the rate of change or other temporal pattern of the total afferent excitation. A purely physiologically addressed system has the character that the morphogenetic specifications define no particular anatomical connexions although afferent excitation can be classified into different kinds, as judged solely by the differential sensitivity and responses of the output; only a quantity of branching and plenty of connexions are required.

In terms of the same analogy with delivery of mail, a chemically addressed system is like an indiscriminate delivery of more than one kind of leaflet. Many recipients receive a copy of many kinds of leaflet and some may receive all kinds but their different sensitivities ensure that only the intended class of recipients respond to the contents of certain classes of leaflet, and they do so in their characteristic manner. It should be noted that both the anatomically and the chemically addressed neurons are distinctively *labelled lines*. These are physiological pathways known to be labelled because they carry a particular identifiable class of excitation, which the next stage into which these neurons run distinguishes from other classes of excitation. The present issue is to suggest that besides the path of progressive differentiation of morphogenetically determined specific connexions, the evolution of labelled lines from the primitive non-addressed system can include the progressive differentiation of the substances secreted by the neurons and their sensitivity to secretions of their neighbours. Labelled lines are neurons which have differentiated along distinctive paths of development, either in structural or physiological features, or in both. The problem of analysis is complicated because these two modes of growth of complexity are progressive and not mutually exclusive and it is possible that physiologically addressed diffusely spreading neurons act among and together with other neurons having various degrees of specificity of anatomically addressed connexions. Also, a physiologically addressed neuron must to some extent be addressed anatomically to a particular region and an anatomically addressed one has specific modes of chemosensitivity. A physiologically addressed system must have a neuropile-like widely ramifying structure but an anatomically addressed system need not be arranged this way.

Neuropile is a word which I shall use for the intermingled processes of dendrites and axon arborizations which branch profusely and ramify among each other in the central nervous systems and outlying ganglia of all animals. It is characteristic of nerve cells that where they meet and apparently generate all interesting aspects of behaviour, they produce this profuse branching and relatively great surface area with multilateral relationships with other neurons in all directions. In the vertebrates there are regularly, in addition, endings on cell bodies, but all invertebrates have nervous systems where all the interesting activity seems to be in the neuropile, as defined in the above way, and a similar neuropile occurs regionally in vertebrates, as, for example, in the optic tectum of the lower forms and the granular layers of the cortex of mammals.

A central problem of invertebrate neurophysiology is the analysis of systems of this type, leading to the understanding of why there should be this dense intermingling of many profusely branching fibres. However, present techniques do not provide the crucial information. The physiological data now available from several convenient preparations of invertebrates, particularly ganglia of arthropods and molluscs, can be represented diagrammatically by sets of simple connexions between stylized neurons where each acts on the next down the line. But neuropile in fact does not look like this, and from anatomical studies of neuropile no one has ever obtained anything which looks like a wiring diagram.

The present ideas leading to a new approach spring from a series of observations on animals which have many reduplicated pacemakers, all of which can be inhibited at the same time. The simplest such systems occur among those coelenterates which have more than one nerve net. In some coelenterates, animals such as sea anemones, corals and hydroid polyps, the nervous system consists of a net of neurons in which every neuron appears to be equivalent to every other, and to be connected by synapses or fusions with any other neurons with which it comes in contact. Considered as a problem in morphogenesis the neurons are merely scattered about and they need have no morphogenetical specifications for forming physiologically significant contacts with only certain other neurons; in fact the net seems to be what it is because synapses are formed at random. Apparently a pattern of only this degree of complexity serves adequately as a nervous system for most polyps, and all known types of their rapid behaviour can be paralleled in a model by changing the parameters of probability of transmission, density of connexions and so forth, in a randomly connected non-addressed net (Horridge, 1957).

A similar set of apparently random connexions between neurons occurs in the sub-retinal layer of the lateral eye of *Limulus*. There are two classes of neurons, retinula cells and eccentric cells, but the branches of both have close relations with their neighbours in a neuropile of only these two components. Their effectiveness in inhibiting their neighbours falls off with distance and only parameters which define this spatial relationship are required to describe the mutual inhibition between the ommatidia (Ratliff and Hartline, 1959; Hartline *et al.*, 1961).

The next grade of complexity is found where there are two overlying nerve nets over much of the animal, and, as compared with the single nerve net, these nets must be kept separate by an additional degree of specificity during their growth. For example, *Heteroxenia*, Fig. 1, is an Indo-Pacific tropical soft coral found in small clumps a few centimetres broad, from which spring a few hundred polyps several centimetres long. The polyps continually beat out of phase and by cutting them into pieces it can be shown that each of their eight arms contains a spontaneously active centre which is apparently nervous. Stimulation anywhere on the colony causes all polyps to stop at once and analysis shows that this is co-ordinated by a distinct inhibitory nerve net which must run to all the pacemakers of the colony (Horridge, 1956b). A second example of widespread inhibition of pacemakers is provided by the tropical anemone *Boloceroides* which swims by simultaneously twitching all its tentacles downwards and outwards. The tentacles are co-ordinated by a through-conducting pathway round the oral disk, and there are many spontaneously active centres or pacemakers. Stimulation anywhere on the anemone by a single shock stops the spontaneous twitching. Again it must be inferred that an inhibitory net spreads to all pacemakers. In these examples the inhibitory pathway must be widespread, anatomically irregular, and addressed in only one respect, that is to seek out the net containing the pacemakers.

In the jellyfish the situation is known in more detail (Horridge, 1956a). There are many spontaneous centres arranged round the margin of the bell,

27

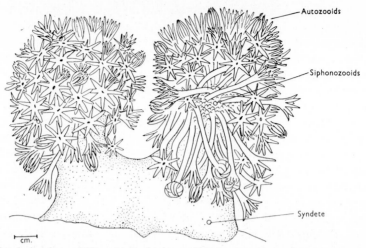

FIG. 1. A colony of *Heteroxenia fuscescens* (Alcyonacea) of the Red Sea, showing the numerous autozooids which are continually and independently spontaneously active except when inhibited by a specialized nerve net which runs over the whole colony. From Horridge (1956b).

each feeding motor impulses into a through-conducting nerve net which co-ordinates the symmetrical beat of the muscles over the whole bell. In the jellyfish these centres are separate ganglia, in which incidentally, neuropile is abundant in the first ganglia which appear in the animal kingdom. There is, in addition, a second nerve net which forms an input to these ganglia but over the surface of the bell, where they overlap, there are no physiological junctions between the two nerve nets. In some species a single shock applied to this second net immediately inhibits the spontaneity of all the marginal ganglia; in other species an impulse in the second net initiates an efferent impulse or accelerates the rhythm. Inhibition, rather than acceleration, of the rhythm of the ganglion is significant here in showing that the modulating pathways are widespread, because inhibition of a number of linked pacemakers shows that they must all have been acted on, but acceleration can be achieved by acting on one of them alone.

The main motor output of the jellyfish ganglion is a nerve net, the so-called giant fibre net, which carries a nerve impulse at each beat of the bell. The pacemaker, lying in the ganglion and physiologically within this motor net, is modulated by a variety of stimuli, including light and mechanoreceptors, in or near the ganglion, in addition to the afferent supply from the primary nerve net. There seems no reason to prefer a set of anatomically addressed connexions of these various inputs rather than a general sensitivity of the pacemakers to transmitter substances from non-addressed afferent neurons.

If only one efferent path were known from the jellyfish ganglion there would not be the necessity for an addressed system within it, except to distinguish between accelerating and inhibiting afferent pathways where these both are observed in the same species. However, there must be some form of addressing within the ganglion in certain species of jellyfish, e.g. *Cyanea*, *Cassiopea*, which have a second efferent path from the ganglion; this runs only locally to muscles of the bell and brings about the asymmetrical component of the beat as the animal rights itself when tilted. This efferent pathway is excited principally by the receptors of the direction of gravity, situated in the region of the ganglion, and the same receptors can also modulate the frequency of the pacemaker in the giant fibre net. There is no *a priori* reason for rejecting either anatomically or chemically addressed connexions for the transmission of excitation to these two efferent pathways within the ganglion. The existence of the neuropile at all, with an enormous number of apparently redundant and haphazardly arranged arborizing neurons in each marginal ganglion, is perhaps more compatible with the chemically addressed system. The point is that evolution from one non-addressed nerve net to two interacting nets and then to a simple ganglion which integrates several types of sensory excitation could have occurred by a differentiation of classes of sensory neurons distinguished by their specific transmitters, and present techniques do not distinguish this from an anatomically addressed system. On the efferent side the differentiation has been very small, in this instance to only two distinct classes of neurons.

There is a limitation of technique which influences any consideration of the modulation of ongoing neuron activity, even at the simple level of the coelenterate pacemaker. The variation between individuals, between similar ganglia where there are several in one animal, and in repeated performances of one preparation, means that the results must be treated statistically. When working with a ganglion with several distinguishable efferent neurons the same consideration applies for each neuron. Therefore the electrophysiological data on which a theory of the ganglionic activity is based, is the influence of various factors on the "probability of motor firing", a term which will recur. Input–output relations of this type cannot, by their nature, discriminate between the suggested mechanisms of preservation of information during transmission through a ganglion. The mechanism within must be studied.

A more complicated example of a widespread effect is the inhibition of crawling in the earthworm (Collier, 1938). Stimulation of the head end puts a stop to forward crawling, causing the movement to "freeze", but the tonus of all the muscles along the body is maintained. Here a pathway, probably a single neuron, runs the length of the worm, and its effect when active is to lower the probability of firing of motoneurons along the whole length of the worm. On account of the distribution of the peristaltic wave, the inhibitory impulses catch adjacent segments at different stages in the sequences of impulses from corresponding motoneurons in different segments. The whole motor output is evidently not stopped, because control of tone remains. The motoneurons of the worm are diverse and run to different muscles but in other respects the situation in any one segment appears superficially to be like that in the crustacean heart ganglion when inhibited.

In the crustacean heart ganglion there are nine motoneurons, about four of which are normally spontaneously active, the others being relays which only multiply the number of impulses in each burst. Except round the smaller cell bodies, the paired inhibitory axon branches apparently indiscriminately in the clumps of neuropile into which also run dendrites from the nine intrinsic neurons (Alexandrowicz, 1932). The inhibitory impulses affect all the cells but not necessarily to the same extent, or in the same order in different preparations (Maynard, 1953, 1961). It looks very much as if the specifications given to the inhibitory axon for growth and formation of synapses are not particular as to details of branching, number or destination of the terminations or their actual site on the heart ganglion neurons. They apparently spread to all the places where the ganglion cells have dendrites, and the specificity of the inhibitory axon could, on present evidence, lie only in its secretion of the appropriate transmitter substance. Similar considerations apply to the acceleratory fibres. This type of widely ramifying termination is perhaps particularly appropriate to this example where the regions of spontaneity are not necessarily static and are changed by stretching the preparation. The nuerons are also modulated by chemically addressed blood-borne hormones.

To this widespread inhibition in the heart ganglion the same general considerations apply as to *Heteroxenia*, to the anemone, the jellyfish and the worm. Other similar phenomena are known elsewhere in less detail, for example the widespread changes in tone following removal of anterior ganglia in many invertebrates, and taken together they suggest that a few axons act more or less indiscriminately on the probability of firing of a group of motoneurons which normally fire together to initiate a co-ordinated movement. Other examples are given below. There is no need to suppose a particular wiring diagram for the general inhibitory or excitatory input; all that is required is that it should be adequately distributed in the volume of neuropile where the motoneurons have their dendrites, and not necessarily anatomically addressed to particular postsynaptic cells.

The cerebral ganglion of the clam *Mya* initiates a sequence of motor impulses in from ten to twelve axons of the anterior pallial nerve when the connective between the posteriorly situated visceral and the anterior cerebral ganglion is stimulated. One impulse in one preganglionic axon is adequate to give a patterned burst of postganglionic motor impulses. There is considerable variation in the pattern seen in different preparations (Horridge, 1958, 1961). In the viscero-cerebral connective there is also at least one preganglionic inhibitory axon, which, when simultaneously stimulated, reduces the probability of firing of the motoneurons with a similar effect on all in the sequence, so that the number of axons and the number of impulses delivered by each progressively diminishes with repeated inhibitory impulses. If the excitatory and the inhibitory effects of the two types of preganglionic neurons are explained by the differential sensitivities of the efferent neurons of the ganglion, the number of anatomically addressed connexions can be minimal. The sequences themselves can also be explained as the consequence of the sensitivity of certain efferent neurons to the activity of others. It requires more postulates, and to my mind less probable ones, to explain these phenomena as arising from chains of anatomically addressed interneurons.

In the locust, the alternation of the antagonistic dorsoventral and longitudinal flight muscle is co-ordinated by a centrally determined sequence of motor impulses, such that impulses alternate in the two sets of motoneurons to the antagonistic muscles (Wilson, 1960). This central sequence, which normally brings about the reciprocatory movements of the wings, goes on irrespective of whether the effector muscles and all the peripheral sensory field of the thorax is removed, except that a stream of impulses must be arriving from certain hair sensilla of the head which are normally excited by the flow of air as the animal flies. However, flight is stopped by contact of the legs with the ground. Again it is reasonable to suppose that relatively few afferent neurons are adequate and that both the excitatory and the inhibitory preganglionic effects are widespread in the sense used here, i.e. they run to a large volume of the neuropile and to no particular neuron.

The ventilatory rhythm of the locust is similarly controlled by centrally determined sequences (Miller, 1960) and in the cricket it has been possible to demonstrate that both inhibitory and excitatory premotor interneurons can be stimulated at definite loci in the brain (Huber, 1960) from which they descend to have an appropriate effect on the probability of motor firing from each of the potentially independent pacemakers which initiate ventilatory movements from the ventral cord.

A rather clear-cut case where one preganglionic axon alone can have a general inhibitory and another a general excitatory effect is found in the feeding response of the fly. One of the three neurons of a single chemosensory hair, for example, of the tarsus, is sufficient to start and keep in activity the complicated pattern of movements which withdraw and fold up the proboscis of the fly and stimulation of another of the neurons is sufficient to reverse these processes. There may be a complicated series of central mechanisms, and in this case internuncial neurons are probably involved. At present, however, it is unnecessary to assume that these two types of sensory neurons have limited specific central connexions; they have opposite effects on the probability of firing of many motoneurons, and excitation from different hairs variously situated over the legs and labellum of the two sides sums together in a way which suggests that the sensory axons all feed into a common pool (Dethier, 1953).

Another preparation where the non-specific inhibition plays a different role is in the last abdominal ganglion of the Mantis (Milburn et al., 1960). When the last connexion of the de-afferentated terminal ganglion is severed from the rest of the nervous system, patterned bursts of impulses soon began to appear in the phallic nerve, similar to those causing copulatory movements if the nerve is intact. Apparently, descending inhibitory impulses are cut off by severing the cord.

Widespread connexions are also a feature of many second-order sensory neurons or interneurons of arthropods, but in these examples it is on the input side that the neuron shows various degrees of specificity. Examples are accumulating which show that one interneuron may collect from a large number of primary sensory axons, not only of many segments of the body but even of differing modality. In his detailed analysis of the crayfish cord, Wiersma (1958) finds examples of differing sizes of the sensory field covered by an interneuron, with examples of overlap and inclusiveness of the fields of different interneurons. For example, one interneuron may respond to sensory field A, another to sensory field B, and a third to A and B. In another type of pattern, an interneuron can be found which responds to any of a number of similar sensory fields repeated in adjacent segments, whereas each of these are also represented individually by other interneurons. Occasionally a very small group of hairs have their own interneuron. It is evident that there are all degrees of specificity in the connexions between sensory axons and interneurons. It is tempting to think that the more specific ones have evolved later. The interneurons are clearly individually differentiated to a high degree and some are unique in that only one is found in each side of the ventral cord. Perhaps here is an ideal situation in which it could be tested whether the various degrees of specificity of the input connexions lie in the exact ana-tomical addressing of sensory endings terminating on them, with a single transmitter, or on the varying sensitivity of different interneurons to a range of transmitters with different ranges of effect, formed by the differentiated peripheral sensory cells.

When we turn to the detailed structure of the neuropile as seen in single sections examined with the electron microscope we find no data which is relevant to the present question. Synapses are identified as contacts between axons having synaptic vesicles at one side of the bounding membranes, but there is no way of telling whether they are anatomically addressed, or whether widespread branches are selective in their contacts. The special methods for single neurons, using Golgi or intravitam methylene blue methods, have shown that the neuropile of many invertebrates consists of branched afferent axon arborizations and branched dendrites of efferent neurons. However, for the finer endings, half a century of detailed work by the best methods on many favourable preparations has failed to demonstrate any pattern or circuit diagram which is evidently anatomically addressed. The finer afferent and efferent branches are jumbled together and consistent specific contacts have been found only in a few instances where they are axon–axon synapses of giant fibres to motor fibres, or in the optic ganglia of arthropods, where spatial relationships must be maintained. In these few instances, as the giant fibre-to-motor synapses of the crayfish (Johnson, 1924) or of the polychaete nerve cord (Horridge, 1959) or the synapses between the giant interneuron and the several giant motor neurons in the squid stellate ganglion (Young, 1939) there is a widespread activation which is anatomically addressed to several motor neurons of a particular class. Here, the connexions, though still widespread, show considerable differentiation of addressing, but these examples are drawn from giant neurons which are concerned with rapid and stereotyped reflexes.

The neuron patterns in the optic ganglia of insects offer examples of great diversity of regional restriction and asymmetrical spread of histologically known arborizations (Zawarzin, 1913; Cajal and Sanchez, 1915). The classes of neurons that are localized radially below their corresponding ommatidia are in a position to conserve the directional aspect of the excitation falling on the eye, but many of these, having long arborizing branches, seem not specific with respect to the depth to which they penetrate. On the other hand, some interneurons spread laterally more widely, and lateral integration between ommatidia could not occur unless some spread occurred. In contrast, however, in all three optic ganglia there are classes of tangential or horizontal neurons having processes which ramify throughout particular tangential layers of the ganglion. They are restricted to certain depths from the outer surface of the ganglion but are in a position to take account of excitation irrespective of the position on the eye of its ommatidia of origin. By its laterally widespread connexions, this output from the optic ganglia contrasts strongly with the other, which has dendrites running more or less vertically and axons which keep their ordered ranks as they run to the next proximal ganglion. There are, therefore, two contrasting types of neurons to the brain, those from particular directions of the visual field and those from various definite depths in the optic lobes irrespective of the axes of the eye. The functional significance of each individual neuron must be a consequence of the directionality, extent and symmetry of the area over which its arborizations are spread in so far as it can have no connexions outside this area. Within individual small areas, we meet the same problem as before in not knowing how the axons are addressed.

On the question of the origin of the differentiation of labelled lines, by whatever mechanism they function, there are hardly any relevant observations. Neither anatomical nor physiological data, obtained by present techniques, are a help in answering the questions raised. Certainly labelled lines can be readily demonstrated physiologically but the mechanism of the channelling of information as the physiological pathways pass through the neuropile is

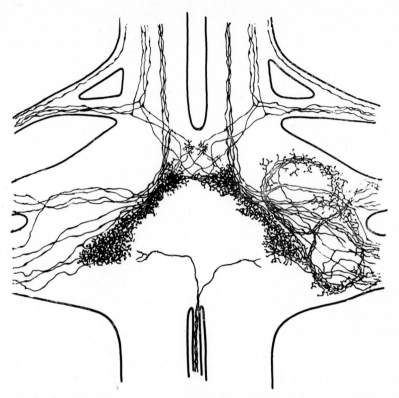

FIG. 2. Dorsal view of some sensory axon arborizations in an abdominal ganglion of the larva of the dragonfly *Aeschna* drawn from methylene blue preparations. This method illustrates the form of the neurons but not their relationships with other neurons and therefore gives no information of the possible occurrence of an anatomically addressed system. The widespread terminations and the general but not detailed symmetry of the two sides are shown. Modified from Zawarzin (1924).

unknown. However, some generalizations may be made about the relevant structures.

(1) Individual neurons can be recognized both physiologically, e.g. in the crayfish (Wiersma, 1958) or anatomically, e.g. in the ragworm (Smith, 1957) progressively more numerously and more clearly as we pass from the coelenterates through the worms to the arthropods.

(2) Widespread activation and depression of probability of motor firing is frequently brought about by widely ramifying neurons, for which only a relatively small degree of anatomical specificity of connexions is required.

(3) Where neurons can be individually recognized by their definite anatomical relations, their dendrites are nevertheless variable in detail from specimen to specimen and branch apparently haphazardly in the neuropile. The pattern

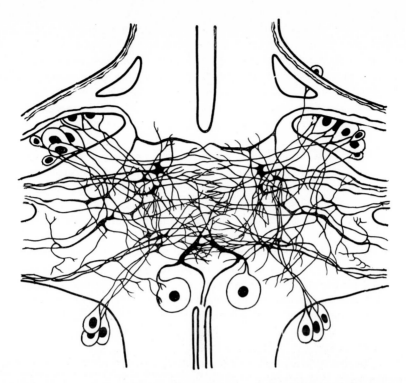

FIG. 3. Dorsal view of the branching dendrites of motor neurons of the same ganglion as in Fig. 1. Many of the neurons have dendrites which ramify over large areas of the ganglion. The patterns shown in this figure and Fig. 1 are typical of the general arrangement in arthropods and, to a less extent, of annelids. Modified from Zawarzin (1924).

of branching frequently still resembles that in nerve nets, where the neurons appear to be non-addressed within each net.

(4) In the simpler ganglia there are fewer classes of neurons, for example only four have been recognized in the jellyfish ganglion (Horridge, 1956a). Therefore fewer morphogenetic specifications are required to determine the pattern of addressing, whether anatomical or physiological. On the other hand in an arthropod, and to a lesser extent in a polychaete, many of the neurons are unique and individually recognizable.

(5) In particular, the number of types of efferent neuron is limited in the simpler ganglia. That of the jellyfish has only two types; even in the relatively complicated polychaete worm *Nereis* there are only about ten motoneurons per ganglion on each side (Smith, 1957). With these ten, reduplicated along the animal, it crawls and swims. This means that the simpler ganglia could possibly operate by relying on the differential responsiveness of the dendrites

of the efferent neurons and not depend on a specific central wiring diagram at all.

(6) Simpler ganglia in the lower animals are homogeneous, rather than divided into regions, and each neuron usually has branches which ramify over the whole ganglion, intermingling with those of many other neurons.

(7) As we go to more complicated animals the neuropile is progressively differentiated into more definite regions, and particular nerve cells have their arborizations confined to one of these regions. However, their branches still have the appearance of not being specified in detail and perhaps each region now acts as I have supposed for a more primitive whole ganglion.

(8) Within one animal, one ganglion may be highly regionalized with exactly delineated spread of the axon arborizations and dendrites, as in the optic ganglia of the dragonfly larva, another may be less regionalized, as in the abdominal ganglia of the same animal (Zawarzin, 1924) and another may be at the simplest level, with little differentiation of neuron types or limitation of the spread of neurons, as in the insect stomatogastric ganglia (Orlov, 1924).

(9) The degree of localization and the directionality of the arborizations range from a few microns, such as the endings of the retinula cell axons in the optic ganglia of insects, to several millimetres, or the whole extent of a ganglion. Most arborizations lie somewhere about the middle of this range.

(10) The pattern of arborization is rarely isotropic. The limitation of growth in a particular direction, with a definite degree of dispersion, sets an interesting problem in morphogenesis.

(11) The degree of bushiness of the arborizations is typical of each neuron, and frequently characteristic of large classes of neurons, e.g. in the corpora pedunculata or the antennal lobes of insects many fine short branches are the rule. A physiological correlate is not known.

(12) The above features apply equally well to the dendrites of efferent neurons and interneurons as they do to the axon arborizations of sensory cells and interneurons, although one normally thinks only of the latter in considering neurons with widespread and apparently non-specific effects.

SUMMARY

A series of examples suggests that inhibitory and excitatory neurons in the nervous systems of many invertebrates have widespread non-specific connexions. The evidence is stronger where such systems are inhibitory because then the afferent pathway must run to all spontaneously active neurons. In general, non-specific systems are considered as the more primitive type, upon which anatomical specificity of contact has evolved to various extents. Except in a single nerve net, each neuron is addressed so that it transmits excitation to some neurons rather than others which it meets. This addressing may be anatomical, in which case synapses occur between recognizable neurons, or physiological, in which case it may depend on differential sensitivities of receptor neurons to transmitter substances released by other neurons. The effect of inhibitory and excitatory transmitter substances on crustacean heart ganglion cells is an example of such a chemically addressed system. The histology of typical invertebrate ganglia is discussed with reference to the suggested mechanisms of the preservation of labelled lines during transmission.

REFERENCES

ALEXANDROWICZ, J. S. (1932) The innervation of the heart in the crustacea—I. Decapoda. *Quart. J. Microscop. Sci.* **75** : 181–249.

CAJAL, S. RAMON Y and SANCHEZ, D. (1915) Contribucion al conocimiento de los centros nerviosos de los insectos. *Trav. lab. inv. biol. Madrid.* **13** : 1–167.

COLLIER, H. O. J. (1938) The immobilization of locomotory movements in the earthworm *Lumbricus terrestris. J. Exptl. Biol.* **15** : 339–357.

DETHIER, V. G. (1953) Summation and inhibition following contralateral stimulation of the dorsal chemoreceptors of the blowfly. *Biol. Bull. Woods Hole* **105** : 257–268.

HARTLINE, H. K., RATCLIFF, F. and MILLER, W. H. (1961) Inhibitory interaction in the retina and its significance in vision. This volume, p. 241.

HORRIDGE, G. A. (1956a) The nervous system of the ephyra larva of *Aurellia aurita. Quart. J. Microscop. Sci.* **97** : 59–74.

HORRIDGE, G. A. (1956b) The responses of *Heteroxenia* (Alcyonaria) to stimulation and to some inorganic ions. *J. Exptl. Biol.* **33** : 604–614.

HORRIDGE, G. A. (1957) The co-ordination of the protective retraction of coral polyps. *Phil. Trans. Roy. Soc. London* B **240** : 495–529.

HORRIDGE, G. A. (1958) Transmission of excitation through the ganglia of *Mya* (Lamellibranchiata). *J. Physiol. (London)* **143** : 553–572.

HORRIDGE, G. A. (1959) Analysis of the rapid responses of *Nereis* and *Harmothoë* (Annelida). *Proc. Roy. Soc. London* B **150** : 245–262.

HORRIDGE, G. A. (1961) The centrally determined sequence of impulses initiated from a ganglion of the clam *Mya. J. Physiol. (London).* **155**.

HUBER, F. (1960) Habilitation Thesis, Tubingen.

JOHNSON, G. E. (1924) Giant nerve fibers in crustaceans, with special reference to *Cambarus* and *Palaemonetes. J. Comp. Neurol.* **36** : 323–373.

MAYNARD, D. M. (1953) Direct inhibition in the lobster cardiac ganglion. Ph.D. Thesis, University of California, Los Angeles, pp. 1–72.

MAYNARD, D. M. (1961) Cardiac inhibition in decapod Crustacea. This volume, p. 144.

MILBURN, N., WEIANT, E. A. and ROEDER, K. D. (1960) The release of efferent nerve activity in the roach, *Periplaneta americana*, by extracts of the corpus cardiacum. *Biol. Bull. Woods Hole* **118** : 111–119.

MILLER, P. L. (1960) Respiration in the Desert Locust—I. The control of ventilation. *J. Exptl. Biol.* **37** : 224–236.

ORLOV, J. (1924) Die Innervation des Darmes der Insekten (Larven von Lamellicorniern). *Z. wiss. Zool.* **122** : 425–502.

RATLIFF, F. and HARTLINE, H. K. (1959) The response of *Limulus* optic nerve fibers to patterns of illumination on the receptor mosaic. *J. Gen. Physiol.* **42** : 1241–1255.

SMITH, J. E. (1957) The nervous anatomy of the body segments of nereid polychaetes. *Phil. Trans. Roy. Soc. London* B **240** : 135–196.

WIERSMA, C. A. G. (1958) On the functional connexions of single units in the central nervous system of the crayfish *Procambarus clarkii* Girard. *J. Comp. Neurol.* **110** : 421–472.

WILSON, D. M. (1960) Private communication.

YOUNG, J. Z. (1939) Fused neurons and synaptic contacts in the giant nerve fibres of cephalopods. *Phil. Trans. Roy. Soc. London* B **229** : 465–503.

ZAWARZIN, A. (1913) Histologische Studien über Insekten—IV. Die optischen Ganglien der *Aeshna*-Larven. *Z. wiss. Zool.* **108** : 175–257.

ZAWARZIN, A. (1924) Zur Morphologie der Nervenzentren. Histologische Studien über Insekten—VI. *Z. wiss. Zool.* **122** : 323–424.

INHIBITION AND OCCLUSION IN
CORTICAL NEURONS*

A. L. Towe

Department of Physiology and Biophysics, University of Washington
School of Medicine, Seattle, Washington

THE activity of individual cortical neurons has been under scrutiny for nearly a decade. During this time, the general features of this activity have been expounded, and we are now moving into a period of more refined measurements and of theory building. From such pursuits will emerge a welter of fine details regarding unit activity and a few general principles that will clarify, to some extent, the functioning of the central nervous system. These principles will rest upon two general processes, as yet poorly understood, termed excitation and inhibition. So far in this symposium the discussion has centered around inhibitory mechanisms in various invertebrates and in several mammalian tissues, especially the spinal cord of the cat. The existence of inhibitory activity in higher synaptic systems, such as the cerebral cortex, remains to be demonstrated. For this discussion we shall confine ourselves to work on the somatosensory system of the monkey (*Macaca mulatta*).

If we isolate a single unit in the postcentral gyrus with a microelectrode and then explore the body surface by deflecting hairs, tapping the skin or passing an electric current through it, we can locate a region of the skin which, when so stimulated, will drive the unit to activity. The precise position, size and shape of this region are not, at the moment, of concern. We will only note that the region does not extend indefinitely, but is bounded; this bounded region is called the unit excitatory receptive field. The various parameters of the cortical unit response change progressively as the point of stimulation is moved from the interior to the edge of this field; stimulation outside it fails to arouse the unit. However, the boundary is not sharp, but is a tenuous region where the excitatory process provoked by the stimulus and impinging upon the unit becomes too feeble to be detectable.

In analyzing the interaction effects, we shall confine our attention to those units whose excitatory receptive fields occupy several digits of the hand. When the skin is stimulated electrically, the extent of current spread must be controlled. This can be accomplished by stimulating digits rather than broad

* This work was supported by a grant (B396) from the National Institute of Neurological Diseases and Blindness, Department of Health, Education and Welfare.

areas of skin on the limb or trunk. Not only is current spread into adjacent digits negligible, but the fibers innervating the skin of the distal portion of one digit ramify within that digit, and not into adjacent digits.

The gradual decline in effectiveness of the stimulus near the margin of the excitatory receptive field suggests that some effect on the unit should be demonstrable by stimulation a little beyond the boundary. Indeed, the standard conditioning-testing procedure clearly shows that stimulation just outside the excitatory field alters the excitability of the unit and of the system leading to it (Amassian, 1952, 1953; Towe and Amassian, 1958). Surprisingly enough, this change takes the form of depressing the responsiveness of the unit to stimulation within the excitatory receptive field (Fig. 1). This depression is

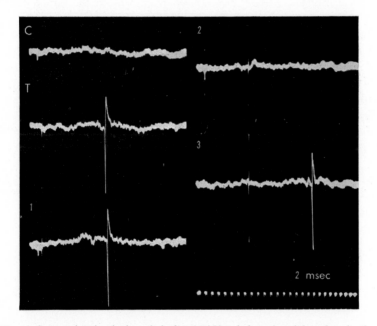

FIG. 1. Interaction in single unit isolated 1050 μ below the pial surface in the postcentral gyrus (p.c.g.) of the monkey. C, conditioning stimulus to digit IV of forepaw failed to discharge unit. T, testing stimulus to digit II of forepaw fired unit after 17·5 msec mean latency. (1) Digit IV stimulated 1 msec before digit II; unit fired after 18·1 msec mean latency. (2) Digit IV stimulated 14 msec before digit II; unit failed to discharge. (3) Testing stimulus alone still fired unit at same mean latency.

sufficiently powerful to render the unit inexcitable for about a tenth of a second, and less excitable than normal for another tenth of a second. Both the duration and intensity of the depression can be diminished by weakening the conditioning stimulus or by applying the conditioning stimulus farther away from the boundary of the excitatory receptive field (Towe and Amassian,

1958). Such a phenomenon can be called an inhibitory interaction in the general sense of the definition used in this symposium.

This inhibitory interaction could result from either of two mechanisms. The conditioning input might discharge some peripheral neurons also discharged from the test field, leaving them refractory or less excitable to the subsequent testing input. This occurrence would reduce the size of the excitatory input aroused by the testing stimulus; the cortical unit might then fail to discharge at all. On the other hand, the conditioning input might directly inhibit some neurons that are ordinarily excited by the testing input, reducing the size of the subsequent test excitatory volley. In order to discover which mechanism prevails, it is necessary to observe more than the response probability changes. Figure 2 shows what happens to the initial discharge latency during the interaction. Two distinct changes occur. When the conditioning stimulus is applied well inside the unit's excitatory receptive field, the latency of the test response clearly and systematically shortens. When the conditioning input is applied on the edge of, or just outside, the unit excitatory receptive field, the latency of the test response lengthens. These two response patterns cannot be dismissed as "random", for they are statistically highly reliable.

We are already familiar with unit response variations of this nature (Kennedy and Towe, 1958). The initial spike latency of a postsynaptic unit varies

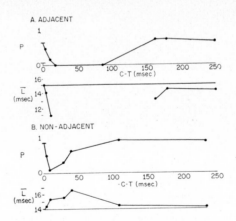

FIG. 2. Two patterns of interaction from two different cortical units. A. Unit from 644 μ down in p.c.g. Conditioning digit V fired unit with probability (p) of 0·08. Testing digit IV fired unit with $p = 0·62$ after 15·2 msec mean latency. In first 15 msec of interaction the test response latency ($\bar{l}$) progressively shortened to more than eight standard deviations (s) below the unconditioned testing $\bar{L}$; $\bar{L}$ was also shorter during recovery. B. Unit from 1829 μ down in p.c.g. Conditioning digit IV never fired unit. Testing digit II fired unit with $p = 0·82$ after 14·0 msec latency. Throughout interaction, $\bar{L}$ of the testing response was greater than 14·0 msec, increasing by more than three standard deviations (s) above the unconditioned testing $\bar{L}$.

as a function of stimulus intensity and hence of the population of presynaptic terminals activated by the stimulus. Very weak stimuli activate a small number of presynaptic terminals; the unit thus excited discharges with only one spike after a rather long latency. Its response probability at such weak stimulus intensities is usually less than one. Strong stimuli, on the other hand, activate a large population of presynaptic elements; the unit then typically discharges several closely spaced spikes after a short latency. The latency of the unit response gradually passes from one extreme to the other as the stimulus is varied from threshold to supramaximal intensity. Figure 3 shows the pattern

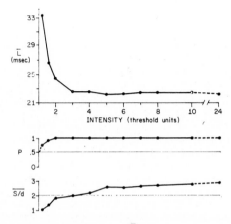

FIG. 3. Unit isolated 680 μ below the pial surface in p.c.g. Intensity of stimulus (i) varied from threshold to twenty-four times threshold intensity (T). When i increased to 2 T, $p = 1 \cdot 00$. The mean number of spikes per discharge (s/d) at each intensity continued to grow, even when $i = 5$ T. $\bar{L}$ shortened rapidly between $i = T$ and $i = 3$ T, stabilizing for all $i = 3$ T; the total latency change was about 10 msec. This pattern of $\bar{L} = f(i)$ has been observed in nearly every central nervous system neuron studied.

of these changes. Response probability grows from the threshold value of 0·5 to unity as the stimulus intensity is raised from threshold to twice threshold value. Simultaneously, the latency of the initial discharge decreases toward a minimum value; all stimulus intensities greater than about three times threshold fire the unit at the same (minimum) latency. Similarly, the number of spikes in each discharge changes with intensity, growing from one spike per discharge at threshold to several at many times threshold intensity. Increasing the stimulus intensity from threshold to much higher values increases the number of fibers activated by the stimulus, and this, in turn, increases the number of active presynaptic terminals on each unit in the system leading to the cortical unit. As the population of active neurons in the system changes, the pattern of unit discharge changes. The proposed mechanism of this dependency on stimulus intensity has been presented elsewhere (Morse and Towe, 1959) and will not be here; it suffices to indicate that the initial latency of the discharge of the unit, the number of spikes per discharge and the interspike intervals are functions of the size and shape of the afferent volley impinging upon the unit.

The latency–intensity relationship just described can be obtained by stimulation anywhere within the unit excitatory receptive field. However, the minimum latency attained at strong stimulus intensities is a function of the position of the stimulus within the field. Figure 4 illustrates this dependency for a unit

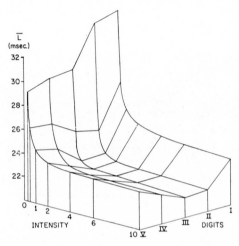

FIG. 4. Change in $\overline{L}$ with change in stimulus intensity and locus. The surface was constructed by finding a best-fit curve of $\overline{L} = f(i)$ for each of the five digits, and inserting some representative intensities; twenty-one different intensities were tested for each digit. The center of this unit's excitatory receptive field was between digits II and III, probably closer to III. Intensity in potentiometric units.

with the center of its excitatory receptive field near the third digit; stimulation of this digit yielded the largest surface primary response in the cortex just overlying the unit. Each of the five digits was stimulated at various intensities from threshold to many times threshold. The mean initial latency of discharge was plotted for each digit as a function of stimulus intensity. As the site of stimulation is moved progressively out from the center of the excitatory receptive field, the minimum latency attained progressively becomes longer, until the unit fails to discharge entirely. Hence, when interaction studies are carried out, some attention must be given to the position of both inputs with respect to the receptive field of the unit under observation. When the conditioning input is applied just prior to the testing input, the latter might effectively excite the unit *before* the former, or the two inputs might affect the unit simultaneously. Table 1 reveals the results of interacting two excitatory

TABLE 1. FACILITATORY INTERACTION AT
SOMESTHETIC CORTEX

The response latency to digit V is significantly shorter than to digit IV, when Student's t, with pooled estimate of error, is used. The response latency to the combined input is significantly shorter than to digit IV or V alone.

Digit	p	$\bar{L}$	s	P	df
IV	0·89	16·60	2·68		114
				<0·01	
V	0·89	14·49	1·42		63
				<0·01	
IV + V (1 msec)	1·00	12·65	0·70		

inputs at a small time interval. The initial response latency is earlier than that to either input alone, and the variation in latency on successive trials is much reduced. Such a change might, as suggested by Figs. 3 and 4, result from an increased population of active neurons in the system leading to the cortical unit; it is like the change produced by interacting stimuli to adjacent digits (Fig. 2). In fact, this sort of facilitatory interaction is observed whenever both the conditioning and testing stimuli are applied well within the boundaries of the unit excitatory receptive field.

When a conditioning input which itself fails to discharge the unit is applied a few milliseconds before the testing input, the latency of the test response increases and the number of spikes in each discharge decreases. Like the facilitatory interaction, this latter effect can be found at all levels within the sensory pathway. Table 2 illustrates this phenomenon in a unit from the

TABLE 2. INHIBITORY INTERACTION AT UNIT IN
CUNEATE NUCLEUS

Stimulation of digit III 12 msec before digit II was stimulated changed the response to stimulation at digit II. Both the change in latency ($D\bar{L}$; note size of standard deviations, s) and interspike interval (ii) were highly significant.

Digit		III	II–1		II–2		II–3
Alone	$\bar{L}$	8·1	7·86		8·51		9·33
	s	—	0·11		0·12		0·13
	P	0·12	1·00		1·00		0·68
	ii			0·65		0·82	
III + II (12 msec)	$\bar{L}$	8·1	8·18		8·89		
	s	—	0·11		0·13		
	P	0·12	1·00		0·94		
	ii			0·71			
	$D\bar{L}$		0·32		0·38		

cuneate nucleus. The conditioning input had a weak excitatory effect, producing one spike in twelve of a hundred trials. The testing input produced three spikes in sixty-eight of a hundred trials and two spikes in the remaining thirty-two trials. When the conditioning digit was stimulated 12 msec prior to the testing digit, the test response latency increased significantly, the number of spikes in each discharge decreased, and the interspike interval increased by a small, but statistically significant amount. The same sort of interaction in the cortex shows considerably greater variability, but also a larger change in latency.

Thus, with any particular unit, both the "increasing latency" and the "decreasing latency" types of interaction should be demonstrable. Figure 5 shows that this is indeed the case, and summarizes both effects. Both digits II and III were near the center of the unit excitatory receptive field; digit V was on the border of the field. Interacting stimulation of digits II (testing) and III

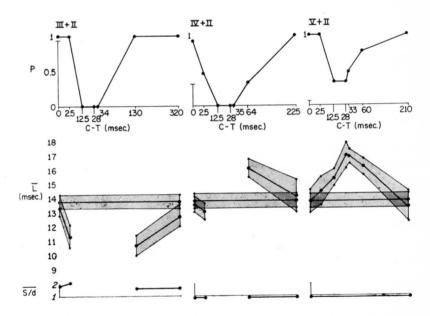

FIG. 5. Unit isolated 832 μ below pial surface in p.c.g. Digit II was center of unit excitatory receptive field; $p = 0\cdot95, \bar{L} = 13\cdot76$ msec, $s = 0\cdot51$ msec, $\overline{s/d} = 1\cdot11$. Unconditioned testing $\bar{L}$ (digit II) shown as line through each $\bar{L}$ graph; shaded area shows one standard deviation in each direction from $\bar{L}$. Height of line at $C - T = 0$ msec, topped by bar, shows conditioning digit response probability. Conditioning digit II by digit III yielded "occlusive" interaction, $\bar{L}$ shortened and $\overline{s/d}$ increased, until $p = 0$ and during recovery. Conditioning II by V yielded "inhibitory" interaction: $\bar{L}$ increased and $\overline{s/d}$ dropped to $1\cdot00$. Conditioning II by IV yielded an intermediate or mixed interaction, i.e. it began like a weak "occlusive" interaction, but other properties suggest the presence of a strong inhibitory effect.

(conditioning) resulted in a facilitatory effect during the early phase and during recovery. The effect in the early phase led us to call this an "occlusive" type of interaction. The late facilitation would not be expected in such an interaction, but may have had its origin in a cortically originating facilitatory effect on lower levels of the sensory system, thus effectively increasing the testing input to the unit. This latter suggestion derives from the observations presented in the subsequent paper of this symposium by Jabbur and Towe (p. 419). When stimulation of digit IV was employed as a conditioning input, the early facilitation of the input from digit II was weaker; the recovery was as expected from an occlusive interaction. Stimulation of digit V effectively diminished the efficacy of stimulation at digit II in exciting the unit. Such an effect could only result from an active inhibition of some neurons in the pathway leading to the unit, and is therefore called an inhibitory interaction. The inhibition is a consequence of stimulation near the boundary of the excitatory receptive field.

This precise timing analysis, combined with the qualitative observations of Mountcastle and Powell (1959), leads to the conclusion that a region just outside and overlapping the excitatory receptive field of any given unit has the net effect of reducing the population of neurons excited by stimulation within the excitatory receptive field. The reduction in population is accomplished, not by prior activation of some elements in the system, so that they are unresponsive, but by an active inhibition of these units. This "ring" around the excitatory field can be termed an inhibitory receptive field or inhibitory surround.

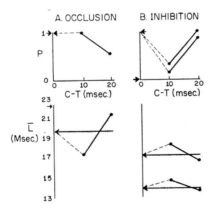

FIG. 6. Two units isolated simultaneously at 759 μ below pial surface in p.c.g., showing both the "occlusive" and the "inhibitory" types of interaction. Arrowhead on left of ordinate axis shows conditioning (digit II) L and p; on right is testing L and p. A. At 10 msec $C - T$ interval, L shortened; when p drops at $C - T = 20$ msec, L increases. B. Very short duration "inhibitory" interaction. Unit discharged two spikes in each discharge, so changes in both are shown.

In nearly every instance where activity in two units has been recorded simultaneously via the same electrode (implying that the two units are close to one another), one unit has shown the occlusive type of interaction while the other has shown the active inhibitory type. Mountcastle and Powell (1959) have reported a related response to tactual stimulation. Figure 6 illustrates this phenomenon, showing a very short inhibitory interaction. It is evident, therefore, that a topographical map of excitatory fields and inhibitory "surrounds" for the units in a small patch of cortex would appear as a jumble of fields. Closely spaced neurons in the cortex can "look back" to the same stimulus input through different input populations, some elements of which are excitatory and some inhibitory.

REFERENCES

AMASSIAN, V. E. (1952) Inhibition and occlusion in single cortical units. *Am. J. Physiol.* **171** : 704.

AMASSIAN, V. E. (1953) Evoked single cortical unit activity in the somatic sensory areas. *Electroencephalog. and Clin. Neurophysiol.* **5** : 415–438.

KENNEDY, T. T. and TOWE, A. L. (1958) Response of somatosensory cortical units to variations in stimulus intensity. *Federation Proc.* **17** : 85.

MORSE, R. W. and TOWE, A. L. (1959) Summation within the somatosensory system. *Physiologist* **2** : 85–86.

MOUNTCASTLE, V. B. and POWELL, T. P. S. (1959) Neural mechanisms subserving cutaneous sensibility, with special reference to the role of afferent inhibition in sensory perception and discrimination. *Bull. Johns Hopkins Hosp.* **105** : 201–232.

TOWE, A. L. and AMASSIAN, V. E. (1958) Patterns of activity in single cortical units following stimulation of the digits in monkeys. *J. Neurophysiol.* **21** : 292–311.

THE INFLUENCE OF THE CEREBRAL CORTEX ON THE DORSAL COLUMN NUCLEI*

S. J. JABBUR AND A. L. TOWE

Department of Physiology and Biophysics, University of Washington
School of Medicine, Seattle, Washington

THE idea of centrifugal modulation of sensory input has developed rapidly in the past decade. Hagbarth and Kerr (1954) described an inhibition of the dorsal root reflex and the dorsal column relay following conditioning stimulation of various supraspinal structures. Since that time, similar depressive effects of central structures on nuclei of the somesthetic, auditory, visual, and olfactory systems have been demonstrated. More recently, fibers have been shown to course directly from the cerebral cortex, via the pyramidal tract, to the dorsal column nuclei and the spinal trigeminal nucleus in both the cat and several primate species (Walberg, 1957; Chambers and Liu, 1957; Kuypers, 1958 a, b, c). The following discussion describes the function of some of these fibers in the cat.

Neurons of the cuneate nucleus are excited not only by axons whose cell bodies are located in dorsal root ganglia, but also by dorsal column relay fibers (Hursh, 1940) and by axon collaterals originating within the cuneate nucleus (Amassian and DeVito, 1957). The monosynaptic input can readily be distinguished from the indirect inputs by its short and relatively invariant response latency and its ability to respond to each shock in a train at frequencies in excess of 100/sec. The indirect inputs produce a discharge after a longer latency (greater than 8 msec) which is more variable; the spikes so produced fail to follow repetitive shocks as high as 50/sec. The same neuron may first be excited monosynaptically and then be excited by either or both of the indirect routes following a single ipsilateral forelimb stimulus (Fig. 1A). This usually results in a short silent interval during the discharge; the spikes appear in two groups.

Bipolar shocks applied to the surface of the precruciate or postcruciate cortex of either hemisphere modify the response of cuneate neurons to a subsequent ipsilateral forepaw shock (Jabbur and Towe, 1960). One cuneate neuron in three is discharged from 5 to 30 msec after single shocks or trains

* This work was supported by a grant (B396) from the National Institute of Neurological Diseases and Blindness, Department of Health, Education and Welfare.

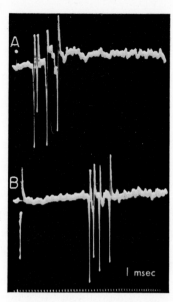

Fig. 1. Cuneate neuron discharged by electrical stimulation of the ipsilateral forepaw (A) and the contralateral motor cortex (B). Peripheral shock artifacts are marked with dot. A short train of shocks applied to the ipsilateral motor cortex would just discharge the neuron. A. Mean initial spike latency following forepaw shocks, $L = 5\cdot77$ msec; mean number of spikes per discharge, $\overline{s/d} = 3\cdot82$; maximum frequency following, $ff = 312$/sec. B. Following stimulation of contralateral motor cortex, $L = 26\cdot70$ msec; $\overline{s/d} = 3\cdot12$.

of shocks to the cortex (Fig. 1B); a subsequent afferent volley finds the neuron less responsive. The remaining two-thirds of the cuneate neurons are rendered less excitable by such conditioning stimulation. As illustrated in Fig. 2, a short train of shocks is usually required. The time course of this decrease in excitability, shown in Fig. 3, is the same as that obtained by interacting two cutaneous inputs; it is fully developed within 20 msec after the end of the conditioning stimulus and the unit has fully recovered 100–200 msec later. Like the monosynaptic inhibitory interaction shown in the Table on p. 415, the response latency of the cortically inhibited cuneate neuron increases, and the number of spikes decreases, until the peak depression is attained. Responsiveness then returns to normal. Conditioning stimulation applied to either hemisphere depresses the unit's responsiveness, but stimulation of the cortex contralateral to the recording site is more efficacious (Fig. 4). The magnitude of the depressive effect can be increased either by increasing the strength of the cortical shock or by decreasing the strength of the forepaw shock. When the conditioning stimulus consists of at least ten strong shocks with a frequency of 300/sec, and the testing stimulus is reduced to near threshold intensity, maximal inhibition is observed. Thus, the inhibition is milder than

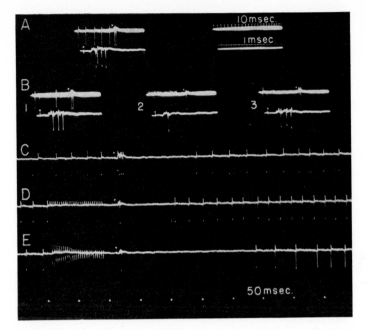

Fig. 2. Evoked and spontaneous cuneate unit activity inhibited by stimulation of the contralateral motor cortex. Peripheral shock artifacts are marked with dot. A (*left*)—Response of unit to maximal ipsilateral forepaw stimulation. $\bar{L} = 7\cdot48$ msec; $\overline{s/d} = 4\cdot0$; $ff = 250$/sec. Lower sweep shows the 40 msec following peripheral stimulation. B1 and 3. Response to near threshold peripheral stimulus intensity before and after a conditioning interaction. $\bar{L} = 7\cdot49$ msec; $\overline{s/d} = 2\cdot85$. B2. Inhibition of peripherally evoked response by 84 msec train of 312/sec shocks to the contralateral motor cortex beginning 106 msec before the testing input. $\bar{L} = 7\cdot47$ msec; $\overline{s/d} = 1\cdot09$. C and D. Continuous film of same interaction, showing effect on spontaneous activity. E. Conditioning pulse durations increased from $0\cdot1$ msec to $0\cdot5$ msec resulting in longer suppression of the spontaneous activity. Lower tips of spikes in C, D and E are indicated by dots.

that between peripheral inputs. It is sufficiently powerful, however, to block the neuron discharge produced by a tactual stimulator or by maintained pressure.

The direction of the changes of response latency and the number of spikes in each discharge during interaction are consistent with the interpretation of an inhibition as defined in another Chapter in this volume (p. 410). Recourse to this argument is not always necessary, however, for inhibition is readily demonstrated in units excited monosynaptically from the skin; an occlusive type of interaction is not possible in these instances.

When the brain stem has been transected at the level of the inferior olivary nucleus so that only the pyramidal tracts remain intact (Fig. 5), then both cortical excitation and cortical inhibition of cuneate neurons can be obtained;

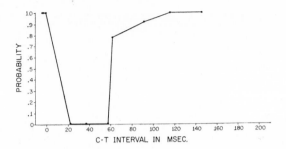

FIG. 3. Time course of the inhibitory interaction. Conditioning stimulus was single 0·6 msec duration shock applied to the contralateral motor cortex at various times before the peripheral testing stimulus. The time course is measured as a decrease in probability of discharge of the first spike of the test discharge; other measures yield a similar time course.

the inhibitory effect, however, is greatly weakened. When, on the other hand, only the pyramidal tract is transected at the same level, leaving the rest of the brain stem intact, the excitatory effect can no longer be demonstrated, but the inhibition still occurs, although it has been weakened. The behavior of units driven by cortical stimulation suggests that the pyramidal tract fibers excite them directly. The corticofugal inhibitory influence is less direct. Perhaps the pyramidal and other projections from the cortex to the bulbar

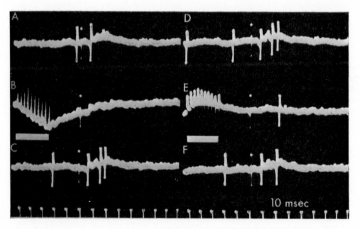

FIG. 4. Comparison of efficacy of contralateral and ipsilateral motor cortex in inhibiting cuneate unit. A, C, D, F. Response to near threshold ipsilateral fore-paw stimulation. Peripheral shock artifacts are marked with dot. $\overline{L} = 6·00$ msec; $\overline{s/d} = 1·8$; probability of discharge, $p = 1·0$. B. Complete inhibition of test response by stimulation of contralateral cortex. E. Incomplete inhibition of test response by similar stimulation of the ipsilateral cortex. $\overline{L} = 20·75$ msec (latency of third spike, when present in unconditioned response was about 19 msec); $\overline{s/d} = 1·00$; response probability at illustrated $C - T$ interval of 53 msec was 0·40. Note suppression of spontaneous activity during interaction.

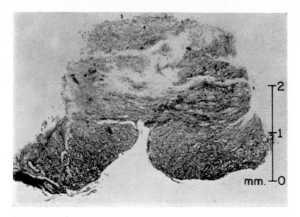

FIG. 5.—Luxol-fast section through brain stem at level of inferior olive, showing the amount of tissue remaining after the transection. The overlying medial lemniscus tissue was effectively transected, as revealed by a comparison of sections at various levels through this region.

reticular formation are involved (Kuypers, 1958a). In any event, it is evident that activation of certain fibers coursing out from the pericruciate cortex ultimately leads to a decrease in the excitability of units in the dorsal column nuclei, as evidenced by the responsiveness of cuneate and gracile units to both monosynaptic and multisynaptic cutaneous inputs. The simplicity of the anatomical arrangement in this preparation makes it ideal for the further analysis of inhibition at higher levels of the central nervous system than the spinal cord.

REFERENCES

AMASSIAN, V. E. and DeVITO, J. L. (1957) La transmission dans le noyau de Burdach (nucleus cuneatus). Etude analytique par unités isolées d'un relais somato-sensoriel primaire. *Coll. intern. centre nat. recherche sci.* (*Paris*) **67** : 353–393.

CHAMBERS, W. W. and LIU, C. N. (1957) Cortico-spinal tract of the cat. An attempt to correlate the pattern of degeneration with deficits in reflex activity following neocortical lesions. *J. Comp. Neurol.* **108** : 23–55.

HAGBARTH, K.-E. and KERR, D. I. B. (1954) Central influences on spinal afferent conduction. *J. Neurophysiol.* **17** : 295–307.

HURSH, J. B. (1940) Relayed impulses in ascending branches of dorsal root fibers. *J. Neurophysiol.* **3** : 166–177.

JABBUR, S. J. and TOWE, A. L. Effect of pyramidal tract activity on dorsal column nuclei. *Science* **132** : 547–548.

KUYPERS, H. G. J. M. (1958a) An anatomical analysis of cortico-bulbar connexions to the pons and lower brain stem in the cat. *J. Anat.* **92** : 198–218.

KUYPERS, H. G. J. M. (1958b) Corticobulbar connexions to the pons and lower brain-stem in man. An anatomical study. *Brain* **81** : 364–388.

KUYPERS, H. G. J. M. (1958c) Some projections from the peri-central cortex to the pons and lower brain stem in monkey and chimpanzee. *J. Comp. Neurol.* **110** : 221–255.

WALBERG, F. (1957) Corticofugal fibers to the nuclei of the dorsal columns. An experimental study in the cat. *Brain* **80** : 273–287.

ONTOGENETIC ANALYSIS OF SOME EVOKED SYNAPTIC ACTIVITIES IN SUPERFICIAL NEOCORTICAL NEUROPIL

DOMINICK P. PURPURA*

Paul Moore Laboratory of the Department of Neurological Surgery,
College of Physicians and Surgeons, Columbia University,
New York

INTRODUCTION

THE superficial neuropil of neocortex is an elaborately organized sub-pial sheet of axons, dendrites and axodendritic synapses which gives rise to a major portion of the electrical activity recorded from the surface of the brain. Information on its intrinsic synaptic organization may be considered fundamental to an understanding of the different varieties of spontaneous and evoked electrocortical potentials observed under different conditions and the relationship of surface potentials to different patterns of neuronal discharges (cf. Purpura, 1959).

Although some cortical synaptic activities have been analyzed with intracellularly located microelectrodes (Branch and Martin, 1958; Buser and Albe-Fessard, 1957; Kandel and Spencer, 1960; Li, 1959; Martin and Branch, 1958; Phillips, 1956a, b, 1959; Spencer and Kandel, 1960), the contribution of axodendritic postsynaptic potentials (p.s.p.'s) to these activities has been a matter of conjecture. Apart from a few attempts to analyze cortical dendritic activity with intracellular recording techniques (Li, 1959; Tasaki *et al.*, 1954), most hypotheses concerning the properties of cortical dendrites have evolved, in part, from physiological and pharmacological studies on the nature and origin of evoked superficial negative cortical responses (Chang, 1951; Clare and Bishop, 1955; Eccles, 1951; Grundfest, 1958; Purpura, 1959; Purpura and Grundfest, 1956). While it is to be expected that further application and development of microphysiological techniques may permit a more detailed

* Work of the author, a Sister Elizabeth Kenny Foundation Scholar, was supported in part by a grant (B-1312 C3) from the National Institute of Neurological Diseases and Blindness, and the United Cerebral Palsy Research and Educational Foundation (R-133-60). The data summarized here were obtained in collaboration with Dr. E. M. Housepia, an Parkinson's Disease Foundation Fellow, and Dr. M. W. Carmichael, a Post-Doctoral Fellow in Neuropharmacology, N. I. N. D. B.

definition of the mode of generation and propagation of these responses and the composition of different superficial axodendritic pathways, the importance of developing other analytical tools cannot be overemphasized.

One approach to the analysis of synaptic activities in superficial cortical neuropil, that described here, takes advantage of the changing morpho-physiological properties of developing cortex in order to provide data on the proportion, magnitude and temporal relations of inhibitory and excitatory synaptic activities in different superficial axodendritic organizations. This approach requires first, consideration of the structural features of elements in superficial cortex and of the overt synaptic activities generated therein during various stages of development. These conditions are satisfactorily met with favorable Golgi–Cox preparations and analyses of the generation and spread of superficial negative cortical responses to local surface stimulation. Elucidation of the distribution of inhibitory activity in overt surface responses requires some method for identifying p.s.p.'s generated in distal dendritic processes. Inhibitory p.s.p.'s may be identified indirectly by the effects of pharmacological agents which eliminate i.p.s.p.'s in responses compounded of excitatory and inhibitory activities and thereby produce profound augmentation in the tested response (Purpura and Grundfest, 1956, 1957; Purpura et al., 1959b).

The present report surveys recent studies that illustrate the usefulness of an ontogenetic approach in analyzing the complex functional activity of the cerebral cortex. The data so obtained not only serve to focus on characteristics of some synaptic organizations involved in the production of different evoked superficial cortical responses but also provide information on the changing composition of these organizations during cortical maturation.

METHODS

Experiments were performed on kittens from litters born in the laboratory. Attempts were made, whenever possible, to use animals from the same litter at different ages. A small series of near-term fetuses were also studied. All kittens were initially anesthetized with ether to permit introduction of tracheal and external jugular cannulas after which the exposed skin margins and scalp were infiltrated with procaine and the ether was discontinued. The animals were then immobilized with succinylcholine chloride and artificially ventilated. Following craniectomy, stimulating and recording electrodes were placed in different arrays on the exposed suprasylvian gyrus. Stimulating electrodes consisted of a pair of 100 μ Teflon-coated wires cemented together. Chlorided-silver wires with 0·2 and 0·5 mm ball tips were used for recording. Monopolar differential recording was employed throughout. Other details as to stimulating and recording techniques and the methods used to study the actions of topically applied ω-amino acid drugs were similar to those described previously (Purpura and Grundfest, 1956, 1957; Purpura *et al.*, 1959b, 1960a).

Postnatal Development of Superficial Neocortical Neuropil

The following survey of the salient morphological features of the major constituents of superficial neuropil is intended to facilitate interpretation of physiological data on the characteristics of superficial cortical responses at different developmental stages. For present purposes useful information may be obtained from Golgi–Cox material on the overall dimensions of dendrites, their general distribution and the origin and distribution of axons in superficial regions of cortex.

Sub-pial neocortical neuropil is extraordinarily well developed in the neonatal and near-term fetal cat. Dendritic components are derived from small, medium, and large pyramidal neurons in all layers (Fig. 1A), and the extensive ramifications of relatively numerous "embryonic" Cajal–Retzius cells (Fig. 1B, C). The apical dendrites of pyramidal neurons emerge from cell bodies whose diameters range from 10–25 μ. Proximal portions of apical dendrites are of considerable thickness relative to cell body diameter (Fig. 1D). Branching of middle or distal segments is minimal, but when this occurs, radial orientation of branches is maintained. Emphasis is to be placed on the fact that tangential branches of apical dendrites in their proximal or middle segments are not observed in the perinatal cat, although a few delicate processes less than 50 μ are occasionally discerned in small superficially located pyramidal neurons. Apical dendrites are densely packed in the molecular layer and terminate within 25 μ of the pial surface or in contact with the latter. Tangential spread in the molecular layer of apical dendrites of medium and giant pyramidal cells is rarely greater than 100 μ, but some small superficially located neurons give rise to apical dendrites whose tangential branching in the molecular layer may approach 150–200 μ (Sholl, 1956). The most conspicuous feature of the pyramidal cell dendritic system in the neonatal period is the relatively poor development of basilar dendrites of medium and large pyramids. Some small pyramidal neurons in the sub-molecular layer may have basilar dendrites three to four times the diameter of their cell bodies. Dendrites of superficially located stellate neurons are poorly developed, but some terminal branches ramify in the molecular layer.

Descending axons of pyramidal neurons of all sizes are well developed but relatively devoid of collaterals in the neonatal cat. Some ascending axons from deep lying pyramidal neurons and others of unknown origin often appear to be intimately related with apical dendrites throughout their entire course. Tangential axons in the molecular layer arise from three sources; the embryonic Cajal–Retzius neurons, pyramidal neurons, and sub-cortical elements. Some of the identifiable axons of Cajal–Retzius cells intertwine with densely

50 μ

FIG. 1. Golgi–Cox preparations of neurons in suprasylvian (A and B) and anterior sigmoid gyrus (C and D) of 5-hr-old kitten. A. Cluster of medium and large pyramidal neurons. Apical dendrites extend to within 25–50 μ of pial surface. Note absence of lateral branches. Axons of two neurons clearly shown extending downward. Basilar dendrites at this stage are short, thin processes. B and C. Embryonic Cajal–Retzius neurons in molecular layer. D. Giant pyramids in motor cortex with massive apical dendrites, but poorly developed basilar dendrites. Further description in text.

packed apical dendrites of pyramidal neurons and may be followed for 100–200 μ before they are lost in a maze of apical dendrites.

The major maturational change observed in neocortical pyramidal neurons consists in a proliferation of basilar dendrites and axon collaterals (Bishop, 1950; Cajal, 1960; Conel, 1939, 1941, 1951; Eayrs and Goodhead, 1959; Purpura et al., 1960a; Schade and Baxter, 1960). In the cat the growth of basilar dendrites of medium and large pyramidal neurons appears to gain momentum within a few days after birth and an accelerated phase of basilar dendritic growth occurs during the second postnatal week. By the end of the third week, basilar dendrites of extraordinary length and large diameter are readily seen in all neocortical areas.

It is a curious fact that during postnatal ontogenesis the density of dendrites in the molecular layer decreases due to the proliferation of non-neural elements and regression of the elaborate dendritic apparatus of Cajal–Retzius cells (Cajal, 1960; Conel, 1951). With advancing age, lateral branching of apical dendrites in middle and proximal segments increases, but such branches never approach dimensions of 1–2 mm as claimed by Chang (1951). Distal segments of apical dendrites undergo moderate proliferation during the second and third postnatal week, but tangential spread of these elements rarely exceeds 200 μ.

In summary, it is to be noted that except for the regressive changes in dendrites of Cajal–Retzius cells, relatively few major alterations are seen in the dendritic components of superficial neuropil during postnatal ontogenesis in the cat. This is in striking contrast to the profound maturational changes which occur in the basilar dendritic system and deep neuropil, as has also been noted in other species. The relative decrease in the density of dendritic elements in the molecular layer during the second and third week occurs pari passu with an increase in the number of axons from various sources. This in turn correlates with the appearance of spines or thorns on apical and basilar dendrites. In view of recent electron microscopical data indicating that the spines observed in Golgi material are loci of synaptic contact (Gray, 1959), it can be expected that the morphological alterations occurring during the second and third postnatal weeks will be reflected in significant changes in the physiological and pharmacological organization of the sub-pial neuropil of neocortex. Support for this is provided by a consideration of the changing characteristics of synaptic activities generated in superficial axo-dendritic pathways by stimuli applied to the pial surface.

Ontogenetic Changes in Evoked Superficial Negative Responses of Neocortex

Graded superficial cortical responses (s.c.r.'s) to local stimulation can be evoked from all parts of the dorsolateral convexity of the cerebral cortex in near-term fetal cats (Fig. 2). In perinatal preparations, s.c.r.'s recorded 1–5

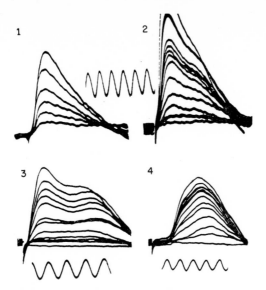

Fig. 2. Characteristics of long-duration superficial cortical responses (s.c.r.'s) recorded 1·5 mm (1–3) and 4 mm (4) from stimulating electrodes on supra-sylvian gyrus. Stimulus frequency 0·5/sec, from six to twenty superposed responses at different stimulus strengths. Negativity upwards in this and all subsequent figures. 1 and 2 from two near-term fetuses; 3, 4-day-old kitten; and 4, 12-hr-old kitten. Duration of s.c.r.'s independent of stimulus strength; threshold of late components in near (3) or distant (4) responses similar to that for the early. Latency of distant responses is not appreciably altered by five to tenfold increase in stimulus strength. Note augmentation of early component in near responses and late components of distant responses with strong stimulus. Cal. 100 c/s; 0·1 mV.

mm from the site of stimulation are of long-duration (50–80 msec) relative to those ordinarily recorded in the adult animal (Adrian, 1936; Brooks and Enger, 1959; Burns, 1958; Chang, 1951; Clare and Bishop, 1955; Purpura and Grundfest, 1956). The 10–20 msec s.c.r. of mature cortex is, however, detectable in the perinatal animal, but a clear dissociation between initial and late components of the response is observed only when care is taken to record responses "at the site of stimulation". With progressive outward displacement of the recording electrode from the site of stimulation, additional 10–20 msec components increase in magnitude and fuse with the early (Fig. 3). During the second and third weeks, dissociation between the early and late surface-negativities of the s.c.r. is more readily obtained at distances comparable to those at which threshold differences in these components are obtained in adult animals.

S.c.r.'s evoked by weak surface stimulation are detectable up to 5–7 mm from the site of stimulation during the first postnatal week (Fig. 4), and 8–10 mm thereafter (Fig. 5). The mean propagation velocity of the s.c.r. in supra-

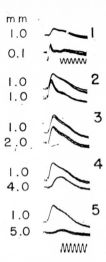

FIG. 3. Characteristics of s.c.r.'s at different distances from stimulating electrodes on suprasylvian gyrus in an 8-hr-old kitten. Upper channel recordings made with large electrode (0·5 mm), the center of which was placed 1 mm from stimulating electrodes. Lower channel responses recorded with wire electrode at sites indicated at left. Note similar characteristics of responses in (3) and fall-off of early component at 4 mm in (4). Further explanation in text. Cal. 100 c/s; 0·1 mV.

sylvian gyrus is 0·3 m/sec in perinatal preparations, and 0·45 m/sec in 2–3-week-old kittens. In the neonatal period, distant s.c.r.'s, i.e. those recorded 3 mm or more from the site of stimulation (cf. Fan and Feng, 1957), are never of greater magnitude than "near" responses recorded 2–3 mm away from the stimulating electrodes (Fig. 4). During the second postnatal week, distant

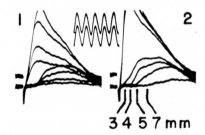

FIG. 4. Relationship between near (upper channel), and distant (lower channel) responses in near-term fetal kittens. (1) Graded responses at near (1·5 mm) and distant (4 mm) sites from stimulating electrodes. Stimulus evoking small near s.c.r. produces detectable distant response after 15 msec latency (propagation velocity, 0·27 m/sec). (2) Characteristics of distant s.c.r.'s to strong stimuli evoking maximal near s.c.r.'s. Note progressively increasing latency of distant responses (mean propagation velocity, 0·25 m/sec). Cal. 100 c/s; 0·1 mV.

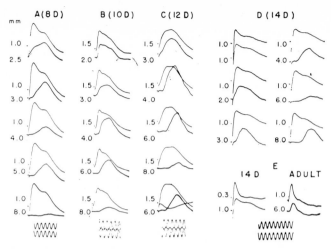

FIG. 5. Changing characteristics of distant s.c.r.'s during second postnatal week.
A–D. Relationship between near (upper channel) and distant (lower channel)
responses recorded at distances from stimulating electrodes indicated at left in
each series; ages shown above. A. S.c.r.'s at 5 and 3 mm larger than at 2·5 and
4 mm. B. Reinforced responses at 4 and 6 mm. C. Note extraordinary magnitude
of response at 4 and 6 mm. D. Reinforced s.c.r. at 8 mm; latency about 25 msec.
In c records at bottom of column taken before and after topical application
of 1 % GABA to near electrode site. In this record, upper channel shows abolition
of surface-negativity and unmasking of surface-positivity after GABA; lower
channel shows two perfectly superposable distant responses. E. Comparison of
responses at indicated distances in a 14 day-old-kitten and adult cat studied
under identical conditions. Wire electrode (0·1 mm) employed to record response
at 0·3 mm in kitten. Compare characteristics of responses at 1 mm. Duration
of the distant response in adult preparation is similar to that of near response.
Cals. 100 c/s; 0·1 mV in A; 0·3 mV in B–E; that for D shown in E.

responses of extraordinary magnitude relative to near s.c.r.'s are detectable
in favorable preparations (Fig. 5). Brooks and Enger (1959) analyzed this
phenomenon in adult cats and concluded on the basis of peak-latency
measurements that distant "reinforced" responses were propagated outward
from the site of stimulation more rapidly than near s.c.r.'s. In the immature
cortex, the latency of s.c.r.'s, as measured to onset of response, increases
linearly with distance (Fig. 5).

In addition to changes in overall duration, propagation velocity, and
spread, s.c.r.'s also exhibit a change in the early phase of their activity cycles
during postnatal ontogenesis (Purpura et al., 1960a). This alteration occurs in
the first week and consists in a decrease in the absolute unresponsive period
(a.u.p.), as determined by short-interval paired conditioning-testing stimuli.
The a.u.p. in neonatal animals (<3 days old) is 4–8 msec, and 1–2 msec by
the end of the first postnatal week. Activity cycles are identical for near and
distant responses. It is of interest that the time of appearance of distant

29

"reinforced" responses coincides with a change in activity cycles, thereby facilitating temporal summation of distant s.c.r.'s. The dual nature of the processes of spread and generation of the s.c.r. in immature cortex is shown by the appearance of distant "reinforced" responses and the fact that elimination of near s.c.r.'s does not alter distant responses (Fig. 5). The latter finding confirms previous observations made in adult animals by Jasper et al. (1958).

The foregoing data, presented in greater detail elsewhere (Purpura et al., 1960a) when considered in relation to histological information on the density and distribution of elements in superficial regions of neocortex provide strong support for the hypothesis that s.c.r.'s are generated postsynaptically in superficial dendrites by conductile pathways of variable length and trajectory (Eccles, 1951; Purpura and Grundfest, 1956). Various lines of evidence compel rejection of alternative hypotheses concerning the nature and origin of the s.c.r. (cf. Purpura, 1959). The fact that basilar dendrites are absent and apical dendrites of pyramidal neurons do not have tangential branches at a time when s.c.r.'s can be detected up to 5–7 mm from the site of stimulation would appear to eliminate the possibility that the s.c.r. is conducted along dendrites (Chang, 1951). Also, the demonstration of variations in s.c.r. amplitude at different loci and the finding that abolition of an s.c.r. at one locus does not alter responses at other loci precludes the possibility that the s.c.r. is both generated in and conducted along a single species of tangential fibers (Burns, 1958).

The relatively long duration of s.c.r.'s recorded in immature cortex at distances (>1 mm) comparable to those at which 15–20 msec responses are observed in mature cortex indicates that in neonatal kittens a single brief weak stimulus to the cortical surface initiates postsynaptic events in superficial dendrites and perhaps other elements in superficial regions of cortex. In the second and third postnatal weeks, distant responses of considerable magnitude are observed indicating that the capacity for temporo–spatial summation of p.s.p.'s in distant elements has been markedly facilitated.

It is abundantly clear from the foregoing brief analysis of the generation and spread of postsynaptic activities in superficial cortex that the sub-pial neuropil is potentially capable of participating in the elaboration of electro-cortical events, even in the near-term fetus. With advancing age changes in its organization are reflected, in part, in the changing electrographic characteristics of s.c.r.'s at varying distances. More importantly, however, such alterations are also apparent in the different effects which selectively acting pharmacological agents produce on superficial axodendritic organizations at different developmental stages.

Ontogenetic Changes in the Pharmacological Properties of Superficial Axo-dendritic Synaptic Pathways

The use of aliphatic ω-amino carboxylic acids as pharmacological tools for dissecting overt axodendritic synaptic activities into excitatory and inhibitory components derives from a large volume of data on the different effects of these compounds on surface evoked responses in neocortex, hippocampus, and cerebellar cortex of adult cats. These effects have been described in detail elsewhere and consequently only features relevant to the present discussion will be reviewed (Purpura, 1960a; Purpura et al., 1959a, b, 1960).

Although a relatively large number of aliphatic ω-amino, ω-guanidino and ω-thioureido carboxylic acids produce rapid and reversible effects on neo-cortical and cerebellar s.c.r.'s in adult animals, the different effects of these compounds are represented by the action of two members of the ω-amino acid series, the four carbon member, γ-aminobutyric acid (GABA), and the six carbon compound, ϵ-amino caproic acid (C_6). Topically applied GABA rapidly eliminates the neocortical and cerebellar s.c.r., but only in neocortex does abolition of surface-negativity reveal a surface-positivity previously "masked" in the overt response. In contrast, C_6 augments neocortical s.c.r.'s recorded 1–2 mm from the site of stimulation, whereas cerebellar s.c.r.'s are relatively unaffected by this and other long-chain ω-amino acids. The effects of GABA are ascribed to selective blockade of depolarizing axodendritic p.s.p.'s, those of C_6 to inactivation of hyperpolarizing, inhibitory axodendritic p.s.p.'s (Purpura et al., 1959b). GABA-induced surface-positivity in the neo-cortical s.c.r. is inferred to be a hyperpolarizing p.s.p. of superficial dendritic elements. Its absence in cerebellar s.c.r.'s is thus attributed to the relative paucity of inhibitory synapses on Purkinje cell dendritic terminals activated by superficial fibers. The lack of effect of C_6 and other long-chain ω-amino acids on cerebellar s.c.r.'s evoked by local surface stimulation is in marked contrast to the action of these compounds on cerebellar responses evoked by stimulation of different afferent pathways (Purpura et al., 1959a). Of particular importance in this respect is that the effects of long-chain ω-amino acids on different varieties of evoked potentials are almost entirely reproduced by topically applied strychnine. Analyses of the alterations in surface responses induced by successive application of GABA and C_6 or strychnine may there-fore provide significant clues concerning the proportion, magnitude and temporal relations of axodendritic and axosomatic p.s.p.'s activated by differ-ent pathways (Purpura, 1960a).

The typical effects of GABA on long-duration s.c.r.'s recorded 1·5 mm from the site of stimulation in the new-born cat are shown in Fig. 6A. These consisted in a rapid decrease in amplitude and duration of the surface-negativity, and "unmasking" of a low-amplitude, late surface-positivity (Fig. 6A, (2), (3)). With continued GABA-action the low-amplitude surface-positivity was further reduced (Fig. 7 (1–3)). During the early stages of recovery from GABA-blockade, s.c.r. amplitude was greater than before treatment with the amino acid, but late components of the response were still depressed (Fig. 6A (4); Fig. 7 (4)). The phase of augmented excitability

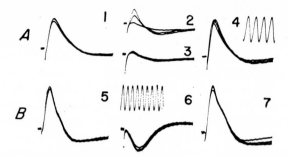

FIG. 6. Effects of topically applied GABA on s.c.r.'s evoked in new-born cat.
A. 5-hr-old kitten: (1) s.c.r.'s recorded 1·5 mm from stimulating electrodes;
(2) 20–30 sec after topical application of 1% GABA; (3) 10–20 sec after (2);
(4) early recovery phase after rinsing cortex with warm Ringer's solution.
B. 15-hr-old kitten: (5) s.c.r.'s recorded 1·5 mm from site of stimulation;
strong stimulus evoked s.c.r.'s followed by prominent surface-positivity;
(6) 30 sec after 1% GABA, unmasking of surface-positivity presumably reflecting sub-surface depolarizing p.s.p.'s; (7) recovery after removal of GABA.
Cal. 100 c/s; 0·3 mV.

following GABA-blockade of the s.c.r. and other responses evoked in mature
cortex has been noted previously (Purpura et al., 1959b). The absence of a
prominent surface-positivity in the s.c.r. after elimination of surface-negativity by GABA was characteristically observed in the neonatal period. There-

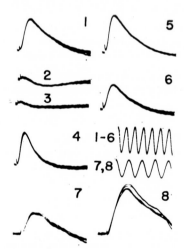

FIG. 7. (1)–(6) 5-day-old kitten; (7)–(8) 5-week-old kitten. (1) Control s.c.r.'s
recorded 1·5 mm from stimulating electrodes; (2) 20 sec after topical application of 1% GABA; (3) 30 sec after (2) and after application of additional
GABA; (4) early recovery of s.c.r. after flushing cortex with warm Ringer's
solution; (5) late phase of recovery; (6) 20 sec after topical application of ε-amino
caproic acid (C_6); (7) s.c.r.'s recorded at 2 mm; (8) 20 sec after topical
application of C_6. Cal. 100 c/s; 0·1 mV.

after, effects similar to those previously demonstrated in adult animals were readily obtained (Purpura *et al.*, 1959b). In some instances when especially strong surface stimulation was employed to evoke s.c.r.'s that were succeeded by a prominent surface-positivity, i.e. the "deep response" of Adrian (1936), GABA unmasked a short-latency surface-positivity of similar time course to the pre-treated s.c.r. (Fig. 6B). Unlike the low-amplitude surface-positivities commonly observed after GABA, those "unmasked" in s.c.r.'s evoked by excessively strong stimulation were not abolished by continued application of the amino acid. It is not unlikely, therefore, that whereas the low-amplitude, late surface-positivity may be a sign of weak inhibitory p.s.p.'s in the s.c.r., that revealed by strong stimulation probably reflects depolarizing p.s.p.'s of sub-surface elements (Purpura *et al.*, 1960b).

FIG. 8. Effects of topical GABA on early and late components of s.c.r.; 3-day-old kitten. S.c.r.'s recorded 1·5 mm from stimulating electrodes. (1) Responses to stimuli of progressively increasing strength, duration of s.c.r. evoked by weak stimulus is identical to that evoked by strong. (2) Effects of topical GABA (0·1%) on s.c.r.'s evoked by stimulus of constant strength (frequency 0·1/sec). Response of greatest amplitude and duration is before GABA. The immediate effect of the amino acid consists in a minimal uniform reduction in amplitude of all components of the s.c.r. (second record from above-downwards). Later effect is exerted primarily on late components which were eliminated by the amino acid at a time when the initial 15 msec component was still prominent. (3) (*a*) and (*b*) s.c.r.'s evoked by strong and weak stimulus, respectively; (*c*) maximum effect of 0·01% GABA on response evoked by strong stimulus as in (*a*). Further explanation in text. Cal. 100 c/s; 0·1 mV.

The disproportionate loss in late components of the s.c.r. following treatment with GABA is of interest with respect to the hypothesis that the long-duration of s.c.r.'s in immature cortex may be due to summated p.s.p.'s in differently oriented elements (Purpura *et al.*, 1960a). This interpretation is supported by observations on the effects of dilute GABA on early and late components of the s.c.r. (Fig. 8). As noted previously (Fig. 2), the duration of s.c.r.'s recorded at distances greater than 1–2 mm in neonatal kittens is independent of stimulus strength (Fig. 8 (1)). After application of weak GABA solutions (0·1%), loss of late components occurred faster than that of the early (Fig. 8 (2)). When very weak GABA solutions (0·01%) were employed, depression of the s.c.r. proceeded to a stage at which the peak-amplitude of the control response (labeled *a* in Fig. 8 (3)) had been reduced by about 40% (*c*). The latter response (*c*), in contrast to the control response of similar peak-amplitude that was evoked by a weak stimulus (*b*) was almost completely devoid of late activity. This suggests that the change in the s.c.r. observed after GABA was not similar to that produced by progressive weakening of the applied stimulus, for if such were the case, it might be expected that when the initial population of responding elements decreased by 40%, the reduced response would have a time course similar to that of the initial response. The fact that the response after GABA has an abbreviated time course suggests that late components in the s.c.r. are more effectively blocked by GABA than the early. Such a situation could arise if the elements contributing to the late components of the s.c.r. were oriented closer to the pial surface than those responsible for the early. Further discussion along these lines is deferred until the effects of long chain ω-amino acids on developing cortex can be considered. Although these differences are clearly shown in Fig. 7 in records from a 5 day-old-kitten (Fig. 7 (5), (6)) and a 5 week-old-kitten (Fig. 7 (7), (8)), they are best summarized with respect to changes that are observed in early and late components of the s.c.r. and the spontaneous electrocortical activity.

The effects of C_6 and ω-amino caprylic acid (C_8) on the s.c.r., the subsequent slow positive–negative sequence, and the background spontaneous electrocortical activity are shown (Fig. 9) in records taken from a 5 hr-old-

FIG. 9. 5-hr-old kitten. Effect of topical ε-amino caproic acid (C_6) and ω-amino caprylic acid (C_8) on s.c.r.'s and succeeding long duration responses. S.c.r.'s recorded $1 \cdot 5$ mm from site of stimulation. Left column, fast sweep (cal. 100 c/s); right column, slow sweep (cal. 10 c/s). A. Control s.c.r.'s, note later positive–negative sequences in slow sweep records. B. 1 min after C_6. C. Recovery of s.c.r. 10 min after flushing cortex with Ringer's solution. D. 20 min after C, control prior to C_8 application. E. 2 min after C_8. F. Recovery 20 min after removal of C_8.

kitten. Both C_6 and C_8 depressed all components of the s.c.r. and increased background activity (Fig. 9B, E). No differences were observed in the depressant effects of these long-chain ω-amino acids on the s.c.r., but C_8 appeared to exert a more pronounced action on late potential sequences in neonatal animals (<5 days old). Differences were more apparent in somewhat older animals. In 5–7 days old kittens, C_6 depressed both near and distant s.c.r.'s and produced some augmentation in background activity, whereas C_8 produced much less depression of s.c.r.'s and initiated local paroxysmal discharges (Fig. 10 (6)).

7 Days

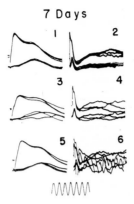

FIG. 10. S.c.r.'s recorded at 1·5 mm (upper channel) and 5 mm (lower channel) from the site of stimulation. Left column, cal. 100 c/s; right column, cal. 10 c/s. (1) and (2) Control; (3) and (4) maximum action of C_6; (5) and (6) after complete recovery from C_6 action and 2 min after topical C_8. Records in (5) taken immediately before development of seizure activity shown in (6).

During the second postnatal week, further differences in the effects of C_6 and C_8 were observed. As shown in Fig. 11, in records from 10 and 12 day-old-kittens from the same litter, C_6 produced depression of near and distant s.c.r.'s. In the older kitten this depression was associated with sporadic spontaneous paroxysmal activity. In contrast, C_8 produced depression of the early component in the near s.c.r., and augmentation of late components. Of particular significance was the finding that during the initial stages of C_8 action on near responses, s.c.r.'s recorded 4–5 mm away from the site of stimulation were depressed by the amino acid or relatively unaffected until the onset of paroxysmal activity.

Towards the end of the third postnatal week, the depressant effects of C_6 and C_8 on near s.c.r.'s were no longer observed. Comparison of the different effects of C_6 and C_8 on near s.c.r.'s evoked in an 8 day-old-animal, and of C_6 on near and 4 mm distant responses in a 3 week-old-litter-mate is shown in Fig. 12. Two features are especially noteworthy. In the 8 day-old-animal, C_6 depressed all components of the s.c.r. (Fig. 12 (3)), whereas C_8 depressed early and augmented late components and induced convulsant activity (Fig. 12 (5), (6)). In the 21 day-old-litter-mate, C_6 rapidly augmented all components of the near s.c.r., but did not significantly alter distant responses (Fig. 12 (9)). Augmentation of the second, late negativity in near s.c.r.'s was more prominent than the increase in the early negativity. The onset of paroxysmal discharges after C_6 resulted in marked fluctuations in late

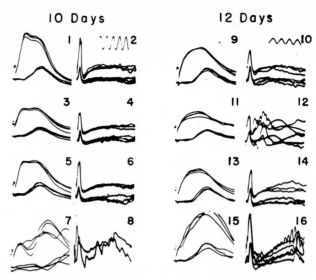

FIG. 11. Comparative effects of C_6 and C_8 on near and distant s.c.r.'s in 10- and 12-day-old litter-mates. (1), (2), (9) and (10) control; s.c.r.'s recorded 1·5 mm (upper channel) and 4 mm (lower channel) from the site of stimulation; (3), (4), (11) and (12) 2 min after topical C_6; (5), (6), (13) and (14) recovery after rinsing cortex with warm Ringer's solution; (7), (8), (15) and (16) 2 min after topical C_8; note depression of early and augmentation of late components in near response in (7) and (15), as well as depression of far response in (7) and minor alteration in far response in (15). Further explanation in text. Fast sweep, 100 c/s; slow, 10 c/s.

components of near responses and depression of distant s.c.r.'s (Fig. 12, (11), (12)). Paroxysmal discharges, apparently triggered by the surface stimulus and initiated close to the site of stimulation, were propagated to distant sites at a velocity similar to that of distant s.c.r.'s. By the fourth postnatal week, both C_6 and C_8 rapidly augmented all components of near s.c.r.'s as in mature animals (Fig. 8 (8)).

In view of the finding that at a developmental stage when near s.c.r.'s were augmented by C_6 and C_8, i.e. 3–4 weeks, no effects were observed on s.c.r.'s recorded 4–5 mm from the site of stimulation, a series of experiments were performed on adult cats to determine whether the differential action of long-chain ω-amino acids on near and distant s.c.r.'s represented a final maturational change. The results of these experiments are summarized in Figs. 13 and 14. Following topical application of C_6 to both near and distant recording sites, s.c.r.'s evoked 1·5 mm from the site of stimulation (suprasylvian gyrus) were rapidly augmented, but no significant change was observed in distant responses (Fig. 13B). When late components of the near s.c.r. exhibited a further increase in amplitude, distant late components were also augmented (Fig. 13C), but the early remained essentially unchanged. The origin of the

8 Days   21 Days

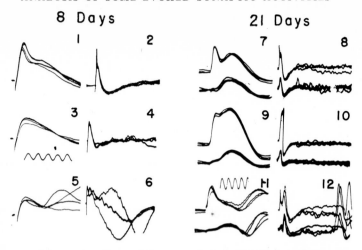

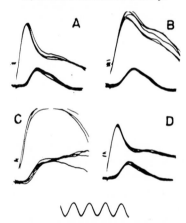

FIG. 12. Comparative effects of C$_6$ on s.c.r.'s in 8- and 21-day-old litter-mates. Sweeps and calibrations as in Fig. 11. (1) and (2) control s.c.r.'s recorded 1·0 mm from site of stimulation; (3) and (4) 2 min after topical C$_6$; (5) and (6) after complete recovery from depressant effects of C$_6$, and 2 min after C$_8$; differences in the action of C$_6$ and C$_8$ are apparent; note in particular changes in late components of s.c.r. after C$_8$; (7) and (8) control near (upper channel) and 4 mm-distant (lower channel), s.c.r.'s; (9) and (10) immediate effects of C$_6$; rapid augmentation of early and late components of near s.c.r. with more pronounced action on late components; distant response unaffected; (11) and (12) onset of C$_6$-induced convulsant activity.

FIG. 13. A. Near (1·5 mm) and distant (6·0 mm) s.c.r.'s evoked in suprasylvian gyrus of adult cat with stimuli threshold for late negative component. B. 20 sec after application of C$_6$ to both recording sites. C. 40 sec after B. D. Recovery after rinsing cortex with Ringer's solution. Cal. 100 c/s; 0·1 mV.

late component appearing in the distant s.c.r. after C$_6$ was established by employing a series of recording electrodes spaced 1 mm apart and adjusting stimulus strength to threshold for the early, but sub-threshold for late

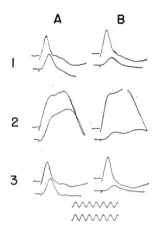

FIG. 14. Adult cat anesthetized with 15 mg/K pentobarbital sodium. Upper channel records in A and B, s.c.r. recorded 1·5 mm from site of stimulation. Stimulus sub-threshold for late negative component in s.c.r. Lower channel records in A, s.c.r. recorded at 3·0 mm and B, at 4·5 mm from stimulating electrodes. (1) Control responses; (2) 20 sec after topical application of C_6 to all recording sites; (3) recovery after flushing cortex with Ringer's. Increase in early and late components of s.c.r.'s recorded at 1·5 and 3·0 mm is clearly shown. Early component of s.c.r. at 4·5 mm is unaffected by C_6. Late activity in 4·5 mm distant response represents propagation of activity initiated by C_6 at site of stimulation. Cal. 100 c/s; 0·1 mV.

surface-negativity in the near s.c.r. (Fig. 14). Cortical "excitability" was reduced by administration of sub-anesthetic amounts of sodium pento-barbital (15 mg/K). Under these conditions, C_6 augmented early and "activated" late components of s.c.r.'s recorded up to 3 mm from the site of stimulation (Fig. 14A (2)). Early components of s.c.r.'s recorded 4·5 mm from the stimulating electrodes were unaltered, whereas a late component developed that appeared to represent propagation of the late component in near responses. Experiments similar to those illustrated in Fig. 14 were also designed to determine the distance at which initial components in s.c.r.'s differed in their response to C_6. Such studies revealed that the action of C_6 was confined to s.c.r.'s recorded within 3–3·5 mm of the site of stimulation. The different effects of C_6 on near and distant responses were reproduced by topical strychnine (0·1 %).

COMMENT

The foregoing survey of the ontogenetic changes in the morphophysio-logical properties of elements involved in the generation and spread of evoked superficial responses in cat neocortex bears on two aspects of the organization of axodendritic synaptic pathways in sub-pial neuropil: (1) the degree to which s.c.r.'s are compounded of inhibitory and excitatory synaptic activities at various developmental stages, and (2) the distribution of components of inhibitory p.s.p.'s in evoked s.c.r.'s recorded at different loci from the site of stimulation. Information is also provided on the effects of aliphatic ω-amino carboxylic acids that permits further analysis of their structure–activity relations (Purpura et al., 1959b).

Weak stimulation of the neocortical surface in neonatal kittens evokes a complex superficial negativity whose duration is presumably dependent on temporal dispersion of "unit" 10–20 msec p.s.p.'s generated in apical dendrites of pyramidal neurons and dendrites of Cajal–Retzius cells. Of considerable interest is the finding that dilute solutions of GABA exert a predominant blocking action on late components of the s.c.r. Since the blockade of super-ficial negativity depends on achieving an effective concentration of the amino acid at synaptic sites responsible for the s.c.r., the relatively rapid elimination of late components suggests that the latter arise in dendritic elements lying entirely within the molecular layer, whereas the initial 10–20 msec response is generated at postsynaptic loci along portions of apical dendritic shafts subtending the outermost layers of cortex (Purpura and Grundfest, 1956; Purpura et al., 1960b). Thus, although all components of the s.c.r. are inferred to be p.s.p.'s, it is not unlikely that the second and successive 10–20 msec negativities characteristically seen in near and distant s.c.r.'s evoked in immature, as well as mature cortex (Brooks and Enger, 1959; Fan and Feng, 1957) arise in different dendritic organizations than those responsible for the initial component. The major developmental changes in these organizations, as revealed by the effects of C_6 and C_8, provide addi-tional support for this hypothesis. In the neonatal period, both long chain ω-amino acids depress all components of the s.c.r., an action which tends to resemble the effects observed on s.c.r.'s evoked in the cerebellar cortex of adult cats (Purpura et al., 1959a, b). At a later stage of development (second postnatal week) C_8 augments late components of the near s.c.r. and, to a lesser extent, C_6 acts similarly. Not until the third and fourth week is it possible to observe effects of C_6 and C_8 on near s.c.r.'s that are entirely similar to those observed in the mature animal. If, as has been proposed elsewhere (Purpura et al., 1959b), the lack of C_6 and C_8 action on an evoked response indicates the absence of a component of inhibitory axodendritic activity in a tested response, the changes in the pharmacological effects of long chain ω-amino acids may be considered reflections of the progressive functional development of inhibitory activity in superficial axodendritic organ-izations; first in organizations involved in the production of late components in the s.c.r., then in those responsible for the early. An alternative explanation of the different actions of long chain ω-amino acids on neocortical s.c.r.'s during postnatal ontogenesis based on the possibility that such differences may result from changes in the pharmacological properties of inhibitory synapses rather than the development of inhibitory synaptic activity must also be considered.

It should be emphasized that the actions of ω-amino acids described here are apart from those exerted on the background spontaneous electro-cortical activity and the long-duration positive–negative potentials which follow in the wake of the evoked superficial negativity. Indeed, the finding that slow "convulsant-like" electrocortical activity may be observed in C_6- or C_8-treated cortex of neonatal animals at a time when all components of the s.c.r. are depressed, serves to focus on complexities of the functional organization of immature cortex that are not apparent from analyses of activity confined to superficial elements. In this connection, it should be noted that despite the relative absence of inhibitory p.s.p.'s in s.c.r.'s evoked in neonatal cat cortex (as indicated by the inertness of C_6 and C_8), inhibitory activities may be generated in neocortex of the new-born cat by corticipetal pathways distributing in a more complex fashion to different synaptic organizations. In the example illustrated in Fig. 15, surface responses similar to those described by Scherrer and Oeconomos (1955) were evoked by weak and strong stimu-

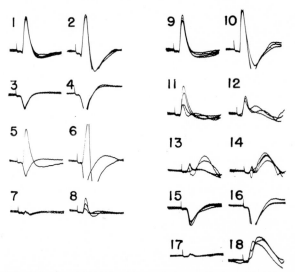

FIG. 15. Effects of topical GABA and strychnine on "primary" response evoked in posterior sigmoid gyrus following lateral thalamic stimulation (stimulus frequency 0·5/sec); 2-day-old kitten. (1) Weak and (2), strong stimulation; (3) and (4) stimulus as in (1) and (2) after topical GABA; (5) and (6) superposed tracing of control response as in (1) and (2) and responses after GABA as in (3) and (4); (7) and (8) early stages of recovery from GABA-effect; (9) and (10) full recovery; (11)–(14) genesis of changes induced by topical strychnine (0·1%) in response to strong stimulation; (15) and (16) immediate effect of GABA applied to strychninized cortex, weak and strong stimulation as in (3) and (4); (17) and (18) recovery from GABA effects and reappearance of strychnine action. Further explanation in text. Sweep duration 150 msec in all records.

lation of lateral thalamic projections. Topical GABA eliminated the initial surface-negativity and unmasked a surface-positivity whose amplitude was dependent on stimulus strength (Fig. 15 (3), (4)). Following recovery from the effects of GABA (9, 10), topical strychnine (0·1 %) first reduced the initial surface-negativity and activated a second, long-latency negativity which progressively increased in amplitude (11–14). During the height of the strychnine action, GABA was reapplied and effects were produced that were entirely similar to those observed before strychnine (15, 16). Upon removal of GABA the initial negativity was barely detectable at first (17), then within a few seconds strychnine effects were again observed (18). Strychnine depression of the early and appearance of late negativity in a surface response evoked by thalamic stimulation in the new-born animal resembles the depression of the early and augmentation of late components in the s.c.r. after C_6 and C_8 in the 2 week-old-kitten. The effect of GABA (Fig. 15 (3)) is similar to that produced in s.c.r.'s evoked by strong surface stimulation (Fig. 6 (6)). Comparison of the effects of strychnine on a thalamocortical response and of C_6 and C_8 on the s.c.r. illustrates that in the new-born animal inhibitory activities may be prominent in some cortical organizations and not in others. In the example shown in Fig. 15, the effects of strychnine are presumably related to its blocking action at axosomatic (cf. Eccles, 1957), as well as axodendritic inhibitory synapses (Purpura and Grundfest, 1957). However, in view of the failure of GABA to reveal a surface-positivity other than that which appears to reflect sub-surface depolarizing p.s.p.'s, it is likely that the late negativity induced by strychnine results exclusively from blockade of axosomatic inhibitory p.s.p.'s. The latter action may also explain the appearance of modified intermittent paroxysmal discharges in the heavily strychninized cortex of the new-born rabbit (Bishop, 1950; Fan, 1957) and 3–4 days old rat (Crain, 1952). Strychnine-induced depression of the initial negative component of the thalamocortical-evoked response and C_6 and C_8 depression of the s.c.r. prior to the second to third postnatal week indicates that although the predominant blocking effect of these convulsants is exerted on inhibitory synapses, depression of excitatory synaptic activity may also occur (Purpura and Grundfest, 1957).

The depressant effects of C_6 and C_8 on s.c.r.'s evoked in neonatal cortex appear to be only partly accounted for by assuming that these compounds have a minor affinity for excitatory axodendritic synapses. C_6 and C_8 markedly depress near and distant s.c.r.'s in neonatal cortex, but at a developmental stage when these compounds cause rapid augmentation of near s.c.r.'s, they produce no significant alteration in distant responses. Failure of C_6 to depress distant s.c.r.'s evoked in mature cortex may indicate that some alteration has occurred during cortical maturation that tends to prevent long-chain ω-amino acids from gaining access to excitatory axodendritic synapses. Possibly some clues to the nature of this alteration may be forthcoming when

electron microscopical data are obtained on the ultrastructure of axodendritic synapses during postnatal ontogenesis.

The differential augmentation of s.c.r.'s recorded within 4 mm of the site
of stimulation is shown to be a final maturational event. Thus, although
s.c.r.'s recorded at various loci are initiated by fundamentally similar processes (Fan and Feng, 1957; Purpura et al., 1960a), it must be allowed that
s.c.r.'s differ with respect to their pharmacological responsiveness to compounds which presumably exert convulsant effects through blockade of inhibitory p.s.p.'s. Viewed from the standpoint of the hypothesis (cf. Eccles,
1957, and elsewhere in this volume) that inhibitory activities in the mammalian CNS are exerted by pathways operating at relatively close range, it is
not unlikely that a weak, localized stimulus to the cortical surface in adult
animals initiates activity in superficial pathways capable of generating excitatory p.s.p.'s in dendrites 8–10 mm from the site of stimulation and inhibitory p.s.p.'s in dendritic elements less than 3–4 mm from the stimulating
electrodes.

If, as proposed here, functional maturation of some inhibitory axodendritic
synaptic pathway in sub-pial neuropil of cat neocortex proceeds at a considerably slower rate than maturation of excitatory axodendritic pathways, the
question may be raised as to why sustained states of paroxysmal activity are
not more commonly observed in new-born cat cortex (Grossman, 1955). An
answer to this may be provided by histological observations on the relative
paucity of neuronal interconnections and the restrictions imposed by the
prolonged post-excitatory depression of processes operating at superficial
neocortical axodendritic synapses in the neonatal period (Purpura et al.,
1960a). Progressive development of neuronal interrelations results primarily
from proliferation of basilar dendritic systems and axon collaterals and is,
in part, reflected in the appearance of spines on basilar and apical dendrites
in Golgi–Cox preparations. In the cat, the phase of maximum neocortical
neuronal development occurs during the second postnatal week and is
heralded by a significant increase in the capacity for temporal and spatial
summation of excitatory p.s.p.'s in superficial dendrites. This period corresponds to the time during which inhibitory synaptic activities in the s.c.r.
become demonstrable with long-chain ω-amino acids. Thus, despite initial
differences in the temporal pattern of development of inhibitory and excitatory processes, both appear to attain full expression by the third to fourth
postnatal week.

The hypothesis that different cortical synaptic organizations exhibit
different rates of functional maturation is supported by observations on the
comparative development of some archicortical synaptic pathways (Purpura,
1960b). Hippocampal pyramidal neurons have morphological features in the
new-born cat that are not observed in neocortical pyramidal neurons until
the second postnatal week. The relatively advanced development of hippo-

campal elements is reflected in the finding that C_6 and C_8 augment evoked activity and induce paroxysmal discharges in the hippocampus in the immediate neonatal period. These observations taken together with those reported here on the time-course of the development of different synaptic activities in superficial regions of neocortex, may provide clues to the physiological processes underlying the maturation of complex behavioral patterns and the factors influencing their normal progression.

REFERENCES

ADRIAN, E. D. (1936) The spread of activity in the cerebral cortex. *J. Physiol.* (*London*) **88** : 127–161.

BISHOP, E. J. (1950) The strychnine spike as a physiological indicator of cortical maturity in the postnatal rabbit. *Electroencephalog. and Clin. Neurophysiol.* **2** : 309–315.

BRANCH, C. L. and MARTIN, A. R. (1958) Inhibition of Betz cell activity by thalamic and cortical stimulation. *J. Neurophysiol.* **21** : 380–390.

BROOKS, V. B. and ENGER, P. S. (1959) Spread of directly evoked responses in the cat's cerebral cortex. *J. Gen. Physiol.* **42** : 761–777.

BURNS, B. D. (1958) *The Mammalian Cerebral Cortex.* Edward Arnold, London.

BUSER, P. and ALBE-FESSARD, D. (1957) Explorations intracellulaires au niveau du cortex sensorimoteur du chat. *Coll. intern. centre Nat. recherche sci.* (*Paris*) **67** : 333–352.

CAJAL, S. RAMON Y (1960) *Studies on Vertebrate Neurogenesis* (translated by GUTH, L.). Charles C. Thomas, Springfield.

CHANG, H-T. (1951) Dendritic potential of cortical neurones as produced by direct stimulation of the cerebral cortex. *J. Neurophysiol.* **14** : 1–21.

CLARE, M. H. and BISHOP, G. H. (1955) Properties of dendrites; apical dendrites of the cat cortex. *Electroencephalog. and Clin. Neurophysiol.* **7** : 85–98.

CONEL, J. L. (1939) *The Postnatal Development of the Human Cerebral Cortex* Vol. I. *Cortex of the Newborn.* Harvard University Press, Cambridge.

CONEL, J. L. (1941) *The Postnatal Development of the Human Cerebral Cortex* Vol. II. *Cortex of the One-Month Infant.* Harvard University Press, Cambridge.

CONEL, J. L. (1951) *The Postnatal Development of the Human Cerebral Cortex* Vol. IV. *Cortex of the Six-Month Infant.* Harvard University Press, Cambridge.

CRAIN, S. M. (1952) Development of electrical activity in the cerebral cortex of the albino rat. *Proc. Soc. Exptl. Biol. Med.* **81** : 49–51.

EAYRS, J. T. and GOODHEAD, B. (1959) Postnatal development of the cerebral cortex in the rat. *J. Anat.* **93** : 385–402.

ECCLES, J. C. (1951) Interpretation of action potentials evoked in the cerebral cortex in the rat. *Electroencephalog. and Clin. Neurophysiol.* **3** : 449–464.

ECCLES, J. C. (1957) *The Physiology of Nerve Cells.* Johns Hopkins Press, Baltimore.

FAN, S-F. (1957) A study of the electrical activity of cerebral cortex of rabbit during the period of postnatal development. *Acta Physiol. Sinica* (*Shanghai*) **21** : 51–62.

FAN, S-F. and FENG, T. P. (1957) Concerning conduction and electrical excitability in the terminal portions of the apical dendrites of the pyramidal neurons. *Acta physiol. Sinica* (*Shanghai*) **21** : 423–434.

GRAY, E. G. (1959) Axo-somatic and axo-dendritic synapses of the cerebral cortex: An electron microscope study. *J. Anat.* **93** : 420–433.

GROSSMAN, C. G. (1955) Electro-ontogenesis of cerebral cortex. *A. M. A. Arch. Neurol. Psychiat.* **74** : 186–202.

GRUNDFEST, H. (1958) Electrophysiology and pharmacology of dendrites. *Electroencephalog. and Clin. Neurophysiol.* Suppl. **10** : 22–41.

JASPER, H., GONZALEZ, S. and ELLIOTT, K. A. C. (1958) Action of γ-aminobutyric acid (GABA) and strychnine upon evoked electrical responses of cerebral cortex. *Federation Proc.* **17** : 79.

KANDEL, E. R. and SPENCER, W. A. (1960) Repetitive firing of hippocampal neurons. *Federation Proc.* **19** : 290.

LI, C-L. (1959) Cortical intracellular potentials and their responses to strychnine. *J. Neurophysiol.* **22** : 436–450.

MARTIN, A. R. and BRANCH, C. L. (1958) Spontaneous activity of Betz cells in cats with midbrain lesions. *J. Neurophysiol.* **21** : 368–379.

PHILLIPS, C. G. (1956a) Intracellular records from Betz cells in the cat. *Quart. J. Exptl. Physiol.* **41** : 58–69.

PHILLIPS, C. G. (1956b) Cortical motor threshold and thresholds and distribution of excited Betz cells in the cat. *Quart. J. Exptl. Physiol.* **41** : 70–84.

PHILLIPS, C. G. (1959) Actions of antidromic pyramidal volleys on single Betz cells in the cat. *Quart. J. Exptl. Physiol.* **44** : 1–25.

PURPURA, D. P. (1959) Nature of electrocortical potentials and synaptic organizations in cerebral and cerebellar cortex. *Intern. Rev. Neurobiol.* **1** : 47–163.

PURPURA, D. P. (1960a) Pharmacological actions of ω-amino acid drugs on different cortical synaptic organizations. In *Inhibition in the Nervous System and γ-Aminobutyric Acid* pp. 495–514. Pergamon Press, New York.

PURPURA, D. P. (1960b) *Third Conference on Central Nervous System and Behavior* (ed. by BRAZIER, M. A. B.). Josiah Macy Jr. Foundation, New York.

PURPURA, D. P. and GRUNDFEST, H. (1956) Nature of dendritic potentials and synaptic mechanisms in cerebral cortex. *J. Neurophysiol.* **19** : 573–595.

PURPURA, D. P. and GRUNDFEST, H. (1957) Physiological and pharmacological consequences of different synaptic organizations in cerebral and cerebellar cortex. *J. Neurophysiol.* **20** : 494–522.

PURPURA, D. P., GIRADO, M. and GRUNDFEST, H. (1959a) Synaptic components of cerebellar electrocortical activity evoked by various afferent pathways. *J. Gen. Physiol.* **42** : 1037–1066.

PURPURA, D. P., GIRADO, M., SMITH, T. G., CALLAN, D. A. and GRUNDFEST, H. (1959b) Structure-activity determinants of pharmacological effects of amino acids and related compounds on central synapses. *J. Neurochem.* **3** : 238–268.

PURPURA, D. P., CARMICHAEL, M. W. and HOUSEPIAN, E. M. (1960a) Physiological and anatomical studies of development of superficial axodendritic synaptic pathways in neocortex. *Exptl. Neurol.* **2** : 324–347.

PURPURA, D. P., GIRADO, M. and GRUNDFEST, H. (1960b) Components of evoked potentials in cerebral cortex. *Electroencephalog. and Clin. Neurophysiol.* **12** : 95–110.

SCHADÉ, J. P. and BAXTER, C. F. (1960) Changes during growth in the volume and surface area of cortical neurons in the rabbit. *Exptl. Neurol.* **2** : 158–178.

SCHERRER, J. and OECONOMOS, D. (1955) Réponses évoquées corticales somesthésèques des mammifères adultes et nouveau-nés. In *Les Grandes Activites du Lobe Temporal.* Mason, Paris.

SHOLL, D. A. (1956) *The Organization of the Cerebral Cortex.* Methuen, London, and John Wiley, New York.

SPENCER, W. A. and KANDEL, E. R. (1960) Firing level and prepotentials in hippocampal neurons. *Federation Proc.* **19** : 290.

TASAKI, I., POLLEY, E. H. and ORREGO, F. (1954) Action potentials from individual elements in cat geniculate and striate cortex. *J. Neurophysiol.* **17** : 454–474.

INHIBITION IN THE NEURO-ENDOCRINE SYSTEMS OF INVERTEBRATES*

WILLIAM G. VAN DER KLOOT

Department of Pharmacology, New York University School of Medicine

OUR present familiarity with inhibition has come about by collecting and comparing data taken from a wide range of animals. By exploiting the riches of the animal kingdom, preparations have been found in which the cellular events in inhibition could be studied precisely and in detail. Comparative studies also give information on another level, as they have begun to show the manifold ways in which animals use inhibition.

My purpose is to point out how frequently inhibition has been used in the evolution of invertebrate neuroendocrine systems. There are two objectives. First, to discuss preparations which deserve further study, especially by physical and chemical methods. Second, to look for the pressures which led to selection for inhibitory links in the control of endocrine function—appreciating that we know more of the cellular details of inhibition than of its biological utility. The examples will illustrate the use of seemingly conventional inhibitory neurons, the existence of inhibitory hormones that are released by neurosecretory cells, and the long-term inhibition of entire sections of the central nervous system. At the outset, a few words of caution—perhaps of conciliation—are needed. If at times my definition of inhibition seems stretched beyond the usual limits, it is the fault of the animals discussed, who do unusual things.

INHIBITION OF A PART OF THE CENTRAL NERVOUS SYSTEM

The first example is of an inhibition persisting for weeks or months that is enforced by profound chemical changes in the nerve cells. For these reasons, inhibition of this type can be of only limited general usefulness to animals. It is worth considering, nonetheless, because it shows that nerve cells can be deprived of excitability for long periods of time, during the course of a life-cycle, and eventually restored to normal activity.

The animal which shows this progression is the *Cecropia* silkworm. At the

* The original studies reported in this paper were supported by grants from the Institute of Neurological Diseases and Blindness, Public Health Service.

time of pupation, the development of the silkworm abruptly stops. For weeks
or for months growth, differentiation, and even cell division are suspended;
the pupa is in diapause. Diapause goes on for many months if the pupa is
stored at 25°C. But after a few weeks at a low temperature, similar to the
cold of winter, if the pupa is returned to 25°C, development is soon resumed.
Twenty-one days after the onset of development, the adult moth emerges.
Diapause is obviously the means by which the pupa passes the winter. The
usual regulation is by the annual temperature cycle. A mistake by the control
mechanism within the insect leads to premature development and to death.

The control mechanism, as Williams (1946, 1956) showed, lies in the brain
of the silkworm. Diapause results from the failure of twenty-six specialized
neurons in the brain to release a neurohormone. The neurohormone from the
brain acts by stimulating a second endocrine organ, the prothoracic glands.
As summarized in Fig. 1, the prothoracic gland hormone, in its turn, acts on
the tissues to promote cell division, growth, and molting.

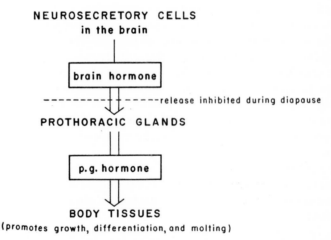

FIG. 1. The control of diapause in the *Cecropia* silkworm. For explanation see text.
⟹ Excitatory hormone.

Why do the neurosecretory cells not release the hormone during the months
of diapause, and how do low temperatures act to restore hormone release?
The scant evidence so far available suggests that neurosecretory cells release
hormone when they conduct action potentials (Knowles *et al.*, 1955; Van
der Kloot, 1960; Hodson and Geldiay, 1960). It therefore seemed reasonable
to study the electrical activity of the neurosecretory cells during diapause and
development.

The surprising result is that in the diapausing pupa all attempts to record
either spontaneous or evoked electrical activity from the brain have been

fruitless. This is in sharp contrast to the condition of the brain only a day or two before pupation, when spontaneous activity is easily recorded. Moreover, spontaneous electrical activity returns to the brains of chilled animals a few days before the visible onset of adult development. There is also a marked contrast between the brain and all of the other ganglia of the central nervous system which are active electrically throughout diapause (Van der Kloot, 1955a). The apparent inexcitability of the brain neurons during diapause is accompanied by a fall in the resting potentials. During diapause, the average resting potential of the brain neurons which were penetrated is only 23 ± 6 (s.d.) mV. This value is to be compared to the 65 ± 8 (s.d.) mV resting potentials of neurons in the brains of caterpillars and of developing adults, as well as to the 65 ± 9 (s.d.) mV resting potentials of neurons in the thoracic ganglia of diapausing pupae. Probably the measurements from the brain include penetrations of the neurosecretory cells, which are large and conveniently sited, but undoubtedly other large neurons were penetrated also (Van der Kloot, 1956).

These results suggest that the changes in electrical activity and in hormone release are part of a causal sequence. Both stop just before the pupa molts and electrical activity returns at just about the time when the hormone must be released to start the development of the adult. It seems that the inexcitability of the brain neurons—including the neurosecretory cells—causes the failure of hormone release during diapause.

The next problem is the chemical basis for the partial depolarization of the brain neurons. The work of Schneiderman and Williams (1954) and of Shappirio and Williams (1957) shows that in many diapausing tissues there is a fall in the titer of cytochrome c. As a consequence, the metabolic rate falls to a low level and the respiration is no longer depressed by cyanide or carbon monoxide. However, the entire central nervous system—the brain included—retains a normal metabolic rate and cyanide-sensitivity throughout diapause (Van der Kloot, 1955b).

On the other hand, measurements of cholinesterase show that at the time of pupation, the activity of this enzyme falls to a level below detection with the methods used. This means that cholinesterase activity falls to 3% (at most) of its former level. Throughout diapause and chilling, cholinesterase remains undetectable and only returns to a high level a few days before the onset of adult development. The experimental evidence suggests that cholinesterase is needed for conduction in *Cecropia* neurons (Van der Kloot, unpublished). In short, it appears that changes in the activity of cholinesterase may account for the loss of electrical and endocrine activites during diapause.

The changes in the brain that are characteristic of diapause do not take place if the brain is removed from a larva just before pupation and transplanted into a brainless pupa (Williams, 1952). This result suggests that the changes in the brain are brought about by the action of some other organ. It will be fascinating to know the source and nature of the influence which can so effectively and selectively inhibit the neurons of the brain.

It will be remembered that low temperatures act to promote the return of cholinesterase to the brain. During diapause there is an accumulation of a cholinergic substance (probably acetylcholine) in the brain. The accumulation is gradual at room temperature, rapid at low temperatures. The chemical, electrical and endocrine changes in the brain during diapause are summarized in Fig. 2. It was proposed that the cholinergic substance accumulates until a critical level is reached and the reappearance of cholinesterase is evoked. This idea is being tested, and the data so far suggest that it is right, but not enough experiments have been completed to be sure. The results already available show that cholinesterase returns to chilled brains implanted into isolated pupal abdomens, which contain no known endocrine organ. This fact argues that the changes leading to the reappearance of cholinesterase take place within the cells of the brain and are not triggered from without.

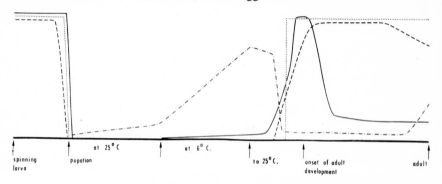

FIG. 2. A diagrammatic summary of the physiology of the *Cecropia* brain during metamorphosis. The time scale during diapause is, of course, greatly condensed. For explanation see text. ————, release of brain hormone; · · · · · ·, electrical activity of the brain; — —, cholinesterase in the brain; — · —, titer of cholinergic substance in the brain. (Reprinted from the *Biol. Bull.*)

To summarize, the neurosecretory cells of the *Cecropia* silkworm are inhibited; this is the cause of the pupal diapause. The inhibition is achieved by an enzymatic change in the brain neurons which may persist for months. Inhibition of this type must be exceptional, because few animals can afford to shut down a considerable portion of the central nervous system for weeks on end. For the silkworm, however, the method guarantees the safe passage of winter in a developmental stage where there seems to be little need for a brain.

INHIBITORY NEURONS IN NEUROENDOCRINE SYSTEMS

Viviparous Insects

In species in which the females hold fertilized eggs in a uterus or in an oöthecal chamber for the period of embryonic development, the maturation of additional eggs must be suppressed. An important step in the maturation of insect eggs is the deposition of the yolk. The incorporation of yolk is promoted by a hormone secreted by the corpora allata, a pair of organs in the head (see Scharrer, 1946). The control of the corpora allata has been studied in a number of Orthoptera.

In the roach *Leucophaea*, for example, Engelmann and Lüscher (1956) and Engelmann (1957) showed that the corpora allata have two distinct innervations: from the subesophageal ganglion and from the protocerebrum of the brain. When a female roach is carrying fertilized eggs, the corpora allata show no sign of secretion. If the nerves from the brain to the corpora allata are severed, the glands secrete, the ovaries become active, and yolk is deposited. If the nerves from the subesophageal ganglion are severed along with the nerves from the brain, the corpora allata do not secrete. Apparently the corpora allata have a dual innervation: excitatory from the subesophageal ganglion and inhibitory from the brain.

The inhibition of the corpora allata does not seem to involve the neurosecretory cells of the brain, whose axons run in the nerves going from the brain to the corpora allata, because inhibition is eliminated by destroying a part of the protocerebrum of the brain that does not contain neurosecretory cells.

When the female *Leucophaea* gives birth, egg development begins once again. This shows that the corpora allata have been released from inhibition. Engelmann showed that the inhibitory center of the protocerebrum is stimulated by a chemical released by the developing eggs. The control system in *Leucophaea* is diagrammed as Fig. 3.

Similar control systems are found in other viviparous roaches. The principal variation from species to species is in the way in which the inhibitory center is regulated. In *Blatella germanica* and in *Pycnoscelus surinamensis*, Roth and Stay (1959) showed that the developing eggs in the oöthecal chamber or uterus stimulate sensory receptors. The sensory messages ascend the ventral nerve cord and stimulate the inhibitory center in the brain. Consequently, during the development of the embryos, secretion by the corpora allata is suppressed.

The roach, *Diploptera punctata*, shows a variation on the same theme. In this species, Engelmann (1959) showed that the corpora allata of the adult female are inhibited as long as the animal remains a virgin. Once the females are mated, the glands secrete and yolk deposition begins. The corpora allata can also be activated by artificial mating with a glass "spermatophore". The mechanical stimuli of mating seem to provide a signal which inhibits activity in the corpora allata inhibitory center of the brain (see Fig. 4). Therefore, this control system relies on the inhibition of an inhibitory nerve supply.

Once the development of the eggs has started in *Diploptera*, the cycle

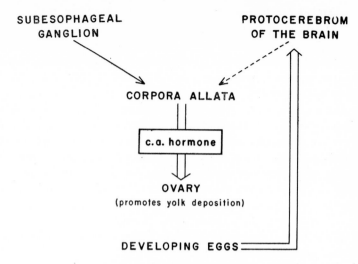

FIG. 3. A diagrammatic summary of the control of egg development in the roach, *Leucophaea* (Engelmann, 1957). For explanation see text.

⟶ excitatory nerve; – – – → inhibitory nerve;

⟹   excitatory hormone.

becomes self-sustaining. Each time the young are born, the mechanical stimulation is equivalent to mating, so the corpora allata are released from inhibition and the next batch of eggs begins to mature.

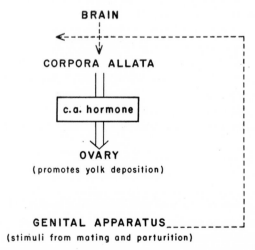

FIG. 4. A diagrammatic summary of the control of egg development in the roach, *Diploptera* (Engelmann, 1959). For explanation see text.

– – – →   inhibitory nerve;   ⟹   excitatory hormone.

Sexual Development in Octopus

Inhibitory nerves also are important in the sexual endocrinology of *Octopus*. In this animal, Wells and Wells (1959), showed that a hormone released by the optic glands promotes sexual maturity in both males and females. In young octopuses the optic gland is inhibited by a nerve that originates in the subpedunculate/dorsal basal region of the brain. Premature release of the optic gland hormone can be experimentally elicited by cutting the inhibitory nerve leading to the optic glands, by destroying the appropriate region of the brain, or by cutting the optic nerves (Fig. 5). The last observation suggests that the inhibitory center in the brain is normally driven by visual stimuli; perhaps it is the diurnal light–dark cycle that is important.

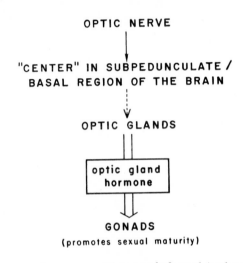

FIG. 5. A diagrammatic summary of the control of sexual development in *Octopus* (Wells and Wells, 1959).

⟶ excitatory nerve;   - - -→ inhibitory nerve;

⟹ excitatory hormone.

INHIBITORY HORMONES FROM NEUROSECRETORY CELLS

Crustacean Molting

Early in this century, Zeleny (1905) found that removing the eyestalks from a crustacean may cause a shortening of the interval between molts. The endocrine mechanism controlling crustacean molting has been worked out by the efforts of many workers (summarized by Knowles and Carlisle, 1956; Carlisle and Knowles, 1959). Hormones are produced in the cell bodies of neurosecretory cells in the central nervous system and in the ganglionic X organ of the eyestalk. The hormones are transported down the axons and are released at the axon endings, which are collected together to form the sinus gland of the eyestalk. One of the hormones released in the sinus gland is molt-inhibiting. The hormone acts by inhibiting the secretion of the Y organ, which is in the cephalothorax (Gabe, 1953; Echalier, 1959). The hormone from the Y organ acts on the tissues to promote growth and molting. Therefore, when the eyestalks are removed, the molt-inhibiting hormone is no longer present, the Y organ is free to secrete, and the animal molts. It is becoming clear that environmental stimuli are important in determining the rate of secretion by the neurosecretory cells (Bliss, 1956).

In the prawns the control system is somewhat more complicated. Both molt-inhibiting and molt-accelerating hormones are produced by neurosecretory cells and released in the eyestalk. The molt-accelerating hormone also acts by stimulating the Y organ (Fig. 6). In these animals then, the removal

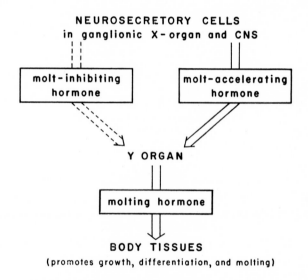

FIG. 6. A diagrammatic summary of the control of molting in the prawn, *Palaemon* (Carlisle, 1959).

⟹ excitatory hormone; ⤏ inhibitory hormone.

of the eyestalks gives a measure of the relative dominance of the two hormones. In *Palaemon* (=*Leander*) *sirratus* collected in Roscoff, removing the eyestalks accelerates molting (Drach, 1944; Carlisle, 1959). The same operation on the same species collected at Plymouth slows molting. The dominant hormone at Roscoff is inhibitory, at Plymouth excitatory (Carlisle, 1959). If there are any differences between Roscoff and Plymouth leading to the selection between acceleration and delay, they are unknown.

Inhibition Between Generations

The final example shows that inhibitory hormones from neurosecretory cells may be used between individuals as well as within a single body. In some races of the silkworm, *Bombyx mori*, the females can lay eggs of either of two types: eggs which promptly go through embryonic development or eggs which enter diapause. For simplicity, the moths laying diapausing eggs will be called "diapause" females, those laying normal eggs will be called "non-diapause" females (Lees, 1955). Whether a female becomes "diapause" or "non-diapause" is determined by the environment in which the animal is reared. If the silkworms are raised in the dark, the mature females are "non-diapause", if reared in the light, they are "diapause". Surprisingly, in making this determination the environment is most influential during the late stages of embryonic life, before the sense organs are exposed to the outside world (Kogure, quoted by Lees, 1955). The fate of the next generation can be decided before the parents have hatched from the egg.

The eggs enter diapause if they have incorporated a hormone from the maternal blood (Fukuda, 1951, 1952; Hasegawa, 1952). The hormone comes from the subesophageal ganglion, which contains neurosecretory cells. The subesophageal ganglion of both "diapause" and "non-diapause" females can produce the hormone. This is shown by experiments in which subeso-phageal ganglia from either "diapause" or "non-diapause" females are isolated and implanted into "non-diapause" hosts. The eggs laid by the hosts enter diapause.

Similarly, when the connectives between the brain and the subesophageal ganglion of a "non-diapause" female are severed, the operated animal lays diapausing eggs (Fukuda, 1953). The conclusion is that the neurosecretory cells of the subesophageal ganglia of the "non-diapause" females are inhibited by the brain (Fig. 7). Darkness in the early life of the female acts to set the

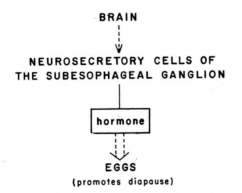

Fig. 7. A diagrammatic summary of the control of egg diapause in the silkworm
(Fukuda, 1951, 1952, 1953; Hasegawa, 1952).

----> inhibitory nerve;   ===> inhibitory hormone.

inhibitory center of the brain into permanent activity. The neurosecretory cells of the subesophageal ganglion are inhibited, hormone release is prevented, and normal egg development is ensured.

DISCUSSION AND SUMMARY

The introduction promised that the term "inhibition" would be extended to cover a wider range of events than is the custom. Whether for example, a neuroendocrine factor producing diapause during embryonic life can reasonably be called an inhibitory hormone is left to others. I think that the evolutionary history, if ever uncovered, would show a close relation between nerve cells which inhibit adjacent cells and neurosecretory cells which inhibit at a distance.

It would be folly to think that the same chemicals are necessarily involved in local and in distant inhibitory effects, although the instance of norepinephrine shows that this is a possibility. Establishing the chemical nature of the inhibitory hormones will be a fascinating task, but the results may not provide answers which can be extended to local transmitters.

Almost all of the examples deserve study by neurophysiologists. The problems are varied and relate to the central questions of integration in the nervous system. The simplest type of control mechanism is the reflex activation of the inhibitory nerve which leads to the corpora allata of the roaches. Here it would be particularly interesting to study in *Leucophaea* the activation of the inhibitory center by chemicals released from the developing eggs.

On a more complicated level are the problems of the long-term control of neuroendocrine systems by the changing external environment. In the *Cecropia* silkworm the control, though still not completely understood, seems relatively simple. The critical controlling events appear to take place within, instead of between, the brain neurons. However, integrative events between nerve cells are surely used in the long-term regulation of the inhibitory center controlling the optic gland of *Octopus* and of the X organ neurosecretory cells of the Crustacea. In these animals changes in the environment are dealt with so that the output of a single nerve tract is altered. The attraction to the experimentalist here is that even though environmental changes are put into the animal through complicated sense organs, the output from the central nervous system converges into a single nerve or tract which could be isolated for recording.

An even more challenging example of central integration driving a neurosecretory pathway is found in the silkworm, where the environment during the late stages of embryonic life sets the level of activity in an inhibitory center of the brain. Weeks later, the activity of the inhibitory center determines the output of the neurosecretory cells of the subesophageal ganglion and, by this means, the developmental fate of the next generation. It is hard to think of a more clear-cut situation for analyzing the effects of early experience on the later activity of the central nervous system.

Although the examples were taken from a wide range of animals and of situations, there seems to be a common principle in the use of inhibition. All involve the long-term control of events within the animal. The time scale in these inhibiting events is weeks or months long, rather than milliseconds. And in each case inhibition is used to insure the animal against a course which would mean complete disaster. If the *Cecropia* silkworm begins adult development before the end of winter, it dies. Premature development of new eggs by a roach would cause a drastic disruption of the reproductive sequence. In the roaches, the corpora allata are innervated by excitatory and inhibitory nerves. If both nerves are severed, the corpora allata do not secrete. This result shows that the absence of excitatory stimuli is usually sufficient to stop hormone release. In normal female roaches, the corpora allata are actively inhibited while the young are being carried. The other examples fit into the same plan. Nevertheless, in these situations it seems undesirable to rely upon the absence of excitatory stimuli to maintain inactivity. Perhaps excitable tissues are too unstable and liable to spontaneous discharge for this solution to be acceptable. Instead, inhibition is used as insurance against premature activation.

This argument is strengthened by considering the control of molting in prawns, where different populations of the same species are dominated by molt-inhibiting or molt-accelerating hormones. This shows that the decision between excitatory or inhibitory control need not be an ancient residue of evolution, but can be selected to fit the circumstances of the animals' life.

In conclusion, remember that the examples were chosen to show inhibitory links in neuroendocrine systems and that a complete review was not attempted. There are undoubtedly many more instances of inhibition remaining to be discovered. Certainly inhibitory links are commonplace in neuroendocrine systems and inhibition plays a vital role in the control mechanisms.

REFERENCES

BLISS, D. E. (1956) *Bertil Hanström. Zoological Papers in Honour of his Sixty-fifth Birthday* (ed. by WINGSTRAND, K. G.). Zoological Institute, Lund.

CARLISLE, D. B. (1959) Molting hormone in *Palaemon* (= *Leander*) (Crustacea Decapoda). *J. Marine Biol. Assoc. United Kingdom* 38 : 351–359.

CARLISLE, D. B. and KNOWLES, F. G. W. (1959) *Endocrine Control in Crustacea.* Cambridge University Press, Cambridge.

DRACH, P. (1944) Etude préliminaire sur le cycle d'intermue et son conditionnement hormonal chez *Leander serratus* (Pennant). *Bull. Biol.* 78 : 40–62.

ECHALIER, G. (1959) L'organ Y et le déterminisme de la crossance et la mue chez *Carcinus maenas* (L.) Crustacé Décopodé. *Ann. sci. nat. Zool.* 12 ser. 1 : 1–59.

ENGELMANN, F. (1957) Die Steuerung der Ovarfunktion bei der Ovoviviparen Schabe *Leucophaea maderae* (Fabr.) *J. Inst. Physiol.* 1 : 257–278.

ENGELMANN, F. (1959) The control of reproduction in *Diploptera punctata* (Blattaria). *Biol. Bull. Woods Hole* 116 : 406–419.

ENGELMANN, F. and LÜSCHER, M. (1956) Die hemmende Wirkung des Gehirns auf die corpora allata bie *Leucophaea maderae* (Orthoptera). *Verhandl. deut. zool. Ges.* 215–220.

FUKUDA, S. (1951) Factors determining the production of non-diapause eggs in the silkworm. *Proc. Imp. Acad.* (*Tokyo*) **27** : 672–677.

FUKUDA, S. (1952) Function of the pupal brain and subesophageal ganglion in the production of non-diapause and diapause eggs in the silkworm. *Annotationes Zool. Japon.* **25** : 149–155.

FUKUDA, S. (1953) Alteration of voltinism in the silkworm following transection of pupal oesophageal connectives. *Proc. Imp. Acad.* (*Tokyo*) **29** : 389–391.

GABE, M. (1953) Sur l'existence, chez quelques Crustaces Malacostraces, d'un organe comparable a la glande de mue des Insectes. *Compt. rend.* **237** : 1111–1113.

HASEGAWA, K. (1952) Studies in voltinism in the silkworm *Bombyx mori* L., with special reference to the organ concerning determination of voltinism. *J. Fac. Agr. Totturi Univ.* **1** : 83–124.

HODGSON, E. S. and GELDIAY, S. (1959) Experimentally induced release of neurosecretory materials from roach corpora cardiaca. *Biol. Bull. Woods Hole* **117** : 275–283.

KNOWLES, F. G. W. and CARLISLE, D. B. (1956) Endocrine control in the crustacea. *Biol. Rev.* **31** : 396–468.

KNOWLES, F. G. W., CARLISLE, D. B. and DUPONT-RAABE, M. (1955) Studies on pigment activating substances in animals—I. The separation by paper electrophoresis of chromactivating substances in arthropods. *J. Marine Biol. Assoc. United Kingdom* **34** : 611–635.

LEES, A. D. (1955) *The Physiology of Diapause in Arthropods.* Cambridge University Press, Cambridge.

ROTH, L. M. and STAY, B. (1959) Control of oöcyte development in cockroaches. *Science* **130** : 271–272.

SCHARRER, B. (1946) The relationship between corpora allata and reproductive organs in adult *Leucophaea maderae.* *Endocrinology* **38** : 46–55.

SCHNEIDERMAN, H. A. and WILLIAMS, C. M. (1954) The physiology of insect diapause VIII. Qualitative changes in the metabolism of the Cecropia silkworm during diapause and development. *Biol. Bull. Woods Hole* **106** : 210–229.

SHAPPIRIO, D. G. and WILLIAMS, C. M. (1957) The cytochrome system of the Cecropia silkworm—I. Spectroscopic studies of individual tissues. *Proc. Roy. Soc.* (*London*) B **147** : 218–232.

VAN DER KLOOT, W. G. (1955a) The control of neurosecretion and diapause by physiological changes in the brain of the Cecropia silkworm. *Biol. Bull. Woods Hole* **109** : 276–294.

VAN DER KLOOT, W. G. (1955b) Neurosecretion and the physiology of the brain of the Cecropia silkworm. *J. Cellular Comp. Physiol.* **46** : 359.

VAN DER KLOOT, W. G. (1956) The resting potentials of neurons in the Cecropia brain during diapause and development. *Proceedings Tenth International Congress of Entomology* **2** : 79.

VAN DER KLOOT, W. G. (1960) Neurosecretion in insects. *Ann. Rev. Entomol.* **5** : 35–52.

WELLS, M. J. and WELLS, J. (1959) Hormonal control of sexual maturity in *Octopus.* *J. Exptl. Biol.* **36** : 1–33.

WILLIAMS, C. M. (1946) Physiology of insect diapause: The role of the brain in the production and termination of pupal dormancy in the giant silkworm, *Platysamia cecropia.* *Biol. Bull. Woods Hole* **90** : 234–243.

WILLIAMS, C. M. (1952) Physiology of insect diapause—IV. The brain and prothoracic glands as an endocrine system in the Cecropia silkworm. *Biol. Bull. Woods Hole* **103** : 120–138.

WILLIAMS, C. M. (1956) Physiology of insect diapause—X. An endocrine mechanism for the influence of temperature on the diapausing pupa of the Cecropia silkworm. *Biol. Bull. Woods Hole* **110** : 201–218.

ZELENY, C. (1905) Compensatory regulation. *J. Exptl. Zool.* **2** : 1–102.

CONCLUSION

THE first published account of a symposium we owe to Plato who, in the year 380 B.C., wrote the famous *Symposion,* that masterful poetic dialog which has influenced occidental culture as few other writings ever have. The term 'symposion' actually means 'drinking party'. Plato's symposion took place in the house of the Athenian Agathon whose circle of friends included Sokrates. The classical—and modern—idea of a symposium was born when Pausanias suggested abstaining for once from compulsory heavy drinking and passing the night with talks on a particular topic, drinking only whenever one felt like doing so. Plato tells us that the friends agreed to this happily since they were still suffering from the after-effects of their drinking bout of the previous night. Following the suggestion of Eryximachos, the theme of this first published symposium was to present laudations to the god Eros. The climax of Plato's symposion is the speech of the visionary Diotima who convinces Sokrates that the cognition of beauty means the recognition of truth through which one acquires the true virtue and immortality.

What would Plato think had he observed this, our Symposium on nervous inhibition? Surely he would be amazed: the duration of this symposium alone would seem incredible to him—would he not be aware that the drinking was confined altogether to a few hours? Truly astonishing, however, he would find the theme of our discussions and arguments: to emphasize and restrict speeches and discussions to concepts of inhibition must surely be disturbing to the mind that dreams of the absolute harmony of all being. I think it is fitting to conclude this Symposium by reassuring the spirit of Plato that we are mindful of the fact that nervous inhibition is only the counterpart of the equally important phenomenon of nervous excitation, and by reminding him that it was our conviction of a universal harmony that prompted us to balance the common emphasis on excitatory processes by giving more weight to the discussion and understanding of inhibition.

Let us hope that one day there will be a truly beautiful symposium where nervous inhibition and nervous excitation will form a theme worthy of the great master.

E. F.

AUTHOR INDEX

ADRIAN, E. D., 15, 327, 429, 435
AITKEN, J. T., 72
ALBE-FESSARD, D., 343, 424
ALBERT, A., 39
ALEXANDROWICZ, J. S., 144, 145, 147, 148, 173, 285, 288, 289, 295, 302, 401
ALVAREZ-BUYLLA, R., 291, 326
ALTAMIRANO, M., 93, 331
ALPERN, M., 275
AMASSIAN, V. E., 411, 423
AMIN, A. H., 357, 358
AMBROSE, E. J., 222
ANDERSSON-CEDERGREN, E., 124, 129
ANGELUCCI, L., 357
ARAKI, T., 51, 53, 62, 76, 79, 80
ARVANITAKI, A., 179, 180, 183, 185, 189, 191, 194, 195, 196, 197, 200, 201, 202, 209, 210, 214, 217, 223, 233, 234
ARNOLD, W., 224
ASANO, M., 358
AUTRUM, H., 326

BACH, L. M. N., 357
BALLIF, L., 21
BARLOW, H. B., 282
BARTELMEZ, G. H., 22
BARRON, D. H., 18, 62, 204
BARTELS, H., 179
BATHAM, E., 233
BAYLISS, W. M., 114
BAXTER, C. F., 428
BAZEMORE, A., 355, 361, 369
BECHT, G., 4
BEIDLER, 332
BÉKÉSY, G. VON, 241
BENNET, M. V. L., 238, 331, 333, 336
BERGMANN, F., 93, 94
BERITOFF, J. S., 17, 18, 21
BERNHARD, C. K., 23, 217, 326
BERNE, R. M., 124, 127
BIEDERMANN, M. A., 4, 364
BIEDERMANN, W., 2, 87, 114
BIRKS, R. I., 346
BISHOP, E. J., 424, 443
BISHOP, G. H., 424, 429
BLASCHKO, H., 346
BLISS, D., 454
BLUM, H. F., 195
BODIAN, D., 22

BOISTEL, J., 81, 83, 87, 102, 119, 179, 364
BONVALLET, M., 179
BRADLEY, D. F., 224
BRANN, A. W., 357
BRADLEY, K., 76
BRANCH, C. L., 424
BRASSFIELD, C. R., 32
BREMER, F., 21, 179
BRIDGER, J. E., 72
BROCK, L. G., 23, 33, 47, 251
BRONK, D. W., 19
BROOKS, C. M., 15
BROOKS, V. B., 27, 61, 66, 69, 76, 429, 431, 441
BROWN, G., 26
BROWN, K. T., 331, 333
BROWN, P. K., 196
BULLOCK, T. H., 3, 5, 145, 149, 151, 158, 162, 167, 179, 180, 204, 217, 233, 238, 291, 301, 319
BUMPUS, F. M., 138
BURGEN, A. S. V., 83, 115, 288, 302
BURNS, B. D., 429, 432
BUSER, P., 343, 424

CAJAL, S., RAMON y, 405, 428
CALDWELL, P. C., 189
CALLAN, D. A., 102, 425, 433, 434, 435, 441
CALVIN, M., 224
CAMPBELL, B., 336
CARDEW, M. H., 224
CARDOT, H., 233
CARLISLE, D. B., 173, 448, 454
CARMICHAEL, M. W., 426, 428, 429, 432, 433, 442, 444
CASTILLO, J. DEL, 16, 87, 111, 115, 117, 342, 345
CERVONI, P., 115
CHALAZONITIS, N., 179, 180, 183, 184, 185, 186, 189, 191, 194, 195, 196, 197, 200, 201, 202, 204, 209, 210, 214, 217, 223, 224, 233
CHAMBERS, W. W., 419
CHANCE, B., 185
CHANG, H. T., 424, 428, 429, 432
CLARE, M. H., 424, 429
CLAUDE, A., 196
COATES, C. W., 93, 331
COHEN, M. J., 145

461

COLE, K. S., 197
COLLIER, H. O. J., 400
CONDOURIS, G. A., 23
CONEL, J. L., 428
COOMBS, J. S., 23, 24, 33, 42, 47, 52, 71, 72, 74, 76, 80, 81, 82, 119, 217, 251, 313, 343, 344, 350, 351, 352
CORABOEUF, E., 179
CORNSWEET, J. G., 282
CORNSWEET, T. N., 282
COUTEAUX, R., 191
CRAIN, S. M., 443
CRAMMER, J. I., 357
CRAWFORD, T. B. B., 357, 358
CRILL, W. E., 121, 127, 130
CROSSLAND, J., 342
CURTIS, D. R., 34, 41, 52, 71, 72, 73, 75, 76, 80, 102, 186, 342, 343, 344, 346

DAVIS, H., 194, 241, 275, 334, 336
D'ARSONVAL, A., 195
DELL, P. C., 18, 23, 179
DENNY-BROWN, D. B., 64
DE ROBERTIS, E., 191, 196, 338, 345
DESMEDT, J. E., 5
DETHIER, V. G., 403
DEVITO, J. L., 419
DIECKE, F. P. J., 69, 217, 255
DIEDERICHS, W., 138
DITCHBURN, R. W., 282
DIVARIS, G. A., 137
DODGE, F. A., 251
DRACH, P., 454
DRAPER, M. H., 127
DUBUISSON, M., 379
DUDEL, J., 83, 111, 112, 115, 124, 204, 313
DUKE, W. W., 114
DUNN, C. E., 114

EASTON, D. M., 76
EAYRS, J. T., 428
ECCLES, J. C., 3, 14, 15, 16, 17, 19, 21, 23, 24, 27, 33, 35, 38, 41, 42, 47, 48, 50, 51, 52, 53, 54, 55, 56, 57, 59, 61, 62, 68, 71, 72, 73, 74, 75, 76, 78, 79, 80, 81, 82, 83, 119, 180, 217, 251, 285, 293, 313, 342, 344, 345, 346, 350, 353, 354, 424, 432, 443, 444
ECCLES, R. M., 25, 50, 53, 56, 57, 59, 68, 69, 81
ECHALIER, G., 454
ECKERT, R. O., 4
EDWARDS, C., 16, 83, 105, 115, 124, 285, 287, 293, 294, 301, 302, 312, 313, 326, 328, 356, 362
EIDE, E., 50
EINTHOVEN, W., 16
ELDRED, E., 64, 288

ELEY, D. D., 224
ELKES, J., 342
ELLIOT, A., 222
ELLIOTT, K. A. C., 222, 355, 361, 380, 432
ENDROECZI, E., 359, 363, 365, 369
ENGELMANN, F., 451, 452
ENGER, P. S., 429, 431, 441
EYZAGUIRRE, C., 204, 217, 251, 286, 287, 289, 290, 291, 292, 293, 296, 298, 300, 301, 302, 305, 307, 308, 309, 310, 312, 314, 318, 319, 326, 327, 328, 361, 362

FABIAN, I., 359, 365
FALK, G., 115
FAN, S. F., 430, 441, 443, 444
FATT, P., 16, 24, 27, 33, 35, 38, 42, 48, 50, 54, 55, 56, 59, 61, 62, 71, 72, 74, 76, 80, 81, 82, 83, 87, 89, 90, 102, 111, 114, 119, 217, 251, 302, 213, 343, 344, 350, 351, 352, 364
FELDBERG, W., 19, 342, 346, 366, 379
FENG, T. P., 430, 441, 443, 444
FESSARD, A., 180
FINEAN, J. B., 196
FLOREY, E., 4, 102, 105, 136, 173, 186, 204, 222, 286, 287, 288, 289, 295, 302, 318, 319, 321, 322, 353, 354, 355, 356, 358, 360, 361, 363, 364, 369, 380
FOLCH-PI, J., 379
FONTAINE, J., 5
FORBES, A., 22
FOSTER, M., 2
FOX, W., 217
FRANK, K., 16, 23, 25, 47, 55, 62, 64, 66, 353
FRITSCH, G., 333
FROEHLICH, F. W., 3, 14
FRY, G. A., 275
FUKUDA, A., 455
FULLAM, E. F., 196
FULTON, J. F., 21
FUORTES, M. G. F., 23, 47, 55, 62, 66, 204, 223, 326, 328, 329, 330, 353
FURUKAWA, A., 98
FURUKAWA, T., 98
FURSHPAN, E. J., 59, 222, 288

GABE, M., 454
GADDUM, H. J., 19, 357, 358
GALAMBOS, R., 194, 241
GALIGER, E., 234
GARTEN, S., 333
GASKELL, W. H., 16
GASSER, H. S., 13, 15, 19, 21, 23, 336
GELDIAY, S., 448
GERARD, R. W., 17, 22, 179
GERNANDT, B., 45
GERNANDT, B. E., 179
GESELL, R., 17, 22, 32

GINSBORG, B. L., 90
GIRADO, M. M., 102, 373, 425, 433, 434, 435, 441
GOLDMAN, L., 233, 239
GOMEZ, J. A., 373
GONZALES, S., 432
GOODHEAD, B., 428
GRAHAM, C. H., 242
GRAHAM, H. T., 15
GRANIT, R., 27, 45, 61, 64, 66, 67, 68, 182, 194, 201, 210, 217, 241, 255, 282, 291, 326, 332
GRAY, E. G., 428
GRAY, J. A. B., 291, 293, 326, 328
GREIG, M. E., 114
GRISWOLD, P., 222
GROSSMAN, C. G., 444
GRUEN, D. N., 222
GRUNDFEST, H., 92, 93, 94, 95, 97, 98, 99, 100, 101, 102, 105, 107, 108, 180, 217, 223, 293, 326, 328, 330, 331, 333, 334, 336, 337, 338, 342, 344, 356, 424, 425, 426, 429, 432, 441, 443
GUERIN, J., 179
GUGGENHEIM, M., 379

HAASE, J., 66, 67
HAGBARTH, K. E., 419
HAGIWARA, S., 56, 83, 149, 204, 214, 291, 305, 314, 315, 356
HARA, J., 173
HARREVELD, A. VAN, 179, 186
HARRIS, E. J., 115, 313
HARTLINE, H. K., 5, 67, 194, 201, 204, 210, 241, 242, 243, 247, 248, 249, 254, 255, 259, 260, 265, 268, 269, 270, 272, 273, 274, 276, 281, 291, 326, 336, 399
HASEGAWA, K. 455
HASHIMOTO, Y., 331
HAYASHI, T., 186, 222, 369, 376, 380, 385, 388, 389
HEBB, C. O., 345
HEYMANS, C., 179
HIRSCH, A., 224
HODGKIN, A. L., 69, 81, 87, 115, 122, 127
HODGSON, E. S., 448
HOERR, N. L., 22
HOFFMANN, H., 233
HOFFMANN, P., 3
HOLLAND, W. C., 114
HOLMGREN, E., 234
HOLMQUIST, B., 41
HONOUR, A. J., 354, 356, 358
HOROWICZ, P., 81, 122
HORRIDGE, G. A., 210, 338, 395, 399, 400, 401, 405, 407
HOSHIKO, T., 124, 127

HOUSEPIAN, E. M., 426, 428, 429, 432, 433, 435, 442, 444
HOWELL, W. H., 114
HOYLE, G., 4, 102, 217, 364
HUBBARD, R., 242
HUBER, F., 403
HUGHES, G. M., 5
HURSH, J. B., 419
HUTTER, O. F., 115, 117, 121, 122, 124, 302, 313

IGGO, A., 68, 69
INOKUCHI, H., 224
ISAACSON, A., 195
ITO, M., 51, 53, 68, 69, 76, 78, 79, 80, 81, 83
IWAMA, K., 373
IZQUIERDO, J. J., 145

JACK, J., 76, 78
JAEGER, J. C., 345, 346
JANCZARSKI, I., 363
JASPER, H., 204, 432
JOHNSON, A. R., 209, 405
JULLIEN, A., 136, 138, 139

KANDEL, E. R., 424
KAO, C. Y., 338
KASHA, M., 224
KATO, G., 14
KATZ, B., 16, 24, 87, 89, 105, 111, 114, 15, 117, 122, 217, 251, 291, 302, 313, 326, 364
KAUTSKY, H., 224
KELLER, R. F. JR., 124
KENNEDY, D., 210
KENNEDY, T. T., 412
KERKUT, G. A., 27, 217
KERR, D. I. B., 419
KEYNES, R. D., 333
KIBJAKOV, A. W., 19
KIMURA, 332
KISSELEFF, M., 16
KLOTZ, I. R., 222
KNOWLES, F. G. W., 448, 453
KOELLE, G. B., 342, 346
KOIZUMI, K., 67
KOKETSU, K., 27, 33, 35, 54, 59, 61, 62, 71
KOLMODIN, G. M., 24, 179, 183, 186, 204
KORNMUELLER, A. E., 359
KOSHINO, C., 358
KOSMAN, A. J., 195
KOZAK, W., 55
KRIJGSMAN, B. J., 137
KRNJEVIC, K., 34

KUFFLER, S. W., 16, 83, 105, 111, 112, 115, 124, 180, 182, 194, 196, 201, 204, 217, 251, 282, 285, 286, 287, 288, 289, 290, 291, 292, 293, 296, 298, 300, 301, 230 303, 304, 305, 307, 308, 310, 312, 313, 314, 315, 318, 319, 324, 326, 327, 336, 361, 362
KUNO, M., 68
KUPERMAN, A., 95
KURIAKI, K., 358
KUSANO, K., 291, 305, 314, 315
KUYPERS, H. G. J. M., 419, 423

LAGET, P., 179
LANDGREN, S., 34, 38, 48, 50, 55, 56
LAPORTE, Y., 25, 26, 33, 41, 47, 76
LASANSKY, A., 196
LE BARON, F. N., 379
LEES, A. D., 455
LEGOUIX, J. P., 179
LENHARTZ, E., 114
LENOIR, J., 183, 184, 196, 200
LETTVIN, J. Y., 18, 23
LI, C. L., 204, 446
LIDDELL, E. G. T., 21, 22
LILLIE, R. S., 32, 195
LIPPAY, F., 195
LISSAK, K., 369, 359, 363, 365
LISSMANN, H. W., 331, 336
LIU, C. N., 419
LLOYD, D. P. C., 3, 16, 18, 19, 20, 21, 23, 24, 25, 26, 27, 33, 47, 50, 52, 76, 78, 179, 186, 204
LOEWENSTEIN, W. R., 204, 291, 326, 328, 337
LOEWI, O., 2, 15, 114
LORENTE DE NÓ, R. 19, 20, 23, 26, 179
LUCAS, K., 14, 15, 16, 23
LUNDBERG, A., 25, 33, 41, 50, 53, 56, 59, 69, 80, 333, 335, 344

MACH, E., 241
MACINTOSH, F. C., 346
MACLAY, H. K., 224
MACLEOD, P., 204
MACNICHOL, E. F. JR., 204, 210, 243, 247, 249, 251, 276, 282, 291, 326, 331, 334
MACRAE, E. G., 224
MACWILLIAMS, J. A., 114
MAGHI, F., 55, 56, 57
MARDUEL, H., 139
MARMONT, G., 3, 105, 362
MARRAZZI, A. S., 19
MARTIN, A. R., 424
MATTHEWS, B. H. C., 18, 62, 204
MAYNARD, D. M., 145, 147, 151, 152, 166, 173, 402
McCOLLOCH, W. S., 18, 23

McDOUGALL, W., 14, 20
McINTYRE, A. K., 76, 78
McLENNAN, H., 186, 222, 353, 354, 356, 358, 360, 364, 369
MECHELSE, K., 5
MERTON, P. A., 64
MEVES, H., 179
MILBURN, N., 404
MILEDI, R., 34
MILLER, P. L., 403
MILLER, W. H., 241, 242, 243, 399
MIYATA, K., 389
MONNIER, A. M., 179
MOODY, M. F., 196, 225
MORIN, G., 136
MORSE, R. W., 418
MOTLEY, H. L., 137
MOUNTCASTLE, V. B., 194, 241, 417, 418
MUELLER, C. G., 282
MUIR, A. R., 124, 129
MURAKAMI, M., 331
MYA-TU, M., 127

NAGAI, K., 369, 380, 389
NAGASHIMA, A., 358
NASTUK, W. L., 343
NOBLE, D., 121, 122
NORO, T., 358

OBRADOR, S., 18
ODORIZ, J. B., 18
OECONOMOS, D., 428
ORREGO, F., 424
ORLOV, J., 408
ORTMANN, R., 336
OSCARSSON, O., 41, 80
OTANI, T., 62, 149, 158, 162
OTTOSON, D., 204, 287, 291, 293, 294, 301, 302, 326, 328, 330
OTSUKA, M., 183

PAGE, I., 138
PAINTAL, A. S., 326, 328
PALADE, G. E., 196
PALAY, S. L., 191, 345
PARFITT, G. D., 224
PASCOE, J. E., 27, 61, 66, 68
PATAKY, I., 359, 365
PATON, W. D. M., 342
PAVLOV, J., 2, 114
PERNOW, B., 358
PERRIN, D. D., 344
PERRY, M. J., 224
PETERSON, P., 316
PFEIFER, A. K., 359, 363, 365
PHILLIPS, C. G., 45, 62, 182, 343, 424
PHILLIS, J. W., 186, 345
PILGRIM, R. L. C., 138, 285

PITTS, W. C., 18, 23
POLLEY, E. H., 424
POTTER, D. D., 59, 337
POWELL, T. P. S., 417, 418
PRESTON, J. B., 55
PROSSER, C. L., 137, 138, 195
PURPURA, D. P., 102, 373, 424, 425, 426, 428, 429, 432, 433, 434, 435, 441, 443, 444

RABINOWITCH, E., 224
RADEMAKER, A. C. A., 16
RALL, W., 72
RAMIREZ DE ARELLANO, J., 291, 326
RATHKAMP, R., 204
RATLIFF, F., 67, 194, 210, 241, 242, 243, 245, 249, 254, 255, 259, 260, 265, 268, 269, 270, 272, 274, 277, 282, 336, 399
RAYNER, B., 117
RENSHAW, B., 3, 18, 23, 27, 47, 61
RETZLAFF, E., 5, 32
REUBEN, J. P., 92, 93, 94, 95, 97, 98, 99, 100, 101, 102, 105, 107, 108, 217
RICHET, C., 2
RICKLES, W. H. JR., 93, 95, 100, 101, 102, 105, 107, 108, 217
RIGGS, L. A., 282
RIKER, W. F. JR., 95
ROBBINS, 105, 364
ROBERTS, J., 95
ROBERTSON, J. D., 196, 225, 345
ROEDER, K. D., 404
ROMANOWSKI, W., 363
ROTH, L. M., 451
RUSHTON, W. A. H., 329, 330
RUTLEGE, L. T., 61, 66, 67

SAITO, N., 149, 291, 314, 315
SAMOJLOFF, A., 16
SANCHEZ, D., 405
SANDOW, A., 195
SANO, T., 127
SATO, M., 291, 293
SATO, Y., 331
SCHAB, R., 38, 39
SCHADE, J. P., 428
SCHARRER, B., 336, 451
SCHARRER, E., 336
SCHERRER, J., 442
SCHEYER, S., 128
SCHIFF, J. M., 114
SCHIMERT, J., 33
SCHLOTE, F. W., 239
SEGAL, J. R., 214
SETCHENOW, I. M., 13
SHAPIRIO, D. G., 449
SHERRINGTON, C. S., 2, 3, 8, 14, 15, 16, 19, 20, 21

SHIMAMOTO, T., 127
SHOLL, D. A., 426
SIGG, E. B., 102
SJÖSTRAND, F. S., 124, 129, 196
SKOGLUND, C. R., 23, 24, 179, 183, 186, 204, 217
SLOCOMBE, A. J., 139
SMITH, J. E., 406, 407
SMITH, T. G., 102, 373, 425, 434, 435, 441
SMITH, R. I., 151
SÖDERBERG, V., 179
SOMJEN, G., 76, 78
SPENCER, W. A., 424
SPERELAKIS, N., 124, 127
SPERRY, R. W., 42
SPRAGUE, J. M., 22, 23, 25, 33
SPYROPOULOS, C. S., 189, 197, 214
STAY, B., 451
STEG, G., 27, 61, 66, 68
STEINMANN, E., 196
STRAUB, R., 179
SUCKLING, E. E., 115
SUGAR, O., 179
SUZUKI, S., 136, 137
SVAETECHIN, G., 204, 331, 332, 334
SZEKELY, G., 42
SZENTAGOTHAI, J. 33, 35, 38, 39, 42, 44, 210, 346
SZENT GYÖRGYI, A., 224
SZABO, T., 336

TAKAGI, T., 98
TAKAHASHI, H., 358
TAKAYAMA, N., 127
TALBOT, W. H., 69, 255
TASAKI, I., 56, 197, 214, 424
TAUB, R., 137
TAUC, L., 5, 83, 162, 179, 180, 233, 239
TAYLOR, B. J. R., 127, 217
TAYSUM, D. H., 224
TCHOU, SI HO, 233, 234
TERROUX, L. G., 83, 115
TERZUOLO, C. A., 5, 149, 151, 158, 162, 167, 179, 291, 319, 325
THERMAN, D. O., 23
THESLEFF, S., 4
THOMAS, J., 179
TOMITA, T., 247, 250, 326, 331
TOSAKA, K., 341
TOWE, A. L., 410, 411, 412, 414
TRAUTWEIN, W., 16, 83, 115, 117, 124, 204, 302, 313
TURNER, R. S., 301

UEXKÜLL, J. VON, 14
USHIYAMA, J., 67

VAN DER KLOOT, W. H., 105, 364, 447, 448, 449
VARTIANIN, A., 19
VERWORN, M., 14
VINCE, E., 369
VINCENT, D., 138
VOGT, M., 357
VON EULER, C., 179, 358
VOORHOEVE, P., 50

WAGNER, H. G., 194, 204, 210, 243, 247, 249, 265, 282, 291, 326
WALBERG, F., 423
WALD, G., 196, 242
WALL, P. D., 209
WATANABE, A., 149, 204, 238
WATANABE, K., 331
WASSERMAN, I., 359
WATKINS, J. C., 186, 342, 344, 345
WEATHERALL, M., 117
WEBER, E., 114
WEBER, E. F. D., 2, 13, 15
WEBER, E. H., 2, 13, 15
WEDENSKY, N., 2, 3, 14, 17
WEIANT, E. A., 404
WEISS, P., 41, 42
WELSH, J. H., 137, 138, 139

WERMAN, R., 92, 95, 99, 102
WERNER, G. 95
WEST, T. C., 115
WHITACKER, V. P., 345
WHITLOCK, D. G., 55
WIEDMANN, S., 125
WIERSMA, C. A. G., 3, 5, 105, 162, 217, 222 285, 288, 362, 364, 404, 406
WIESEL, T. N., 331, 333
WILLIAMS, C. M., 448, 449
WILSKA, A., 5
WILSON, D. M., 403
WILSON, V. J., 16, 24, 25, 27, 33, 48, 52, 61, 66, 69, 78, 255
WINSBURY, G. J., 34, 38, 56
WITZLEB, E., 179
WOLBARSHT, M. L., 282
WOODBURY, J. W., 130

YAKUSHIJI, T., 358
YOUNG, J. Z., 183, 405

ZAWARZIN, A., 405, 406, 407, 408
ZELENY, C., 453
ZETLER, G., 358
ZOTTERMAN, Y., 179

SUBJECT INDEX

Absorption bands of pigments and vital dyes, 196, 200
Accommodation, 69, 318, 321, 323
Acetate, 80
Acetyl-γ-aminobutyrobetaine, 388
Active excitatory processes, 11
Active inhibitory processes, 11
Adaptation, 152, 156, 167, 177, 318, 319, 322, 323
Adrenaline, 19, 336, 357
  inhibitory action of, 19
Acetylcholine, 4, 11, 114, 115, 117, 118, 119, 120, 121, 124, 133, 136, 137, 138, 319, 321, 335, 346, 347, 357, 360, 363, 365, 378, 382, 383
  actions compared with those of Factor I, 363
  actions on molluscan hearts, 136ff.
  action on vertebrate hearts, 114ff., 133
  desensitization to, 4
  effects on current spread, 133
  not inhibitory transmitter, 138
  to increase K⁺-permeability, 134
Afternegativity, 295, 309
Afterpositivity, 297, 309
Agmatine (γ-guanidino butylamine), 362
β-Alanine, 344, 356, 362
β-Alanyl-1-histidine (see Carnosine)
Alleviatin (diphenol hydantoin), 390
ω-Amino acids, 102, 103, 432, 433, 436
γ-Amino butyric acid (GABA), 93, 101, 102, 105, 107, 109, 112, 173, 186, 222, 315, 322, 344, 355, 361, 362, 365, 369, 370, 372, 373, 374, 380, 386, 388, 433, 435, 436, 443
γ-Aminobutyric acid, action compared with that of Factor I, 356ff.
  not inhibitory transmitter, 362
  effect on presynaptic terminals, 96
γ-Aminobutyrobetaine, 388
γ-Amino-β-hydroxy butyric acid, 356, 369, 370, 372, 373, 380, 382, 389, 391, 394
γ-Amino-β-hydroxybutyrobetaine (see Carnitine)
γ-Aminobutyrocholine, 388
ε-Aminocaproic acid, 433, 437, 438, 439, 441, 443
ω-Aminocaprylic acid, 436, 437, 438, 441, 443
δ-Aminovaleric acid, 336, 362

Anatomically addressed systems, 396ff.
Anatomy of *Aplysia* visceral ganglion, 180, 233ff.
  of crustacean heart ganglion, 144ff.
  of crustacean stretch receptor organs, 285ff.
Anelectrotonus, 15, 16
Annulospiral afferents, 33
Anodonta, 2
Anoxic depolarization, 181ff., 183
Anterior cerebellum, 67
Anterior commissure, 33
Anterior midbrain central grey matter, 38
Antidromic inhibition, 61
  stimulation, 26
  of ventral roots, 51
Antidromically evoked potentials (stretch receptors), 295
Aplysia Californica, 234, 238
Aplysia varica, 234
Aplysia fasciata, 179, 180, 218
  anatomy of visceral ganglion, 180ff.
Aplysia, ganglion cells, 83, 179ff., 194ff., 233ff.
Apparent suppression of rebound, 168
Artificial endolymph currents, 38
Aspartic acid, 378, 379
Astacus fluviatilis, 87
Astroscopus, 9, 11
Asymmetrical reciprocal innervation, 69
Atrial trabeculae, structure of, 129
Atropine, 345, 360
Auditory receptors, 336
Autoactivity (see Spontaneous activity)
Axodendritic postsynaptic potentials, 424

Ba⁺, 101
Bicarbonate, 80
Biceps-semitendinosus motor neurons, 351, 352
Biphasic i.p.s.p., 162
Bisynaptic (see Disynaptic)
Bisynaptic excitatory responses, 38
Blatella germanica, 451
Boloceroides, 399
Bombyx mori, 455
Bordercontrast, 273, 275
Brain transplantation, 449
82 Br, 112

467

Bromate, 81
Bromide, 80, 84, 313
BST motoneurons, 78

Cajal-Retzius cells, 426, 441
Cambarus clarkii, 163
Cambarus virilis (*see also Orconectes*), 321, 322
Cancer magister, 107
Cancer productus, 107
Carbamylcholine, 11
Carcinus, 69
Cardiac ganglion (*see* Crustacean heart ganglion)
Cardiac inhibition in decapod crustacea, 144ff.
  in molluscs, 136ff.
  in vertebrates, 114ff.
Cardiac pacemaker cells, 204
Carnitine, 378, 379, 382
Carnosine, 378, 379
Carotenoid pigment in *Aplysia* nerve cells, 183, 184, 196, 200, 201, 223
Carotenoids in *Nitella*, 196
Cassiopea, 401
Cecropia, 447, 449, 456, 457
Cellena eucosmia, 136
Cellena nigrolineata, 136
Cellular photosensitivity, 194ff.
Central inhibition, 13, 22
Central inhibition latency, 50ff., 78
Central inhibitory transmitter, 84, 342ff., 350ff.
Central latency, measurements of, 50
Centrifugal modulation of sensory input, 419
Cephalopods (*see also Sepia*), 137
Cerebral cortex, 343, 410ff.
Charged pores, 84, 89
Charpentiers bands, 280
Chemical hypothesis of inhibitory synaptic transmission, 16, 24, 25 (*see also* Inhibitory transmitter substance; Criteria for inhibitory transmitter)
Chemical transmitters (*see* Excitatory transmitter substance; Inhibitory transmitter substance)
Chemopotentials, 179ff.
  definition of 179
Chemically addressed systems, 397
Chemical stimulation of receptor neurons, 319ff.
Chemical transmitter hypothesis 15, 16, 19, 24, 25, 222, 223
Chloride (*see* Cl⁻)
Chlorophyll, 196, 224

Cholinesterase, 449, 450
Citrate, 71
36 Cl, 119
Cl⁻ concentration, effect of alteration of, 88, 90
  -conductance, 9
  contribution of to total membrane conductance, 88
  distribution, 100
  permeability, increase during inhibition, 80, 81, 83, 88, 89, 313ff.
  pump, 81, 83
Clarke's column, 39, 80, 343
Clarke neurons, 41
Clinocardium nutalli, 142
Coelenterate nerve nets, 395ff.
Comital, 390
CO_2, depolarizing action, 186ff.
  excitatory and inhibitory actions, 179
Co-axial electrodes, 343
Coiled fibre system, 41
Competitive inhibition of transmitter-receptor interaction, 137
Conditioning stimulus, 412, 414, 415, 416, 420
Cocaine, 11
Cochlear nucleus, 5
Cockroach, inhibitory fibers in, 4
Cortico-spinal neurons, 11, 12
Crab (*see Cancer; Carcinus*)
Crayfish (*see also Astacus; Cambarus; Orconectes*), 2, 3, 87, 105, 204, 285ff., 404, 405
Cricket, 403
Cristae acusticae, 37
Criteria for inhibitory transmitter, 342ff., 351ff.
Crude excitine, 381
Crustacean heart ganglion, 105, 144ff., 204
  anatomy 144ff.
Crustacean heart, inhibition in, 144ff., 360, 402
Crustacean molting, 453
  muscle, charged pores, 83
  muscle fiber, electrical behaviour, 89, 92ff., 105ff., 281
  neuromuscular junction, 92ff., 105ff., 313
  receptor muscles, physiology, 289
  stretch receptors, 9, 83, 84, 204, 285ff., 291, 293, 318ff., 327, 353, 361
    anatomy 285ff.
Cs⁺, 99, 100
Cuneate nucleus, 415, 416, 419ff.
Curare, 347
Cyanea, 401
Cyanide, 449
Cyprea tigris, 136
Cysteine, 378, 379

Cytochemical organization of *Aplysia* nerve cells, 183ff.
Cytochromes, 196, 225, 449

Darkschewitsch nucleus, 37, 38, 39
Decremental conduction, 15, 22, 23
Definition of inhibition, 13
  chemopotentials, 179
  neuropile, 398
  stimulation, 325
  stimulus, 325
Delay paths, 22
Demarcation current, 16
Dendritic arborzations as stretch receptors, 145
Dendritic conduction, 23
Depolarizing action of inhibitory impulses, 313, 359ff.
Depolarizing inhibition, postsynaptic potenials, 158, 304ff.
Depolarizing pressure, 62, 63, 64, 65
Depolarizing p.s.p.s., 9
Desensitization, 11
  to acetylcholine, 4
Diamox, 390
Diapause, 448ff.
Dicarboxylic amino acids, 344
Differential inhibition by GABA of the pacemakers, 174
Dimethyl-γ-butyrylcholine, 388
N:N-Dimethyl-5-hydroxy tryptamine, 138
Diphenol hydantoin (alleviatin), 390
Diploptera, 451, 452
Direct inhibition, hypothesis of, 15
  of motoneurons, 33, 47
Disynaptic reflex system, 25, 26, 28, 38
Dog, motor cortex, 376, 383
Dorsal column relay fibers, 419
Dorsal nerve, 147
Dorsal root afferent volleys, 20
Dorsal root reflex, 12
DPN, 185, 186
D-Tubocurarine, 93, 383, 385
Dual action of individual neurons, 2, 160
Dual inhibitory action, 78
Dual nature of inhibitory fiber, 160

Earthworm, 338, 401
  giant fibers, 301
Eccentric neurons of *Limulus* eye, 5, 326, 328, 329
Eel electroplaques, 93
  heart, 114
Eighth nerve, 6
Electric fishes, 9, 93, 333, 336
Electric time constant, 71
Electric transmission in cardiac tissue, 132
Electrical guidance system, fishes, 331

Electrophoretic injection of ions, 80ff., 102, 103
Electroplaques, 93, 333
Electrotonic potentials, 149
Electrically excitable membrane, 92, 328
Electrically inexcitable membrane, 9, 328, 330
Electrotonus in Purkinje fibers, 125
  non-uniform spread of, 127
Energy transfer in organized cytostructures, 224
Ephatic connections, 12
Epilepsẏ in dogs, cure of, 389ff.
  in humans, 389ff.
Epinephrine (*see* Adrenaline)
E.p.s.p., potentiation of i.p.s.p., 75
  equilibrium potential, 102, 351
  recorded from ventral roots, 78
Equilibrium potential, effect of electrodes on, 315
  of Cl⁻, 81
  of e.p.s.p., 102, 351
  of i.p.s.p., 73, 74, 82, 88, 100, 162, 305, 309, 313, 344, 351
Equilibrium potention of K⁺, 81
Equivalent circuit of local current spread, 128
Eserine, 93, 137
Excitation by hyperpolarization, 326ff.
Excitation, post-inhibitory, 152
  produced by infra-red radiations, 194
  light, 194
Excitatory drive (surplus excitation), 62, 64, 65, 66
Excitatory effects of inhibitory fibers, 164, (*see also* 307, 318ff.)
Excitatory junction potentials, crustacean muscle, 96ff, 105ff, 111 (*see also* E.p.s.p.)
Excitatory junctional activity, creation of pores, 89
Excitatory minature potentials, 111
Excitatory nerve terminals, 111
Excitatory postsynaptic potential (*see* E.p.s.p.)
Excitatory substance (Hayashi), 376ff.
Excitatory synaptic membranes, 9
Excitatory transmitter substance, 24, 110, 321, 409
  from GABA 385ff.
Excitine, 377
Excitine-Inhibitine hypothesis, 378ff.
Excitine N, 382
Excitine NC, 380, 382, 383
Experimental embryology, 32
Experimental neurohistology, 32
Extensor motoneurons, 65
Extensor reflexes, 62

Extensor tonus, 26
Extracellular microelectrodes, 293
Extrapyramidal centers, 354
Extrasynaptic hypothesis of inhibition, 18
Extrinsic cardioregulatory fibers, 147
Extrinsic impulses, Crustacean heart ganglion, 149

Facilitation, 19, 27, 306ff.
    of antidromic invasion by inhibitory action, 312
Facilitatory interaction, 415
Factor I, 105, 322, 353, 354, 355, 359, 360, 361, 362, 280
    actions compared with those of acetylcholine, 363
        of GABA, 356ff.
    central actions, 355
    distribution in mammalian central nervous system, 354
Faiscau moyen of Cajal, 33
Field effects, 4, 12
Fishes, electric, 9, 93, 333, 336
    electrical guidance system, 331
Flavoprotein, 196
Flexor reflex, 15, 19
Fly, 403
Folic acid, 385
Follower cells, crustacean heart ganglion, 5, 148, 158, 174
Formate, 81, 84
Frequency limitation, 64
Frog auricle, 121
    brain stem, 13
    muscle, 87, 89, 98, 378ff.
    nerve, 115, 379ff.
    sinus venosus, 360

Gamma-amino butyric acid (*see* γ-Amino butyric acid)
Ganglion cells (*see* Anatomy of *Aplysia* visceral ganglion; *Aplysia*, *Aplysia* ganglion cells; Crustacean heart ganglion; Mollusc heart)
Gaskell effect, 15
Gasserian ganglion, 33
Gastrocnemius-soleus, 61, 63
Gastropods, ganglia of, 5 (*see also* Anatomy of *Aplysia* visceral ganglion; *Aplysia*)
Generator potential (generator depolarization), 9, 149, 159, 162, 197, 198, 202, 223, 225, 243, 291, 293, 326, 333, 334, 361
Giant axons, earthworm, 301
    Sepia, 195, 196, 199, 210, 215, 223
Giant fiber nerve net, 401
Giant interneuron, 405
Giant nerve cells, 179

Giant synapses (parallel contact synapses), 40, 41
Gland cells, 9, 333
Glial invasion of nerve cells, 234, 237
Glutamate, 314, 385
Glutamic acid, 222, 378, 379
L-glutamic acid decarboxylase, 222
Goldfish, 12
Golgi cells, 32
Golgi methods, 44
Grouped discharges, stretch receptors, 299ff.
Guanidine, 386
Guanidino acetic acid, 362
γ-Guanidinobutyric acid, 356
γ-Guanidinobutylamine (agmatine), 362
β-Guanidino propionic acid, 356, 362
Gymnotids, 336

Haemoglobin, semi-conducting properties, 224
    in *Aplysia* nerve cells, 194
Hair cells, 336
Heart, inhibition (*see* Cardiac inhibition; Crustacean heart ganglion; Inhibition in mollusc hearts; Inhibition of pacemaker neurons)
Helix, 239
    cardiac fibers, cytochromes, flavoproteins, 196
Heteroxenia, 399, 402
Heteroxenia fuscens, 400
Hippocampus, 433, 442
Hipponyx pilosus, 136
Histamine, 357
Histological basis of Renshaw inhibition, 35ff.
Homarus, 148, 149, 151, 173, 174, 176, 177
Homarus americanus, 92, 105, 108, 144
Humoral theory 15 (*see also* Transmitters)
Hypothalamus, 357
Hypothesis, interference, 22, 23
    neurin, 20
    of direct inhibition, 15
    of extrasynaptic inhibition, 18
    of indirect inhibition, 15
    sieve, 83, 89
5-Hydroxy tryptamine (= Serotonine), 94, 98, 99, 137, 357

Identification of inhibitory transmitter, 342ff., 350ff.
Ideopathic epilepsy, 389ff.
Impulse conduction, mammalian atrium, 124
Indirect inhibition, hypotheses of, 15, 17, 19
Inferior rectus, 39

Information (*see* Transmission of information; Preservation of information)

Infra-red, inhibitory effects, 210ff.

Inhibitine N, 382

Inhibitine NC, 382, 383

a-Inhibition, 105, 107, 362

β-Inhibition, 105, 364

Inhibition, antidromic 61
  as consequence of action, 14, 15, 17
  between generations, 455
  by depolarization, 182, 304
  by depolarizing potentials, 4
  by excitatory impulses, 3
  by extremely fine synaptic structures, 36
  by Ia volleys, 76
  by infra-red radiation, 194ff., 210ff.
  by light, 194
    synaptic origin, 210
  by reticular stimulation, 68
  by subnormality, 19
  chemical hypothesis, 16, 24, 25
  definition of, 13
  direct, 17, 21, 22, 23, 47
  due to fatigue, 3
  due to superposition of inhibitory current and hyperpolarization, 77
  during anoxia, 181ff.
  extrasynaptic hypothesis of, 18
  in cortical neurons, 410ff.
  in crustacean hearts, 144ff, 360, 402
  in crustacean stretch receptors, 83, 84, 302ff.
  in mollusc hearts, 136ff.
  in polysynaptic systems, 26
  in sensory processes, 241ff., 285ff.
  in sympathetic ganglia, 19
  in the cutaneous system, 241
  in the spinal court, 13ff, 41ff. 47ff., 61ff., 71ff.
  long lasting, 447ff.

Inhibition, monistic view of, 21
  of crustacean muscle fibers, 24, 87ff., 92ff., 105ff.
  of neuroendocrine systems, 447ff.
  of neurosecretory cells, 447

Inhibition of pacemaker neurons, 156
  orthodromic, 62
  peripheral, 3, 24, 87ff., 92ff., 105ff., 144ff., 302ff.
  pluralistic view of, 21
  respiratory, 2
  without iinhibitory postsynaptic potentials, 204

Inhibitory action, by creation of pores, 84, 89, 90, 122
  of adrenaline, 19

Inhibitory connections of primary afferents, 33

Inhibitory current, 75, 76, 78

Inhibitory factor of Florey (*see* Factor I, Substance I)

Inhibitory fibers, history of their discovery, 1ff.

Inhibitory interaction, 241ff., 420, 422

Inhibitory interneurons, 33, 41, 38, 210 (*see also* Renshaw cells)

Inhibitory hormones, 447ff.

Inhibitory neurons in neuro-endocrine systems, 450

Inhibitory latency, 50ff., 78

Inhibitory nerve net, 399

Inhibitory neurons, history of their discovery, 1ff.

Inhibitory pathways, 32ff, 47ff.
  of oculomotor neurons, 36ff.
  to motoneurons, 47ff.

Inhibitory postsynaptic potential = I.p.s.p.

Inhibitory receptive field, 417 (*see also* 241ff.)

Inhibitory substance, 24, 43, 80, 81, 84, 105, 110,, 111 173, 315, 342ff., 350ff., 369, 409 (*see also* Factor I, Substance I)

Inhibitory substance, of Lissak *et al.*, 359, 365, 369ff.
  of Pfeifer and Pataky, 359, 363, 365

Inhibitory surround (*see* Inhibitory receptive field)

Inhibitory transmitter, acting on plugs of membrane pores, 84, 90 (*see also* 81, 122)

Intercellular resistance, 130

Interference hypothesis, 22, 23

Intermediate nucleus of Cajal, 33

Intermittent conduction, 18

Interneurons, 19, 20, 24, 26, 33, 41, 38, 66, 210 (*see also* Renshaw cells)

Intracellular approach, limitations, 65

Intracellular pH measurements, 189

Intracellular resistance, 130

Intrinsic burst, 149

Ionic mechanisms of inhibitory process, 79ff., 87ff., 114ff., 313ff.

I.p.s.p., 23, 74, 158, 209, 214, 304ff., 343, 350, 351, 352, 361, 424, 436, 443 (*see also* Equilibrium potential of i.p.s.p., Ionic mechanism of inhibitory process)
  facilitation of, 167
  inversion of by electrophoretic injection, 80
  recorded from ventral roots, 78

Isolated ventral horn preparation, 35

Isonicotinic acid hydrazide (INH), 383, 385, 386

I—synapses, 74

Janthina janthina, 136
Janus green B, 183
Junctional potentials (*see* Excitatory junctional potential, E.p.s.p.; Inhibitory junctional potential, I.p.s.p.)

42 K, 116ff., 121, 132, 313
K^+ conductance, 9, 11
K^+ concentration, effect of alteration of, 88, 90, 136ff., 313
K^+ distribution, 314
K^+ flux during i.p.s.p., 81, 82, 83 (*see also* 116ff., 313ff).

Labelled lines, 397, 398
Lactic acid, depolarizing action, 185
Lamellibranch hearts, 142
Latent pause, 153, 168
Lateral funiculus, 41
Lateral inhibition, 67
Leucophaea, 451, 452, 456
Lementina imbricata, 136
Lengthening reaction, 25, 26
Limbs, transplanted, 42
Limulus eye, 4, 5, 67, 137, 210, 242ff., 324, 331, 336, 399
    eccentric cell, 5, 326, 328, 329
    structure of, 242ff.
    final path neuron, 330
    heart, 137
Lipochondria, 183, 196, 200, 223, 225
Lobster, 92, 97, 99, 105, 108, 144, 148, 149, 151, 173, 174, 176, 177, 285ff., 293 (*see also Homarus, Palinurus, Panulirus*)
    muscle fiber, 92ff., 105, 107
    action of K^+ and Cs^-, 99
Local transmissional sites, 98
Locust, 403
Long lasting facilitation, 167
Lophius, spikes in neurosecretory cells, 337
Lutraria maxima, 137

Macaca mulatta, 410ff.
Mach bands, 275
Mach pattern, 274
Mactra, pigmented pallial nerve, 210
Mg^+, 138
Maia, pericardial organs, 173
Malapterurus, electroplaques, 333
Mammalian cortex, 102 (*see also* Neocortex)
Mantis, 404
Mautner cells, 5, 6, 12, 22
Measurements of central latency, 50
Mechanism of infra-red inhibition, 222
Medial longitudinal fasciculus, 37, 38
Membrane resistance, 101, 132, 329
Mesencephalic tract of trigeminus, 33

Method of persisting elements, 32, 35
Methylene blue, 196, 214, 215, 225, 386
Metrazol, 371, 372, 382, 385
Mice, 389
Midbrain, 38
Miniature postsynaptic potentials, 90, 97 (*see also* Miniature potentials; Prepotentials)
Miniature potentials, 197
Model nervous system, 32, 41, 42
Modifications of acetylcholine molecule, 137
Mollusc heart, effect of acetylcholine, ions, 136ff.
    inhibition, 136ff.
    nervous pacemaker, 137
Monistic view of inhibition, 21
Monkey (*Macaca*), 410ff.
Monocarboxylic aminoacids, 344
Monochromatic activation of nerve cells, 201ff.
Monosynaptic reflex, 20, 25
Monosynaptic inhibitory pathway, 50
Monosynaptic system, spinal cord, 25
Motoneuron membrane, 71
Motor axons, specific inhibitory endings of, 3
Motor cortex, 382
Motor units, 144
Murex trunculus, 137
Muscle spindle, 25, 29, 62, 64, 291, 326
Muscular afferent neurons, 40
Muscular pacemaker, 137
Mya, 139, 402
Mya arenaria, 138
Myotatic reflex, 25, 27
Myotatic reflex, pathways, 21
Myotatic unit, 26
Mytilus, 139
Mytilus Californianus, 138
Mytolon, 137, 138

Na^+ conductance, 8, 11
$Na^- - K^+$ pump, 82
Negative feedback control, 27
Neocortex, neuropile, ontogenetic development, 424ff.
Neocortical neuropile, morphology, 426ff.
Nereis, 407
Nerve net, model of, 395
Nervous pacemaker of mollusc heart, 137
Nervous system, models, 32
Net depolarizing current, 62
Neurin hypothesis, 20
Neuro-endocrine systems, inhibition in, 447ff.
Neurogenic heart (Crustacea), 144ff.

Neuromuscular transmission, Crustacea, 92ff., 105ff., 313ff.
Neurons, dual action of, 2
"Neuropil" (*see* Neuropile)
Neuropile, 18, 145, 240, 395ff., 424ff.
    definition of, 398
    neocortex, morphology, 426ff.
Neurosecretory cells, 331, 333, 336, 337
    electrical activity, 448ff.
Neurosecretory granules, 338
Neutral red, 196, 214, 215
NH$_4$Cl, 97
Nitella, 196, 223
Nitrate, 80, 313
Noise, 4
Non-addressed systems, 397
Non-uniform spread of electrotonus, 127
Nor-adrenaline, 357

Occlusive interaction, 417
Occlusion, 410
Octopus, sexual development, 453, 456
Oculomotor neurons, 19, 38
Oculomotor nucleus, 38
"Off" response, 5, 201, 202, 214, 217 (*see also* 241ff., 323, 324; *see also* Postinhibitory excitation; Postinhibitory facilitation; Postinhibitory rebound; Rebound)
Olfactory epithelium, 330
Olfactory receptors, 291
"On" response, 201, 202, 214 (*see also* 241ff., 323, 324)
Opener muscle, crayfish, 87ff.
Orconectes virilis, 111
Orthodromic inhibition, 62
Oscillatory activity, *Sepia* giant axon, 215
Oscillatory potentials, *Aplysia* nerve cells, 197, 214
Ostrea, 139
Ostrea circumpicta, 136
Ostrea gigas, 136
Oxygen consumption of illuminated axons, 225
Oxygen, required for repolarization, 185
Oxymethyl pyrimidine, 385, 386

Pacemaker, 138, 144, 149, 302, 360, 398, 399, 400, 401
Pacemaker cells, 5, 149ff.
Pacinian corpuscle, 204, 291, 293, 326
Palaemon sirratus, 454
Panulirus, 159, 160, 163, 165, 176
Panulirus argus, 144, 147
Panulirus interruptus, 144, 151, 158
Paradox, 142

Paradoxical driving, 154, 158
Parallel contact synapses ("giant synapses"), 40
Paratya, 173
Pathways of recurrent inhibition, 35
Patterning, 163ff., 171ff.
Pedal ganglion, 5
Pericardial organ, 147, 173
Peripheral inhibition, 3, 24, 87ff., 92ff., 105ff.
Permeability, *see* Cl$^-$, K$^+$ (*also* Equilibrium potential)
Pharmacology of neocortical neurons, ontogenetic changes, 432ff.
pH, intracellular, 189
Phenethylamine, 93
Phenobarbitol, 390
Phosphate, 80
Photoactivation of nerve cells, 194ff.
Photons, 194, 223
Photoreceptors, 223 (*see also* 241ff.)
Photosynthesis, 223
Physiologically adressed systems, 397
Picrotoxin, 93, 94, 95, 96, 102, 105, 107, 109, 110, 358, 361
Pigmented nerve cells, *Aplysia*, 194ff.
Pilocarpin, 335
Pit Vipers, facial pit sense organ, 217
Place theory, 22, 23
Pleurodeles Waltli, 42, 43
Pluralistic view of inhibition, 21
Polysynaptic system, 26
Pons, 38
Pores, charged, 84, 89
    opening of by inhibitory transmitter, 84, 90, 122
Porifera, 338
Positive variation, 16
Posterior biceps-semitendinosus, 78
Post-excitatory depression, 150, 318ff.
Post-inhibitory depression, 170, 306
Post-inhibitory excitation, 152, 308, 318ff.
Postinhibitory facilitation, 306, 307
Post-inhibitory rebound, 153, 156, 162, 177, 214, 217 (*see also* "Off" response)
    compared with release from hyperpolarizing currents, 162
    without membrane potential shift, 162, 307
Postsynaptic inhibition, 71ff., 84ff., 87, 92ff., 105ff., 114ff., 151ff., 302ff.
Postsynaptic potential (*see* Axodendritic postsynaptic potential; Axosomatic postsynaptic potential; E.p.s.p.; Excitatory junction potential; I.p.s.p.)
Potassium (*see* K$^+$, 42 K)
Potential field, 59

Prepotentials, 197, 291, 300 (*see also* Miniature postsynaptic potential; Miniature potential)
Preservation of information, 401
Presynaptic block, 23
Presynaptic inhibition, 47, 55ff., 111ff., 353
Presynaptic interaction, 18
Presynaptic terminals, 95, 98, 413
Primary afferent fibers, 24
Primary sensory neurons, 42, 326, 327, 330
Primitive central nervous system, 395ff.
Probability of firing, 401ff.
Procaine, 11, 93, 345
Propagated action potentials, 149
Proprioceptive afferents, 22
Prothoracic gland, 448
Protothaca, 139
Protothaca staminea, 138
Puctada martensi, 136
Purkinje neurons, 45
Pycnoscelus surinamensis, 451
Pyramidal tract, 419

Quantal release of transmitter, 111, 112

Radioactive isotopes in analysis of synaptic inhibition, 116, 119, 121, 132, 144ff. 313
Ragworm, 406
Raia electroplaques, 9
Random connections, neuropile, 395, 396
Rat atrium, 125
Rebound (*see also* Postinhibitory excitation; Postexcitatory inhibition; "Off" response; "On" response) excitation 154, 318ff.
Receptor cells, 241ff., 285ff., 318ff., 326ff.
Reciprocal inhibition, 38
Reciprocal innervation, 25
Recurrent collaterals of Golgi, 61
Recurrent conditioning, 27
Recurrent excitation, 69
Recurrent facilitation, 27
Recurrent inhibition, 61ff., 64, 66, 255, 275 physiological role of, 66
Recurrent inhibitory system, spinal cord, 26
Regulator fibers of crustacean heart, 144ff.
Remote inhibition, 23, 353
Renshaw cells, 5, 27, 35, 36, 61, 66, 67, 347 not automatic, 68
Renshaw inhibition, histological basis of, 35ff.
Repolarization, 24
Resistance changes, produced by light, 197 to inhibition, 64
Respiratory inhibition, 2
Reticular formation, 12, 37, 38, 357, 374, 423

Retina, generator potentials, 333 inhibitory interactions in, 241ff.
Reversal of inhibitory synaptic current, 73
Reversal potential of i.p.s.p. (*see* Equilibrium potential)
Rhodopsin, 196
Role of inhibition, 25 (*see also* 318ff.)
Rotation of acetylcholine-sensitive sites, 138

Salivary gland, hyperpolarization, 333, 335
Salt-contraction, 378
SCN$^-$, 313
Scratch reflex, 2, 5
Sea-urchin, esophagus, 358
Secondary degeneration of synapses, 32
Secondary sensory cells, 327
Secondary vestibular fibers, 38
Seizures, 385ff.
Selfinhibition, 261
Sensitization to light by dyes, 195
Sensory field, 404
Sensory ganglia, 42
Sensory input, centrifugal modulation, 419
Sensory neurons (*see* Primary sensory cells; Receptor cells; Secondary sensory cells)
Sepia stained giant axon, 195, 196, 199, 210, 215, 223
Serotonin (*see* 5-Hydroxytryptamine)
Shadow reflex, 323
Sheep myocardium, 132
Sieve hypothesis, 83, 89
Silent period, 279, 280, 318
Simple inhibition, 105, 364
Sinus venosus, eel heart, 114 effect of vagus stimulation, 115 of tortoise, 115
Sodium (*see* Na$^+$)
Sodium pentobarbital, 440
Somesthetic cortex, 415
Spatial summation, 50, 258, 259, 278
Spinal cord interneurons, 19, 20, 24, 26, 41, 66, 67, 210 (*see also* Renshaw cells)
Spindle and tendon receptors, 27
Spontaneous activity (autoactivity), 42, 179ff., 200, 201, 299 in regulator neurons, 151 of presynaptic terminals, 97, 209
Squid axon, 11, 89 (*see also* *Sepia* stained giant axon)
Stained axon as detector of infra-red, 214
Stenarchus albifrons, 337
Stimulation, definition, 325
Stimulus, concept of, 318ff.
Stretch deformation of dendrites, 289
Stretch receptor cells of crayfish (*see* Crustacean stretch receptors)
Stretch reflex, 27, 28, 64, 65

Structure activity relationship, 137
Strychnine, 11, 42, 103, 347, 348, 354, 358, 359, 361, 371, 373, 433, 440, 443
Substance I, 4, 320, 363, 364, 365
Submicroscopic synapses, 38
Substance P, 358
Subnormal period, 14, 19
  process, 19
Subsynaptic membrane, 9, 71, 84, 89, 90, 92, 122, 328, 330
Sulphate, 71, 80
Superficial cortical responses (S.C.R.) ontogenetic changes of, 428ff.
Supplemented inhibition, 105, 362
Superior obliquus, 39
Suprasylvian gyrus, 425, 430, 438
Surplus excitation (excitatory drive), 62, 64, 65, 66
  concepts of 64
Sympathetic ganglia, 19, 363
Sympathin (see Adrenaline, Nor-adrenaline)
Synpatic knobs, 22 (see also Terminal knobs)
Synaptic potentials (see E.p.s.p.; Generator potential; I.p.s.p.; Junctional potential)
Synaptic vesicles, 191, 338, 345

Tastebuds, 331, 332, 334
Taurine, 378, 379, 382
Temperature sensitivity of nerve cells and synapses, 217
Tendon organ, 27
Terminal degeneration, 22
Terminal knobs, 17, 33, 37, 38, 40, 41, 42
  generally excitatory, 35
  of motoneurons, 35
Testing stimulus, 414, 415, 416, 420
Tetrapyrrolic pigments, Aplysia nerve cells, 196
Theory of decremental conduction, 14
Thiocyanate, 80
Tibialis anterior, 65

Time course of inhibitory current, 72
Tonic reflex, 65
Tonic stretch reflex, 62
Tortoise auricle, 16
  sinus venosus, 115
Transmission of information, 322, 334, 336, 395ff., 401, 406ff.
Transmissional components at synapse, 99
Transmissional membranes of terminals, 97
Transmitter agents (see Transmitter substances)
Transmitter, bound form, 345
Transmitter-Receptor interaction, 343, 346
Transmitter substances, 12, 58, 71, 105, 401
  (see also Excitatory transmitter substance Inhibitory transmitter substance)
Transmitter, enzymatic inactivation, 346
  free form, 345
Trigeminal system, 33
Triturus cristatus, 42
Trophospongium, 234
d-Tubocurarin, 93, 383, 385

Unit excitatory receptive field, 410, 411, 414, 416, 417, 418

Vagal inhibition, 13, 15, 16, 114ff.
Vagus action, 114ff.
  nerve, 114
Venus, 138
Venus mercenaria, 137
Vertebrate heart muscle, 84
Vestibular nucleus, 38
Visceral ganglion, mollusca, 138, 179ff., 194ff., 233ff.
Vision, 5, 241ff.
Visual pigment of Limulus, 242
  (see also Rhodopsin)
Vitamin B_1, 380, 385
Vitamin B_6, 380
Vitamin B_{12}, 380, 386